SALT DOMES
Gulf Region, United States & Mexico

STRATIGRAPHIC COLUMN
GULF REGION—UNITED STATES
(Northeast Mexico Equivalent)*

ERA	SYSTEM	SERIES	GROUP	FORMATION
CENOZOIC	QUATERNARY	RECENT		*Undifferentiated*
		PLEISTOCENE	*HOUSTON*	*Beaumont* / *Lissie* / *Willis*
	TERTIARY	PLIOCENE		*Goliad*
		MIOCENE	*FLEMING*	*Lagarto* / *Oakville* / *Catahoula*
		OLIGOCENE UPPER		*Anahuac*
		OLIGOCENE MIDDLE		*Frio* *Hackberry*
		OLIGOCENE LOWER		*Vicksburg*
		EOCENE	*JACKSON*	*Whitsett* / *Mc Elroy* / *Caddell* / *Moodys Branch*
		EOCENE	*CLAIBORNE*	*Cockfield-Yegua* / *Cook Mountain* / *Sparta* / *Weches* / *Queen City* / *Reklaw*
		EOCENE	*WILCOX*	*Carrizo* / *Sabinetown* / *Rockdale* / *Seguin*
		PALEOCENE	*MIDWAY*	*Wills Point* / *Kinkaid*
MESOZOIC		UPPER CRETACEOUS	*NAVARRO*	*Upper Navarro (Kemp, Escondido)* / *Nacatoch (Olmos)*
			TAYLOR	*Upper Taylor (San Miguel)* / *Pecan Gap (Anacacho)* / *Wolf City* / *Lower Taylor (Gober)*
			AUSTIN	*Austin* / *Sub-Clarksville*
			EAGLEFORD	*Eagleford*
			WOODBINE	*Woodbine*
		LOWER CRETACEOUS	*WASHITA*	*Buda* / *Del Rio* / *Georgetown* (*Mainstreet* / *Paw Paw* / *Weno* / *Denton* / *Fort Worth* / *Duck Creek*)
		COMANCHEAN	*FREDERICKSBURG*	*Kiamichi* / *Edwards* / *Comanche Peak* / *Walnut*
			TRINITY	*Paluxy* / Glen-Rose Sub-Group: *Upper (Ferry Lake Anhydrite)* / *Middle* / *Lower* (*Rodessa* / *Pearsall* / *James (Cow Creek)*) / *Travis Peak (Pine Island)* — *Stuart City Reef*
			COAHUILA	*Sligo* / *Hosston*
	JURASSIC	SABINAS	*COTTON VALLEY (LA CASITA*)*	*Schuler* / *Bossier*
				Haynesville / *Buckner (Olvido*)* / *Smackover (Zuloaga, La Gloria*)* / *Norphlet*
		MIDDLE		*Louann Salt* / *(Minas Viejas*)* *Werner* *Huizachal Red Beds*
		LOWER		
	TRIASSIC			*Eagle Mills (La Boca*)*
PALEOZOIC	PERMIAN			*Undifferentiated* / *Deformed & Metamorphosed Rocks*

SALT DOMES

Gulf Region, United States & Mexico

MICHEL T. HALBOUTY

Geologist and Petroleum Engineer
Houston, Texas

GULF PUBLISHING COMPANY
HOUSTON, TEXAS

SALT DOMES

Gulf Region—United States and Mexico

Copyright © 1967 by Gulf Publishing Company
Houston, Texas

Library of Congress Catalog Card Number 67-24628

DEDICATED TO

PATTILLO HIGGINS
SCOTT HEYWOOD
MILES FRANK YOUNT
MARRS McLEAN

*the four great salt dome explorers, who,
although not geologists, changed the
geological thinking of our time*

SPECIAL ACKNOWLEDGMENT

Special recognition is extended to Thomas E. Kelly, geologist, who is associated with the author, for his most valuable assistance in the preparation of the entire volume. His painstaking efforts in researching the subject of salt domes in general were outstanding; his editorial contributions, suggestions, recommendations, criticisms, and discussions on various topics helped the author immeasurably; and, many of his ideas are incorporated in the text. In fact, it is very doubtful the volume could have been completed in its present form without his unqualified and enthusiastic cooperation. The author gratefully acknowledges and extends his thanks and sincere appreciation to Thomas E. Kelly for his superb assistance in the completion of this work.

Acknowledgments

The preparation of this volume in recognition of the importance of salt structures in the production of hydrocarbons in the Gulf Region, United States and Mexico, is an outgrowth of many separate but related studies, many conducted by the author, but mostly by other dedicated students of salt dome geology, whose work over more than half a century has stimulated and kept alive the keen interest in salt domes. Space would not permit the individual acknowledgment of the many geologists and engineers with whom I have enjoyed an intellectual comradeship for over thirty-five years and who have inspired, encouraged, and assisted me in general and specific salt dome projects, but more importantly have generously shared their thoughts and ideas which helped broaden my own knowledge on the complexities of salt structures and salt basins.

It is a privilege to acknowledge, with deep appreciation the efforts of Abe W. Wagner, Jr., geologist, who is on the author's staff, for his assistance in compiling the bibliography. His research in listing such a bibliography as published herein required a major effort of time and patience.

Thanks are also extended to Mrs. Lois Cloud, secretary, for her assistance in the editing and typing of the bibliography and text; also to the author's executive secretary, Mrs. Viola Vermillion, for an over-all effort in just keeping the files of this massive work in proper and usable order.

The author gratefully acknowledges to Eduardo J. Guzman, Pemex; Dr. Zoltan de Cserna, Instituto de Geologia, University of Mexico; and, Luis Benavides, Pemex for their assistance in obtaining information on salt structures of Mexico; D. C. Ion, British Petroleum, London, England; and, H. G. Graham, Esso International, London, England, for their help in obtaining published information on salt structures and salt basins in Africa and the Middle East; the New Orleans Geological Society and Wallace Mann, and his Salt Dome Committee of the New Orleans Geological Society, for permission to reprint, with some of the author's modifications, certain salt dome maps and information; Transcontinental Gas Pipe Line Corporation for furnishing a base map which was used in the preparation of the text's salt dome location map; and to *World Oil* and

The Oil and Gas Journal for their cooperation in securing data from their respective
libraries.

The author also extends his thanks to
James J. Halbouty, consultant, who rendered
invaluable assistance in the compilation of the
many statistical tables which were made a
part of the text, and who offered pertinent
suggestions on the subject material, some of
which were incorporated in the manuscript;
and to Thos. D. Barber, Exploration Man-

ager, Michel T. Halbouty Oil and Gas Interests, for timely suggestions on specific portions of the text.

There is an observation made by the pub-
lishers—that "no appreciable piece of work
is done alone." This statement is very true
in this case—without the diligent efforts,
cooperation and assistance of all of these
people, this book could not have been completed.

Foreword

Salt Domes by Michel T. Halbouty is a big book about a big subject by a leading student of the structures involved. Moreover, the author's encyclopedic knowledge of their notable intricacies has been responsible for significant financial rewards as well as important scientific concepts. In the present volume Halbouty generously shares the latter with a predictably large audience. Careful readers are also likely to share the former because, as the author makes clear, there is much more black gold to be found associated with the grey salt.

The fact is, salt and salt deposits have concerned man since before the dawn of recorded history, and salt domes, specifically, have been the subject of scientific investigations for well over a century. Such studies have increased in scope and intensity during the twentieth century. Nevertheless, as Halbouty correctly points out, at this day and time, the study of salt dome geology has been attracting relatively few apprentices, and their training in the subject cannot yet be considered extensive. Meanwhile, the older experts in the field now comprise a waning cadre.

The trend toward a partial neglect of an important, if a difficult, subject is all the more surprising because, as the author correctly contends, salt movement has geologically affected perhaps 80 percent of all the oil and gas fields in the Gulf Coast province. This is true because a wide variety of shallow and deep modifications of the thick Tertiary sediments has resulted from the growth of the numerous and varied salt structures characterizing the Gulf Coast area.

Actually, the modern liquid fuel age was spawned at Spindletop. And the productivity of some of the domes—even some of small areal extent such as Spindletop—has been little short of phenomenal. In fact Spindletop, discovered in 1901 and still productive after 65 years, has now yielded approximately 145 million barrels of oil from a total productive area of about 500 acres; and some small flank leases have produced more than a million barrels per acre!

In view of such production records, it is little wonder that whenever a new oil or gas discovery is made on any dome, exploration activity quickens on many other salt structures. Moreover, the drilling activity tends to center on those areas which appear to be similar to the geological position of the new production on the bellwether structure. As Halbouty remarks, this is a logical and safe method since such slavish following of precedent in well location and drilling methods has tended to "pay off." But unfortunately such a procedure ultimately leads to diminishing returns. To use the author's words—and, indeed, to follow his example—it is the "imaginative, creative, unproven concept" which is "necessary to advance geological thinking steadily. This *forces* new exploration." The italics are mine.

Salt Domes is divided into nine chapters plus a *Preface,* an *Appendix,* and elaborate bibliographies and indices, the latter skillfully and completely cross-referenced. The *Preface* and the *Introduction* are chiefly presentations of historical and background materials, but nevertheless they also mirror much of the author's geological philosophy. Chapters 2 and 3 have the accurately descriptive titles: *Evaporite Deposition in the Gulf Region,* and *Origin and Growth of Salt Structures.* Valuable summaries of old and new knowledge of the *Configuration and Composition of Salt Structures* and their *Classification* are presented in the two following chapters.

Chapters 6 and 7 are excellent discourses on the *Accumulation of Oil and Gas* and the *Factors Affecting the Quantity of the Hydrocarbon Accumulation.* Chapter 8, entitled the *Economic Significance of Salt Structures,* has been elaborated from a rich background of practical experience. Similarly Chapter 9, *Salt Dome Drilling and Production Problems,* is particularly valuable because it is based on the exploration, engineering and production practices of the author and his associates.

Altogether the book deals with general observations on, and actual experience with, many of the some 370 salt domes and structures which have been penetrated by the drill—not to mention many other structures which probably are to some degree salt controlled. These structures are located in the Gulf States—chiefly in Texas and Louisiana—and in the states of Veracruz and Tabasco, Mexico. But throughout the text—for comparative or explanatory purposes—reference is commonly made to pertinent salt structures in other foreign countries.

There is a well-selected quick reference bibliography at the end of each chapter; and the illustrative material—much of it in uniformly keyed colors—has been especially prepared for this volume. The maps, figures and cross sections have been skillfully selected and reproduced. Many are partly or wholly original and almost all—though well placed with reference to the text itself—are so fully and informatively captioned that they are particularly valuable in their own right.

The Appendix includes a number of excellent structure maps contoured on top of the salt. These are all the more valuable because the corresponding field data sheets are also provided for the eleven Texas and Louisiana Domes which have been chosen for detailed illustration.

The bibliographies and indices are little short of remarkable in their completeness. The papers and articles cited number close to a thousand. They are listed by author—even by junior as well as by senior author—and by subject matter generally as well as by separate domes. They are also indexed by the county, parish or offshore block in which each particular structure occurs. In short, if the reader cannot find what he is looking for regarding salt dome structures in this new volume, it certainly is not the fault of the author.

Michel Thomas Halbouty is listed in *Who's Who in America* as a "geologist, petroleum engineer, independent producer and operator." This is an accurate but all too succinct a description of an uniquely remarkable oil man, even among a legion of remarkable Texas oil men. "Mike" Halbouty, as he is widely and affectionately known, is a salt dome buff whose notable personal dynamism and aggressive courage in backing his scientific convictions, however unorthodox, have carried him to substantial financial successes while concurrently proving the validity of many of his pioneering geological theories.

Born on a salt dome, and thus almost preordained for his later central preoccupation, Halbouty grew up in the atmosphere of Spindletop not too many years after its discovery. It was only natural then for him to choose a career in the petroleum field. He was graduated in geology and petroleum engineering from Texas A&M in 1930, and received his M.S. from that institution in 1931. Although the Great Depression was then on the land, young Mike Halbouty—immediately after obtaining his advanced degree—secured a position as geologist and petroleum engineer with the Yount-Lee Oil Company of Beaumont, and was appointed chief geologist of that organization some two years later when he was only 24 years of age. In 1935, however, he became associated with Glenn H. McCarthy, Inc., of Houston, as chief geologist and general manager. In 1937, only six years after leaving Texas A&M, Mike Halbouty became the owner of a firm of consulting geologists and engineers—a highly successful organization which he still heads. In 1956 he was awarded the Professional Degree of Geological Engineering, the first and only degree of its kind ever conferred by Texas A&M.

Halbouty, with a sort of majestic understatement, admits that he has been the "discoverer" of numerous oil fields in Louisiana and Texas. He has, indeed. Possibly the reason for his success is to be found in the fact that he possesses a rare combination of talents —for he is a creative and imaginative scientist with a very high degree of business acumen—or perhaps it is the other way around. At any rate, his activities have carried him into many kinds of economic activity, and notably into the banking business.

But whatever his other activities or the ramifications of his financial interests, Mike Halbouty is first and last a geologist and petroleum engineer, still actually doing scientific research, as well as directing it, and continually writing and speaking on subjects pertaining to the oil and gas industry. He is a member of too many scientific societies to list in this brief introduction, but sufficient to say, he has recently been elected president of The American Association of Petroleum Geologists, which, with more than 15,000 members scattered throughout North America and some 80 foreign countries, is the largest and most influential geological society in the world.

There is no doubt that Michel Halbouty treasures his presidency of the AAPG as an accolade of acceptance by his fellow professional geologists. All the more so because it appears increasingly more difficult these days for one who has enjoyed great financial as well as professional success to receive the plaudits of his associates. But above all Mike Halbouty probably cherishes most his deserved reputation as *the* salt dome expert—a reputation which will not suffer as a result of the publication of this significant volume.

CAREY CRONEIS
Chancellor and Wiess Professor
of Geology
Rice University

Preface

Although geological thinking, as applied to petroleum exploration, has gradually progressed throughout the world since the discovery of Spindletop in 1901, it is evident that the more complicated the geology in any particular province, the slower the rate of progress. For example, it is recognized that the most important geological structures in the Gulf region are the salt domes. Yet these features reflect subsurface geology in its most difficult form: highly complicated and not wholly understood.

Many experienced Gulf Coast geologists are growing increasingly concerned because relatively few practicing geologists have more than a cursory understanding of these saline uplifts. This author is of the opinion that the study of salt dome geology is gradually becoming a dying art in which the apprentices have had no sustained training, and others have not paused long enough on their way to understand it. There is no doubt that this lack of geological understanding has resulted in a slowing down of the exploration effort on domes.

The key to the geology of the Gulf Region is a thorough knowledge and familiarization with the geology of salt domes. More than four-fifths of all oil and gas accumulations (fields) in the Gulf Coast province have been geologically affected by the growth of the many domes through the thick Tertiary sediments or by depositional conditions that were a result of dome growth throughout Tertiary time. A geologist who understands the complex geology of salt domes simplifies the task of interpreting correctly the true geology of the Gulf region and of its many other features.

*　　*　　*

Three significant events have greatly influenced the course of the modern petroleum industry in the United States: (1) Drake's discovery of oil at Titusville, Pennsylvania, in 1859; (2) the discovery of Spindletop field in 1901 by Higgins and Lucas; and (3) the discovery of oil in East Texas in 1931 by Joiner. Each of these three events had a profound effect not only on the growth but on the scientific thinking of the industry. None of these discoveries were recommended or encouraged by geologists or geophysicists. Drake overcame seemingly insurmountable odds in drilling to a depth of $69\frac{1}{2}$ feet—an unusually shallow depth by present standards. The discovery gave hope to a few determined men that oil might be found in large quantities within the continental United States. When subsequent discoveries in other geological provinces resulted in relatively small production, hope diminished that oil would revolutionize energy consuming industries.

The discovery of oil at Spindletop changed the thinking of geologists, engineers, chemists, and economists the world over because it proved that vast quantities of oil could be produced in a short time from a single source. The age of liquid fuel was born at Spindeltop. The United States, as a result of the discovery, rapidly surpassed Russia, the largest oil country of that day, in oil production and in proven reserves. Spindletop was a symbol of the economic might of a fledgling industry—portrayed by a towering gusher of oil. Pattillo Higgins, the man of the hour at Spindletop, with his associate Anthony F. Lucas, discovered oil, in a place where the best geologists said it was impossible. A new era of geological thinking was born which, once born, remained unchanged for three decades.

Skeptics were plentiful at the time Columbus "Dad" Joiner began drilling for oil on a non-existant geological feature which he termed "the Overton anticline." In reality the Overton anticline was a nondescript topographic feature devoid of subsurface expression. Learned professionals surmised and believed that oil was to be found only on structural highs. Scientists accepted the anticlinal theory of accumulation as dogma and they publicly stated that any deviation from its principle was not only foolish but destined for certain failure. Fortunately, Joiner did not heed the advice of the learned explorationists of his day. It is now evident that he did not know the correct geologic picture but he believed strongly that his efforts were right. This he proved by the discovery of the East Texas field, the largest oil field on the continent and one of the largest purely stratigraphic oil accumulations yet found in the world.

Undoubtedly, if Joiner had not discovered East Texas field, it would have been found shortly thereafter by some other enterprising wildcatter. Joiner's most significant contributions were: (1) he discovered oil in a newly recognized type of trap and this heralded another new era of geological thinking and (2) he persevered in his ideas in the face of doubting contemporaries who were the experts of that day. The latter contribution emphasizes the fact that the growth and strength of the petroleum industry and the creative aspects of new exploration ideas have stemmed from the perseverence of such men as Higgins, Drake, Lucas, Joiner, and others like them who were willing to risk everything they possessed to further their beliefs. In each case, new concepts of scientific thinking were established.

Following a discovery, geological thinking is generally confined to the precedent established by the success. For example, Higgins at Spindletop, proved the existence of cap rock overlying the main salt core. The initial production of oil from Spindletop was from this cap rock. Therefore, for years after the Spindletop discovery every well that was drilled on a dome either produced from the cap rock or was promptly abandoned. Twenty-four years elapsed before Miles Frank Yount, drilling again at Spindletop, discovered oil off the supradome area in sediments pinching out against the immediate flanks of the dome. This resulted in every operator going back to the domes and drilling, and finding millions of barrels of new reserves, off the immediate flank of the domes.

Analogous reasoning characteristic of human nature largely governs the approach to geological investigations. After a new discovery is made on or near a salt dome, drilling efforts focus on the areas of other domes which are geologically similar to the new discovery. This is a sound and safe approach but because this approach is one of simply following a precedent, it eventually reaches a point of diminishing return. The imaginative, creative, unproven concept is necessary to advance geological thinking steadily. This forces new exploration.

The many studies made on salt domes have brought out certain concepts unique to this phase of geology of special academic and economic importance. For example, some of these concepts are generally applicable to explain why some domes are productive while others are not. Other concepts are useful not only in retrospect but are the basis for hopes of finding new reserves in the areas influenced by the uplift of the salt domes. Through the years many of the ideas have been proven by drilling. Still there are many others yet unproven but maybe of utmost economic importance. The undertaking of all of these ideas and their practical application are the most valuable assets of the salt dome geologist.

This work reviews, describes, and illustrates the geological concepts and economical significance of salt domes of the Gulf region: a complete and ready reference in one volume.

MICHEL T. HALBOUTY

Houston, Texas

June, 1967

Contents

SALT DOMES
Gulf Region, United States and Mexico

Chapter 1

Introduction

"If the coast is bold and rocky, it speaks a language easy to be interpreted." With these words Playfair (1802) began his support of Hutton's principle of uniformitarianism, the basic premise of modern geology. Certainly, without the concept that the present is a key to the past the earth sciences would be little more than fable.

Purpose and Scope

Perhaps if there is one phase of geology on which we have accumulated more data, yet have more to learn about, it is salt dome geology. True, these subsurface and subaerial prominences are among the most easily recognized structural features. Their description, composition, and economic importance are described in great detail in countless publications. Statistics of every nature are available on salt domes, particularly in the Gulf region, where they first became so important as a result of the geyser of oil that was Spindletop.

Much remains to be learned about salt structures, and what is known is difficult to interpret and often fraught with misjudgment. Ideas on origin and mode of development have not progressed significantly from the stage of theory, despite widespread acceptance today of a few basic concepts.

For many years this author has believed there is a need for a book which presents, in a concise manner, the major segments of salt dome geology in the Gulf region. There are many excellent publications, both new and old, which treat various aspects of salt domes; indeed many papers discuss domes in as many ways as is presented herein, some with more detail. This book, however, is the first attempt to devote a text *solely* to these most interesting, amazing, and important geologic features.

This book reviews the fundamentals of salt dome geology, including the ideas of many previous writers on the depositional framework of the source bed from which domes have grown, the origin and development of

1

domes and their descriptive and structural characteristics, the accumulation of oil and gas, the economic importance of domes in all aspects, and the engineering practices common to the exploitation of the mineral resources from domes. In addition to the compilation of the works of others which dated back about a hundred years, a number of new approaches and ideas are presented on the domes of the Gulf region in hope that new and heightened interest in salt domes may be stimulated. Many people believe that the importance of domes in our industrialized world is on the wane. The author fails to share this view, and believes that there are tremendous opportunities remaining for both academic and economic progress in salt dome geology.

Salt dome geology is the most documented geological topic in the Gulf region. This book is concerned with the more important segments of salt dome geology of the region, but obviously could not contain all of the ideas expressed in a century of study. Therefore, a comprehensive Bibliography pertaining directly to salt dome geology in the Gulf region is presented with the text. With possibly few exceptions, the Bibliography includes every available reference to Gulf region salt domes.

Evaporite deposits are widely distributed in both hemispheres of the world and occur in every system from Precambrian through Quaternary. A complete evaporitic sequence from carbonates through bitterns is not common to all evaporite basins; and this book is concerned with those basins which contain significant deposits of rock salt (halite).

Types of Salt Basins

Salt basins are of two definite types: one containing bedded salt which, if deformed, is the result of *halo-tectonism* (compressive tec-

tonic forces) and the other containing salt structures which are the result of *halokinesis* (autonomous, isostatic salt movement). These descriptive terms, proposed by Trusheim (1960), for the Zechstein salt masses in Northwestern Germany, are now in widespread use by European geologists. This book adapts Trusheim's terms because of their complete adaptability to the salt deposits in the Western Hemisphere, particularly the Gulf region of the United States and Mexico.

Salt basins where halokinesis is evident are termed salt dome basins in this book. It should be clear to the reader that salt dome basins are considered, by use of this term, in the broadest sense. The locale of salt structures that have formed through predominantly isostatic processes is a salt dome basin regardless of the shape or form of the structures or the amount of deformation including diapirism. The Paradox basin of southeastern Utah, for example, contains elongate salt anticlines but no salt domes. Nonetheless, the salt structures are halokinetic in origin; therefore the basin is classified a salt dome basin.

The major salt basins and salt dome basins of the Eastern Hemisphere are shown in Figure 1-1. The age and geographic location of the salt deposits are listed in Table 1-1. Since this book is primarily concerned with the salt deposits of the Gulf region of the United States the occurrences of salt structures in other areas is only briefly described and then for comparison or analogy. Recent works describe in more detail the salt deposits of Europe, Africa, and Asia. (See Eby, 1956; O'Brien, 1957; Trusheim, 1960; Kennedy, 1965; Kent, 1965; Belmonte, *et al*, 1965; Aymé, 1965; Demaison, 1965; Gill, 1965.)

The major salt basins and salt dome basins of the Western Hemisphere are shown in Figure 1-2. Table 1-2 lists the age and geo-

TABLE 1-1

Major Salt Basins in the Eastern Hemisphere

Age of Salt	Country or Region	Basin or Province	Bedded Salt and Halo-tectonic (Salt Basin)	Halokinesis (Salt Dome Basin)
Tertiary	Northeastern France	Rhine	X	
Miocene	Romania	Transylvanian		X
		Romanian	X	
		Ploesti		X
	Hungary, Ukraine	Solotvin	X	
	Ukraine	Carpathian	X	
	Southern Iran	Central Foothills	X	X
	Gulf of Suez	Red Sea	X	
	Farsan Is., Dahlak Is.	Red Sea	X	
	Yemen	Red Sea		X
Eocene	Pakistan	Potwar	X	
Cretaceous	Gabon	Gabon		X
	Congo	Congo	X	(probable)
	Angola	Angola	X	
pre-Cretaceous	Senegal	Senegal-Mauritania		X
Jurassic	Bulgaria	Provadia	X	
	Soviet Union	Kuljab	X	(probable)
	Aden Protectorate	Red Sea		X
Triassic-Jurassic	Tanzania	Mandawa	X	
Triassic	Germany	South German	X	
	Northern France, England	North Europe	X	
	Southwest France	Aquitaine	X	(probable)
Permo-Triassic	Spain, France, Morroco, Algeria, Tunisia, Libya, Sicily, Italy, Adriatic, Cyprus, Syria	Mediterranean		X
Permian	Soviet Union	Emba		X
		Solikamsk	X	
	Germany, Denmark, Netherlands, England, North Sea, Poland	Northwest German (Zechstein)		X
Devonian	Russia	Nordvik	X	
		Sary-Su	X	
	Ukraine	Kharkov		X
Cambrian	Siberia	Kimpendzjal	X	
	Iran, Persian Gulf	Persian Gulf		X
	Iran	Qum		X
Proterozoic	Australia	Amadeus	X	

graphic location of these salt deposits. The salt deposits of South America are small in comparison to those of North America principally because of the limited data available concerning the subsurface stratigraphy of South American basins. Future exploration probably will prove the existence of other evaporite basins as well as expand the limits of the presently known deposits.

The major basins containing evaporites in North America are in the Maritime Provinces of eastern Canada; the Appalachian basin in New York, Ohio, and Ontario; the Michigan basin in Michigan and Ontario; the Williston basin in North Dakota, South Dakota, Montana, and Saskatchewan; the Alberta basin in northern and eastern Alberta; the Mackenzie basin in the Northwestern Territories; the

TABLE 1-2
Major Salt Basins in the Western Hemisphere

Age of Salt	Country or Region	Basin or Province	Bedded Salt and Halo-tectonic (Salt Basin)	Halokinesis (Salt Dome Basin)
Pliocene	Nevada	Virgin Valley	X	
Eocene	Wyoming	Green River	X	
Pre-Tertiary	Dominican Republic	Enriquillo	X	
Mesozoic	Argentina	Neuquen	X	
Cretaceous	Cuba	Cuba		X
	Florida	Sunniland	X	
	Colombia	Zipaquira	X	
	Brazil	Aracaju (Sergipe)	X	
Jurassic	Dakotas, Montana	Williston	X	
Triassic-Jurassic	Southern United States	Gulf Coast		X
		Sabinas		X (mainly gypsum)
	Mexico	Veracruz		X
		Tabasco-Campeche		X
	Gulf of Mexico	Sigsbee Deep		X (probable)
Triassic	Peru	Rio Huallaga		X
Permian	West Texas, New Mexico, Oklahoma, Kansas	Permian	X	
	Dakotas, Montana	Williston	X	
Post-Pennsylvanian	Brazil	Manaos	X	
Pennsylvanian	Utah, Colorado	Paradox		X
	Arizona	Supai	X	
	Canadian Arctic Islands	Sverdrup		X (mainly gypsum)
Mississippian	Maritime Provinces, Newfoundland	Cumberland-Moncton		X
	Dakotas, Montana	Williston	X	
Devonian	Alberta	Alberta (Elk Point)	X	
	N. Dakota, Montana, Saskatchewan, Manitoba	Williston	X	
Silurian	New York, Ohio, Ontario	Appalachian	X	
	Michigan, Ontario	Michigan	X	
Cambrian-Ordovician	Northwest Territories	Mackenzie	X	

Permian basin of West Texas, New Mexico, Oklahoma and Kansas; the Paradox basin in southeastern Utah and southwestern Colorado; the Supai basin in New Mexico and Arizona; and the Gulf region of the United States, Mexico, and Cuba. Salt-controlled structures are known only in the Moncton basin of the Maritime Provinces, the Paradox basin, and the Gulf region.

Elongate salt anticlines are found in the northern part of the Paradox basin, eliptical salt plugs occur in the Moncton basin; and both anticlinal and diapiric salt masses are concentrated in basinal segments of the greater Gulf region.

The Gulf Coast basin of the southern United States contains five depocenters (areas of maximum deposition) which comprise the salt dome basins shown in Figures 1-3. These salt dome basins include:

1. The Rio Grande basin
2. The East Texas basin
3. The Texas-Louisiana Coastal basin
4. The North Louisiana basin
5. The East-Central Louisiana-Mississippi Interior basin

Salt structures are characteristically limited to depocenters where a greater than normal thickness of sediments overlies the salt source bed. Salt may be present over parts of the major structural elements of the Gulf region, such as the Monroe and Sabine uplifts, Coahuila and Tamaulipas peninsulas, but is undoubtedly much thinner because of, (1) less salt deposition over positive features, or, (2) possible flowage from areas of higher relief to areas of lower relief.

Gulf Region Salt Domes

Four hundred and nine domes where salt has actually been penetrated by drilling are located in the United States Gulf region and in the Isthmian embayment of southeastern Veracruz and western Tabasco, Mexico. In addition there are scores of probable deep, onshore domes and other lesser relief structures where salt has not yet been penetrated by the drill. But on the basis of geological and geophysical information, they are judged to be salt controlled. Notable in this category is the Conroe field, Montgomery County, Texas, which has all the geologic criteria for a deep salt intrusion. On the outer continental shelf of Texas, Louisiana, and Mexico several hundred probable domes await confirmation; indeed, the abyssal depth of the Sigsbee Deep adjacent to the Yucatan shelf probably con-

tains clusters of needle-shaped salt spines. Geophysical evidence indicates that some of the probable domes in the Sigsbee Deep protrude from the sea floor.

Evaporite deposits comprise approximately 40 different salts—however, only a few are present in more than trace quantities. The most common salts are the calcium sulphates including gypsum ($CaSO_4 \cdot 2H_2O$) and anhydrite ($CaSO_4$). The best known occurrence are rock salt deposits (halite-NaCl) which are found as low relief bedded salt and as salt structures. Potash and magnesium salts are commercially important but constitute only a small portion of the world's evaporites.

Only in comparatively recent years has sufficient information been available to establish the geochronology of the Gulf region salt dome basin. Deeper drilling, improved geophysical techniques, and new stratigraphic interpretation have helped to date the period of salt deposition and to form concepts on the most probable mode of deposition.

Fortunately, the information has brought about revision of paleotectonic and paleogeographic concepts which are applicable not only to the Gulf region but to most of the major evaporite basins in the world.

Several important conclusions may be drawn from these concepts:

1. The major salt basins of the world (e.g., Gulf region, Mediterranean, Northwest Germany, Western Africa) are not simple arbitrarily positioned evaporite pans, tidal or supratidal flats occasionally separated from open marine waters; but rather, they reflect major negative elements which are probably related to re-activation of basement structure. The present continental margins which include many of the major coastal salt basins and their bounding orogenic belts and cratonic

elements are positioned along ancestral zones of orogenesis.

2. The above premise explains why the many separate coastal salt basins (U. S. Gulf Coastal, Veracruz; North African, Adriatic) cannot be considered in isolation but must be viewed as segments of much larger marine basins.

3. Throughout the world salt deposits tend to increase in thickness toward the deepest part of the basin. Plastic salt flowage into low areas may, in part, explain local variation in salt thickness; however, on a regional basis the two factors which appear to have a greater bearing on the thickness of the salt are (1) subsidence related to orogenesis and (2) synchronous deposition. Basin depocenters in the Gulf region which contain thicker salt deposits are intimately related to the major orogenic belts describing the basin architecture and are discussed in Chapter 2. Synchronous deposition, on the other hand, envisions a stratigraphic interval of pure salt represented by equivalent deposits of the major constituents of an evaporitic facies (marine marl, dolomite, anhydrite, gypsum or nonmarine red beds).

Literature Cited

Aymé, J. M.: "The Senegal Salt Basin," *Salt Basins Around Africa* (1965), The Institute of Petroleum, London, pp. 83-90.

Belmonte, Y., Hirtz, P. and Wenger, R.: "The Salt Basins of the Gabon and the Congo (Brazzaville): A Tentative Paleogeographic Interpretation," *Salt Basins Around Africa* (1965), The Institute of Petroleum, London, pp. 55-78.

Demaison, G. J.: "The Triassic Salt in the Algerian Sahara," *Salt Basins Around Africa* (1965), The Institute of Petroleum, London, pp. 91-100.

Eby, J. B.: "Salt Dome Interest Centers on Gulf Coast," *World Oil* (1956), v. 143, no. 5, pp. 143-150; *Proc.*, International Geol. Cong. (1956).

Gill, W. D.: "The Mediterranean Basin," *Salt Basins Around Africa* (1965), The Institute of Petroleum, London, pp. 101-111.

Kennedy, W. Q.: "The Influence of Basement Structure on the Evolution of the Coastal (Mesozoic and Tertiary) Basins," *Salt Basins Around Africa* (1965), The Institute of Petroleum, London, pp. 7-16.

Kent, P. E.: "An Evaporite Basin in Southern Tanzania," *Salt Basins Around Africa* (1965), The Institute of Petroleum, London, pp. 41-54.

O'Brien, C. A. E.: "Salt Diapirism in South Persia," *Geologie en Mijnbouw Niewve Serie*, 19e Jaargang (1957), pp. 357-376.

Playfair, John: *Illustrations of the Huttonian Theory of the Earth*, Edinburgh, 1802.

Trusheim, F.: "On the Mechanism of Salt Migration in Northern Germany," *Bull.*, AAPG (1960), v. 44, no. 9, pp. 1519-1540.

Chapter
2

Evaporite Deposition
in the Gulf Region

The processes controlling the precipitation of salts were established long ago by the experiments of Usiglio (1849) on the evaporation of sea water. Usiglio noted that salts precipitated from brines fall within closely defined salinity and density ranges. The concentration of normal sea water when increased beyond its equilibrium constant causes solutes to settle out of solution. Usiglio demonstrated that when sea water is reduced to about one-fifth of its volume, calcium sulphate (anhydrite) is precipitated. Further reduction results in the precipitation of halite, then potassium and magnesium bearing salts (bitterns). If a 1,000-foot column of sea water were precipitated, the resulting deposits would be 15 feet thick and comprise 0.4 foot of calcium sulphate, 11.6 feet of halite, and 3.0 feet of bitterns (Pettijohn, 1957).

The origin of thick evaporite deposits in nature has interested geologists ever since Ochsenius (1888) developed his classic "bar theory" hypothesis to explain salt deposits. Precipitation of great volumes of salt in nature requires an environment where, over long spans of geologic time, evaporation exceeds rainfall and surface run-off, and where restriction to free circulation of sea water exists. Ochsenius' bar provided the seaward barrier to restrict commingling of saturated brines with sea water except under conditions of storm elevated sea levels. During brief storm periods sea water of normal salinity would spill over the bar and replenish the brines which were evaporating.

Brine crystallization actually is more complex than ordinarily believed. It is influenced by a number of variables including brine concentration, temperature, and solubility of the salts in the brine. In turn, these factors are controlled, at least in part, by basin architecture—depth of the water, bathymetry of the basin, and geomorphological characteristics of the adjacent land bodies. Although the order of precipitation under natural conditions agrees in general with the experiments of Usiglio, there are many exceptions. Because of these exceptions, geologists have studied evaporite sequences in basins throughout the world and have offered different theories to explain the mode of deposition.

There is voluminous geologic information available on the Louann salt of the Gulf region, often referred to as the "mother salt bed." Perhaps more laboratory studies have been conducted to explain the structural relationships of the Louann salt to the host sediments than any other salt deposit in the world. Many of this country's most renowned geologists have worked on the age and mode of deposition of the Louann salt and their findings are well documented. These excellent studies have contributed much to our knowledge of surface and subsurface geology, paleontology, palynology, and other means of establishing stratigraphic relationships as possible solution of the problem. In spite of this, there is more disagreement among geologists on the Louann salt of the Gulf region than any other evaporite deposit in the world. At present, there are two schools of thought on the age and mode of deposition of the Louann salt. An early belief holds that the Louann salt is Permian in age and is, in part, a stratigraphic equivalent of the Permian Castile formation of the Delaware basin in West Texas. A later concept holds that the salt is Triassic to Middle Jurassic in age and represents a widespread evaporite deposit of an ancestral gulf similar in size and shape to today's Gulf of Mexico. There is sound evidence and reasoning behind both beliefs.

The Louann—A Permian Salt Basin

First let us review the ideas supporting the concept of a Permian age for the Louann salt and its mode of deposition. Many students draw considerable support by analogy of similar events. The Permian period was extremely arid as is evidenced by the worldwide occurrence of evaporites of Permian age. The Zechstein Salt of northern Germany is of Permian age and the structural growth of many salt stocks in that basin is similar to the salt domes of the Gulf region. There are Permian salt basins in Russia. The Permian of West Texas and the Williston basin of North Dakota contain thick evaporite deposits.

Admittedly, the widespread salt deposits of Permian age do not necessarily mean that the salt of the Gulf region should be assigned to the Permian. However, detailed work by many writers on the Permian of West Texas is a good starting point for reconstructing the sedimentational process governing deposition of the Louann Salt.

The early work of Branson (1915) suggested modifications to Ochsenius' theory wherein marine waters entered a barred basin, precipitated most of their carbonates and sulfates, and then moved on to an adjoining barred basin where salts of the upper salinity ranges were deposited. Adams' (1944) excellent paper on the Permian Ochoa Series of the Delaware basin applied the "modified bar" concept to partially explain the deposition of the Castile Anhydrite. He noted the predominance of anhydrite over salt in the formation which is not consistent with phase relations during the evaporation of brine.

To account for the absence of sodium salts in the Delaware basin, Adams (1944) concluded that concentrated brines containing sodium chloride must have escaped from the basin. Two methods of escape were suggested, either through a deep breaching and subsequent sealing of the barrier which created the evaporite basin, or, more plausibly, that the heavy brines escaped through a permeable barrier. Adams (p. 1620) states, "with limited permeability, outflow would occur when the gravity and pressure of the brine in the barred basin was higher than that of the water at the same level outside."

King (1947) enlarged on the process by which anhydrite was deposited at the expense of halite and proposed the theory of reflux. The Delaware basin, according to King, was connected to the sea by a channel through which new sea water entered the basin to replace water lost by evaporation. The concentrated brine, he reasons, sank to the bottom of the barred basin and returned as a reflux to the open sea either by overflowing the barrier or by percolating through it. Calculation shows that the rate of influx to reflux was about 10:1. The salinity of the Castile sea within the Delaware basin was nearly saturated with sodium chloride, and thus the calcium sulfate and less soluble materials were precipitated, but the heavy soluble brines were discharged as a reflux before they could settle out.

Scruton (1953) reviewed the results of several oceanographic studies in estuaries and restricted arms of the sea and noted that particular circulation patterns exist. These circulation patterns, due to the flow of less saline or dense waters to regions of greater salinity under influence of hydrostatic head, would appear to support the reflux theory of King.

The hypersaline brines of the Castile sea refluxing from the evaporite basin altered the metastable limestones to bedded dolomites (Adams and Rhodes, 1960). This most interesting concept may have application in explaining the association of anhydrites with dolomites in many other evaporite basins of the world. According to these two authors, the heavy brines on the bottom of the barred evaporite basin were dense enough to displace the connate waters and seep down through the slightly permeable carbonates of the basin floor. During this seepage, magnesium in the brines replaced part of the calcium which later recrystallized as dolomite.

The stratigraphic relationships of pre-Smackover (Upper Jurassic) rocks gleaned from data obtained in deep wells drilled in south Arkansas, northeast Texas, and north Louisiana caused a revision of the correlation and stratigraphic nomenclature of these pre-Upper Jurassic age rocks and resulted in the concept that the Louann salt basin was of Permian age (Hazzard, Spooner, Blanpied, 1947). The work of these authors is a recognized contribution to the knowledge of the Louann-Werner (anhydrite) evaporite sequence. Supported by the experiments of Usiglio (1849) and the multiple-basin hypothesis of Branson (1915) they envisioned that the Louann-Werner evaporite sequence represented the deposits laid down in a large enclosed basin separated by one or more barriers from a body or normal marine water. The evaporites in the Permian basin of West Texas, and the Louann-Werner sequence of the Gulf region are geographically close enough to reasonably expect a related mode of deposition and an age equivalancy, particularly if a theory could explain the extreme range in the salt to anhydrite ratios between the two basins. At the conclusion of their work, Hazzard, Spooner, and Blanpied (p. 502) state:

> In light of Usiglio's principles, the Castile formation represents the stage of calcium sul-

phate precipitation with six or eight possible interruptions in the cycle, during which the salinity of the brines reached the point of sodium chloride precipitation. During Castile time brines entered the Delaware Basin from the southwest . . . with a continuous outward movement of denser brines carrying sodium chloride in solution. It is thought that these brines moved eastward into the Louann-Werner Basin, perhaps through a channel located to the northeast of the Central Mineral Region, but that more probably it trended in a southeast direction, to the south of the Central Mineral Region. The unconformity at the base of the Werner Formation is correlated with the unconformity at the base of the Castile Formation. It is thought that the channel was permanently closed prior to Salado time. The hiatus between the Louann Salt and the Norphlet Formation would represent post-Castile Permian time and all of Triassic and Lower and Middle Jurassic time.

Halbouty and Hardin (1956) supported the ideas of Hazzard, *et al.,* with their belief of a probable correlation between the Louann salt and the Castile Anhydrite of the Delaware basin. In explaining the mother salt bed deposit, Halbouty and Hardin (1956) reasoned that the salt basin area began to subside with the Llanoria land mass (Ouachita tectonic province) which was much more extensive than previously believed. The sinking was probably the beginning of the Gulf coast geosyncline and the present Gulf of Mexico. Their report (pp. 739, 740) says:

> The sinking continued through Lower and Middle Permian time, so that at the beginning of Upper Permian time a large restricted basin existed [Fig. 2-1].
>
> Also, during this time, seas covering West Texas were greatly restricted, so that at the beginning of Castile time (Upper Permian), only the Delaware basin was submerged.
>
> The lands surrounding the basin were low

and tidal flats existed east of the basin; these flats were not receiving sediments, nor were they being eroded.

In these flats existed narrow flow channels, with intermittent permeability barriers, which connected the Gulf Coast basin with the Castile sea. The Castile sea was intermittently connected and separated by a bar area with a marine sea on the southwest, thus making the Castile basin a barred basin. Referring to the bar area and the intermittent flow of open sea waters in the Castile basin, Adams (1944, p. 1617) stated:

> All the geological evidence indicates that the marine waters that entered the Castile sea entered from the south or southwest through one or more narrow channels. A sand-dune ridge, perhaps made up of calcareous sands and protected by organic reefs, would be a logical type of barrier to shut off migration through such channels. Breaches could be produced by storm waves and sealed off by normal wind action. Alternate breaching and sealing of a barrier of this type might well be a seasonal occurrence. Recurrent closing and opening of the barrier would allow the waters in the basin to be lowered by evaporation or to be raised by freshening floods.
>
> Initially the waters of the Castile sea were fairly well uniform in composition, and because they were derived from the open sea, salt concentrations would be those normal to the waters of the Permian oceans, which probably closely approached those of the present sea. . . .

Sea waters from time to time entered the Castile basin over the bar area, and the waters were evaporated to the extent that $CaSO_4$ was largely deposited. The level of the sea would be lowered, with only concentrated brines remaining. New waters from the marine sea from the southwest would break over the bar area and enter the Castile basin with a rush, so that the velocity and volume of these new waters would be of sufficient force to push out eastward the remaining brine waters into the tidal-flat channels and on into the Gulf

Coast basin, where these highly concentrated brine waters would deposit their salt. Cycle after cycle of this procedure followed, thus accounting for the small amount of salt present in the Castile basin and the small amount of anhydrite deposited in the Gulf Coast basin (Hazzard, *et al*).

The Louann Salt—An Upper Triassic-Lower Jurassic Salt Basin

Much data has been collected on the pre-Upper Jurassic age rocks in the coastal province of the United States and Mexico subsequent to the ideas advanced by Hazzard and his colleagues, and by this author and his associates. The careful work of Imlay (1943, 1948) on the distribution and stratigraphic relationships of clastic-evaporitic rocks of Jurassic age in northeastern and southern Mexico was augmented by the studies of several other geologists (see Humphrey, 1956; Humphrey and Diaz, 1958; Mixon, Murray and Diaz, 1959; and Murray, 1961). The results of these works suggest that the Louann salt of the Gulf region of the United States is related in age and mode of deposition to the pre-Zuloaga age rocks of northeastern Mexico.

In attempting to explain the vast evaporite basin which collected thick Louann salt deposits, the age and distribution of the salt or its equivalents (if exactly known) would dispel much of the controversy surrounding salt deposition. Unfortunately, the precise age has not yet been determined, but reasonable stratigraphic relationships have been worked out for overlying and underlying rocks whose age and facies equivalent are now established.

The excellent and unusually complete synopsis of Murray (1961), which combined the work of hundreds of previous authors with much of his own material, has contributed immeasurably to the clear understanding of the geologic framework of the Gulf region.

Murray (1961) believes that the salt of the Gulf Coast basin is probably post-Triassic and pre-Oxford in age and is stratigraphically equivalent to the clastic-evaporite sequences of eastern and southern Mexico and to the anhydrite and gypsum deposits of the Sabinas basin of northeastern Mexico (southwestern portion of Rio Grande embayment). These conclusions are based in part on the works of Imlay *et al.,* (1948) who correlated the red beds of the Huizachal Formation (probably Lower-Middle Jurassic) with the Eagle Mills Formation of the Gulf region, and suggested a correlation between the main mass of salt in the southern United States and the time represented by the disconformity between the Huizachal Formation and the overlying upper Oxfordian limestone in eastern and northern Mexico.

The observations of Murray (1961 p. 284) on the Eagle Mills-Werner-Louann sequences based on regional studies of the Gulf basin (where there appear to be equivalent strata in south Texas and northeastern Mexico to northeastern Texas, southern Arkansas, northern Louisiana, and Alabama) are as follows:

(1) They (Eagle-Mills-Werner-Louann) underlie beds of generally accepted Late Jurassic age (Smackover and Norphlet Formation) and overlie Paleozoic strata (Permian and older) and Paleozoic-Precambrian.

(2) They are similar lithologically and occupy an equivalent stratigraphic position to that of evaporites and red clastics (Huizachal Group) in Mexico which at places partially overlie Early Jurassic strata. In different localities these red beds have yielded Middle Jurassic and Triassic plants.

(3) More than 2,000 feet of evaporites, principally anhydrite, occur in the Sabinas basin

and adjacent area of northeastern Mexico beneath the Smackover equivalent (Zuloaga limestone of Upper Jurassic Oxfordian age). These and upper Huizachal red beds which underlie Zuloaga in other areas appear to be continuous with the strata of the coastal province. The evaporites might therefore be the sulphate concentrate of the Louann Salt, which is deficient in sulphates, rather than such a concentrate being the sulphate deposits in West Texas and New Mexico. (Halbouty and Hardin, 1956; Hazzard, Blanpied, Spooner, 1947).

(4) Thick salt of the coastal area appears to be restricted to areas basinward (Gulfward) of inner-boundary fault systems, these fault systems apparently also limiting the inner extent of thick deposits of Late Jurassic age.

(5) Salt from domes in northern Cuba has yielded spores of Mesozoic age, probably no younger than Early Cretaceous (letter from H. J. Morgan, Jr., dated November 12, 1956). Persistent rumors have circulated verbally in the coastal area for several years that the salt has yielded definite Permian spores; however, to date it has not been possible to verify them, although certain paleontologists admit that in their opinion some spores from the lower part of the Louann salt might be as old as Permian.

DeGolyer and others (1926) reported that red algae of Permian age were found in potash salt of the Rycade Oil Corporation #1 Gray well drilled on Markham dome, Matagorda County, Texas in 1924. To the writer's knowledge this report of Permian age salt based on palynological determination is the only documentation of this type ever recorded.

Andrews (1960 p. 227) reviewed the opinions of previous writers on the age of the Louann salt and concluded:

> . . . most Gulf Coast geologists agree that the Louann salt of the Gulf Coast basin is definitely no older than Pennsylvanian, probably no older than the West Texas Upper Permian, but is older than Upper Jurassic. Within these upper and lower age limitations, no definite con-

clusive proof for either Upper Permian, Triassic, Lower or Middle Jurassic, or a combination thereof, can be presented at this time. However, after a careful consideration of all the available material, the writer (Andrews) believes that a preponderance of the existing data and interpretation seems to more strongly favor an age younger than Permian, probably near the Early Jurassic.

More recent information on the age relationships of the Eagle Mills-Werner-Louann sequence was reported by Scott, *et al*, (1961) from cores of the Eagle Mills Formation recovered from a well in southern Arkansas. The Humble Oil & Refining Company's No. 1 Royston, Hempstead County, Arkansas, contained impressions of the plant fossil *Macrotaeniopteris magnifolia* in cores of the Eagle Mills Formation. To date, this plant fossil is known in North America only from the Upper Triassic. However, closely related species range into the Jurassic both in North American and Eurasia. Based on this identification, which might be conclusive if verified in other wells, the Louann salt which is stratigraphically above the Eagle Mills would be no older than Upper Triassic and probably was deposited during Early to Middle Jurassic time.

The most recent evidence that directly relates to the age of the Louann salt concerns palynologic data obtained from intruded and bedded salt of mines in Texas and Louisiana and from cores of wells in north Louisiana (Jux, 1961). Examination of 24 different sporomorphs (wind-deposited microfloral fossils) taken from the various mines and well cores showed a predominance of Upper Triassic types, with a few species ranging up into the Jurassic. Jux believes an Upper Triassic-Lower Jurassic age for the diapiric salt of the Gulf region is therefore most probable, and states, "the sporomorphs encountered in each

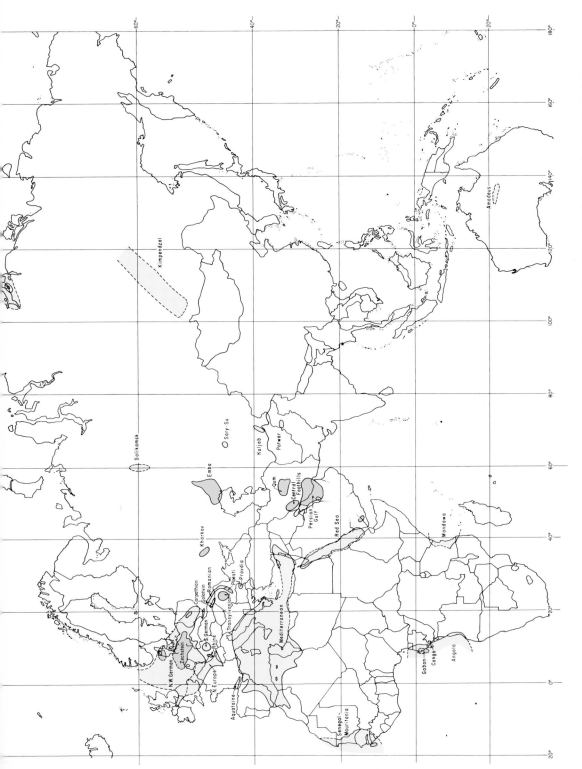

Figure 1-1. Map shows location of major salt basins in the Eastern Hemisphere. The depositional habitat of salt deposits include: salt basins containing bedded salt which is essentially little deformed or, if folded, is the result of basin tectonics (compression, tension, shear); salt dome basins containing salt controlled structures where isostatic salt movement has created the structural form. (Modified in part after Eby, 1956)

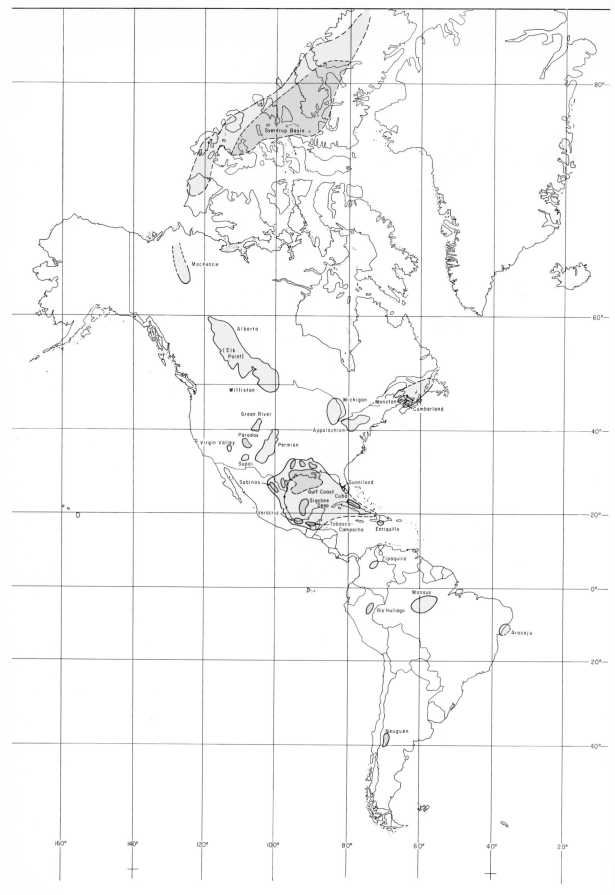

Figure 1-2. Map shows location of major salt basins in the Western Hemisphere. The Gulf Coastal province of the United States contains five separate salt dome basins within the larger Gulf region salt basin.

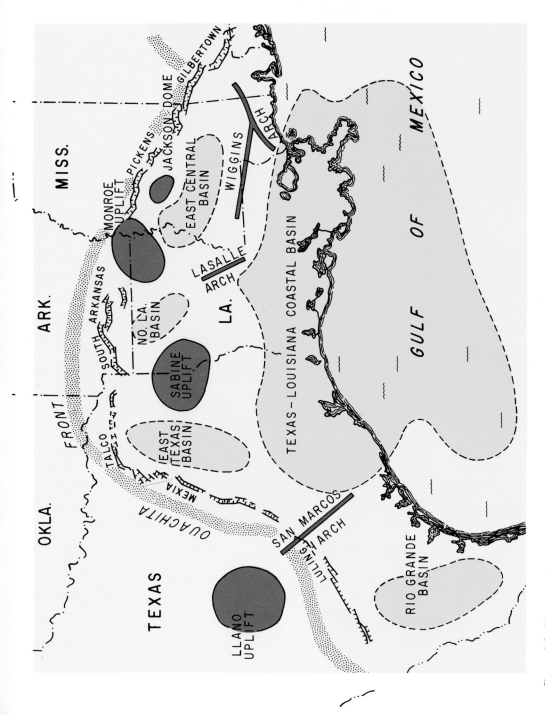

Figure 1-3. Diagrammatic map outlines the major structural features of the U.S. Gulf region including the five salt dome basins and their relationship to positive elements. Salt-controlled structural features are located in the salt-dome basins shown in deep yellow. Light yellow areas are part of the evaporite basin of deposition but in these areas the salt source layer is less thick and no salt structures are known to exist.

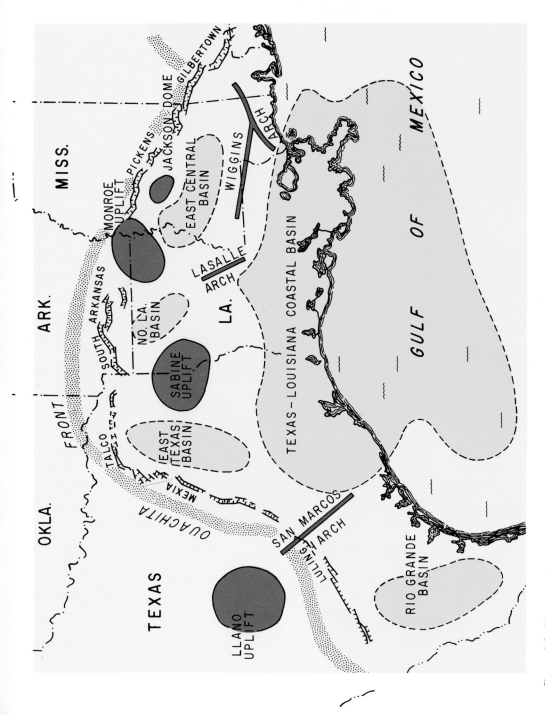

15

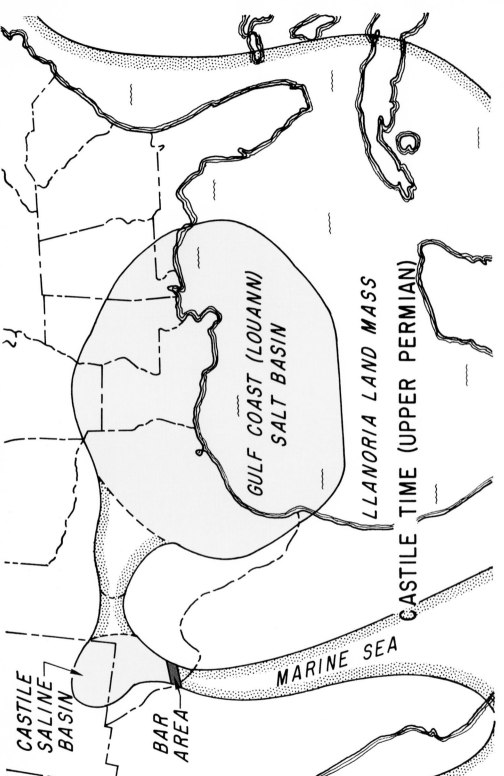

CASTILE SALINE BASIN

BAR AREA

GULF COAST (LOUANN) SALT BASIN

LLANORIA LAND MASS

MARINE SEA

CASTILE TIME (UPPER PERMIAN)

Figure 2-1. This paleogeographic map shows a concept of conditions at beginning of Upper Permian time. Concept suggests a relationship between the Permian anhydrite deposits of the Castile Saline basin and the rock-salt deposits of the Louann salt basin. The concept envisioned that sea waters from time to time entered the Castile basin over the bar area, and less soluble evaporites (anhydrite) were precipitated. The level of the sea was lowered, with only concentrated brines remaining in solution. Normal marine waters from the southwest intermittently broke over the bar area with enough velocity to force the concentrated brines eastward into the tidal-flat channels and into the Gulf Coast basin. Here, the concentrated brines precipitated as halite. This concept is useful in explaining the difference between the relative proportion of salt to anhydrite in the Castile basin and the Louann basin. (After Halbouty and Hardin, 1956)

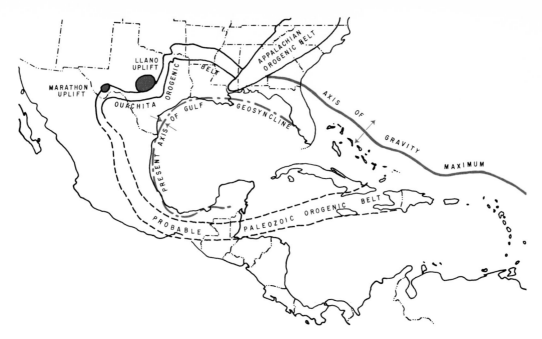

Figure 2-2. Late Paleozoic (Pennsylvanian?) orogenic belts outlining the Gulf region. These belts probably initiated the present basin architecture. The orogenic belt in Mexico was later obscured by movements reflected in the present Sierra Madre Oriental. The gravity maximum extending from the east coast of Florida probably coincides with the continental margin. The influx of marine waters into the Louann salt basin probably entered from the east across a sill or bar. (Modified after Lyons, 1957)

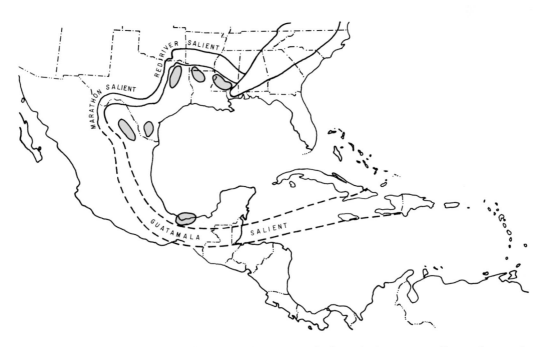

Figure 2-3. Map shows possible relationship of interior salt dome basins to arc salients of orogenic belts. The salt dome basins in the Isthmanian embayment of Mexico, and interior portion of the Gulf Coastal province of the United States are depocenters adjacent to salients of the Paleozoic orogenic belts. Areas adjacent to recesses of the orogenic belt (e.g. Central Texas) were more stable and received a lesser volume of sediments including salt.

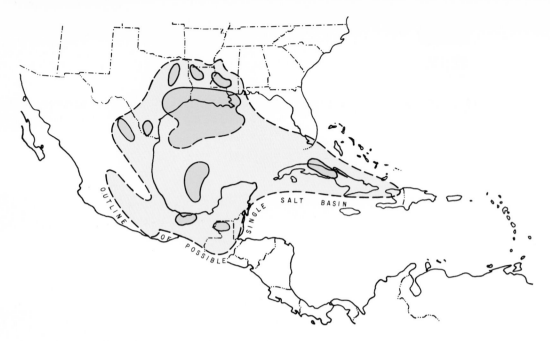

Figure 2-4. Map shows known extent of salt dome basins in the Gulf region and their relationship to enclosing salt basins. The dashed line outlines the boundary of a postulated single salt deposition basin representing a vast, silled ancestral Gulf of Mexico. (Single basin outline after concepts of Imlay, 1943 in Lyons, 1957)

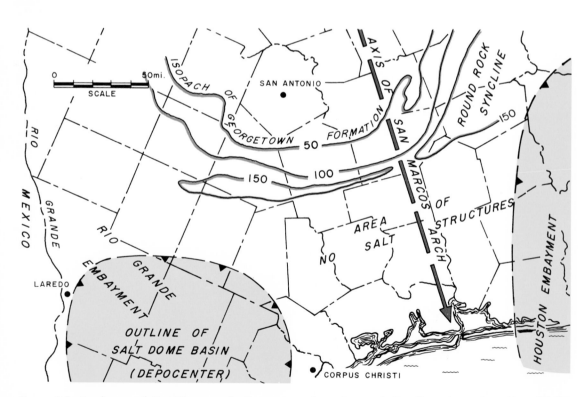

Figure 2-5. Areal map of San Marcos arch, Texas. Isopach contours of the Georgetown formation (Washita group—Lower Cretaceous) show the gentle nosing of the arch in an updip position. Downdip, the influence of the arch is reflected by the absence of known salt structures in a wedge-shaped area which separates the Rio Grande and Gulf Coastal (Houston Embayment segment) salt dome basins.

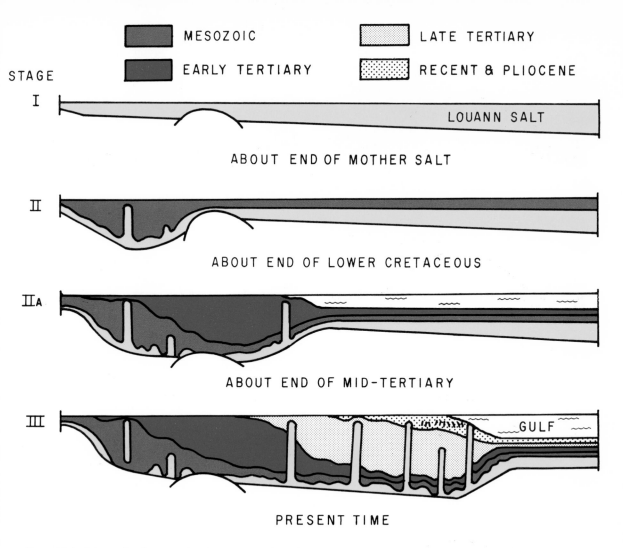

STAGE

I

LOUANN SALT

ABOUT END OF MOTHER SALT

II

ABOUT END OF LOWER CRETACEOUS

IIA

ABOUT END OF MID-TERTIARY

III

GULF

PRESENT TIME

MESOZOIC

EARLY TERTIARY

LATE TERTIARY

RECENT & PLIOCENE

Figure 2-6. Schematic diagram showing structural evolution of interior and coastal salt dome basins of Gulf region. (Modified from Hanna, 1959, in Andrews, 1960).

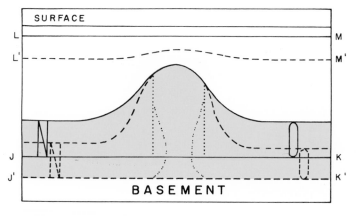

SURFACE

L   M

L'   M'

J   K

J'   K'

BASEMENT

Figure 3-1. Diagrammatic representation of downbuilding of salt dome. (After Barton, 1933)

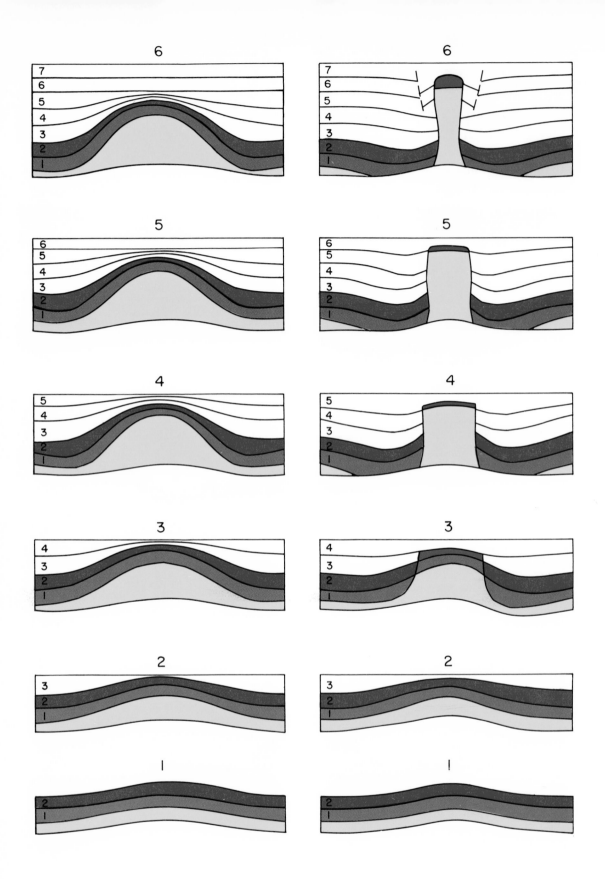

Figure 3-2. Stage development of a shallow piercement dome (right) and deep-seated, non-piercement dome (left). (After Nettleton, 1934).

of the samples are so small in total abundance, that nothing but a Rhaetic-Liassic age could be stated for the whole region investigated." From the preponderance of data which place the Louann salt in the Upper Triassic-Lower Jurassic age, it is reasonable to predict that the second school of thought will eventually become firmly established. In recognizing a younger than Permian age for the Louann Salt, a different theory of the mode of salt deposition is now widely accepted.

Development of the Basin and Its Structures

Most geologists believe that the depositional history and structural development of the salt basins and salt dome basins of the Gulf region coincide with the post-orogenic phase of the Gulf Coast province of North America. Recent interpretations of geophysical studies of the Gulf of Mexico by Ewing, *et al,* (1955) and Lyons (1957, 1965) have helped establish the structural evolution of the Gulf Coast basin and its relationship to the Gulf geosyncline and present Gulf of Mexico. The geologic history of the Gulf Coast of the United States is clearly a part of the history of the greater Gulf region including the Mexican and Antillean segments.

Enough work has been done by previous authors to relate structural alignments and tectonic features of the Gulf region to earlier controls established by the Ouachita system in the United States and its orogenic counterparts in Mexico and the Antilles. It is not just coincidental that zones of faulting along the inner edge of the Gulf region (Balcones, Luling-Mexia, Arkansas, Pickens-Gilbertown, and zones of igneous activity of Cretaceous and younger age, closely follow the Ouachita trend. The comprehensive work of Flawn,

et al., (1961) resolved many of the questions about the Ouachita structural belt and its influence on positive and negative elements of the inner margin of the Gulf region.

The depositional basin that accumulated post-orogenic (Permian and later) sediments developed as part of the much larger Gulf Coast basin, the paleogeography of which was similar to the present Gulf of Mexico. The configuration of the Gulf Coast basin and Gulf of Mexico is outlined by Paleozoic fold belts except along the eastern margin. Here a zone of gravity maxima probably indicates downfaulting on the edge of the continental platform, or a possible eastward extension of the Ouachita orogenic belt. Figure 2-2 shows the approximate outline of the Ouachita tectonic belt and its probable Mexican and Antillean counterparts. The belt in the United States curves toward and over the craton in broad salients, and recesses around buttressing elements of the stable craton margin. In the Gulf region of the United States, regional negative and positive elements are coincident with salients and recesses respectively of the Ouachita belt. In Mexico and northern Central America this relationship is reversed, *i.e.,* salients of the Paleozoic fold belt are adjacent to positive elements of the coastal province and recesses are adjacent to negative elements. This feature was pointed out by Murray (1961 pp. 90, 91) who explained:

> . . . the anomalies of the eastern flank of the Sierra Madre Oriental orogenic belt, which apparently control late and post-Cretaceous structures in adjacent portions of the coastal province, were in turn positioned by the now covered Paleozoic and Precambrian trends. It is suggested that the areas (salients and recesses) of the flank of the Sierra Madre Oriental respectively reflect recesses and salients of stabilized Paleozoic fold belt or belts. If so, the

large negative anomalies of the coastal province in this region are also adjacent to the salients of the Paleozoic orogenic belt and vice versa.

The salt dome basins within the Veracruz-Tabasco, Rio Grande, East Texas, North Louisiana, and East-Central Louisiana-Mississippi basins are depocenters within salt basins adjacent to arc salients of the Paleozoic orogenic belts (Fig. 2-3). These sites of maximum deposition probably were inherited from earlier zones of weakness which resulted in crustal downbuilding from isostatic adjustments occasioned by the Paleozoic orogeny.

The salt dome basins of the Gulf region are believed to be encircled by salt basins where little salt deformation has occurred, or at least where no diapiric structures are observed. Undisturbed, bedded salt in "domeless" areas of the Gulf region has not been penetrated except in a few widely scattered localities. Therefore, the subcrop area is largely derived from geophysical evidence. Although salt has been penetrated in hundreds of test wells and many wells have drilled through the salt into older sediments, most of these wells are located on known or inferred salt structures.

Many geologists generally agree that a continuous bed of Louann salt underlies the Gulf region including the Gulf of Mexico. A single salt basin (Fig. 2-4), representative of a vast closed ancestral gulf, has been suggested by Lyons (1957) based in part on the works of Imlay (1943), who carefully reconstructed the distribution of Jurassic sediments which correspond to an extensive Gulf area. Domeless areas which separate the salt dome basins and such major tectonic features as the San Marcos arch, Sabine uplift, Monroe uplift, Jackson dome, etc. (Fig. 1-3) may be covered in part by a thin veneer of Louann salt. In

some localized areas, however, the absence of salt may be due to nondeposition, erosion, or flowage from "highs" into adjacent "lows."

The San Marcos arch has had the greatest influence (geographically) on salt sedimentation and lack of development of salt structures of any tectonic element in the upper Gulf region. In the updip areas of the Gulf Coastal plain (Atascosa to Bastrop Counties, Texas), the San Marcos arch in the subsurface is reflected by thinning of most Cretaceous sequences, notably the Georgetown Formation (Fig. 2-5). The arch has been a persistent positive area since Late Triassic or Early Jurassic time as indicated by apparent thinning or absence of Louann salt and consequently by an absence of salt domes or salt-controlled structures in a wedge-shaped region extending from northeastern Live Oak County to southwestern Colorado County and from Aransas to Matagorda Counties along the Gulf of Mexico (Halbouty, 1966).

The arch, therefore, effectively separates the Rio Grande and Texas-Louisiana coastal (Houston embayment) salt dome basins which are depocenters within their respective salt basins.

The Texas-Louisiana coastal salt dome basin and newly discovered Sigsbee knoll area are believed to contain salt of Louann age. The evaporite was deposited in these local areas about the same time the Louann salt was deposited in the other salt dome basins of the Gulf region. This belief is consistent with the concept of a single contemporaneous salt basin as shown in Fig. 2-4. Growth of piercement salt structures in the interior salt dome basins, hence evolution of the salt dome basin as described herein, is definitely believed to have preceded growth of salt structures in the gulfward-lying salt dome basins. Hanna (1959) pointed out this significant factor and

Andrews (1960), enlarging on the concept of Hanna, illustrated this concept as shown in Figure 2-6. Andrews writes (pp. 231, 232):

Stage I: Would be near the end of Louann or Mother salt time. The basin illustration shown is, of course, very diagrammatic. Salt was deposited thinly, and, in some cases may have been completely missing over a postulated low relief, pre-existing high or highs [schematically shown left of center of Fig. 2-6].

Stage II: Would be near the end of the Lower Cretaceous. During Upper Jurassic and Lower Cretaceous time, sediments were being deposited nearshore in the area of what is now the East Texas and Louisiana-Mississippi Interior basins. Assuming Nettleton's 'Fluid Mechanics' theory to be correct, growth of domes would begin during and after deposition of first, the Jurassic, and second, the Lower Cretaceous overburden. This combined overburden caused this portion of the basin to subside, which, in effect, could have accentuated (or possibly even created) the west-east trending high or highs to the south. Evidence indicates that the greatest amount of sediment overburden from the Norphlet-Smackover formations through the Lower Cretaceous Travis Peak Formation was concentrated in the area of the Interior basins. The downdip (basinward) facies of these formations in what is now the Coastal basin would consist primarily of deep water marine shales and oozes.

According to Forgotson (1956), a marine shale character is implied for these basinward sediments, which now underlies the Coastal basin. These shales and oozes would theoretically have insufficient density contrast to initiate domal growth on a comparable scale to that of the Interior basins. Furthermore, the lip or rim of the south flank of this earlier Mesozoic basin was correspondingly "high," and may have been in relatively shallow, clear, probably warm waters that would be ideally suited for a type of "bank lime" or biohermal development. This area was probably far enough from shore to be unaffected by turbulence, muddy waters, etc., that are usually associated with nearshore clastic deposition. Forgotson (1956) reports that a tectonic sill in southern East Texas and southern north Louisiana separated the (Cretaceous) basin area from the shelf area. He believes that biohermal growth along the tectonic sill was an important factor in producing the restricted environment which periodically favored the deposition of calcium sulphate (Ferry Lake anhydrite) updip from the reef development.

Perhaps this bioherm or "bank lime" could have begun to develop during Travis Peak time, or more likely, it started during Lower Glen Rose. Certainly the Lower Glen Rose units would be susceptible to biohermal or "bank lime" development, and regionally these units also deposited the majority of their load updip in the area of the present interior basins. This further contributed to overall subsidence and resultant domal growth.

Stage II-A: Would be near the end of the mid-Tertiary. The center of deposition has shifted basinward. Again, domes are growing in response to the overburden.

Stage III: Represents present time. The center of deposition has continued to shift basinward (to the right) and has been concentrated in a much smaller area. The Texas-Louisiana Coastal basin salt dome theoretically did not really begin to grow until sufficient overburden existed to initiate the necessary triggering action. The great amount of overburden in this area consists mainly of Tertiary sediments, therefore, the primary age of growth for the Coastal basin domes would be much later than that of the interior domes.

Hatten and Meyerhoff (1965, 1967) and Meyerhoff (1965) wrote on the occurrence of Cretaceous age salt domes reported from northern Cuba. If the paleogeologic concepts reviewed here hold true for the Mexican and Antillean segments of the Paleozoic tectonic belts which controlled post-Paleozoic structures and trends, is it unlikely that the salt deposits of Cuba are contemporaneous with those of the Gulf region of the United States and that the age of Cuban salt dome growth is possibly Cretaceous, but more probably after Middle Eocene time through Recent.

The foregoing discussion of Louann salt and development of the salt dome basins has not only retraced the evolution and growth of ideas on this most interesting subject, but has also suggested that all of the questions to the multiphase problem have not been answered. As more data is obtained, new and revised ideas can be advanced. As an example, consider the writer's earlier belief that the salt was Permian in age and related to the Castile deposits of West Texas. While this idea remains unshaken as to certain basic evaporite basin concepts, new facts have led the author to revise his earlier opinions and support a different age and mode of deposition for the mother salt bed. It is likely that further revisions in these ideas will come from new information now being rapidly collected with more deep drilling of salt domes.

In light of current information the author's new conception of the age and deposition of the Louann salt may be summarized as follows:

1. The depositional basin that accumulated post-orogenic sediments, including the Louann Salt, was similar in size and shape to the Cenozoic Gulf Coast basin including the present Gulf of Mexico. Sub-basins such as the East Texas and Rio Grande embayments probably were initiated by crustal weaknesses caused by arching in the Ouachita fold belt (arc salients). The Gulf Coast geosyncline, which encompasses the Texas-Louisiana coastal salt dome basin, has been continuously downbuilding under the influence of sedimentary load since its positioning along flexure or down-to-the-coast fault zones.

2. The Louann salt is probably Upper Triassic through Lower Jurassic in age but evidence is not conclusive to rule out that part of the salt may be of Permian age or that the salt may, in fact, span the entire interval from Permian to Middle Jurassic.

3. The Louann salt may underlie the entire Gulf Coast basin including the present Gulf of Mexico except in local areas where non-deposition, erosion, or flow is responsible for absence of the salt. The central part of the Gulf of Mexico is a large gravity maximum which Lyons (1957) points out is contrary to what we would expect if the Gulf were a conventional basin. According to Lyons, this pronounced anomaly probably reflects an excess of mass or great high on the Mohorovicic surface which effectively masks the influence of whatever thickness of salt may be deposited over the area.

4. The depocenters within the Gulf Coast basin are also the locales of the known salt dome basins. Unfolded Louann Salt is much thicker in the salt dome basins than in the surrounding domeless areas.

5. The Louann or mother salt bed probably was deposited contemporaneously throughout the basin. However, the development of the interior salt dome basins (hence the growth of diapiric salt structures) probably preceded development and growth of similar features in the coastal salt dome basins.

Literature Cited

Adams, J. E.: "Upper Permian Ochoa Series of Delaware Basin, West Texas and Southeastern New Mexico," *Bull.*, AAPG (1944), v. 28, no. 11, pp. 1598-1625.

Adams, J. E. and Rhodes, M. L.: "Dolomitization by Seepage Refluxion," *Bull.*, AAPG (1960), v. 44, no. 12, pp. 1912-1920.

Andrews, Donald I.: "The Louann Salt and Its Relationship to Gulf Coast Salt Domes," *Trans.,* GCAGS (1960), v. 10, pp. 215-240.

Branson, E. B.: "Origin of Thick Gypsum and Salt Deposits," *Bull.,* GSA (1915), v. 26, no. 6, pp. 231-242.

DeGolyer, E.: "Origin of North American Salt Domes," *Bull.,* AAPG (1925), v. 9, No. 5, pp. 831-874; *Geology of Salt Dome Oil Fields,* AAPG (1926), pp. 1-44.

Ewing, M., et al: "Geophysical and Geological Investigations in the Gulf of Mexico," *Geophysics* (1955), v. 20, pp. 1-18.

Flawn, P. T., Goldstein, A., Jr., King, P. B. and Weaver, C. E.: "The Ouachita System," *Pub. 6120,* Tex. U. (1961), 399 pp.

Forgotson, J. M., Jr.: "A Correlation and Regional Stratigraphic Analysis of the Formation of the Trinity Group of the Comanchean Cretaceous of the Gulf Coastal Plain; and the Genesis and Petrography of the Ferry Lake Anhydrite," *Trans.,* GCAGS (1956), v. 6, pp. 91-105.

Halbouty, Michel T.: "Stratigraphic-Trap Possibilities in Upper Jurassic Rocks, San Marcos Arch, Texas," *Bull.,* AAPG (1966), v. 50, no. 1, pp. 3-24.

Halbouty, Michel T. and Hardin, George C., Jr.: "New Exploration Possibilities on Piercement Type Salt Domes Established by Thrust Fault at Boling Salt Dome, Wharton County, Texas," *Bull.,* AAPG (1954), v. 38, no. 8, pp. 1725-1740.

Halbouty, Michel T. and Hardin, George C., Jr.: "Genesis of Salt Domes of Gulf Coastal Plain," *Bull.,* AAPG (1956), v. 40, no. 4, pp. 737-746.

Hanna, Marcus A., et al: "Salt Domes: Favorite Home for Oil," *Oil and Gas Jour.*

(1959), v. 57, no. 6, pp. 138-142.

Hatten, C. W. and Meyerhoff, A. A.: (abs.) "Pre-Portlandian Rocks of Western Cuba," *Spec. Paper 82,* GSA (1965), p. 301.

Hatten, C. W. and Meyerhoff, A. A.: "Diapiric Structures in Central Cuba, *in* Diapirism and Diapirs," *Memoir,* AAPG (in press).

Hazzard, R. T., Spooner, W. C. and Blanpied, B. W.: "Notes on the Stratigraphy of Formations Which Underlie the Smackover Limestone in South Arkansas, Northeast Texas, and North Louisiana," *Ref. Rept.* (1945), Shreveport Geol. Soc. (1947), v. 2, pp. 483-503.

Humphrey, W. E.: *Notes on Geology of Northeast Mexico,* Corpus Christi Geol. Soc. (1956), 41 pp; *Guidebook Laredo to Monterrey Field Trip* (Supp.), Corpus Christi Geol. Soc. (1956), pp. 9-11: *Guidebook.* Corpus Christi Geol. Soc., 11th Annual Field Trip (1961), pp. 6-8.

Humphrey, W. E. and Diaz Gonzalez, T. E.: "Secuencia Mesozoica. Anticlinal de las Grutas de Garcia en la Sierra del Fraile, a 30 Kilometers al NW de la Cuidad de Monterrey," *Congreso Geologico Internacional* (1958), pp. 26-31.

Humphrey, W. E. and Diaz Gonzalez, T. E.: "Secuencia Mesozoica. Portal de la Muralla, Sierra de la Gavia, Coahuila," *Congreso Geologico Internacional* (1958), pp. 41-45.

Humphrey, W. E. and Diaz Gonzalez, T. E.: "Secuencia Mesozoica en la Arroyo de San Rogue, Cerro de la Silla, Nuevo Leon, Approximadamente a 15 Kilometres al SE de la Ciudad de Monterrey, Nuevo Leon," *Congreso Geologico Internacional* (1958), pp. 18-23.

Imlay, R. W.: "Jurassic Formations of Gulf Region of North America, Including United States, Mexico and Cuba," *Bull.,* AAPG (1943), v. 27, No. 11, pp. 1407-1533.

Imlay, R. W., Cepeda, E., Alvarez, M. and Diaz, T.: "Stratigraphic Relations of Certain Jurassic Formations in Eastern Mexico," *Bull.,* AAPG (1948), v. 32, No. 9, pp. 1750-1761.

Jux, Ulrich: "The Palynologic Age of Diapiric and Bedded Salt in the Gulf Coastal Province," *Bull. 38,* La Geol. Svy. (1961) Dept. of Conserv., 46 pp.

King, R. H.: "Sedimentation in Permian Castile Sea," *Bull.,* AAPG (1947), v. 31, No. 3, pp. 470-477.

Lyons, P. L.: "Geology and Geophysics of the Gulf of Mexico," *Trans.,* GCAGS (1957), v. 7, pp. 1-10; (abs). *Bull.,* AAPG (1965), v. 49, No. 3, p. 348.

Meyerhoff, A. A.: (abs) "Cuban Evaporite Diapirs," *Bull.,* AAPG (1965), v. 49, no. 3, pp. 350-351.

Mixon, R. B., Murray, G. E. and Diaz, Teodoro: "Age and Correlation of Huizachal Group (Mesozoic), State of Tamaulipas, Mexico," *Bull.,* AAPG (1959), v. 43, No. 4, pp. 757-771; (addendum), v. 43, p. 2499.

Murray, G. E.: *Geology of the Atlantic and Gulf Coastal Province of North America,* Harper Bros. (1961), New York, 692 pp.

Ochsenius, C.: "On the Formation of Rock Salt Beds and Mother Liquor Salts," *Proc.,* Acad. Natural Sci. of Philadelphia (1888), v. 40, pp. 181-187.

Pettijohn, F. J.: *Sedimentary Rocks,* Harper & Brothers (1957), Second Edition, New York, 484 pp.

Scott, K. R., Hayes, W. E. and Fietz, R. P.: "Geology of the Eagle Mills Formation," *Trans.,* GCAGS (1961), v. 11, pp. 1-14.

Scruton, P. C.: "Deposition of Evaporites," *Bull.,* AAPG (1953), v. 37, No. 11, pp. 2498-2512.

Usiglio, J.: "Analyse de l'Eau de la Mediterranee sur la Cote de France," *Ann. Chim. et Phys.* (1849), ser. 3, v. 27, pp. 92-172.

Chapter 3

Origin and Growth
of Salt Structures

The modern theory of salt dome origin postulates that salt has flowed into structures by means of plastic deformation in response to density differences between the salt and surrounding sediments. This concept, now generally accepted by geologists the world over, has evolved from 100 years of speculation and interesting controversy.

A Short History of Salt Dome Knowledge

The history of ideas on the formation of salt domes began with the observations of Thomassy (1860), who visited the Five Islands area of South Louisiana, and announced that Petite Anse (Avery Island) "comes from a volcano of water, mud, and gas." Posepny (1871) was the first to realize the diapiric nature of salt domes in Rumania. The many different ideas of dome origin have been well documented and at intervals the ideas have been collected and ably reviewed (see De-Golyer, 1926; Barton, 1926; Stille, 1926; and Nettleton, 1935). The works of these authors are so complete and clearly stated that another review of all the ideas would serve little purpose. However, brief mention of a few of the concepts that were popular during their respective periods will provide the necessary background for better understanding the problems of salt-dome formation which are not yet wholly answered.

In general, all of the ideas advanced on salt dome origin ascribe to one or more of three basic concepts. These broad classifications include:

1. From the earliest reference to the discovery of Spindletop dome in 1901—characterized by casual, unrelated ideas.

2. From 1901-1916 during which time keen interest in domes was shown as a result of the economic impact of Spindletop and other

giant salt dome oil fields—the deposition-from-solution era.

3. From 1916-1924, when there was widespread acceptance of salt-flow principles to explain dome formation.

DeGolyer (1919) and others[1] championed the third concept which could reasonably be demonstrated in the flow structures present in the walls of salt dome mines. The present salt-flow theory has been modified and greatly refined from the early concept.

Many of the early ideas offered by American geologists resulted from studies of the Five Islands of South Louisiana. The islands are circular, forested hills of gentle to moderate relief that rise above flat-lying marshland. From a distance the hills resemble islands in the sea. Brine springs, salt, and sulphur deposits of these hills were known to Indians and early settlers long before Thomassy's expedition. The salt core of the islands is overlain by a thin cover of alluvial material and was comparatively easy to study; hence, a logical example to support the theories on dome origin.

Lockett (1871), Hopkins (1870), and Hilgard (1872) advocated simple structural or erosional theories for the occurrence of salt at Five Islands. Hopkins and Hilgard believed the domes and salines were erosional remnants of an old Cretaceous range; Lockett concluded that the hills were segments of an ancient natural levee breached by flood waters. Clendenin (1896), and Harris and Veatch (1899) held to a structural explanation for the Louisiana domes. They recognized the uplift of the hills with respect to the surrounding areas and believed that the hills resulted

from folding and faulting during recent geologic time. These early theories may appear humorous in light of present knowledge, but when we consider that little was known about similar features anywhere in the world, these early ideas can be appreciated, especially since they were supported by (1) geomorphic criteria and (2) evidence of structural deformation. Later sophisticated theories were far more speculative and unrealistic than these ideas.

It is interesting to note that the first theories of origin of domes in Rumania and Germany were tectonic theories. Barton (1926) reports that Mrazec, a student of Rumanian salt domes, believed the salt diapirs represented the first stage of an overthrust.

Following the discovery of Spindletop dome, Adams (1901) and Veatch (1902) published reports showing the location of many other dome-like features on the Texas-Louisiana Gulf Coast. Salt dome oil discoveries at Sour Lake, 1902; Humble, 1905; and Goose Creek, 1908 greatly intensified the search for other oil accumulations associated with domes, and with heightened interest geologists advanced deposition-from-solution theories of dome origin in rapid succession.

The deposition-from-solution concept originated years earlier with Goessmann (1867) who also reported on the salt at Avery Island. He concluded that the salt resulted from the evaporation of brine springs ascending through older deposits of bedded salt—a theory similar to later ideas advanced during the height of popularity of the solution concept.

There were three principal lines of thought proposed by advocates of the deposition-from-solution concept. The first and simplest explanation is essentially a restatement of Goessmann's ideas; that is, saline waters emanating from deep within the earth rise hydrostatically

---

[1] Van der Gracht (1917), Rogers (1918), Dumble (1916).

through the overlying sediments along zones of weakness (faults or fractures). Then they precipitate the minerals in solution near the surface in the form of stocklike masses.

A variation in the solution concept suggested by Harris (1907, 1908) dealt with the forces of crystallization of the salt as the mechanism for pushing salt upward through the overlying sediments. DeGolyer's (1926, p. 17) summary of the Harris theory is so interesting that it is worthy of quoting.

> Artesian waters, which had entered outcropping formations north of the general salt dome areas, having descended to great depths along pervious beds, becoming heated by the high earth temperatures existing at such depths, and taking into solution salts encountered in the Paleozoic and Mesozoic formations, rose under hydrostatic pressure at points of weakness, occurring mainly at the crossing of faults in the pre-Tertiary formations. Deposition of salt by the cooling of this hot saline solution resulted in the formation of a slender pencil-like cone of rock salt. The forces exerted by the power of the growing crystals of salt, especially at the bottom of this salt cone, resulted in the cone being pushed continuously upward as long as deposition continued, the one being beheaded by solution as it reached the zone of circulating underground fresh waters. Overlying sedimentary rocks were lifted and contiguous rocks tilted by the upthrust of the salt cone.

The Harris theory remained popular for many years and was supported by Campbell (1911) and Matteson (1918) who reviewed the principal theories of dome origin in their respective publications.

The third variation in the deposition-from-solution concept vigorously upheld some sort of volcanic influence as the major factor in the initiation or continuation of dome formation. The first mention of a volcanic origin was, of course, the work of Thomassy (1860).

Coste (1903) was one of the staunchest advocates of the volcanic influence concept. He believed the domes were a result of volcanic action which forced water, salt, sulphur, and oil, in a gaseous state, to pierce upward "boldly through the plains" and condense near the surface. Hager (1904) presented yet another approach where heated waters carrying salt and other minerals vented to the surface along channels previously formed by volcanic gases. The salt was precipitated from saline waters into necklike masses.

One of the last theories to stress volcanic influence was perhaps the most speculative. Norton (1916) concluded that the domes were deposited in the dissolved portion of a pipe of calcareous sinter which accompanied the intrusion of molten rocks.

Writers who supported volcanic influence recognized that there was no positive evidence of volcanic activity in the salt dome basins, the nearest occurrences being located in the Central Mineral Region of West Texas, and in the Tampico region of eastern Mexico. Nevertheless, the solution concept associated with vulcanism endured longer than any other concept. We now accept the salt-flow concept but here also can be found volcanic implications (see O'Brien, 1957).

European scientists first advanced the idea that salt could flow in a plastic or semiplastic state under natural conditions and form structures. In the manner of the other basic theories, the salt-flow concept has been explained in several different ways. Two principal schools of thought include (1) salt structures produced by lateral or tangential compression—a tectonic motivation, and (2) salt structures produced by gravitational nonequilibrium resulting from density differences between salt and surrounding sediments—an isostatic motivation.

Until recently salt domes in northern Germany had been explained by German geologists as tectonically controlled structures. Trusheim (1960) reports that present opinion favors "geostatic" principles similar to current American thought. However, the original isostatic concepts were developed by German scholars.

Harbort (1910, 1913) believed that the motive force for at least part of the salt upthrust of German domes was due to the loading of the salt masses by overlying sediments. Arrhenius (1912) proposed an hypothesis that comes closest to a general statement of the modern theory—that the upward movement of the salt mass was caused by its lesser specific gravity, compared with that of the surrounding rocks.

Lachmann (1910 a, b, 1917), an eminent student of German salt domes, approached the problem differently in advocating a "salt eczeme" or ulcer-type projection of the salt through the earth's crust. Although his so called "autoplastic" upthrust of salt was more tectonic than isostatic in principle, he recognized the importance of forces inherent in the salt mass and not in the surrounding sediments. That is, forces located substantially in the salt were responsible for the upward movement through overlying rocks.

Proponents of tectonically motivated salt flow finally prevailed in Europe, as well as in the United States. It was many years before gravity concepts were revived. In Germany, Stille (1911, 1917) was the chief exponent of the idea that upward movement of salt occurred in the same manner as the folding of normal sediments by lateral compression.

DeGolyer (1926), who contributed greatly to the salt-flow concept in America, believed

a tectonic influence for salt flow was the most acceptable and rational theory. He concludes (pp. 34, 35):

> . . . the north American salt domes, i.e., the salt structures of the Texas-Louisiana province, are plugs of salt intruded into previously almost undisturbed Tertiary and Cretaceous formations from deeply buried salt structures; that these deeply buried salt structures were formed by orogenetic forces; and that the flowage of the salt in a plastic or semi-plastic state from original bedded deposits was induced by compression resulting from folding.

Barton (1926) reviewed the ideas of the Rumanian geologist Krejci (1926), who proposed a combination tectonic-isostatic theory for the domes in Rumania. Three stages of dome development were postulated by Krejci which Barton summarized as (p. 185):

> (1) The formation of wavelike folds in the competent cover through the effects of thrust by the overthrust sheet.
>
> (2) The transformation of the folds into piercement folds through the yielding upward of the mobile plastic underlying formation under the effect of the same thrust, the upward movement being augmented at the points of least resistance along crests of the folds.
>
> (3) The transformation of the piercement folds into outbreaks through the extrusion of the plastic core vertically upward into the overlying sediments, the movement taking place isostatically under the effect of the pressure of the overlying sediments.

The idea that salt was less dense than the surrounding sediments and that the difference in density constituted a buoyancy force which caused the salt to rise was alluded to several times after Arrhenius' original hypothesis. However, the concept was only casually mentioned and generally was discarded because the forces were not believed adequate for the magnitude of the salt uplifts.

During the early 1930's the gravimeter was used extensively in locating deep salt structures in the Gulf Coast. The negative gravity anomalies associated with naturally occurring salt deposits definitely established that salt was less dense than the surrounding sediments. Substantiated by basic geophysical evidence, Barton (1933) proposed the theory of "isostatic downbuilding" to explain the motive force of salt uplifts while Nettleton (1934) developed a somewhat similar theory, independent of Barton's, known as the "fluid mechanical concept." This is basically the same theory that is widely accepted by American geologists today.

The theory of downbuilding postulates that the salt structure remained more or less constant in depth, while the overlying sediments sank downward past it; that with the general subsidence of the sedimentary section, horizontal flowage of salt from the mother salt bed moved in toward the base of the salt core and built the base of the salt downward in reference to the surface. The process is shown diagrammatically in Fig. 3-1.

Barton (pp. 1030, 1031) explains the diagram and process of downbuilding as follows:

> The top of the basement, JK, of the salt series subsides to a new position, J'K'; the surface is maintained at a constant level by continuous deposition of the sedimentary material. But any bed, LM, sinks concomitantly with the subsidence of the basement, JK. The mother salt bed, NO, sinks concomitantly to the new position, N'O'. If the salt of the mother salt bed were an ordinary sediment, the salt core would sink at the same rate as the mother salt series. But, as the salt is lighter than the surrounding sediments, the salt core of the dome by its buoyancy tends not to sink with the sur-

rounding sediments. Under the pressure of the overlying sediments the plastic salt of the mother salt bed is forced to flow inward under the base of the salt core and thereby tends to build the root of the dome downward in earth space and in reference to the surface. The movement of the salt should not wholly be horizontally inward from the mother salt bed. The flaring flanks concomitantly should be pressed down and the salt of the flanks should flow plastically downward and slightly inward. The dotted vertical line [Fig. 3-1] represents an assumed vertical straight line in the salt at the stage of the solid lines. The corresponding curved line of double dots shows the position to which that line should have moved by the time of the stage of the dashed line. This downbuilding takes place concomitantly with the subsidence of the basement and must cease when the subsidence ceases. The rate of flowage of the salt into the roots of the dome presumably approaches zero (1) as the thickness of the mother salt bed approaches zero, (2) as the salt and sediments approach isostatic equilibrium, and (3) as the rate of subsidence decreases. The continuance of the flowage of the salt and of the downbuilding is not dependent, however, on the continuance of deposition of new sedimentary material, although the cessation of that deposition may affect the rate of flowage slightly.

The mechanics of salt-dome formation proposed by Nettleton's "fluid mechanical theory," are consistent in most respects with the salt-flow principles cited by Barton. However, Nettleton stressed the upward intrusion of the salt masses in which both the salt and surrounding sediments behave as highly viscous liquids and flow through a long period of geological time. Nettleton recognized that the prime motive force was the density contrast between salt (specific gravity 2.2) and sediments (specific gravity ranging from 1.7-2.0 at the surface to 2.4-2.8 at depth). He conducted experiments on different materials to simulate model domes and concluded (p.

1193) that the final form of a dome depends largely on the following factors:

(1) the initial configuration which localized the dome.
(2) the thickness of the mother salt layer.
(3) the strength or viscosity of the overlying rocks.
(4) the strength or viscosity of the salt.

Nettleton's conception of the initiation and growth of a dome is shown by the hypothetical example in Fig. 3-2. The dome initiated by some sort of tectonic movement after deposition of the mother salt bed. Note here again the mention of orogenic or tectonic influence in the early stages of dome growth. The tectonically motivated uplift does not alter the salt thickness. In stage 2, flow has begun and sediments continue to accumulate above the rising salt plug. In stage 3, the salt stock has pierced through the overburden and carried some of the rocks which immediately overlie the salt ahead of it. At stage 3 the salt supply flowing toward the dome is cut off by the drop in the peripheral sink. Flow is now away from the dome and further growth is at the expense of the material within the peripheral sink and salt core. At stage 4 the original material over the dome has been nearly removed by erosion. At stage 5 the rocks carried up by the dome have been completely eroded and circulating ground water acting on the salt has produced the caprock material. Stage 6, the final stage of dome growth, shows the collapse of the steeply upturned beds into the peripheral sink in the form of block fault segments.

The dome illustrated in the left hand column represents the deep-seated salt structure. It is formed in an area of relatively thin bedded salt and less mobile overlying rocks. Nettleton believed the strength of the overlying rocks would inhibit the development of

peripheral sink such that salt flow would be cut off by actual meeting of the rocks above and below the salt.

Halbouty and Hardin (1956) supported the general ideas expressed in Nettleton's fluid mechanic theory but placed more emphasis on the static weight of the overlying sediments as the motive force of the intrusion. They recognized that a tectonic impulse was not prerequisite to the initiation of salt dome growth and that any irregularity in the overlying sediments, or in the salt, or sediments below the salt, which might influence the salt bed, triggers the plastic salt into its initial upward movement. They stated (pp. 743-745):

> The initial upward movement of the salt from the mother salt bed did not begin until sufficient sediments had been deposited over the salt bed to cause an appreciable weight differential on the salt bed (Fig. 3-3). The thickness and weight of the sediments above the mother bed constitute the most important factor in the upward movement of the salt, since the bouyancy causing this upward movement is a result of the difference in the specific gravities of the salt and sediments.

> Once the initial upward movement of the salt begins, the salt stock continues to move in stages through geologic time, depending on the thickness and the resulting weight of the sediments above and around the salt intrusion. The upward movement of the salt core would gradually become slower, but not necessarily stop altogether, as it approached the surface. Generally, when such equilibrium is reached between sediments and the salt, a stage of semi-dormancy, if not complete quiescence, prevails. Erosion then predominates over the super-dome area, whereas deposition predominates on the flanks of the intrusion. As more sediments are deposited over the flanks of the salt-core area, the static weight of the sediments and the density of the beds being buried are increased. Thus differential pressure is increased between the sediments and the salt, reviving the forces

of buoyancy and causing the upward movement of the salt stock to begin all over again.

Cycle after cycle of this procedure occurred until the salt domes gradually pierced their way through the sediments to their present positions. It is apparent that there was wide variation in the rate of the upward movement of various salt stocks. Some moved upward rather slowly, because of lack of salt from the mother salt bed in the surrounding area of the origin of the dome, or because of encountering one or more resistant formations which retarded a continuous uplift of the dome. The great variation in the rate of rise of the salt plugs resulted in the intricate structural and sedimentational complexes that characterize the sediments on the flanks of piercement salt domes. Each salt plug apparently had its own rate of penetration, and the quiescent periods of one salt dome did not correspond with those of nearby domes. Each quiescent period generally resulted in erosion of the flanking sediments and the forming of a local unconformity around the salt plug. This condition complicated the interpretation of structural conditions around a salt dome because each local unconformity must be thoroughly understood before short sections in drilled wells can be attributed to faulting.

The rise of some of the salt domes did not keep pace with the rapid deposition of sediments and the salt plug eventually became buried beneath many thousand feet of sediments. These domes are referred to as "deep-seated." Other salt stocks seem to have developed under conditions that resulted in the salt intrusion remaining near the surface throughout their growth history, thus permitting the salt to pierce the sediments shortly after deposition. These salt domes are commonly referred to as "piercement-type" domes. Those in between are referred to as "intermediate-type" domes.

Recent Study

Although isostatically induced salt diapirism has been the established thought in the Gulf region for many years, and more lately in Germany, relatively recent work by O'Brien[2] (1957) in south Persia (Iran) suggests that a combination of both tectonic and isostatic forces may initiate salt flow.

O'Brien visualized the evolution of salt structures in the Masjid-i-Sulaiman area in five stages (Fig. 3-4). Development of the Imam Reza and Sar-i-Naftak diapirs in the southwest portion of the section was attributed to squeezing of the salt (Lower Fars-Stage 1) into salt bulges as a result of increasing pressures from a rising Asmari anticline. As folding became more intense greater compressional forces were exerted, eventually causing the salt to extrude in flow-sheets, "overthrusting" and nearly submerging the Tembi syncline.

In contrast are the diapirs of Sar-i-Gach and Andakah shown in the northeast portion of the section. According to O'Brien, the Sar-i-Gach plateau is held at its present elevation, which is higher than the adjacent Turk-i-Diz syncline by the isostatic effect of the northeastern section of the Turk-i-Diz syncline sinking into a less dense salt series. O'Brien points out that in a conformable sequence the salt generally occupies lower ground than the overlying sediments because of its greater solubility and rate of erosion; however, in the Sar-i-Gach area the salt plateau is nearly 1,000 feet above rocks which normally stratigraphically overlie the salt.

Undoubtedly there are geologists who disagree with the tectonic nature of salt diapirism as described by O'Brien for the Imam Reza and Sar-i-Naftak diapirs. This author does not propose to question the structural evolution of the area, and indeed O'Brien presents convincing arguments in support of his ideas. However, it is important here, as in the other aspects of salt dome geology, to emphasize that

---

[2] O'Brien was describing salt flow in a belt of compressional folding. Therefore, his proposed mechanism was meant only to apply to compressional belts. He did not imply a similar origin of domes on the Gulf Coast.

all of the problems are not solved and it is not likely that a panacean explanation for the growth of salt structures will hold for all salt domes in all salt-dome basins of the world.

The preceding discussion on the origin and growth of salt structures, outside of tracing the evolution of major ideas on the subject, has been generalized in its approach to the mechanics of salt migration. As a result of sophisticated model studies in recent years together with field measurements made by Gulf Coast and German geologists, certain numerical parameters have been established for the initiation of salt flowage. In addition, physical and chemical aspects of salt movements have been added to the overall refinement of theories of the origin of salt structures.

Model Studies of Salt Domes

Following widespread acceptance of the salt-flow concept in the 1920's, salt dome geologists carried out a number of model experiments to simulate the form of salt structures and the deformation of surrounding sediments. The various types of early model experiments are not discussed here, but are covered in detail in publications of each contributor (see Torrey and Fralich, 1926; Escher and Kuehner, 1929; Link, 1930; Hubbert, 1937). The early experiments were based primarily on the idea that the motive force of salt flow was tectonic. Early models used externally applied forces which were enormous compared to the size of the model and strength of the material used. Scalar factors were largely ignored and the mechanical properties of the material used were not carefully measured.

Nettleton (1934) constructed the first models to produce artificial domes by purely gravitational forces and without external pressures or constraints. Some sort of initial uplift was induced by external objects; but thereafter, the growth and form taken by the dome resulted from isostatic non-equilibrium due to the difference in density between the materials.

Probably the most refined and accurate model studies were conducted by Parker and McDowell (1951, 1955). They initiated the growth of model domes by several different methods, including:

1. Irregularities on the surface of the overburden, either depressions or projections from the general level of the surface.
2. Variations in the thickness of the overburden.
3. Natural variations in the density of the overburden.
4. External stresses producing faults or folds in the overburden which produced varying pressure differentials on the salt equivalent surface.

One of the primary objectives in model studies, which has important application to naturally occurring domes, is the depth of burial necessary to start salt flow. Balk (1949) conducted studies which reflect that salt deformation can result from shearing stress of 30 kg/cm^2 (427 lbs./in^2). Parker and McDowell determined that the shearing stress of 427 lbs./in^2 will result from a difference in compressive stress of 853 lbs./in^2 and that if these forces act over a long period of time, even lower stress could initiate flow. Therefore, they recognized that very deep burial is not prerequisite for salt flow and that sufficient pressure differentials might be established if an area underlain by salt is covered by approximately 1,000 feet more of sediments than an adjacent area.

An important corollary to the flow of plastic materials derived from the model studies of Parker and McDowell is that if the overburden exceeds a certain amount, no further movement of salt material will occur, providing the overburden has a finite shear strength.

According to Trusheim (1960), experience with the German Zechstein salt basins showed that an overburden of about 1,000 meters and a thickness of at least 300 meters of salt were necessary to initiate the flow process. This is closely compatible with the parameters now used for salt flow in the Gulf region.

Strain, temperature and pressure influence rock viscosity, or in the case of salt, its plasticity. These physical factors vary, of course, with increased overburden. Restated, an increase in burial depth will be accompanied by increases in strain, temperature and pressure of the salt mass. Although it has been difficult to make direct laboratory measurements of rock viscosity, certain general numeral parameters have recently been cited by Gussow (1965).

Below 25,000 feet of overburden, salt behaves as a perfect plastic and is entirely mobile. Above 200° C, salt will flow without rupture. From what has been previously stated, this obviously is not to imply that the salt domes of the Gulf region, or elsewhere, did not begin to form until 25,000 feet of overburden was accumulated or that the rock temperature reached 200° C. If these quantitative values are necessary for salt to become completely plastic, domes undoubtedly have commenced to grow under less than ideal conditions of viscous flow.

The condition may have been partly influenced by plastic flow and partly by creep. Creep—a slow, continuous movement of solid or semi-solid rock from higher to lower levels because of gravitational nonequilibrium—may have caused salt to flow downward into a peripheral sink and inward toward a rising salt mass.

This author believes that on a regional scale, very small dip on the basement or pre-salt surface is necessary to initiate creep or plastic flow. Trusheim (1960) similarly believes that if the dip of the basement exceeds one degree the salt migration in the Zechstein basin was facilitated. He states that according to the mechanical consideration advanced by Durschner (1957), the presence of a sufficiently deep sedimentary trough in the shape of a shallow saucer would start the salt moving.

The different methods by which model domes have been initiated in the laboratory and the different structural and sedimentary associations of naturally occuring domes suggest that not all salt structures were initiated in the same manner and that one or more of several geologic processes may have started formation of a particular dome.

The experiments conducted by Parker and McDowell showed that after an original dome began to develop, other domes or ridges began to form, concentric to the original dome. They termed the original feature a master dome and the subsequent structures secondary domes. If the process continued, third and fourth order uplifts would develop in the same pattern.

Based on the behavior of model domes, Parker and McDowell postulated that as a primary or master salt dome continued to grow, a peripheral sink developed in the mother salt bed, and a series of graben fractures developed around the margins of the sink. A peripheral sink is that depression in the source layer of salt resulting from the thinning of the source layer as salt flows into the dome. The development of graben-type fractures around the margins of the peripheral sink, the development of the sink, and the growth of the master dome disturbed the equilibrium between the salt and overlying sediments and initiated the growth of mounds or ridges on the edge of the sink which eventually grew into domal uplifts similar to the master dome but generally smaller.

Determining Master and Secondary Domes

According to Parker and McDowell the best criterion for determining master and secondary domes is their distribution or pattern of arrangement. A single salt dome far removed from any other salt uplifts would be considered a primary or master dome. A dome near the center of an arc or circle formed by other domes, anticlines, or ridges may be a master dome, and the features comprising the arc would be regarded as secondary salt structures.

The Texas-Louisiana coastal salt dome basin contains clusters of salt domes and apparent salt structures which may be genetically related in development and may possibly reflect a master dome-secondary dome association. The structure contour map of the Frio Formation in a part of Jefferson County, Texas, (Fig. 3-5) shows that Spindletop dome lies east of an arc of anticlines (Lovell Lake, North Cheek, Amelia, and West Beaumont) associated with normal faults. A pronounced synclinal area separates the arc of structures from Spindletop. The Port Neches salt dome is east of Spindletop at a distance approximately equal to the radius of the arc of producing structures on the west. Parker and McDowell consider the Spindletop area as a possible master dome-secondary dome association. They conclude (p. 2422):

> The evidence available strongly suggests that Spindletop is a master dome and that the anticlinal features forming the arc west of Spindletop were produced by deep-seated secondary

domes. Port Neches may also be a secondary dome, though its relationship to the deep-seated domes on the west is not clear. The normal fault along the west side of the arc may have its counterpart in the outer graben fault in the models. Since in many of the models this fault is the largest observed, it might be expected to affect horizons high above the source beds.

Although the map of the Spindletop area is not to be regarded as conclusive proof that the concept of secondary dome development is valid, it does indicate several similarities between the models and a group of actual salt domes. The presence of an arc of structurally high features centered on Spindletop, the diameter of this arc as compared with the diameter of Spindletop, and the pronounced synclines adjacent to the several domes suggest that these features were produced in a manner comparable with that by which the model domes were formed.

Identifying master and secondary domes may be extremely difficult and, even when indicated, the geometry of concentrically arranged domes may be misleading. A natural assumption is that the master dome, which originates earlier, should have more salt available to flow into the dome and should, therefore, contain a greater volume of salt than secondary domes. Parker and McDowell found in some models that many secondary domes reach a size comparable with the master dome. Factors that may reduce the theoretical volume of salt a master dome should contain, as estimated from the size and shape of the rim syncline, include:

1. The derivation of cap rock from the upper portion of the salt mass.

2. Subaerial or submarine erosions or dissolving action of ground waters on the original volume of salt as the mass approaches the surface.

3. The possible outward flow of salt from the peripheral sink.

Regarding the third factor, Nettleton (1934) demonstrated mathematically that if the sedimentary overburden is of low strength and if the peripheral sink is sufficiently deep, the salt pressure beneath the lowest part of the sink should exceed the pressure in the source layer outside the sink. Under these conditions salt should flow outward from the bottom of the sink as well as inward toward the dome, thereby reducing the apparent volume of salt that a master dome should contain.

The Texas-Louisiana coastal basin contains several clusters of domes with geometric arrangement similar to the Spindletop area but with different genesis.

Calcasieu Lake dome is a shallow dome located in the approximate center of a well-defined low or "rim basin" which exhibits quaquaversal dip inward toward the dome from other domes and/or salt anticlines (West Hackberry, East Hackberry, Big Lake, Grosse Savanne, Sweet Lake, Creole, Cameron, etc.) concentrically arranged around Calcasieu Lake dome (Fig. 3-6). Major normal faults are located on the northeast, south, and southwest perimeter of the rim basin.

Applying the master dome-secondary dome concept to this area, Calcasieu Lake dome would be the master dome whose uplift triggered the growth of surrounding structures. Coincidentally with subsidence of the peripheral sink and movement of the salt into the dome, faulting and fracturing occurred on the rim of the sink. Secondary domes and salt mounds, whose long axes were parallel with the strike of the faults, then developed along the margins of the sink.

The form of the Calcasieu Lake area has many of the criteria to support the master dome-secondary dome concept. However, close study indicates that Calcasieu Lake dome and the rim basin are late-occurring structural features that developed after the formation of the ring-like pattern of salt structures encircling Calcasieu Lake. The rim syncline at Calcasieu Lake dome is small and the structure is nearly barren of hydrocarbon accumulation. It may be reasonably concluded that migration of oil and gas in the host sediments surrounding the dome took place before the dome developed. All of the concentric structures around Calcasieu Lake are good producing fields and if Calcasieu Lake dome was formed before or even contemporaneous with the concentric structures it should have trapped abundant hydrocarbons.

More recently, Sannemann (1960, 1965) and Trusheim (1960) have collaborated in their work to present a well-organized and reasonable explanation for the apparent genetic relationships among salt structures or groups of structures. Their studies in the Northwest German basin indicate that certain regional salt patterns are in no way coincidental, but have developed in the manner of a chain-reaction once the initial movement of salt began.

Sannemann (1965) refers to the larger group of salt stocks as "salt stock families" which consist of a number of salt domes grouped around the genetically oldest dome or "mother salt stock." "Mother" structures arising may have initiated "daughter," "grandchild," etc., generations parallel with and on both sides of the mother structures.

The regional pattern of the Zechstein salt structures in northwest Germany is that of elongate, meandering salt walls or ridges in the deepest part of the basin adjoined by an area of salt domes which in turn is surrounded by a girdle of salt pillows in the shallower part of the basin. Similarly, this arrangement is found in the salt dome basins of the Gulf region. Figure 3-7 is a block diagram (modified after Trusheim) that shows the types of salt structures in the Northwest Germany basin and is also applicable to the Gulf region.

Two different ideas attempt to explain the origin of the regional patterns of salt structures in northwest Germany. One view holds that a rhythmical wavelike phenomenon is set in motion with the growth of a mother salt stock. Much like ripples emanating from a stone thrown into water, the salt travels in a wavefront from the deeper part of the salt basin toward the rim of the basin after an initial dome disturbs the equilibrium of the mother salt bed. This concept is supported, in part, by the master dome-secondary dome development demonstrated in the model studies of Parker and McDowell.

The second view is that the regional salt pattern reflects a network of faults in the pre-salt basement rocks. According to Trusheim the existence of such faults has actually been proved, or at least shown to be probable, by information from wells drilled near the edge of the basin. In addition, Trusheim states (p. 1524):

> . . . the salt lines along the Aller River and between the Aller and Elbe Rivers, linking together various elongate salt domes and running transversely to the old relief, could be connected with disturbances in the basement, following the northwest-striking tectonic lineaments which predominate throughout Central Europe.

Trusheim postulates that salt structures begin with a pillow stage and, under a continuous supply of salt from the source layer, the flanks of the pillow grow increasingly steeper until the salt breaks through the overlying sediments and the diapir stage begins (Fig. 3-8).

Peripheral Sinks

One of the most significant observations brought out by Trusheim and Sannemann concerns the development of peripheral sinks. A primary peripheral sink is considered an attribute of salt pillow development and is characterized by a thinning of the overlying sediments within the rim syncline toward the salt structure. Trusheim envisions that the periphery of the salt surface subsides as the pillow rises and the resulting depression fills with sediments.

With the culmination of the pillow stage a diapir extrudes from the pillow and as the piercement stock grows the pillow supplying the salt to the dome begins to shrink. Gradual destruction of the pillow is accompanied by a subsidence of the adjacent overlying sediments which thicken toward the dome and indicate a secondary peripheral sink (Figs. 3-8, 3-9).

Trusheim's description of peripheral sinks is not consistent with American thought and some confusion arises from the illustration (Fig. 3-8), which does not show a marked depression in the source layer or pillow due to withdrawal of salt to form the rising salt structure. Reference to peripheral sinks in these instances could probably be stated in terms of stratigraphic thickness of sediments in the rim syncline. This is a moot point and is not the important factor of Trusheim's contribution. To this writer's knowledge, American geologists have placed minor emphasis on the sedimentational maxima of specific stratigraphic units adjacent to a dome and herein lies the importance of Trusheim's work.

A unique application of peripheral sink development (thickness of stratigraphic systems of adjacent sediments) was made by Sannemann (1960). The lateral migration of salt in a direction toward the salt structures is reflected by the progressive shifting with time of the primary peripheral sinks, or, as indicated stratigraphically, by a shifting of the corresponding thickness maxima in the overlying sediments. It is assumed that the migration took place continually throughout several geologic time units (epochs or periods) and since the duration of these time units is known to a certain extent, the speed of the salt movement can be approximated. Sannemann's schematic diagram (Fig. 3-9) shows a thinning of Upper Jurassic through Middle Jurassic age rocks toward the salt dome which corresponds to the pillow stage of development. Upper Jurassic and Lower Cretaceous rocks increase in thickness toward the structure which dates the beginning of the diapir stage.

The model experiments of Parker and McDowell (1955) show that the size of peripheral sinks of domes is directly related to the diameter of the dome or to the salt volume within the dome. This relationship would hold true for the size relationship of peripheral sinks to salt pillows in the Zechstein basin. If the salt volume in the final stage of pillow development, before the diapir stage begins, has migrated from the area of the peripheral sink and not from outside of the area of the peripheral sink, and the time of development of the pillow is known from the shift in sedimentational maxima of rocks in the rim syncline, then the speed of salt movement can be ascertained.

On the basis of this principle Sannemann concluded that the rate of salt flow on the geological time scale averages 0.3 mm. per year. He admits this value is only a rough approximation and is applicable to regional salt migration which lasts over long periods of geologic time. There are many examples of more rapid salt movements but these are local and probably tectonically accelerated.

Surprisingly, Sannemann found that the mean rate of flow of about 0.3 mm. per year was constant both in the lateral flow during the salt pillow stage and in the more vertical flow during diapir stage. A salt pillow, therefore, took about as long to form as the diapir that developed from it. A chart showing this relation is shown in Fig. 3-10.

The decrease or increase of a particular stratigraphic unit or units when applied to an interpretation of genetic relationship of one salt structure to another or, as in Sannemann's work, to the relationship of a diapir to a pillow is economically important in the search for hydrocarbon accumulations on salt domes.

The mother salt bed has not been reached by drilling in the vicinity of the salt domes of the Gulf region. Therefore the presence of a peripheral sink, proven in model studies, can only be inferred from sedimentation in the rim synclines bounding many domes. Although it is believed that all salt structures probably have some manifestation of a peripheral sink surrounding them, not all domes have rim synclines. The influence of regional dip on the gulfward side of the dome may overcome opposing dips necessary to form a rim syncline. This raises a question of whether the change in the thickness of stratigraphic units adjacent to a dome can unequivocally be used to demonstrate probable genetic relationship of one salt structure to another.

This writer believes that the change in thickness of specific stratigraphic units around many domes in the Gulf region relates directly to the history of development of the dome and suggests a genetic relationship between dome and an ancestral structure (pillow?).

The change in thickness of stratigraphic units pierced by the salt plug at High Island, Galveston County, Texas, suggests that the dome had at least two phases of growth—not unlike what would be expected if the dome has evolved from an initial pillow stage.

A pronounced unconformity occurs at the base of the Amphistegina shale (Middle Miocene). Lower Miocene beds below the unconformity are in sharp angular contact with the overlying shales (Fig. 3-11). Correlative units above the unconformity on the western side of the dome are considerably thicker than on the eastern side. Below the unconformity the reverse is true. Siphonina davisi and Bigenerina sp. sands of the Lower Miocene are thickest on the eastern side of the dome.

In all probability the locus of domal growth has shifted between Lower and Middle Miocene time. Initially the salt dome, perhaps in the pillow stage, caused uplifting and thinning of the overlying Lower Miocene units. The area to the east of the pillow or relict dome was structurally lower and accumulated a greater thickness of equivalent Lower Miocene strata. Subsequent to the time of the unconformity the salt mass shifted its path of movement to the east and the area that was structurally low became high and vice versa. Continued uplift influenced sedimentation and resulted in thinning the Middle Miocene section adjacent to the eastern side of the dome with respect to equivalent beds on the structure's western side. As the uplift continued, the Miocene section was pierced and tilted to its present position. The development of High Island along the lines discussed is diagramatically shown in Fig. 3-11.

Literature Cited

Adams, G. I.: "Oil and Gas Fields of the Upper Cretaceous and Tertiary Formations of the West Gulf Coast," *Bull.*, USGS (1901), pp. 37-62.

Arrhenius, S. V.: "Zur Physik der Salzlagerstatten," *Meddelanden fran K. Vettenskabsakodemiens Nobelinstitut* (1912), v. 11, no. 20.

Balk, Robert: "Structure of Grand Saline Salt Dome, Van Zandt County, Texas," *Bull.*, AAPG (1949), v. 33, no. 11, pp. 1791-1829.

Barton, D. C.: "The American Salt-Dome Problems in the Light of the Rumanian and German Salt Domes," *Bull.*, AAPG (1925), v. 9, no. 9, pp. 1227-1268; *Geology of Salt Dome Oil Fields,* AAPG (1926), pp. 167-208.

Barton, D. C.: "Mechanics of Formation of Salt Domes with Special Reference to Gulf Coast Salt Domes of Texas and Louisiana," *Bull.*, AAPG (1933), v. 17, no. 9, pp. 1025-1083; *Gulf Coast Oil Fields,* AAPG (1936), pp. 20-78.

Campbell, M. R.: "Historical Review of Theories Advanced by American Geologists to Account for the Origin and Accumulation of Oil," *Econ. Geol.* (1911), v. 6, pp. 363-395.

Clendenin, W. W.: "A Preliminary Report Upon the Florida Parishes of East Louisiana and the Bluff, Prairie, Hill Lands of S.W. Louisiana, Louisiana State Experimental Station," *Geology and Agriculture* (1896), v. 3, pp. 236-240.

Coste, Eugene: "The Volcanic Origin of Natural Gas and Petroleum," *Canadian Mining Institute Journal* (1903), v. 6, pp. 73-123.

DeGolyer, E.: "The Theory of Volcanic Origin of Salt Domes," *Bull. 137,* AIME (1919), v. 61, pp. 456-477.

DeGolyer, E.: "Origin of North American Salt Domes," *Bull.,* AAPG (1925), v. 9, no. 5, pp. 831-874; *Geology of Salt Dome Oil Fields,* AAPG (1926), pp. 1-44.

Dumble, E. T.: "The Occurrence of Petroleum in Eastern Mexico as Contrasted with Those in Texas and Louisiana," *Trans.,* AIME (1916), v. 52, p. 263.

Durschner, H.: "Einige Physikalische Uberlegungen zum Problem der Halokinese," *Zeits Deutsch. Geol. Ges.* (1957), v. 109, pp. 152-158.

Escher, B. G., and Kuehner, P. H.: "Experiments in Connection with Salt Domes," *Leidsche Geologische Mededeelinger* (1929), Aflevering 3, II, pp. 151-182.

Goessmann, C. A. and Buck, C. E.: "On the Rock Salt Deposit of Petite Anse, Louisiana Rock Salt Co.," *Rept.,* Amer. Bur. of Mines (1867), 35 pp.

Gussow, W. C.: "Energy Source of Intrusive Masses," (abs.) *Bull.,* AAPG, (1965), v. 49, no. 3, p. 343.

Hager, Lee: "The Mounds of the Southern Oil Fields," *Eng. and Min. Jour.* (1904), v. 78, pp. 137-139, 180-183.

Halbouty, Michel T. and Hardin, George C., Jr.: "Genesis of Salt Domes of Gulf Coastal Plain," *Bull.,* AAPG (1956), v. 40, no. 4, pp. 737-746.

Harbort, E.: "Zur Geologie der Nordhannoverschen Salzhorste," *Monatsber. d. Deutsch. Geol. Ges.,* 62 (1910), p. 326.

Harbort, E.: "Zur Frage der Aufpressungsvorgiiange und des Alters der Nordwestdeutschen Salzvorkommen," *Kali* (1913), Heft 5, p. 112.

Harris, G. D.: "Notes on the Geology of the Winnfield Sheet," *Rept. of 1907,* Geol.

Svy. of La. (1907), Bull. 5.

Harris, G. D.: "The Salt Domes of Louisiana and Texas," *Science* (1908), new ser., v. 27, pp. 347-348.

Harris, G. D.: "Rock Salt," *Rept. of 1907,* Geol. Svy. of La., (1908), Bull. 7.

Harris, G. D. and Veatch, A. C.: "A Preliminary Report on the Geological Survey of Louisiana," *Rept. for 1899,* Geol. Svy. of La. (1899), pp. 9-138.

Hilgard, E. W.: "On the Geology of Lower Louisiana and Salt Deposit of Petite Anse Island," *Art. 3,* Smithsonian Contr. Knowledge (1872), no. 248, 34 pp.

Hopkins, F. V.: *First Annual Report of the Louisiana State Geological Survey; Annual Report of Board of Supervisors of the Louisiana State Seminary of Learning and Military Academy for the Year Ending Dec. 31, 1869,* New Orleans (1870), pp. 77-109.

Hubbert, M. K.: "Theory of Scale Models as Applied to the Study of Geologic Structures," *Ph.D. Dissertation,* Chicago U. (1937), Dept. of Geol.; *Bull.,* GSA (1937), v. 48, pp. 1459-1519.

Krejci, Karl: "Der Bau der Rumanischen Olgebiete," *Geological Rundschau Band 16* (1926), Heft 1, S. 1-16; Heft 2, S. 99-127.

Lachmann, R.: "Studien Uber den Bau von Salzmassen," *Kali* (1910a), Heft 9, pp. 188.

Lachmann, R.: "Uber Autoplaste (Nichttektonische) Formelemente in Bau der Salzgesteine Norddeutschlands," *Monatsber d. Deutsch Geol. Ges.,* Bd. 62 (1910b), pp. 113-116.

Lachmann, R.: *Ekzeme und Tektonik,* Zentralbl. f. Min. usw. (1917), 414 pp.

Link, Theodore A.: "Experiments Relating to

Salt Dome Structures," *Bull.*, AAPG (1930), v. 14, no. 4, pp. 483-508; (abs.) *Pan-Am Geologist*, v. 53, p. 221.

Lockett, S. H.: "Report of Topographical Survey of Louisiana," *Rept. of Superintendent for 1870*, LSU (1871), pp. 16-26.

Matteson, W. G.: "Principles and Problems of Oil Prospecting in the Gulf Coast Country," *Trans.*, AIME (1918), v. 59, pp. 435-491.

Nettleton, L. L.: "Fluid Mechanics of Salt Dome," *Bull.*, AAPG (1934), v. 18, no. 9, pp. 1175-1204; *Gulf Coast Oil Fields*, AAPG (1936), pp. 79-108.

Nettleton, L. L.: "History of Concepts of Gulf Coast Salt-Dome Formations," *Bull.*, AAPG (1935), v. 19, no. 12, pp. 2373-2383.

Norton, E. G.: "The Origin of the Louisiana and East Texas Salines," *Bull.*, AIME (1915), no. 97, pp. 93-102; no. 101, pp. 1120-1122; *Trans.*, AIME (1916), v. 51, pp. 502-513.

O'Brien, C. A. E.: "Salt Diapirism in South Persia," *Geologie en Mijnbouw Niewve Serie*, 19e Jaargang (1957), pp. 357-376.

Parker, Travis J. and McDowell, A. N.: "Scale Models as Guide to Interpretation of Salt Dome Faulting," *Bull.*, AAPG (1951), v. 35, no. 9, pp. 2076-2086.

Parker, Travis J. and McDowell, A. N.: "Model Studies of Salt Dome Tectonics," *Bull.*, AAPG (1955), v. 39, no. 12, pp. 2384-2470; Review by W. T. Born, *Geophysics*, v. 21, no. 4, p. 1121.

Posepny, F.: "Studien aus dem Salinargebiete Siebenburgens, zweite Abteilung," *K. K. Geol. Reichsanstalt Jahrb.* (1871), Bd. 21, Heft 1, pp. 123-188.

Rogers, G. S.: "Intrusive Origin of the Gulf Coast Salt Domes," *Econ. Geol.* (1918), v. 13, p. 468.

Sannemann, D.: *Zur Entwicklung von Salzstock-Familien* (1960), in preparation.

Sannemann, D.: "Salt Stock Families in Northwestern Germany," (abs.) *Bull.*, AAPG (1965), v. 49, no. 3, p. 357.

Stille, H.: "Das Aufsteigen der Salztebirges," *Zeitschr. f. Prakt. Geologie*, 19 (1911), p. 91.

Stille, H.: "Injektivfaltung und damit Zusammenhangende Erscheinungen," *Geol. Rundschau*, 8 (1917), p. 89.

Stille, H.: "The Upthrust of Salt Masses of Germany," *Bull.*, AAPG (1925), v. 9, no. 3, pp. 419-441; *Geology of Salt Dome Oil Fields*, AAPG (1926), pp. 142-166.

Thomassy, R.: *Geologie Pratique de la Louisiana*, Paris, (1860).

Torrey, Paul D. and Fralich, Charles E.: "An Experimental Study of the Origin of Salt Domes," *Jour. Geol.* (1926), v. 34, no. 3, pp. 224-234; (abs.) *Oil & Gas Jour.*, v. 23, no. 45, p. 133.

Trusheim, F.: "Uber Halokinese und Ihre Bedeutung fur die Strukturelle Entwicklung Norddeutschlands," *Zeits. Deutsch. Geol. Ges.* (1957), v. 98, pp. 7-29.

Trusheim, F.: "On the Mechanism of Salt Migration in Northern Germany," *Bull.*, AAPG (1960), v. 44, no. 9, pp. 1519-1540.

Van der Gracht, W. A. I. M. von Waterschoot: "The Saline Domes of Northwestern Europe," *Southwestern Assoc. Pet. Geol.* (1917), v. 1, pp. 85-92.

Veatch, A. C.: "The Salines of North Louisiana," *Rept. of 1902*, Geol. Svy. of La., (1902), pp 47-100.

Chapter
4

Configuration
and Composition

Configuration

Salt masses in domes of the Gulf region are circular to broadly elliptical. In the Gulf region of the United States circular or modified circular slopes are most common; in the southern Gulf area (Isthmian embayment) elongate or ellipitical shapes predominate.

Barbers Hill, Lost Lake and Moss Bluff, Chambers County, Texas (Fig. 4-1), are three closely-spaced domes that illustrate similarities and differences in size and shape of their salt masses.

The tops of individual salt stocks range in diameter from one-half mile to four miles or more; the average diameter of domes in the Gulf region is two miles. Salt stocks in cross-section are generally cylindrical, but downward enlargement is common such that any or all of the dome's flanks may be vertical to inclined. Many large salt domes are bell-shaped masses which might best be described as truncated cones of salt. Some stocks are

vertical at one depth and inclined at others. The top surface of the salt masses may be flat to slightly convex upward; or in some cases, highly irregular to steeply inclined. In a few instances sharp salt projections extend above the salt mass. A mushroom-like development, or overhang, is common at the apex of the salt stock and may occur around all or part of the stock.

Composition

The composition of salt masses of domes in the Gulf region is remarkably pure sodium chloride (halite) with minor amounts of calcium sulfate (anhydrite). Excellent descriptions of megascopic and microscopic properties of salt in Gulf region domes were given by Taylor, 1938; Balk, 1949, 1953; Hoy, *et al*, 1962; and Kupfer, 1962, to which the reader is referred for detail. According to Kupfer (1963) the anhydrite content in Gulf Coast salt domes is less than three percent. Practically all of the insoluble impurities in rock salt are anhydrite but traces of other minerals including dolomite, calcite, barite, pyrite, quartz, iron minerals, celestite, and sulphur have been reported.

The salt is coarsely crystalline with individual crystals ranging from ¼ to ½-inch in diameter. Pods of extremely coarse-grained halite occur in the salt mines of the Gulf region and Balk (1953) reported poikiloblasts (irregular areas of uniform orientation) of halite as large as 16 inches long.

Layering in the salt is the dominant physical characteristic. The layers average one to 10 inches thick and consist of interbedded white and gray-to-black salt bands with minor impurities, chiefly anhydrite and dolomite. The layers observed in mines are folded, recrystallized, or otherwise deformed but preserve their sedimentary character. Folding is characteristically isoclinal with axial planes nearly vertical.

Across the top of most shallow, piercement salt domes is a mantle of associated minerals called cap rock (Fig. 4-2). The amount of cap rock associated with domes decreases with depth but has been found on domes more than 10,000 feet deep. The average thickness of cap rock on shallow domes is between 300 and 400 feet, but more than 1,000 feet has been penetrated on some domes (*e.g.,* Jefferson Island, Iberia Parish, Louisiana, Fig. 4-2). Cap rock is usually thick over the center of a dome, thinning towards the periphery, and very thin or absent on the flanks.

Cap rock is composed chiefly of granular anhydrite, and in many instances is the only constituent of the supradomal material. On most shallow domes anhydrite grades upward into gypsum and limestone (calcite) with or without accessory minerals (e.g. sulphur, barite). Cavities are common within the cap

rock. Taylor (1938) in his excellent paper states:

> Cap rock cannot be divided into a satisfactory series of continuous beds or layers because of its great complexity and irregularity. There are, however, three fairly well-defined zones that can be distinguished where cap rock is well-developed. The most important of these is the zone in which anhydrite predominates . . . A calcite zone is found above the anhydrite zone in the thicker and better developed cap rocks. It is separated from the anhydrite zone by a transition zone containing, in addition to calcite and anhydrite, the greater part of the sulphur, gypsum, and less important cap-rock minerals.

Associated with many domes is a zone of hard, secondarily cemented sediments that immediately overlies the cap rock or salt where cap rock is absent. The hard strata, commonly called "false cap rock," may grade into the cap rock itself. The sands of the false cap rock are usually cemented by calcite or other water insoluble minerals such as pyrite.

Origin of Cap Rock

Several theories have been advanced on the origin of cap rock but most geologists now agree that anhydrite in cap rock is an accumulation of insoluble residues precipitated from ground waters acting on the dome's salt mass (Goldman, 1952). Gypsum, calcite, sulphur, and other minerals are products of anhydrite alteration. A recent theory on limestone origin in cap rock has been advanced by McLeod (1960), who believes that ground waters in the supradomal area circulating under the influence of osmotic pressure deposited limestone cap rock above the anhydrite. He contends previous theories failed to account for the rather complete separation of the calcite layer from the anhydrite zone.

In contrast to McLeod's concepts is the work of Feely and Kulp (1957) who performed experiments and isotopic analysis on the mineralogic constituents of cap rock and concluded:

1. Free sulphur and hydrogen sulphide are formed by sulphate-reducing bacteria acting on sulphate ions of anhydrite.

2. Carbon of calcite cap rock is derived from oxidation of hydrocarbons.

Thus, there appears to be room for further refinement of the exact process by which the various mineral zones of cap rock are emplaced. However, it is apparent that all accessory minerals in addition to anhydrite were derived directly from the salt mass itself.

Literature Cited

Balk, Robert: "Structure of Grand Saline Salt Dome, Van Zandt County, Texas," *Bull.,* AAPG (1949), v. 33, no. 11, pp. 1791-1829.

Balk, Robert: "Salt Structures of Jefferson Island Salt Dome, Iberia and Vermilion Parishes, Louisiana," *Bull.,* AAPG (1953), v. 37, no. 11, pp. 2455-2474.

Feely, H. W. and Kulp, J. L.: "Origin of Gulf Coast Salt Dome Sulphur Deposits," *Bull.,* AAPG (1957), v. 41, no. 8, pp. 1802-1953.

Goldman, M. I.: "Deformation, Metamorphism, and Mineralization in Gypsum-Anhydrite Cap Rock, Sulphur Salt Dome, Louisiana," *Memoir 50,* GSA (1952), 169 pp.

Halbouty, Michel T. and Hardin, George C., Jr.: "Factors Affecting Quantity of Oil Accumulation Around Some Texas Gulf Coast Piercement Type Salt Domes," *Bull.,* AAPG (1955), v. 39, no. 5, pp. 697-711.

Hoy, R. B., Foose, R. M. and O'Neill, B. J., Jr.: "Structure of Winnfield Salt Dome, Winn Parish, Louisiana," *Bull.,* AAPG (1962), v. 46, no. 8, pp. 1444-1459.

Kupfer, Donald H.: "Structure of Morton Salt Company Mine, Weeks Island Salt Dome, Louisiana," *Bull.,* AAPG (1962), v. 46, no. 8, pp. 1460-1467.

Kupfer, Donald H.: "Structure of Salt in Gulf Coast Domes," *Symposium on Salt,* Northern Ohio Geol. Soc., Inc. (1963), Cleveland, Ohio, pp. 104-123.

McLeod, Richard R.: "A Theory for the Formation of Limestone Cap Rock of Salt Domes," *Trans.,* GCAGS (1960), v. 10, pp. 151-153.

Taylor, R. E.: "Origin of the Cap Rock of Louisiana Salt Domes," *Bull. 11,* La. Geol. Svy. (1938), Dept. of Conservation, 191 pp.; *Ph.D. Dissertation,* LSU, Dept. of Geol.

Chapter 5

Classifying Salt Structures

Salt structures occur in a wide variety of forms, sizes, and relationships to host sediments. As a result the structural and stratigraphic conditions of surrounding areas are influenced in different ways by their development. Notwithstanding these variables, individual salt structures and groups of structures often have certain common characteristics which provide the basis for a usable classification system.

Salt structures in the Gulf region have been classified according to structural and descriptive schemes. Barton (1926) presented one of the first descriptive outlines to distinguish salt domes from each other and Murray's (1961) comprehensive work leaves little room for improvement in classificatory methods. The following discussion attempts to use the most clearly understood and easily demonstrable criteria for classification from all previous writers.

Descriptive classifications refer to:

1. Depth of burial of the salt mass below the surface.

2. Form or shape of the salt structures.

3. Genetic relationship of salt structures or group of structures.

Structural classifications include the relationship of:

1. The upper portion of the salt to adjacent sediments.

2. The lower portion of the salt mass to the source bed.

3. The salt stock to structural features in adjacent strata.

4. The salt core to numerous typical fault patterns.

Descriptive Classification— Depth of Burial

Teas (1935) classified Gulf region salt domes as shallow, intermediate, or deep, based on the depth of the cap rock or salt. Shallow domes ranged from the surface to 2,000 feet and pierced all or most of the geologic section. Intermediate domes included those whose cap rock or underlying salt was found from about 2,000 to 6,000 feet below the surface. Intermediate domes pierced much less of the geologic section than the shallow domes. Resulting structures were considered less complicated with fewer faults and associated unconformities. Deep domes included those where salt had not been reached by the drill, and domes below 6,000 feet.

Wallace (1944) used the same arbitrary depths as Teas but divided the deep domes of South Louisiana into the following groups:

1. Deep-seated salt domes: top of salt definitely encountered below 6,000 feet.

2. Deep-seated domes: several deep wells drilled but no salt encountered.

Wallace (p. 1250) stated: "the deep-seated domes represent the end members of the series of structures known as salt domes. The only evidence of salt movement appears as deeply buried faults in gently uparched strata."

In the late 1940's and early 1950's, deep drilling on the flanks of domes and over gravity minimums which indicated deep-seated salt uplifts, led Parker and McDowell (1955) to redefine the classification as to depth of burial. Domes at less than 4,000 feet were considered *shallow,* those between 4,000 and 10,000 feet were *intermediate,* and those at still greater depths were *deep* (Fig. 5-1). Using this depth system in the U. S. Gulf region there are 340 proven domes (salt has been penetrated) including 188 shallow, 98 intermediate, and 54 deep structures.

In addition, there are scores of other domal or anticlinal anomalies, both onshore and in the Gulf of Mexico, which have not been penetrated by drilling but are almost certainly salt-controlled structures. A list of the known salt domes classified according to depth of burial is shown in Tables 5-1, 5-2, 5-3.

Descriptive Classification—Form

Salt structures of the Gulf region vary greatly in size, shape, and form. The largest salt-controlled structures within a particular salt dome basin (*e.g.* East Texas, Texas-Louisiana coastal basins) are generally located in the deepest part of the basin. Salt structures tend to be smaller and exhibit less intense folding as they approach the updip limit of salt deposition. This arrangement is governed by the amount of salt available to form structures (thickness of source bed) and density contrast between salt and sediments (thickness of overburden).

The various forms of salt structures found in salt dome basins of the Gulf region include monoclines, pillows, anticlines, domes, and ridges or massifs (Figs. 5-2 and 5-3). All of the forms shown in the diagrams may not occur in each basin. However, the general sequence is from simple, homoclinal dip on the salt surface at its updip limit, to large diapiric salt masses, some with individual stalks or dome-like apophyses extending from a parent salt intrusion in the deepest part of a basin.

The salt domes and anticlines in Texas, Louisiana, and Mississippi are located coastward of the Mexia-Talco, Arkansas, Pickens-Gilbertown fault systems. In fact, the updip limit of the Louann salt roughly coincides with these fault systems.

Similarly in Mexico, known salt structures of the Isthmus of Tehuantepec region are restricted to the area gulfward from the Santa Elena fault system (Fig. 5-4).

Table 5-1

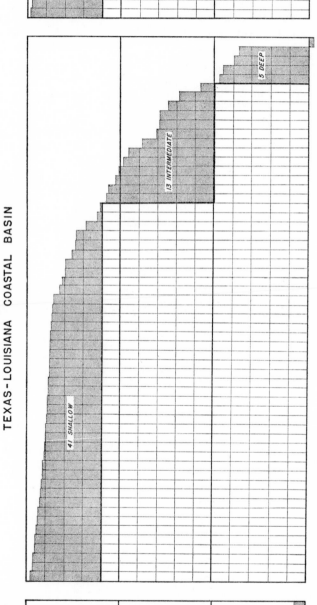

TEXAS PORTION
TEXAS-LOUISIANA COASTAL BASIN

EAST TEXAS
BASIN

16 SHALLOW

2

ELKHART
CONCORD
LA RUE
KITTRELL
BRUSHY CREEK
KEECHI
WHITEHOUSE
BOGGY CREEK
BETHEL
HAINESVILLE
EAST TYLER
OAKWOOD
MOUNT SYLVAN
BULLARD
BUTLER
STEEN
BROOKS
GRAND SALINE
PALESTINE

41 SHALLOW

13 INTERMEDIATE

5 DEEP

RED FISH REEF
MANVEL
RACOON BEND
WEBSTER
CEDAR POINT
THOMPSON
CLAM LAKE
HANKAMER
ORANGE
MYKAWA
PORT NECHES
ESPERSON
LOST LAKE
MILLICAN
DANBURY
SAN FELIPE
SOUTH HOUSTON
SUGARLAND
ARRIOLA
FERGUSON CROSSING
DAY
STEWART BEACH
MC FADDIN BEACH
CLAY CREEK
FANNETT
BATSON
SARATOGA
BLOCK 144
MARKHAM
CLEMENS
ALLEN
BIG HILL
STRATTON RIDGE
HIGH ISLAND
HUMBLE
DAVIS HILL
SPINDLETOP
BRENHAM
BRYAN MOUND
HOSKINS MOUND
GULF
MOSS BLUFF
HOCKLEY
BARBERS HILL
BOLING
NASH
LONG POINT
PIERCE JUNCTION
NORTH DAYTON
WEST COLUMBIA
SOUR LAKE
BIG CREEK
HULL
DAMON MOUND
SOUTH LIBERTY
HAWKINSVILLE
ORCHARD
SAN LUIS PASS
BLUE RIDGE

RIO GRANDE
BASIN

3

2

PESCADITO
DILWORTH
MOCA
PIEDRAS PINTAS
GYP HILL
PALANGANA

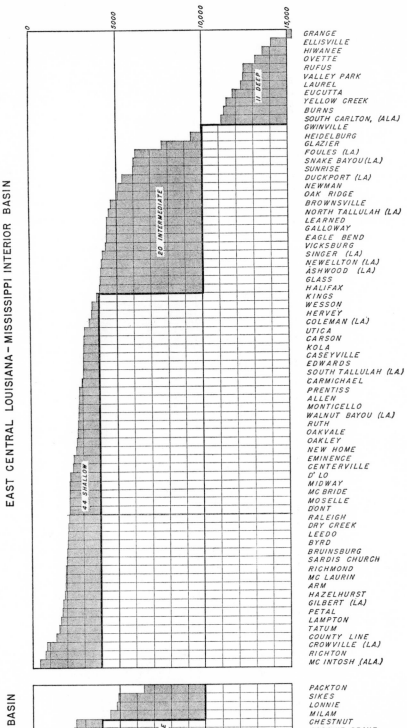

TABLE 5-2

EAST CENTRAL LOUISIANA-MISSISSIPPI INTERIOR BASIN

GRANGE
ELLISVILLE
HIWANEE
OVETTE
RUFUS
VALLEY PARK
LAUREL
EUCUTTA
YELLOW CREEK
BURNS
SOUTH CARLTON, (ALA.)
GWINVILLE
HEIDELBURG
GLAZIER
FOULES (LA.)
SNAKE BAYOU (LA.)
SUNRISE
DUCKPORT (LA.)
NEWMAN
OAK RIDGE
BROWNSVILLE
NORTH TALLULAH (LA.)
LEARNED
GALLOWAY
EAGLE BEND
VICKSBURG
SINGER (LA.)
NEWELLTON (LA.)
ASHWOOD (LA.)
GLASS
HALIFAX
KINGS
WESSON
HERVEY
COLEMAN (LA.)
UTICA
CARSON
KOLA
CASEYVILLE
EDWARDS
SOUTH TALLULAH (LA.)
CARMICHAEL
PRENTISS
ALLEN
MONTICELLO
WALNUT BAYOU (LA.)
RUTH
OAKVALE
OAKLEY
NEW HOME
EMINENCE
CENTERVILLE
D' LO
MIDWAY
MC BRIDE
MOSELLE
D'ONT
RALEIGH
DRY CREEK
LEEDO
BYRD
BRUINSBURG
SARDIS CHURCH
RICHMOND
MC LAURIN
ARM
HAZELHURST
GILBERT (LA.)
PETAL
LAMPTON
TATUM
COUNTY LINE
CROWVILLE (LA.)
RICHTON
MC INTOSH (ALA.)

11 DEEP

20 INTERMEDIATE

44 SHALLOW

NORTH LOUISIANA BASIN

PACKTON
SIKES
LONNIE
MILAM
CHESTNUT
COOCHIE BRAKE
MINDEN
BISTINEAU
ARCADIA
GIBSLAND
DRAKES
VACHERIE
CEDAR CREEK
PRICE'S
PROTHRO
WINNFIELD
KING'S
RAYBURN'S

4 INTERMEDIATE

14 SHALLOW

5000
10,000
15,000

0
5000
10,000
15,000

TABLE 5-3

LOUISIANA PORTION OF THE TEXAS—LOUISIANA COASTAL BASIN

EUGENE ISLAND, BLOCK 32	
NORTH MALLARD BAY	
GOLDEN MEADOW	
CROWLEY	
NORTH CROWLEY	
SOUTH TIGRE LAGOON	
SOUTH SECTION 28	
SOUTH MARSH ISLAND, BLK. 79	
LAFITTE	
BOSCO	
PARADIS	
STELLA	
BIG LAKE	
EUGENE ISLAND, BLOCK 238	
LAKE CHICOT	
VERMILION, BLOCK III	
EUGENE ISLAND, BLOCK 292	
CREOLE	
EAST CAMERON, BLOCK 155	
EAST CAMERON, BLOCK 152	
SOUTH MARSH ISLAND, BLK. 57	
ROANOKE	
EAST CAMERON, BLOCK 160	
SOUTH TIMBALIER, BLOCK 54	
LAKE SALVADOR	
ST. GABRIEL	
ST. MARTINSVILLE	
WOODLAWN	
JEANERETTE	
MAIN PASS, BLOCK 46	
VERMILION, BLOCK 245	
CHARENTON	
SOUTH MARSH ISLAND, BLK. 66	
CUTOFF	
GOOD HOPE	
SOUTH PASS, BLOCK 27	
EAST CAMERON, BLOCK 139	
DELTA DUCK CLUB	
SOUTH MARSH ISLAND, BLK. 41	
SHIP SHOAL, BLOCK 230	
NORTH STARKS	
EUGENE ISLAND, BLOCK 231	
SOUTH TIMBALIER, BLOCK 176	
PLUMB BOB	
SWEET LAKE	
WEST DELTA, BLOCK 133	
WEST BAY	
SHIP SHOAL, BLOCK 113	
RACELAND	
LOCKPORT	
SOUTH MARSH ISLAND, BLK. 7	
VERMILION, BLOCK 190	
SOUTH MARSH ISLAND, BLK. 48	
BAY DE CHENE	
IOWA	
BARATARIA	
EAST CAMERON, BLOCK 126	
BAYOU DES ALEMANDES	
SHIP SHOAL, BLOCK 72	
WEST COTE BLANCHE BAY	
EAST CAMERON, BLK. 189	
EUGENE ISLAND, BLOCK 205	
EAST CAMERON, BLOCK 187	
LAKE MONGOLOIS	
VERMILION, BLOCK 102	
HESTER	
CHENEYVILLE	
SOUTH TIMBALIER, BLOCK 131	
VALENTINE	
TIMBALIER BAY	
WELSH	
SOUTH MARSH ISLAND, BLK. 8	
GRAND ISLE, BLOCK 72	
BAYOU COUBA	
SOUTH MARSH ISLAND, BLK. 6	
EAST CAMERON, BLOCK 151	
SOUTH TIMBALIER, BLOCK 135	
COON POINT	
CAMERON MEADOWS	
BAY JUNOP	
GUEYDAN	
DARROW	
SOUTH TIMBALIER BAY, BLK. 86	

32 DEEP

51 INTERMEDIATE

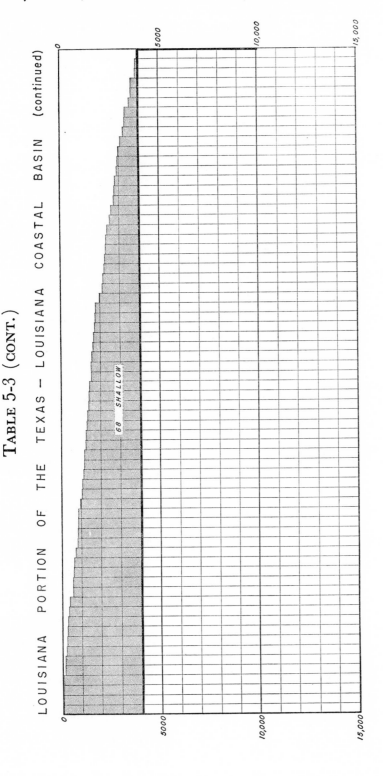

TABLE 5-3 (CONT.)

LOUISIANA PORTION OF THE TEXAS – LOUISIANA COASTAL BASIN (continued)

68 SHALLOW

EUGENE ISLAND, BLOCK 208
LEEVILLE
EDGERLY
EUGENE ISLAND, BLOCK 128
PORT BARRE
SOUTH MARSH ISLAND, BLK. 73
EAST HACKBERRY
SHIP SHOAL, BLOCK 208
BAYOU DES GLAISE
VERMILION, BLOCK 120
VERMILION, BLOCK 162
EAST CAMERON, BLOCK 118
SHIP SHOAL, BLOCK 154
BAYOU BLUE
WEST DELTA, BLOCK 30
CAILLOU ISLAND
EUGENE ISLAND, BLOCK 110
SHIP SHOAL, BLOCK 32
JENNINGS
CALCASIEU LAKE
WHITE CASTLE
SOUTH MARSH ISLAND, BLK. 38
GRAND ISLE, BLOCK 18
EUGENE ISLAND, BLOCK 188
BAY MARCHAND
LAKE PELTO
WEST HACKBERRY
GRAND ISLE, BLOCK 16
SORRENTO
EUGENE ISLAND, BLOCK 77
GARDEN ISLAND BAY
DOG LAKE
LAKE WASHINGTON
STARKS
SULPHUR MINES
BAY ST. ELAINE
LAKE HERMITAGE
VENICE
BULLY CAMP
BAYOU BOUILLION
SECTION 28
CLOVELLY
EUGENE ISLAND, BLOCK 184
CHACAHOULA
POTASH
BLACK BAYOU
FOUR ISLE
FAUSSE POINT
IBERIA
WEST CAMERON, BLOCK 386
LAKE BARRE
VINTON
BAYOU CHOCTAW
VERMILION, BLOCK 164
SOUTH PELTO, BLOCK 20
NAPOLEONVILLE
EAST CAMERON, BLOCK 115
PINE PRAIRIE
COTE BLANCHE ISLAND
EUGENE ISLAND, BLOCK 126
VERMILION BAY
EUGENE ISLAND, BLOCK 175
ANSE LA BUTTE
BELLE ISLE
WEEKS ISLE
JEFFERSON ISLAND
RABBIT ISLAND
AVERY ISLAND

The various forms of salt structures in the Gulf region, excluding diapiric intrusions, are probably best revealed in the East Texas basin (Fig. 5-5) where there is a sufficient density of wells that penetrated pre-Cretaceous rocks. Currently one of the most active and promising exploratory areas in the Gulf region is the Smackover (Jurassic) trend in the East Texas basin. Information from recent Smackover wells provides control for extrapolating depths to the top of the salt. These data, together with scattered salt control points, indicate the probable form of salt structures in the updip part of the basin. Updip to downdip, the salt surface is monoclinal from its wedgeout adjacent to the inner margin of the Mexia-Talco fault zone southeastward into a narrow, sinuous trough. Flanking this trough on the south is an elongate, arcuate anticlinal belt comprising separate folds formed during Middle to Late Jurassic time and not rejuvenated during the Cretaceous. These Jurassic anticlines are the major producing Smackover fields.

Probably several, if not all, of these anticlines are salt-controlled structures. Salt uplifts within this belt vary from small salt pillows to large salt anticlines (Fig. 5-2). Gravity interpretations suggest that many of the folds along the anticlinal belt are salt anticlines. Many of the Smackover fields in this area are gravity minima. Adjacent synclinal areas are maxima. Updip from the known salt wedgeout, gravity anomalies with structural manifestations are reversed—anticlines are maxima, synclines are minima.

The major salt domes in the East Texas basin occur basinward (downdip) from the belt of probable salt anticlines. The structural alignments of the domes, salt anticlines, and fault zones conform with the basin's dominant north to northeast trending structural grain established by earlier Ouachita movements.

Huge diapiric salt intrusions occurring as single salt domes or as salt ridges with several stalk-like projections are more characteristic of the Texas-Louisiana coastal basin than any other salt dome basin. These immense salt structures occur in the area of maximum deposition in the Gulf region (Gulf geosyncline). Deep drilling on the flanks of three prominent piercement salt domes of coastal Louisiana indicates that they are components of a huge, deep-seated salt intrusion (Fig. 5-6). Atwater and Forman (1959) proposed the term "salt massif" for this form of salt structure. Bay Marchand, Timbalier Bay, and Caillou Island domes were previously considered three separate and unrelated salt stocks. Regarding this massif, Atwater and Forman state (pp. 2601-2602):

> The Marchand-Timbalier-Caillou Island salt massif, at a depth of 20,000 feet is more than 27 miles long and slightly more than 13 miles wide. It has an east-west orientation. The massif has an area of 200 square miles, as mapped at a depth of 20,000 feet, and contains 265 cubic miles of salt to that depth. When the massif is projected downward with vertical sides from that depth to 50,000 feet [postulated depth to the mother salt bed], it contains 1,400 cubic miles of salt . . . these figures, impressive as they are, probably present only a part of the picture, for it is likely that this salt massif extends eastward in an arc to include the Block 16 and Block 18 salt domes of the offshore Grand Isle Area. If this proved to be true by future drilling, the figures presented here for the salt volumes would be substantially increased.

It is probable that many clusters of domes, previously considered separate stocks, are connected at depth to a large salt massif.

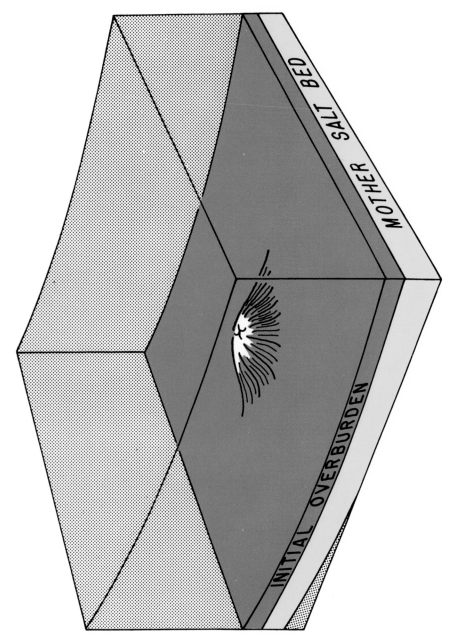

Figure 3-3. Block diagram shows initial movement of salt dome in response to increase overburden. Isostatic movement of salt is created by the density contrast between salt and overlying sediments. Factors which may initiate the growth of domes include: (1) irregularities on the surface of overburden; (2) variations in the thickness of overburden; (3) lateral variations in density of overburden; and (4) external stresses causing pressure differentials on the salt surface.

54

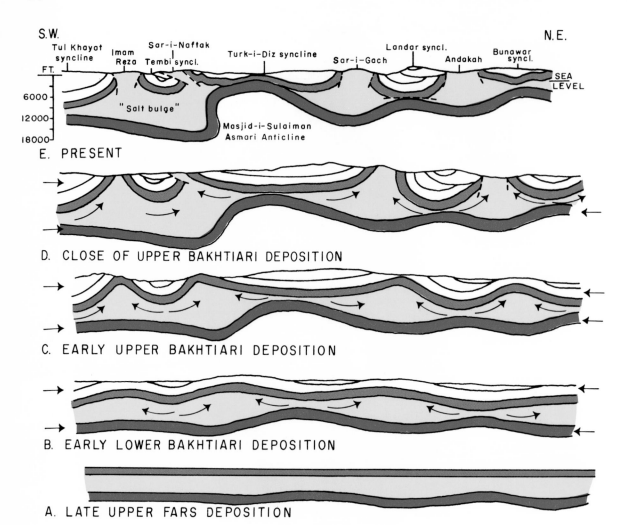

S.W.   N.E.

Tul Khayat syncline · Imam Reza · Sar-i-Naftak · Tembi syncl. · Turk-i-Diz syncline · Sar-i-Gach · Landar syncl. · Andakah · Bunawar syncl.

FT.

SEA LEVEL

6000

"Salt bulge"

12000

Masjid-i-Sulaiman Asmari Anticline

18000

E. PRESENT

D. CLOSE OF UPPER BAKHTIARI DEPOSITION

C. EARLY UPPER BAKHTIARI DEPOSITION

B. EARLY LOWER BAKHTIARI DEPOSITION

A. LATE UPPER FARS DEPOSITION

Figure 3-4. Structural evolution of Masjid-i-Sulaiman area, Iran. Both halo-tectonic (compression) and halokinetic (isostatic) forces are displayed in development of the salt structures and are indicated by the stress arrows. (After O'Brien, 1957)

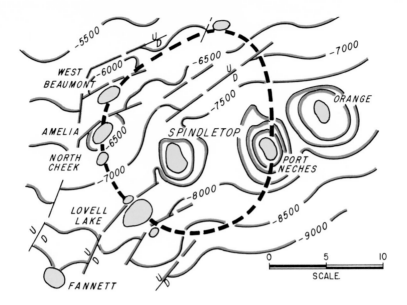

Figure 3-5. Generalized structural contour map of Spindletop area, Jefferson County, Texas shows possible relationship of master dome (Spindletop) to secondary dome (Port Neches, Lovell Lake, etc.). Spindletop dome lies on a southerly plunging nose and east of an arch of anticlines, (North Cheek, Amelia, and West Beaumont) that are associated with normal faults. The Port Neches salt dome is east of Spindletop a distance approximately equal to the radius of the arc of the producing structures on the west. These structures are believed to be deep-seated salt structures. Model studies conducted by Parker and McDowell showed concentric development patterns similar to naturally occurring salt structures as shown on the map. Contoured on Frio formation (Oligocene). (After Parker and McDowell, 1955)

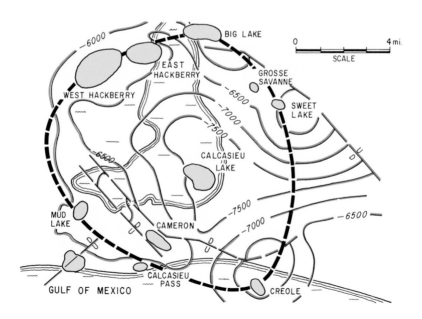

Figure 3-6. Generalized structural contour map of Calcasieu Lake area, Cameron Parish, Louisiana showing concentric arrangement of salt structures similar to the Spindletop area. The masterdome, secondary-dome explanation for the concentric pattern does not hold true in this particular case because evidence shows that Calcasieu Lake dome is a late-occurring salt uplift which developed after the surrounding domes.

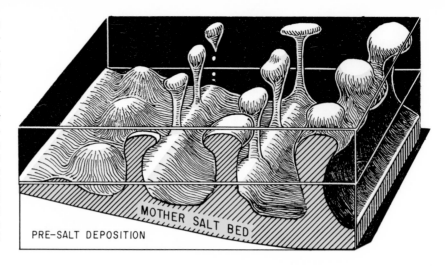

Figure 3-7. Block diagram showing shapes of salt structures in the Northwest (German (Zechstein) basin. The shapes of salt structures in the Gulf region are comparable to those in the diagram. The horizontal line about half-way up in the block diagram indicates the relative thickness of the salt prior to dome formation. Note the conjectural teardrop-shaped dome that has been severed from the source layer and "floated" upward through the host sediments. (Modified after Trusheim, 1957.)

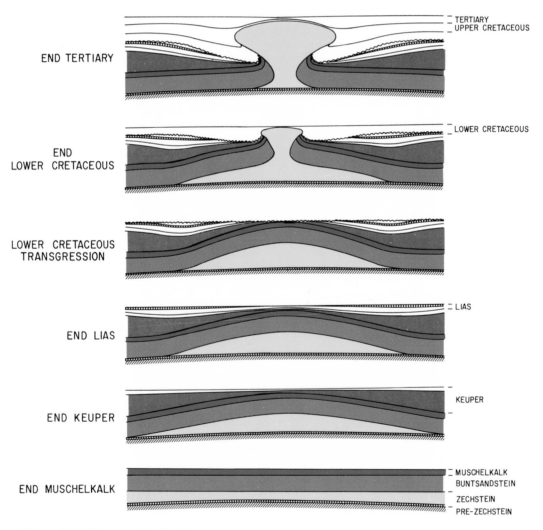

Figure 3-8. Diagrammatic development of Zechstein salt stock. Note that the primary peripheral sink increases in thickness away from the dome, whereas the secondary peripheral sink increases in thickness toward the dome. (After Trusheim, 1960)

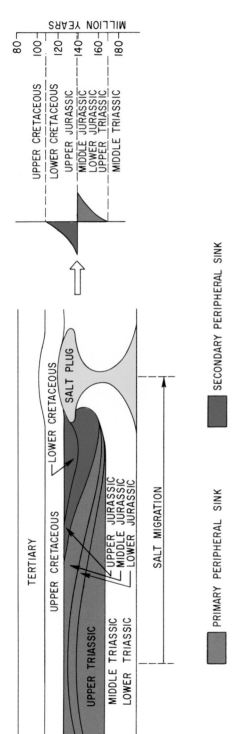

Figure 3-9. Diagrammatic method for determining speed of salt migration by development of primary and secondary peripheral sinks. (After Sannemann, 1960, in Trusheim, 1960)

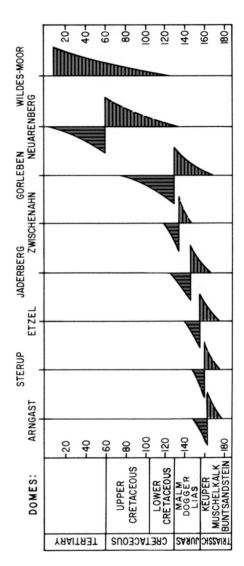

Figure 3-10. Time chart of development of some German salt domes. Blue denotes diapiric stage, green denotes pillow stage. Note that a salt pillow took about as long to form as the diapir developing from it. (After Sannemann, 1960, in Trusheim, 1960)

58

WEST   EAST

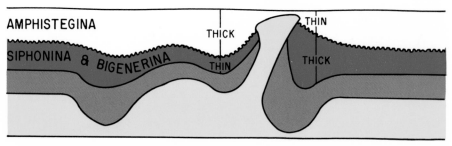

AMPHISTEGINA   THICK   THIN

SIPHONINA & BIGENERINA   THIN   THICK

MIDDLE MIOCENE

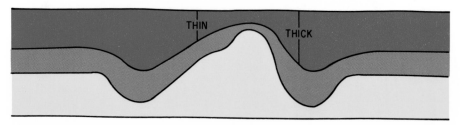

THIN   THICK

LOWER MIOCENE

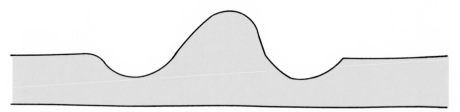

PRE MIOCENE

Figure 3-11. Diagrammatic development of High Island Dome, Galveston County, Texas, illustrating growth of a piercement structure from an earlier salt uplift (pillow). The change in thickness of stratigraphic units on different flanks of the dome suggests that the dome had at least two phases of growth which could be expected if the dome has evolved from an earlier salt uplift.

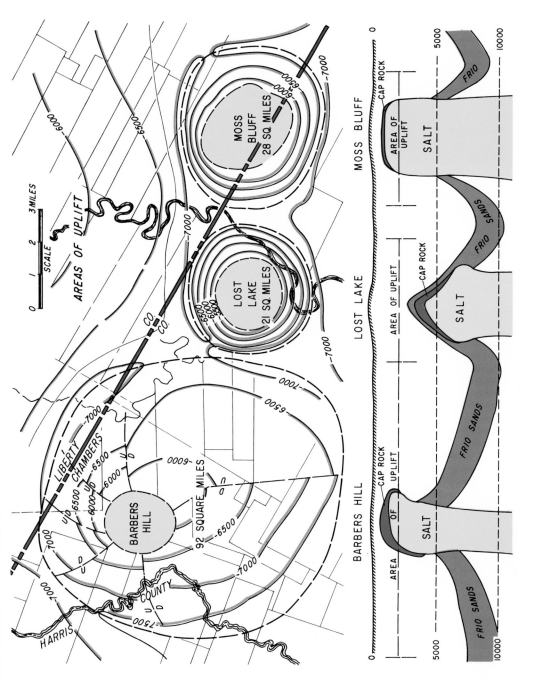

Figure 4-1. Structural contour map and cross section of Barbers Hill, Lost Lake, and Moss Bluff domes, Chambers and Liberty Counties, Texas. These three closely spaced domes are representative of the common shapes and sizes of Gulf region domes. The map shows a comparison of the areas of uplift in square miles of the three structures. The area of uplift at Barbers Hill dome is approximately three times greater than at the other domes. The amount of hydrocarbon accumulation at Barbers Hill is many times greater than at the other domes. Contoured on top of the Frio formation (Oligocene). (After Halbouty and Hardin, 1955)

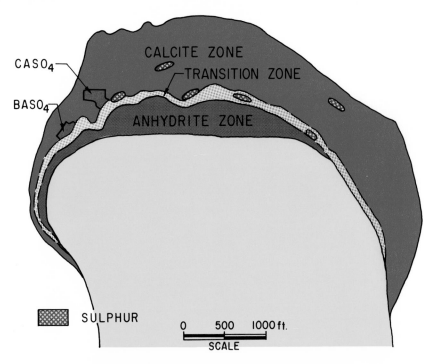

Figure 4-2. Cross section of Jefferson Island dome, Iberia Parish, Louisiana showing three mineralogical zones typical of cap rock on many domes. Accessory minerals such as gypsum and sulphur, if present, are usually associated with the transition and calcite zones overlying the lower anhydrite zone. (Modified after Taylor, 1938)

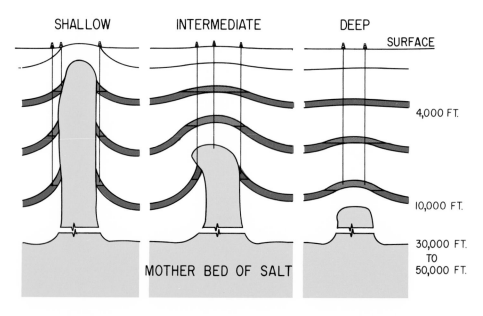

Figure 5-1. Diagrammatic section of typical piercement domes classified according to depth of burial. Note that the domes have been greatly foreshortened between the upper part of the salt stock and source layer.

Descriptive Classification— Genetic Relationships

There is mounting evidence that the pattern or geometric arrangement of salt structures is not by coincidence and that some domes, especially clusters of domes, are related in their history of development. Trusheim's work on the Zechstein salt structures in northern Germany and Atwater and Forman's findings in South Louisiana suggest that a group of domes may be the offspring of a single earlier salt movement. This concept was demonstrated, more or less, by the laboratory studies of Parker and McDowell. A very meaningful scheme of classification is needed to compare development of individual nearby structures to each other—a genetic method of classification. This method is of obvious economic importance because future discoveries of oil and gas may depend on determining the age relation of one structure to another or to ancient salt structures.

The primary or master dome-secondary dome concept of Parker and McDowell (1955) has been explained previously. Add to this distinction the relict salt structure and the three types comprise a usable genetic classification. Briefly, here are the criteria for distinguishing primary, secondary, and relict salt structures:

A. Primary

1. Well defined and extensive peripheral sink.

2. Concentric arrangement of structures (secondary domes) around primary dome. This is an optimum criterion but is not prerequisite—some linear patterns may include both primary and secondary structures.

3. Size of the dome not an identifying criterion—primary domes may be larger or smaller than secondary structures.

B. Secondary

1. Area of peripheral sink small or poorly defined—late-occurring domes may rise rapidly and have virtually no peripheral sink.

2. May form with other domes a ring-like pattern around a primary dome or may be a subordinate feature of a linear massif or salt wall.

3. Major unconformities may be present at depth—secondary domes according to Parker and McDowell would not develop under a very great thickness of overburden. Rather, their growth would be favored by a prolonged interval of nondeposition or erosion following the deposition of a relative thin layer of overburden material.

C. Relict

1. Change in thickness of specific stratigraphic units from one side or one flank of a piercement salt dome to the other sides or flanks (see Fig. 3-11, High Island dome).

2. Presence of a primary peripheral sink (after Trusheim, 1960) where old salt migrations at depth are indicated as local maxima of sedimentation with decrease in thickness *toward* the salt pillow. In subsequent stages, this may not be wholly destroyed by diapirism and remain as a relict structure.

As stressed in Chapter 2, applying the primary or master dome-secondary dome concept is difficult even when basic criteria can be recognized. The Spindletop area, Jefferson

County, Texas (Fig. 3-5), seems to fit the requirements with Spindletop dome the primary structure and Lovell Lake, North Cheek, Amelia, West Beaumont, North Vidor, and Port Neches the secondary structures. High Island dome (Fig. 3-11) as a possible relict structure.

Another possible example of genetically related salt structures is the Katy area, Waller County, Texas (Fig. 6-12). Discovered in 1935, Katy was the largest gas-condensate reserve in the Gulf Coast province at that time. The field, comprising more than 30,000 productive acres, is structurally a broad domal anticline unbroken by major faulting. Geologists generally agree that the field overlies a deep salt structure, though salt has never been reached and probably never will be because of its depth (+ 30,000 feet).

There are two different opinions on the origin of the Katy structure: (1) an earlier idea advanced by Allison, *et al*, (1946) that the structure is a residual or intradomal "high" resulting from the development of peripheral sinks around San Felipe and Hockley domes while Katy remained structurally stable; and (2) this writer's belief that the structure is a relict salt structure where initial uplift ceased and began later along a different path.

The earlier idea, presented by Allison, *et al*, reasons as follows (p. 169):

> The Katy structure does not appear to be due to uplift as the wells on the crest of the structure encounter the Yegua formation at depths that are normal for the area, while the wells on the north flank encounter the Yegua at depths that are several hundred feet below normal. This anomaly appears to be a classical example of a residual high. It is between and downdip from the overlapping rim synclines of the Brookshire (San Felipe) and Hockley salt domes. Closure on the north, east, and west is due to subsidence of these flanks which took

place as the peripheral sinks were formed. The salt mass moved from the forming synclines toward the center of the growing salt plugs, leaving a residual high in the interdomal area.

This theory for the origin of the Katy structure, first advanced by C. H. Ritz, is further supported by the fact that there is an abnormal thickening of the formation on the flanks affected by the peripheral sinks. The interval from the top of the Frio to the base of the Yegua Formation increases from 4,787 feet over the crest of the structure to 5,165 feet on the north flank. The total thickening is 378 feet, with 138 feet in the Yegua Formation, 107 feet in the Jackson Formation, 33 feet in the Vicksburg Formation, and 100 feet in the Frio Formation. This leads to the assumption that subsidence began prior to the deposition of the Yegua Formation and continued throughout that of the Frio.

The alternative explanation, based on additional well information from nearby, off-structure wells, considers the thinning in the Upper Eocene (Yegua) and Oligocene (Frio) a result of structural uplift of a primary salt structure. Deep drilling on the flanks of Katy provided information which showed similar thinning over the crest of the structure in the deepest horizons penetrated (Upper Wilcox).

Structural datums on the top of the Yegua on opposite sides of San Felipe dome reflect the dip of one flank of an initial salt uplift. If projected from the east side of the dome to the west, the dip is relatively constant into a sub-basin whose synclinal axis is immediately west of San Felipe dome. The Yegua Formation increases in thickness from one side of this immense piercement dome to the other, which is contrary to what would be expected if the dome was actively growing during Yegua time.

The geology of San Felipe and Hockley domes suggests that the two are similar in time and mode of growth. A significant datum relationship on both domes can best be explained by relating the two structures to a common plane from which they emerged. San Felipe dome is approximately 20 miles southwest of Hockley dome, yet the deepest Yegua datum penetrated on the northwest flank of San Felipe is only 20 feet structurally low to correlative Yegua strata on the north flank of Hockley. This datum relationship suggests that both domes extruded from the deepest part of a common trough which partially encircled the Katy uplift.

Consider also other similarities between Hockley and San Felipe. Neither has produced significant quantities of hydrocarbons; they are classic examples of uniquely barren domes within a prolific oil-producing trend. Katy, on the other hand, is a giant field.

The lower Yegua section at San Felipe is unusually calcareous, and although reefal limestone has never been definitely cored in wells at San Felipe, electric log characteristics suggest a possible reef facies around the dome. If San Felipe dome was just beginning to grow during lower Yegua time, a sea-mound would logically provide the habitat for reef development. San Felipe and Hockley domes are apparently younger than Katy, and their growth, commencing during Yegua time (Upper Eocene), was quite rapid. The peripheral sinks around the domes are very narrow; on some sectors of the periphery of the dome they are almost non-existent. On the southwest flank of Katy, Eocene beds dip into a "low" that is closely adjacent to the salt stock of San Felipe.

The structural evolution of the Katy area, with regard to genetic relationships among the three features (Katy, San Felipe, Hockley), is envisioned as a broad *primary* salt uplift of gentle-to-moderate relief. Growth continued until Middle Oligocene time. Be-

cause the energy for the uplift salt mass was distributed over a large geographical area the mound or pillow stage did not pierce the overburden and was never diapiric, at least not in the area of initial uplift. A change or addition of other geological factors—structural, sedimentational, or both—probably occurred during Late Eocene or Early Oligocene time causing a shift in locus of growth at Katy. Two new loci were initiated —San Felipe and Hockley domes began to extrude from the extreme flanks of Katy. With the growth of Katy directed into two rapidly rising domes, it ceased to be a primary structure and became relict in nature (Figure 6-12).

Structural Classification of Domes

For many years the popular category of classification has been the relationship of the salt to adjacent sedimentary strata; i.e., whether or not a dome actually broke through the overburden and became a piercement structure. On deep domes where it could not be actually established that salt broke through the overlying sediments, the dome was generally classified as nonpiercement.

The failings of this scheme are obvious. The determining factor was one of *well control* and *not of the relationship of the salt to sediments*. Any dome with sufficient vertical relief from the mother salt bed must be piercement in some stage of growth regardless of the thickness of the present overburden. By definition all salt diapirs are piercement, and domes as we know them in the Gulf region are diapirs.

Petroleum geologists are interested in the distinction between piercement and nonpiercement structures as they affect potential reservoir beds. If potential reservoir beds are pierced by the salt stock, whether they lie adjacent to the uppermost part of the salt mass or are confirmed by later drilling to be at much greater depths, the dome is a piercement structure. Use of the non-piercement category should be confined to salt structures that have not pierced potential reservoir beds. If strata pierced by a dome lack favorable reservoir characteristics, regardless of the thickness of the beds pierced, the dome should be non-piercement.

A structural classification is commonly combined with descriptive classification. A shallow salt dome may be non-piercement if it fails to penetrate potential reservoir beds— the reservoir beds are draped over the structure, faulted, but not pierced. Conversely a deep-seated dome may be piercement-type. The most common cases are, of course, shallow, piercement or deep, non-piercement domes.

All stages of piercement to a maximum of approximately 50,000 feet occur in the Gulf region (Fig. 5-1). Sedimentary strata which have been ruptured or pierced by a rising salt plug may be gently to steeply upturned or completely overturned.

In general, beds are more steeply upturned with increasing depth. However, this condition is not always present. The structural dip of beds into a local depositional trough from which a dome has emerged (*e.g.,* San Felipe) may not be reversed by uplift of the dome to the degree that deeper beds have steeper attitudes than shallower beds. "Salt dome breccia," a desiccated fragmental shale, occurs in a broad domal uplift surrounding a number of salt domes in South Louisiana (Kerr and Kopp, 1958). The contact between salt dome breccia and overlying normal shale is not a plane but has the shape of an in-

verted bowl which transects the strata surrounding the dome. Sedimentary beds in this case would not be sharply upturned as would beds in direct contact with the salt core since the breccia would act as a buffer zone and absorb most of the energy of the uplift.

The relationship of the lower portion of the salt mass to the mother salt bed is an excellent method of distinguishing a very special diapir from the normal type. Most Gulf region domes are attached to the source bed, rising as apophyses from the salt source layer or from earlier salt structures (pillows, walls or ridges). A few domes may become detached from the source bed and continue to rise through the enclosing sedimentary strata.

As salt flows into a growing structure from a radius of several times the diameter of the structure, a peripheral sink is formed. The depression formed by salt withdrawal may eventually thin the source layer to such an extent that the layer is blocked off from the salt dome. Bethel dome, Anderson County, Texas (Fig. 6-7), is a possible example of a teardrop-shaped dome severed from the mother salt bed and "floated" upward in the sedimentary sequence to become a present shallow, piercement dome. Similar structural peculiarities of diapirs in northern Germany have been established by drilling. The drop-like salt stock of Eilte with accumulation below the salt body is shown in Fig. 5-7. Trusheim (1960) stated that down-thrown faults associated with salt structures are part of the salt movement processes in regions where halokinesis (isostatic movement) was active. The faults are not attributable to orogenic forces which might have caused or influenced the salt to rise. If this situation holds true, the salt mass at Eilte has actually "floated" upward and the faulting did not provide a conduit for migration. What better example can illustrate the tremendous forces of buoyancy!

Just as the structures of salt stocks vary considerably, so do the structures of the sediments enclosing them. Excluding fault structures, which will be treated separately, structural features in adjacent strata include the following:

1. Simple doming of sediments over both high and low relief salt stocks. Thinning is commonly associated with arching of strata over a salt dome indicating that uplift was contemporaneous with deposition. A simplified section (faulting eliminated) of South Liberty dome, Liberty County, Texas (Fig. 5-8), shows sedimentary beds gently arching over the salt stock. Over the supradome area, uplift coupled with submarine erosion predominates, thus accounting for thinning of some members of the Yegua and Cook Mountain (Claiborne) formations.

2. Gentle to steep folding of strata by salt intrusion. In some instances the beds may actually be overturned and truncated by erosion, then overlapped by younger sediments which have been considerably less deformed. A radial cross-section of Nash dome, Fort Bend County, Texas (Fig. 6-5), shows near vertical attitude of Frio sands that have been uplifted by the salt, truncated by erosion, and overlapped by younger Marginulina shales whose angle of dip is approximately one-half that of the Frio beds below the unconformity.

3. "Diapiric shale" is a lithologic term proposed by Atwater and Forman (1959) for an intrusive deep-water marine shale that may form a sheath or dome over the rising salt plug and pierce the overlying sedi-

ments in the same manner as salt. Plastic qualities of the shale allow it to move under the influence of the more buoyant underlying salt.

Vicksburg and Jackson shale "wedges" lie adjacent to the salt in many Gulf region domes. The cross-section through Nash dome (Fig. 6-5) illustrates the relationship of the shale "wedge" to the salt core and the overlying sediments. The shale has sharply uplifted and nearly overturned the Upper Frio sands. The angular unconformity at the top of the Frio resulted from erosion of the Frio during a static period in the growth of the dome, and subsequent deposition of overlying marine shales.

Continued deposition of Oligocene sediments resulted in renewed uplift of the salt and shale "sheath." In this illustration, the shale wedge was probably dragged upward by the salt but because of its plasticity it continued to rise with the salt uplift through post-unconformable sediments instead of the salt piercing the sheath and leaving it behind.

There are several domes where the diapiric shale has flowed en masse and is not merely a veneer dragged upward by the salt. Atwater and Forman (1959) describe diapiric shale at Valentine dome, LaFourche Parish, Louisiana (Fig. 5-9), flowing upward as much as 7,000 feet above its normal stratigraphic position. Roach (1962) describes an intrusive shale dome at South Thornwell field, Jefferson Davis and Cameron Parishes, Louisiana, which is similar to the diapiric shale at Valentine and probably resulted from shale flow.

Diapiric shale, while common to the coastal salt dome basins of the Gulf region, has not been penetrated and probably is not present in the interior salt dome basins. Tertiary sediments in the interior salt dome basins do not contain a thick sequence of deep water marine shale comparable to coastal salt dome basins. Diapiric shale has been reported, however, in other parts of the world, notably in northwest Borneo (Shaub and Jackson, 1958). Regarding diapiric shale Atwater and Forman (1959) p. 2594 state:

> The necessary requirement for the development of diapiric shale in salt dome structures of the lower Gulf Coast appears to be the presence of a thick, deep-water marine shale facies (of relatively incompetent nature) in the sequence of sediments above the mother salt bed. The closer this shale facies lies to the present surface in its normal stratigraphic position, the better developed within drillable depths will be the diapiric shale component of the domal core. Inasmuch as the Tertiary sediments of the lower Gulf Coast grade seaward from shallow marine sand and shale facies into deep-water marine shale facies, there is in this region an abundance of source beds from which the intrusive diapiric shale of the individual structures is derived. It is likely that the domal cores of all salt domes in this area, at some depth, contain diapiric shale as a component part. The absence of any similar well-developed deep-water marine shales in the interior salt basins of Texas, Louisiana, and Mississippi has apparently precluded the development of diapiric shale as a constituent part of the cores of salt domes in those areas.

Classification of Fault Structures

Faulting is commonly associated with most piercement salt domes, as well as with many structures judged to be salt-controlled but where salt has not actually been encountered. Faulting is predominantly normal or gravity-type, although reverse or

thrust faulting has been reported in a few cases. Although certain classic fault patterns can be recognized on many domes, no two domes have exactly the same fault pattern. The most common pattern is highly complex and comprises a variety of different faults. Fault patterns are usually not consistent at all depths—characteristically they are more complex with depth. Typical fault patterns associated with known or inferred salt domes include:

I. Over or adjacent to salt plug.
   A. Offset
      1. Simple offset—single major fault.
      2. Multiple offset—more than one major fault in same direction.
      3. Compound offsets—many major and minor faults with no particular orientation.
   B. Radial—normal faults emanating from apex or flank of dome.
   C. Graben—prominent pattern over apex of many domes.
   D. Horst—uncommon fault pattern sometimes formed by multiple offset.
II. Away from dome.
   A. Tangential or Peripheral—normal faults up or down-thrown toward dome some distance away from plug.
   B. Regional—major fault may influence structure on more than one dome.

Offset fault patterns were first classified by Wallace (1944). An example of domes with various offset fault patterns is shown in Fig. 5-10. The simplest pattern is a dome without major faulting. Minor faults with little displacement could be present but would not influence hydrocarbon accumulation. Mallalieu dome, Lincoln County, Mississippi, is an example of a dome with no major fault pattern.

Simple offset patterns comprise a single major fault. Minor complementary faulting is usually present. Erath dome, Vermilion Parish, Louisiana, is an example of a dome with simple offset faulting.

Multiple offset fault patterns are characterized by more than one major fault offset (downthrown) in the same direction. In general, the major faults are aligned in the same direction. Krotz Springs, St. Landry Parish, Louisiana, is an example of a multiple offset fault pattern in which the two major faults trend northeastward.

Compound offset faulting forms a complex pattern without particular alignments. Anahuac field, Chambers County, Texas, displays a compound offset fault pattern over a probable deep-seated salt dome. The illustration shows intersecting radial and multiple offset faults. A common compound offset pattern comprises a central graben system with numerous intersecting radial faults.

Separate faults emanating from a central point are termed radial faults. Radial patterns are commonly characteristic of shallow, circular-shaped domes. If the upper portion of the salt mass is symmetrically shaped in horizontal section, a radially arranged fault pattern is usually the dominant pattern. Branching radial faults create fault segments which resemble pie slices. At Fannett dome, Jefferson County, Texas (Fig. 5-11), a large southeast trending radial fault intersects several smaller faults. Radial faults which are continuous over the supradome area form transverse faults. On individual domes there is usually no orientation in the direction of displacement; *i.e.,* progressive faults may be downthrown in opposing directions to form grabens, or downthrown in the same direction to produce a series of step blocks. Factors which influence the direction of displacement are undoubtedly as varied as the fault patterns themselves. However, Parker and McDowell (1955) found that with experimental domes the direction of displacement on major faults paralleling the long axis of a dome could be controlled by the configuration of the peripheral sink. If a sink was wider on one side of a dome than another, faults tended to be downthrown in that direction. It is possible to apply the size of the peripheral sink to the direction of fault displacement on naturally occuring domes. However, there must be adequate information on the size of the sink.

Simple and complex graben fault systems are found over the crests of a large number of deep-seated and shallow salt domes. Pescadito dome, Webb County, Texas, is a large deep-seated salt dome with a well-defined central graben (Figs. 5-12, 5-14). The graben is believed to have been created by compensating movements that occurred after a principal offset fault pattern was formed. Fig. 5-12, seismic section and schematic illustration of Pescadito dome, shows the relationship of a major offset fault to a compensating fault which forms the central graben system.

The mechanics of graben-type fault occurrence over deep-seated domes in South Louisiana were described by Wallace (1944). The progressive development of a central graben which is probably similar to the origin of the fault pattern at Pescadito is as follows (Fig. 5-13):

STEP I. Contemporaneous with deposition, the salt mass moved upward arching the sediments above the salt plug.

STEP II. Continued uplift of the salt caused shearing and fracturing of the overlying sediments. A simple, offset fault developed with maximum throw near the salt.

STEP III. As throw on the principal offset fault increased, a compensating fault developed downthrown in the opposite direction. Compensating faults normally develop when deformation of the sediments results in stresses that cannot be relieved by the principal fault.

STEP IV. Additional compensating faults began to develop as uplift continued, creating a complex graben system.

Over circular domes the direction of orientation of a central graben has no particular alignment. However, grabens formed over elongate domes are most apt to align parallel with the structure's long axis. The alignment of the graben at Pescadito dome, whose outline is broadly eliptical, is in the direction of the long axis of the dome (Fig. 5-14).

Salt domes with horst-block fault patterns are rare and only a few have been documented. Nolan Edward dome, Wood County, Texas (Fig. 5-15), is an example of a dome with horst pattern (after Moore, 1951 in Murray, 1961).

The occurrence of thrust or reverse faults on domes of the Gulf region has aroused much discussion and controversy among geologists. Some state categorically that thrust faulting is just not associated with Gulf region domes. Those who believe thrust faulting improbable explain that the repetition of the fault zone is less than the dip of the faulted strata. Halbouty and Hardin (1954) made an extensive study of the structural conditions at Boling dome, Wharton County, Texas and describe what they believe to be

a definite case of thrusting in the Texas-Louisiana coastal province. They (pp. 1734, 1735) state:

It has been suggested that this structure might have originally occurred as a rather steep normal fault and that the subsequent rise of the salt mass rotated the plane of the fault in such a manner as to give it the appearance of a thrust fault. Such a sequence of events is depicted in the six illustrations shown in Fig. 5-16. If the structure had thus developed, the Frio beds would have been rotated in such a manner as to create a dip of 90° or more; the beds of this section would have necessarily become practially veritical, or else would have been overturned. Such is not the case, as is demonstrated by cross section [Fig. 5-17]. In fact, the dips on the Frio sands range from 45° to 70°. Lack of complete overturn is also proved by the fact that the Frio sections, penetrated by wells that have drilled through the Jackson shales in the South Boling field, are correlative with wells drilled a considerable distance from the dome, and thereby show that the Frio section over the represented distance is in normal sequence.

The possibility of "shale overhang" was also considered. If this were the case, the outline of the "shale wedge" would follow the general curvature of the salt mass. Such is not the condition because the outline of the wedge is essentially a straight line that is approximately 600 feet from the 5,000-foot salt contour at the closest point, and is more than one-half mile from the same contour near the western end of the thrust fault.

The possibility of reworked Jackson sediments being eroded from the higher parts of the dome during Frio time and redeposited with the Frio sands was considered when the Jackson was originally found out of place above the Frio. This explanation was quickly ruled out as more data became available and it became apparent that the content, shape, size, and extent of the shale wedge precluded this as a possible explanation.

Completely overturned sections are commonly found on the flanks of salt domes. This

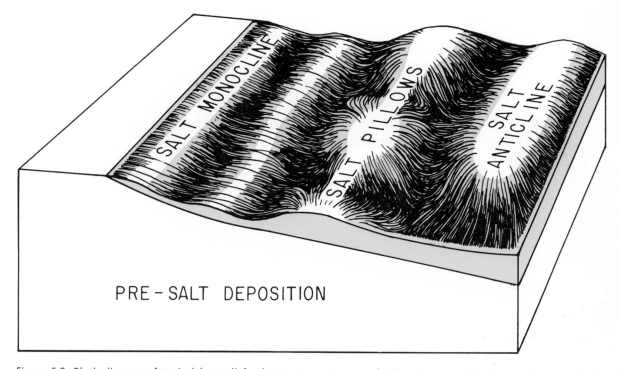

Figure 5-2. Block diagram of typical low relief salt structures. In general, these forms are located on the outer flanks of salt dome basins where the salt source layer is relatively thin.

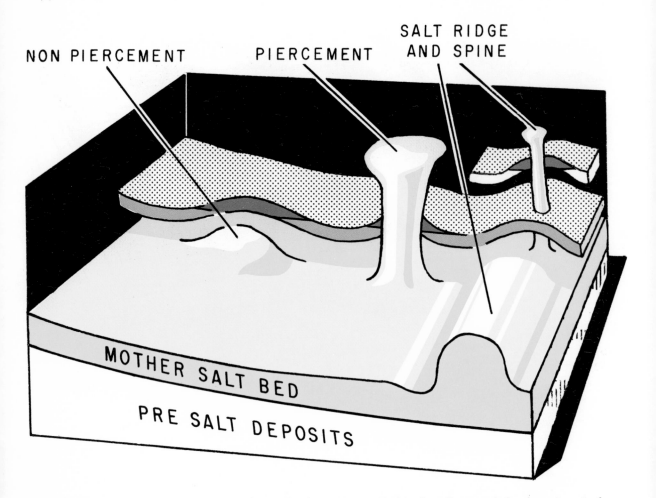

NON PIERCEMENT

PIERCEMENT

SALT RIDGE
AND SPINE

MOTHER SALT BED

PRE SALT DEPOSITS

Figure 5-3. Block diagram showing larger forms of salt structures. Moving downdip toward the deepest part of any particular salt dome basin, structures that occur normally in order of their magnitude include non-piercement domes, piercement domes, and great salt ridges or massifs with or without spines rising from the major salt uplift. See Figure 5-6 and salt dome map of Mexico (Pocket).

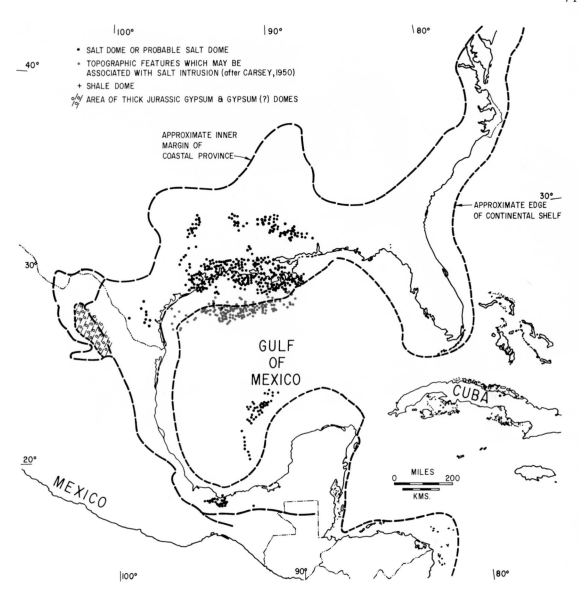

Figure 5-4. Known distribution of salt domes in the Gulf region. (After Murray, 1961).

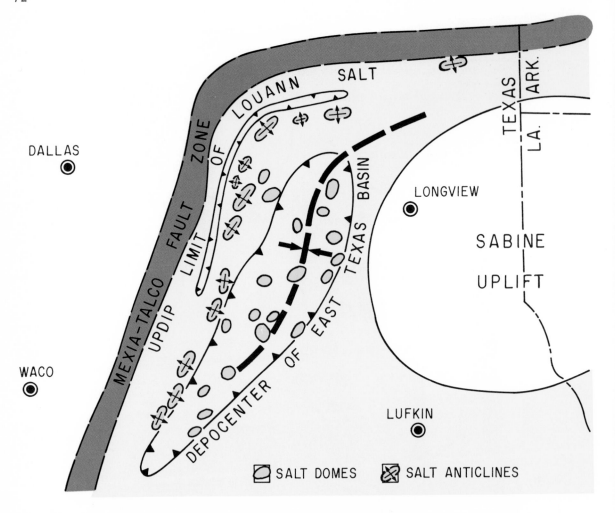

Figure 5-5. Generalized map of the East Texas basin showing major structural features including known and probable salt structures. The various forms of salt structures in the Gulf region excluding diapiric intrusions are probably best revealed in the East Texas basin where there is a sufficient density of wells that penetrated rocks of pre-Cretaceous age. In the northern part of the East Texas basin the salt exhibits monoclinal dip from its wedge-out adjacent to the inner margin of the Mexia-Talco fault zone into a narrow regional low. Flanking this trough on the south is an elongate arcuate anticlinal belt. The strucutures from the Smackover Formation (Upper Jurassic). The anticlines are probably salt-controlled structures. The major domes in the East Texas basin occur downdip from the belt of salt anticlines.

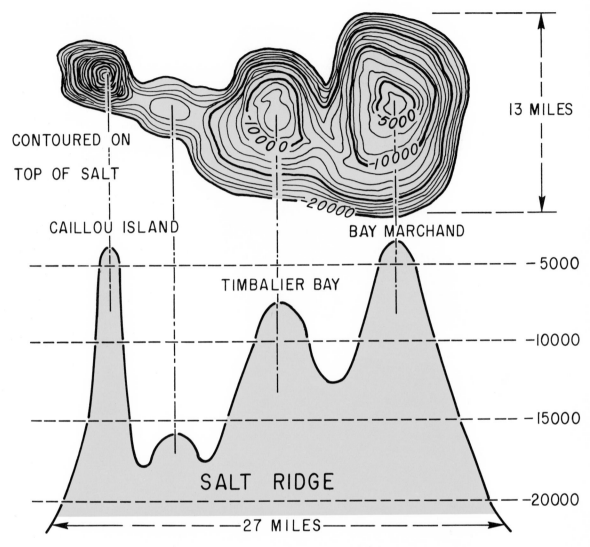

Figure 5-6. Structure contour map and section of salt core, Bay Marchand, Timbalier, Caillou Island Salt massif, LaFourche and Terrebonne Parishes, Louisiana. Huge diapiric salt instrusions occurring as single salt domes or as salt ridges with several stock-like projections are more common in the Texas-Louisiana Coastal basin and Veracruz basin than in other salt dome basins. The three salt stocks are part of a single giant salt ridge or massif. Earlier it was thought that these salt structures were three unrelated salt domes. Contours are on top of salt. (Modified after Atwater and Forman, 1959).

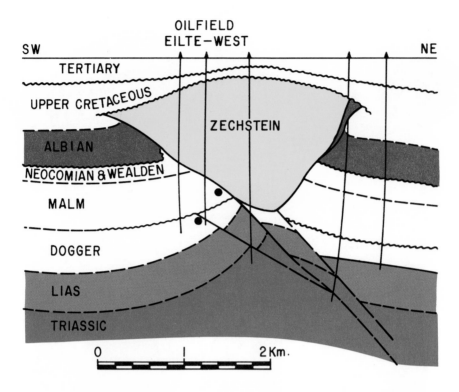

Figure 5-7. Cross section of drop-like salt stock of Eilte (with oil field Eilte-West below salt body). Ascent of salt might be associated with fault zone below salt body. (Interpretation by E. Plein, in Trusheim, 1960).

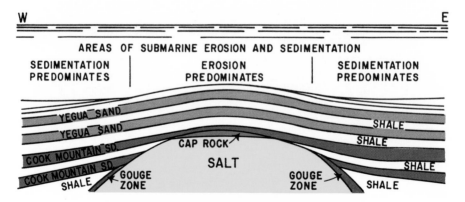

Figure 5-8. Schematic section South Liberty dome, Liberty County, Texas showing geologic conditions during Yegua time. Faulting eliminated. (After Halbouty and Hardin, 1951).

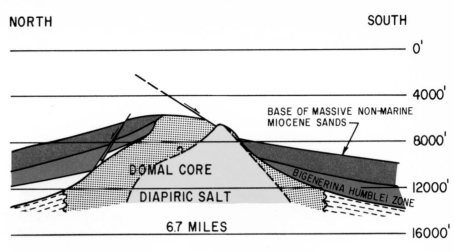

NORTH   **SOUTH**

Figure 5-9. Cross section of Valentine salt dome, LaFourche Parish, Louisiana showing relationship of diapiric shale to salt core and host sediments. (After Atwater and Forman, 1959).

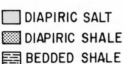

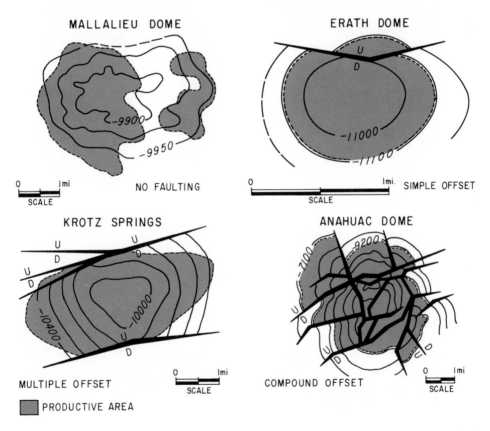

Figure 5-10. Structure contour maps of principal types of offset fault patterns defined by Wallace (1944). The simplest form is a domal type structure with no major faulting, such as Mallalieu field, Lincoln County, Mississippi. Erath field, Vermilion Parish, Louisiana is an example of a domal type structure with simple offset faulting. A multiple offset fault pattern is characterized by more than one major fault downthrown in the same direction, as exemplified by Krotz Springs field, St. Landry Parish, Louisiana. Compound offset faulting forms a complex pattern in which no particular type is dominant, as in the case of Anahuac field, Chambers County, Texas. (After Murray, Steig, Bader and Louisiana Department of Conservation in Murray, 1961).

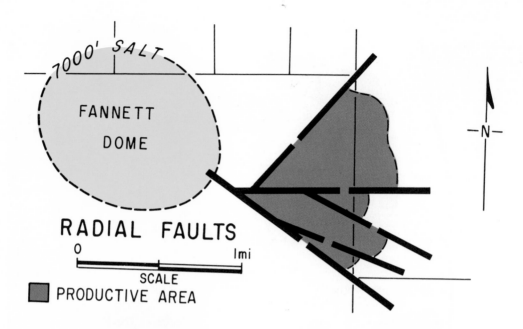

Figure 5-11. Radial fault pattern (greatly simplified), Fannett dome, Jefferson County, Texas.

77

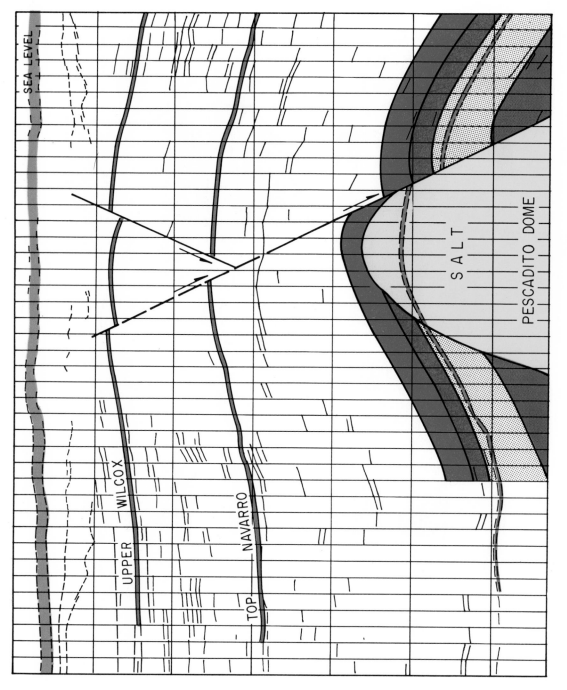

Figure 5-12. Seismic cross section of Pescadito dome, Webb County, Texas showing relationship of a major offset fault to a compensating fault. The intersecting faults create a central graben pattern over the dome.

78

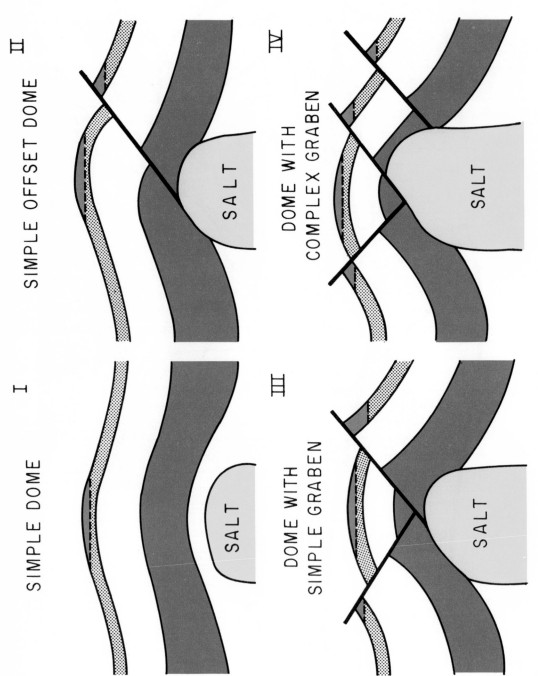

Figure 5-13. Diagram showing development of a central graben. (Modified from Wallace, 1944).

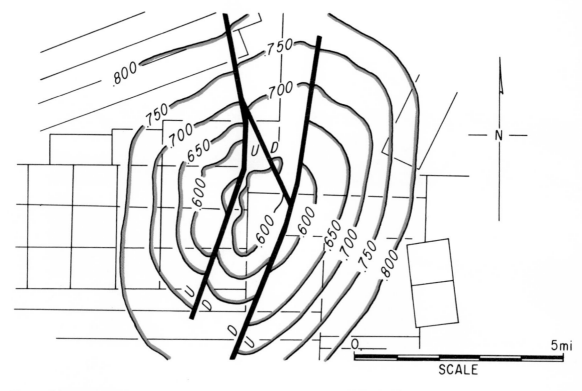

Figure 5-14. Seismic structure map of Pescadito dome, Webb County, Texas showing well-defined central graben. Contours are on top of a phantom horizon in Wilcox Formation (Eocene).

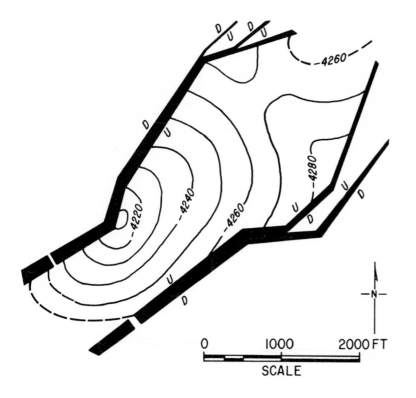

Figure 5-15. Structure map of Nolan Edward field, Wood County, Texas showing uncommon horst fault pattern. Contours are on top of sub-Clarksville sand of Eagle Ford stage (Upper Cretaceous). (After Moore in Murray, 1961).

80

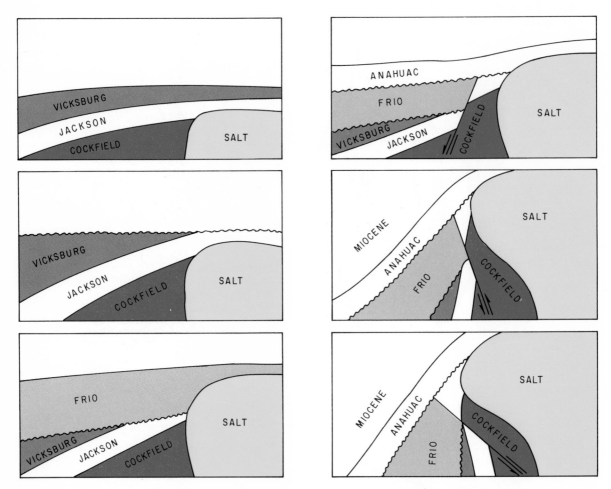

Figure 5-16. Sequence of cross sections showing theoretical results of normal faulting with subsequent overturn of fault by rotation as intrusion of salt mass progressed. This possible interpretation for South Boling structure was ruled out because Frio beds at South Boling do not have dip as steep as would result from overturn of normal fault as shown above. (After Halbouty and Hardin, 1954).

81

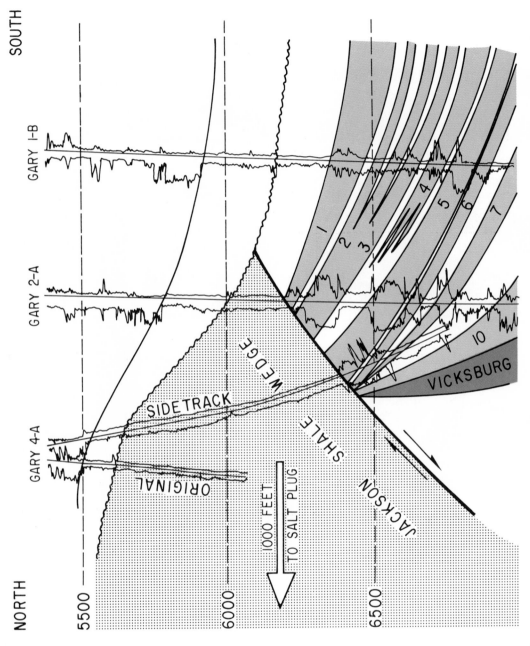

Figure 5-17. Cross section through South Boling field showing relation of productive Frio sands to overthrust body of Jackson shale. Frio sands are arbitrarily numbered for ease in correlation. (After Halbouty and Hardin, 1954).

82

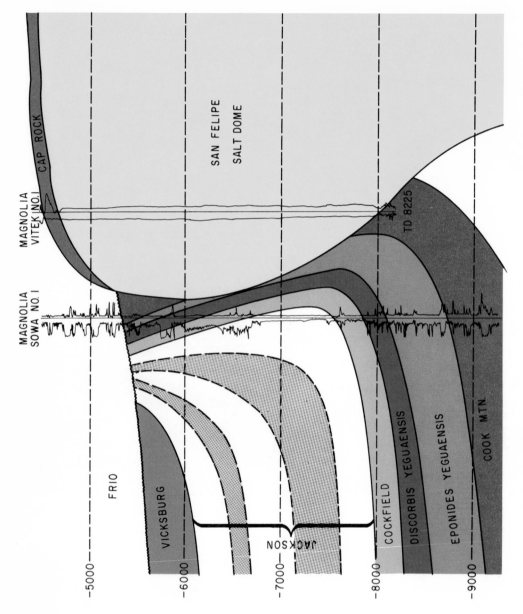

Figure 5-18. Cross section through west flank of San Felipe dome, Austin and Waller counties, Texas, showing overturn of beds caused by salt overhang. Beds were penetrated by Sowa No. 1 well in reverse sequence, and were then penetrated below in normal sequence. (After Halbouty and Hardin, 1954).

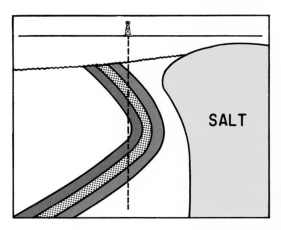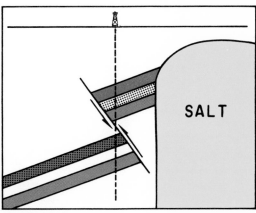

Figure 5-19. Diagrammatic cross section showing result of overturn of beds on piercement-type salt dome flank (A) as compared with result of thrust faulting (B). In overturned section, beds are penetrated by drill in reverse sequence and then in normal sequence. In thrust-faulted section, beds are penetrated in normal sequence both above and below fault structure. Conditions at South Boling are comparable with cross section B. (After Halbouty and Hardin, 1954).

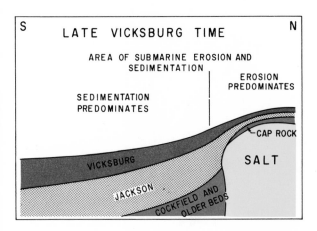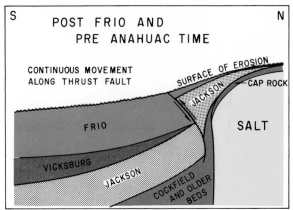
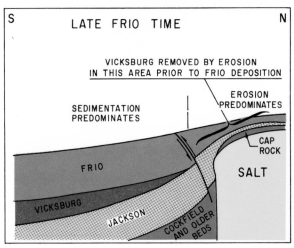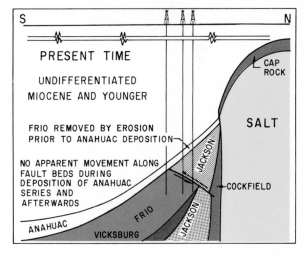

Figure 5-20. Sequence of cross sections showing the concept of formation of South Boling overthrust in connection with growth of Boling salt dome. (After Halbouty and Hardin, 1954).

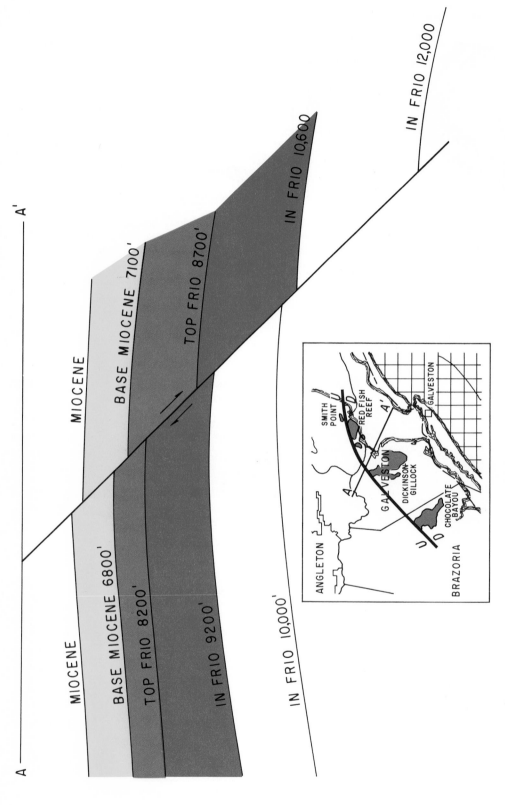

Figure 5-21. Schematic cross section showing thickening of Miocene and Frio (Oligocene) beds across regional fault, Brazoria and Galveston Counties, Texas. The growth of a salt ridge or salt wall may have originated the fault on the inland side of the ridge. Following initial fault movement diapiric salt structures began to extrude from the salt ridge. Movement on the fault, contemporaneous with growth of the salt structures, influenced the difference in stratigraphic thickness of formations across the fault.

condition exists on the west flank of the San Felipe dome as shown in cross section in Fig. 5-18. The Magnolia Petroleum Company's Sowa well No. 1 penetrated the Eponides yeguaensis, Discorbis yeguaensis, Cockfield, and Jackson in that order. Below the Jackson, the well penetrated the same zones in normal sequence. In this way, the Jackson shale could be dragged up over the Frio at South Boling in somewhat the same manner as at San Felipe. However, in such a condition, the overhanging beds would be reversed in sequence. This is not the case at South Boling because the Humble Oil and Refining Company's Gary No. 2 penetrated the Jackson and Cockfield sections in normal sequence and then penetrated the Frio. The contrast between the sequence in which the overhanging beds would be penetrated in an overturned section as against a thrust-faulted section is shown [in Fig. 5-19]. Also, if overturning were the cause of this feature, the fault would necessarily follow approximately the periphery of the salt mass.

The writers' concept of the formation of the overthrust in connection with the growth of the salt dome is illustrated [Fig. 5-20].

Peripheral faults are developed away from the dome itself and form circular or arcuate traces in plane view. Well-documented examples of peripheral faulting are few, principally because exploration has been concentrated over the supradome area or on the flanks immediately adjacent to the salt uplift. At South Liberty dome several peripheral faults are believed to occur. One such peripheral fault, downthrown toward the dome, is shown in Fig. 6-9. Note that the direction of displacement may be either toward or away from a dome. Halbouty and Hardin (1951) believe the peripheral faults at South Liberty were initiated with the first stages of uplift of the dome, and were progressive with dome growth.

Tangential faulting, as the word implies, is tangent to the circular or eliptical uplift area. These faults probably were formed during the initial stages of dome growth similar to peripheral faults. An example of tangential faulting is on the north flank of Hull dome, Liberty County, Texas (Fig. 6-10).

Regional faults associated with salt structures are undoubtedly the most significant of all fault structures. However, their great influence on sedimentation and ultimately on the occurrence of oil and gas is in the realm of sound geologic concept rather than conclusive evidence. The regional fault as depicted here probably preceded the growth of individual salt domes but was initiated by a regional salt swell. As previously stated, regional salt walls in the Northwest German basin indicate that here too, are the same problems of proving relationship between regional fault systems and salt tectonics.

A large depositional fault extends from southern Chambers County to Brazoria County, Texas. The fault is not specifically described in the literature, but may, in fact, be a northeast extension of the Sam Fordyce-Vanderbilt fault system (sometimes referred to as the Vicksburg flexure) in southeast Texas. This regional fault can be traced continuously from the vicinity of Smith Point-Red Fish Reef fields in Galveston Bay through Dickinson-Gillock field to Danbury dome (Fig. 5-21). On the north (or upthrown) side of the regional fault, Oligocene and Miocene sediments are thin as compared to equivalent strata on the south (or downthrown) side. This abrupt change in stratigraphic thickness of sediments is characteristic of depositional or contemporaneous faulting and occurs both over and away from major structural features judged to be salt-controlled, regardless of whether or not salt has been penetrated. For example, at Danbury dome, which is bisected by this fault, the Oligocene strata south (downthrown) of the fault are much thicker than correlative beds north of the fault but over the structure. Away from the dome the stratigraphic thickness of a correlative section thickens across the fault in an amount comparable to the thickening across the fault over the structure.

This writer believes that the growth of a salt wall or ridge initiated the regional fault which extended on the north side of the ridge. Following the initial fault movement, individual piercement salt structures (*e.g.,* Danbury) and deep-seated domes (*e.g.,* Dickinson-Gillock) began to extrude as diapirs from the salt wall. Movement on the fault continued as the salt structures developed and greatly influenced sedimentation over the structures.

Literature Cited

Allison, A. P., Beckelhymer, R. L., Benson, Don G., Hutchins, R. M., Jr., Lake, C. L., Lewis, Ray C., O'Bannon, P. H., Self, S. R. and Warner, C. A.: "Geology of Katy Field, Waller, Harris and Fort Bend Counties, Texas," *Bull.,* AAPG (1946), v. 30, no. 2, pp. 157-180.

Atwater, Gordon I. and Forman, McLain, Jr.: "Nature and Growth of Southern Louisiana Salt Domes and Its Effect on Petroleum Accumulation," *Bull.,* AAPG (1959), v. 43, no. 11, pp. 2592-2622; (abs.) *Trans.,* GCAGS (1958), v. 8, pp. 20-21.

Barton, D. C.: "The American Salt Dome Problems in the Light of the Rumanian and German Salt Domes," *Bull.,* AAPG (1925), v. 9, no. 9, pp. 1227-1268; *Geology of Salt Dome Oil Fields,* AAPG (1926), pp. 167-208.

Halbouty, Michel T. and Hardin, George C., Jr.: "Types of Hydrocarbon Accumulation and Geology of South Liberty Salt Dome, Liberty County, Texas," *Bull.,* AAPG (1951), v. 35, no. 9, pp. 1939-1977.

Halbouty, Michel T. and Hardin, George C., Jr.: "New Exploration Possibilities on Piercement Type Salt Domes Established by Thrust Fault at Boling Salt Dome, Wharton County, Texas," *Bull.,* AAPG (1954), v. 38, no. 8, pp. 1725-1740.

Kerr, Paul F. and Kopp, O. C.: "Salt Dome Breccia," *Bull.,* AAPG (1958), v. 42, no. 3, pp. 548-560.

Moore, Hastings: "Nolan Edwards Field, Wood County, Texas," *Pub. 5116,* Tex. U. (1951), pp. 266-268.

Murray, G. E.: *Geology of the Atlantic and Gulf Coastal Province of North America,* Harper Bros. (1961), New York, 692 pp.

Parker, T. J. and McDowell, A. N.: "Model Studies of Salt Dome Tectonics," *Bull.,* AAPG (1955), v. 39, no. 12, pp. 2384-2470; Review by W. T. Born, *Geophysics,* v. 21, no. 4, p. 1121.

Roach, C. B.: "Intrusive Shale Dome in South Thornwell Field, Jefferson Davis and Cameron Parishes, Louisiana," *Bull.,* AAPG (1962), v. 46, no. 12, pp. 2121-2132.

Shaub, H. P. and Jackson, A.: "The Northwestern Oil Basin of Borneo," *Habitat of Oil,* AAPG (1958), pp. 1330-1336.

Teas, L. P.: "Natural Gas of Gulf Coast Salt Dome Area," *Geology of Natural Gas,* AAPG (1935), pp. 683-740.

Trusheim, F.: "On the Mechanism of Salt Migration in Northern Germany," *Bull.,* AAPG (1960), v. 44, no. 9, pp. 1519-1540.

Wallace, W. E., Jr.: "Structure of South Louisiana Deep Seated Domes," *Bull.,* AAPG (1944), v. 28, no. 9, pp. 1249-1312.

Chapter 6

Accumulation of

Gas and Oil

Types of Traps

The mode of oil accumulation controlled by salt uplifts in the Gulf region is as varied as the geometry of the salt structures themselves. Practically all known types of hydrocarbon traps occur in connection with salt dome structures.

An idealized section through a salt dome (Fig. 6-1) shows the more common types of traps where oil and gas have been found. A single dome may have several, if not all, of the types shown in this illustration. It is more unusual to have a single type of trap associated with a salt plug than to have several types. Figure 6-1 shows the following distinct types of traps:

1. Simple domal anticline
2. Graben fault trap over dome

3. Porous cap rock (limestone or dolomite)
4. Flank sand pinchout and sand lens
5. Trap beneath overhang
6. Trap uplifted and buttressed against salt plug
7. Unconformity
8. Fault trap downthrown away from dome
9. Fault trap downthrown toward dome.

Historic Spindletop, birthplace of the modern American oil industry, initially produced from cap rock accumulation about 1,000 feet below the surface. The dissolving action of circulating ground waters on cap rock at Spindletop and many other shallow domes has produced a highly porous—honeycombed to cavernous—reservoir. Oil and formation waters migrated from sediments surrounding the salt plug and were trapped in porous sections of the cap rock, overlain by impervious strata. Cap rock production is not uniform— parts of it may contain oil and other minerals while other parts of the same cap rock are dense and non-productive. Many domes, particularly deeper structures, with a well-developed cap rock do not produce because of insufficient porosity in the material.

Simple Domal Anticlines

Simple domal anticlines with hydrocarbon accumulations in gently arched sands above the salt or cap rock are rare in the Gulf region. The distribution of hydrocarbons over the top of a salt plug is usually complicated by faulting, lenticularity of separate sand bodies, or local unconformities. Some of the early discoveries on domes apparently did produce from domal anticlinal traps. But subsequent development often indicated that the accumulation was not uniform over the supradome area and that structural and stratigraphic complexities were, in fact, present. Sugarland dome, Fort Bend County, Texas, is an example of a dome with essentially simple anticlinal accumulation (Fig. 6-2). Simple as the accumulation appears, local unconformities in the Vicksburg, Frio, and Middle Oligocene (Anahuac) Formations were clearly recognized shortly after the discovery (McCarter and O'Bannon, 1933). Sugarland is another historical milestone in the annals of salt-dome exploration because it was the first of the moderately deep domes discovered by seismic methods where the producing sands were gently arched over the uplift. The Sugarland discovery brought about a new phase of geophysical exploration for salt domes. Following this discovery much of the entire Gulf Coast area was "re-shot" by refraction seismograph.

Sugarland Salt Dome Growth

Sugarland is a dome with producing sands dipping at a relatively constant rate in all directions from the apex. Although the Anahuac Formation (Discorbis, Heterostegina and Marginulina zones) is uplifted more than 2,000 feet, the reservoir is unbroken by faulting. Uplift of this magnitude without faulting is unusual.

The geologic history of Sugarland dome is comparable to that of many other shallow, less complicated domes of the Gulf region. McCarter and O'Bannon (1933) p. 1378 described the history of uplift of the dome as follows:

> As recorded by unconformities, the Sugarland salt-dome growth was initiated prior to Tertiary and continued through Miocene time. Prior to the Vicksburg Stage, a large part of the salt uplift was either a submarine or subaerial knoll, dating from pre-Tertiary time; indeed, possibly older formations covered it and had been stripped. The top of the cap rock was considerably eroded prior to its burial in the Vicksburg sediments, as evidenced by the contact of sedimentary formations with the normally lowest anhydrite cap-rock zone over the apex. After the Vicksburg Formation was deposited, the dome again was brought above the plane of deposition of the ensuing early Frio seas, for during that time the greatest part of the Vicksburg Formation was stripped from the crest of the uplift. Possibly at this period the highest calcite zone was eroded down to the anhydrite zone, for the area of the stripped calcite zone is almost coextensive with the stripped part of the Vicksburg (Fig. 6-2). The stripping of the Vicksburg Formation and the calcite cap zone was evidently the result of subaerial or submarine erosion contemporaneous with structural uplift, for these zones thin out up the slope of the dome, and possibly some Vicksburg sand zones also show the angular unconformity. The Frio and Middle Oligocene formations were also considerably reduced.

These formations were planed after deposition, but the greater part of their attenuation was more probably accomplished by means of local submarine or subaerial erosion, within the planes of many small disconformities (diastems). During the Heterostegina period, the top of this salt dome was certainly in relatively shallow waters, which inhibited the growth of coral reefs, such as those which flourished on the neighboring West Columbia and Damon Mound salt domes. During Miocene time, possibly the uplift was a barrier upon which little or no sediments were deposited. The salt growth had almost completely subsided at the beginning of Pliocene time, since nearly the entire Lagarto Formation was deposited.

Central Graben System

Formation of a central graben system over a rising salt plug controls the position of oil pools on many domes. Either or both the downthrown or upthrown segments may be productive or barren. Over some deep-seated domes the producing sands may be several hundred feet downthrown to correlative barren sands.

In contrast are domes which have never produced from the area of the central graben. The structural pattern of Dickinson, Gillock, and South Gillock fields, Galveston County, Texas (Fig. 6-3), is representative of many deep-seated domes in the Gulf region. The central graben system may be well defined but virtually all grabens are complicated by other types of faults (radial at Dickinson-Gillock).

The accumulation at Dickinson-Gillock is due primarily to doming, but faulting and lenticular character of pay sands control accumulation within separate fault segments.

Although many of the early salt dome discoveries were from sands in the supradome area or from cap rock, later production was often found in reservoirs adjacent at varying distances to the salt stock. By far the greatest oil and gas production has come from traps on the flanks of the salt core.

Flank Traps

Flank traps exist in many relationships to the salt core as shown in the idealized section (Fig. 6-1). Flank traps are of two broad types: those created by sedimentation and/or erosion prior to or contemporaneous with uplift of the salt mass; and those actually created by upward salt movement. One of the most common types of traps on the flanks of piercement domes is formed by lenticular sands that pinch out or shale out before reaching the salt core, shale sheath, or gouge zone. At South Liberty dome, multiple Yegua sand reservoirs (Fig. 6-4) have been uplifted by the rising salt mass and shale out in an upstructure position before reaching the dome. A well drilled near the shale-out position would encounter several sand stringers which develop downstructure into a single reservoir. Other sand stringers pinch out downstructure as well as laterally and form sand lenses.

A lens trap such as those at South Liberty is a volumetric closed reservoir. Sands that occur regionally have not been found in wells drilled near the salt plug. Detailed studies of such occurrences have resulted in the location of stratigraphic traps on the salt dome flanks with the upstructure edges of many such traps being as much as a mile from the salt plug. Excellent examples of fields of this type are the North Port Neches field, Orange County, Texas, and the North Blue Ridge field, Fort Bend County, Texas. In the North Port Neches field, Hackberry (Oligocene) sands, occurring regionally in the area, pinch out across the nose formed by the north flank of the domal uplift, and result in accumulation of a large oil and gas reserve. In the North Blue Ridge field, the Vicksburg (Oligocene) sand pinches out across the north flank of the uplifted area and results in trapping oil and gas.

Where salt plug growth was intermittent, uplifted sediments may have been partially or totally removed by aerial or submarine erosion. The erosional surface was then over-lapped by younger sediments forming trun-cated sand bodies. Truncated sands below unconformities are excellent potential reser-voirs and may have trapped oil and gas some distance from the salt core. Accumulation at Nash dome (Fig. 6-5) is from truncated Frio sands below an unconformity. Although the resulting traps may be small in lateral extent and at variable distances outward from the salt plug, the oil column can be extremely thick because of the attitude of the individual beds. In general, traps of this nature yield greater amounts of hydrocarbons per acre than other types of traps regardless of the size of the geologic structure.

Flank traps created by upward intrusion of salt through the host sediments include:

1. Sands which terminate under salt or cap rock overhang.
2. Sands which are buttressed against the salt stock, or, if present, against the gouge zone, or shale sheath.
3. Simple and complex fault traps.

Traps formed in the uplifted sands below salt or cap rock overhang on mushroom-shaped domes were recognized in the early stages of salt-dome exploration. Prolific production was established beneath the overhang at Barbers Hill, Chambers County, Texas (Fig. 6-6), in 1962, and at High Island, Galveston County, Texas, in 1931. More than 100 million barrels

of oil have been produced from sands below the overhang at Barbers Hill. An early but detailed study which showed the relationship of the overhang to oil accumulation at High Island dome was made by Halbouty (1936). More than 1,300 feet of salt was penetrated at High Island before oil-bearing sands were encountered below the overhang. Prominent overhangs have also been discovered at San Felipe dome (Fig. 5-18), Bethel dome (Fig. 6-7), and Lost Lake dome in Texas, and at Calcasieu Lake dome and Weeks Island dome in Louisiana. Cote Blanche Island, St. Mary Parish, Louisiana (Fig. 6-8), is one of the most striking examples of accumulation below the overhang. Here the overhang is confined to the north flank of an eliptical-shaped salt plug. Some wells penetrated the top of the salt at less than 1,000 feet and drilled through more than 14,000 feet of salt before encoun-tering Miocene sands. Other boreholes close to the scalloped flank of the salt plug have drilled in and out of the salt as many as three times to a depth of 8,000 feet.

Porous and permeable reservoir rocks which are uplifted and terminate against the salt, gouge zone, or shale sheath, are common types of flank traps. In most traps of this nature, faulting has influenced the amount of en-trapped hydrocarbons. Radial, peripheral, or tangential fault patterns characteristic of domal structures control the vertical and hori-zontal extent of flank reservoirs.

A fault trap controlling oil and gas accu-mulation at variable distances from the salt core is another type of flank trap which has produced hydrocarbons in vast quantities. The multiple sands of the Tertiary sequences of the Gulf region when downfaulted, uplifted, or overthrust (*e.g.,* Boling dome) against im-pervious shales, form excellent reservoirs. Tan-gential and peripheral faults on the flanks of domes (*e.g.,* South Liberty, Fig. 6-9, and Hull, Fig. 6-10) have created traps which have accumulated large quantities of hydrocarbons.

Structurally, South Liberty field is a shallow piercement dome with an eliptical outline. The top of the cap rock overlying the salt plug rises to within 275 feet of the ground surface. The periphery of structure is broken by many radial faults with displacements ranging from a few feet to more than 1,000 feet. Major tangential or peripheral faults downthrown toward the dome are located on the northeast and northwest flanks of the dome near the salt mass. Sands uplifted by the dome but on the downthrown side of the tangential fault are barren of oil.

No production of significance has ever been found on the supradome structure. Present production is from Frio, Yegua, and Cook Mountain sands which produce from pinchout and fault traps adjacent to the plug. More than 25 separate reservoirs occur on the dome's northeast flank. Accumulation is primarily controlled by tangential faulting with separate reservoirs formed by the radial faults which intersect the main tangential fault.

The discovery of an up-to-the-dome tangential fault trap on the north flank of Hull dome extended production more than one mile beyond the then known field limits. A large area between the tangential fault and the old production on the near north flank of the dome had been condemned by early drilling. Many other instances of tangential faulting have been found on other salt domes such as Sour Lake, Hardin County, Texas; High Island, Galveston County, Texas; and Pierce Junction, Harris County, Texas. These discoveries have added many tens of millions of barrels to the Gulf region's proven oil reserves.

On many domes of the Gulf region which have produced for years from a variety of common fault traps, a different type of fault associated with salt structures may provide large new oil and gas reserves. These newly recognized fault traps comprise a series of down-to-the-coast parallel strike faults that extend along the inner flank of elongate salt ridges. One such salt ridge extends from Brazoria to Calhoun County, Texas, and from the ridge, individual salt stocks extrude. Figure 6-11 shows one of these domes, Bryan Mound, Brazoria County, where parallel fault traps created by faulting across a north-plunging structural nose produce from deep reservoir strata. Frio and Miocene rocks thicken into the downthrown side of the faults indicating that growth was contemporaneous with deposition. Movement on the ridge occurred as late as Oligocene and Miocene time because Frio and younger beds dip to the north (opposite normal regional southeast dip) toward a narrow, elongate trough on the upland side of the salt ridge. Faulting in the north dipping strata has created traps on the upthrown side of down-to-the-coast faults (Fig. 6-11). Peach Point field, Brazoria County, is an example of a fault trap field formed in this manner.

A recent discovery on the northeast flank of Clemens dome, Brazoria County, may be structurally comparable to Peach Point field. Accumulation is probably controlled by faulting across the nose of a plunging salt swell from which Bryan Mound extruded. Accumulation probably took place prior to the growth of Clemens dome. The growth of Clemens dome, a late-occurring movement, complicates a geological interpretation of the area but does not directly control accumulation.

Practically all of the known or apparent piercement domes of the onshore Gulf region

have not been adequately explored for hydrocarbons.

Non-Productive Domes

A large percentage of the domes which are
either nonproductive or have produced only
minor amounts of oil or gas can be explained
as late-occurring domes. Generally, growth
has been vertical to near-vertical and has
occurred after hydrocarbons migrated from
nearby source rocks and were trapped.

Some domes apparently did not rise vertically through the sediments; they may have
extruded from the source bed or salt pillow
along an inclined path, or during periodic
growth the apex may have shifted from one
geographical position to another. This has resulted in the formation of relict salt structures
associated with present piercement domes.
The present position of a dome may be considerably removed from its former position
during oil accumulation.

Relict Structures

Relict structures are probably the locales
for old hydrocarbon accumulations which
may have been modified or left undisturbed
by later growth. The location of old domal
highs and correct interpretation of their structural history hold promise for discovery of
important new oil and gas reserves.

The relict dome can be expected to have
various traps similar to a known piercement
dome. Simple doming of the beds over the
relict structure could provide excellent deep
reservoirs if subsequent salt movement did not
destroy structural closure of the relict structure by disruption of one flank. If a flank of a

relict structure has been deformed by late
domal movement, the flank becomes part of
the newer uplift and much of the entrapped
hydrocarbons probably will have migrated to
a position on the dome adjacent to the relict
structure.

Faulting, lenticular character of sands, and
unconformities could, of course, influence oil
and gas accumulations on relict structures and
cause permanent entrapment regardless of
subsequent growth of a salt stock.

San Felipe and Hockley domes, in Waller
and Harris Counties respectively, are relatively nonproductive. These shallow piercement domes are surrounded by the same host
rocks which have produced great quantities
of oil and gas in other areas of the Gulf
region. One of the largest gas fields in the
Gulf province, Katy field, is located between
the two domes.

Katy Field

Katy field, Waller County, Texas, probably
overlies a relict salt structure (Fig. 6-12). Although salt has never been penetrated at
Katy, geophysical information suggests the
presence of a deep-seated salt uplift probably
more than 30,000 feet deep. Most geologists
concur that Katy field overlies a salt swell or
uplift but there are varying opinions on the
mode of development of the salt structure.

Previous theories consider the Katy structure to be a residual or intradomal high,
formed by subsidence in the surrounding areas
while the field proper remained at its original
structural position. Closure on the north, east
and west was ascribed to subsidence of these
flanks which took place as peripheral sinks
were formed in response to salt flow toward
the center of rising salt plugs (San Felipe and

93

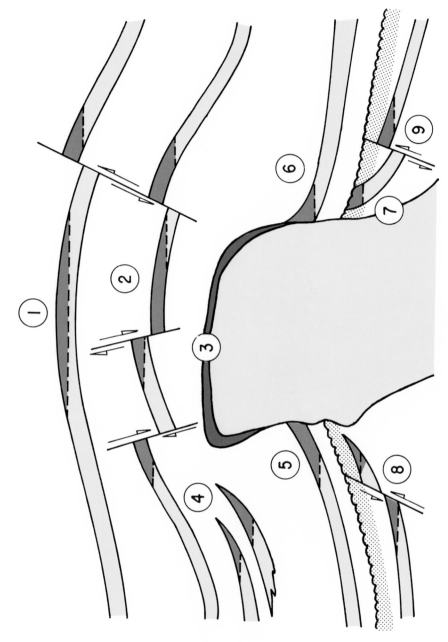

Figure 6-1. Idealized section showing common types of hydrocarbon traps associated with salt domes. Various traps include (1) simple domal anticline draped over salt; (2) graben fault trap over dome; (3) porous cap rock; (4) flank sand pinchout and sand lens; (5) trap beneath overhang; (6) trap uplifted and buttressed against salt plug; (7) unconformity; (8) fault trap downthrown away from dome; (9) fault trap downthrown toward dome.

94

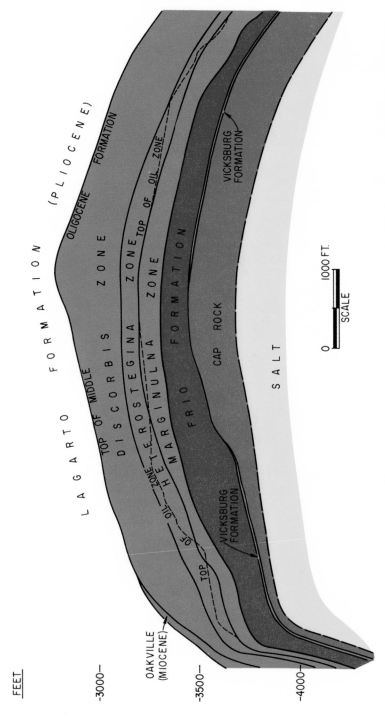

Figure 6-2. Cross section of Sugarland dome, Fort Bend County, Texas showing simple anticlinal trap arched over crest of salt mass (modified after McCarter and O'Bannon, 1933).

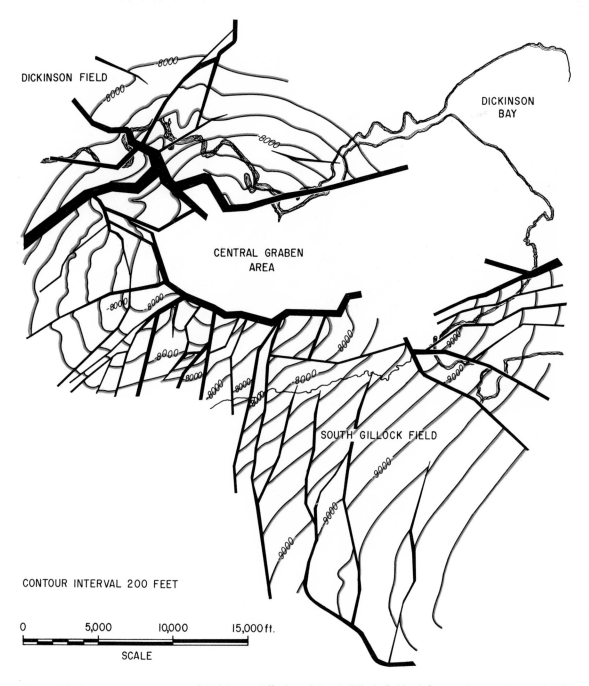

Figure 6-3. Structure contour map of Dickinson, Gillock and South Gillock fields, Galveston County, Texas, showing central graben and complex radial fault pattern. Contours are on top of a producing gas sand (after Gahagan, 1953).

WEST

EAST

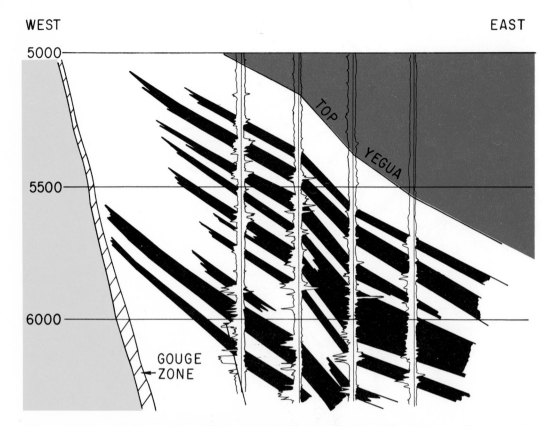

Figure 6-4. Cross section, northeast flank of South Liberty salt dome, Liberty County, Texas showing multiple Yegua sand reservoirs that have been uplifted by the rising salt mass. The sands tend to shale out updip before reaching dome. Individual sand stringers may coalesce downdip to form thick sand bodies. Other sand stringers pinch out downdip to form sand lenses (after Halbouty and Hardin, 1951).

97

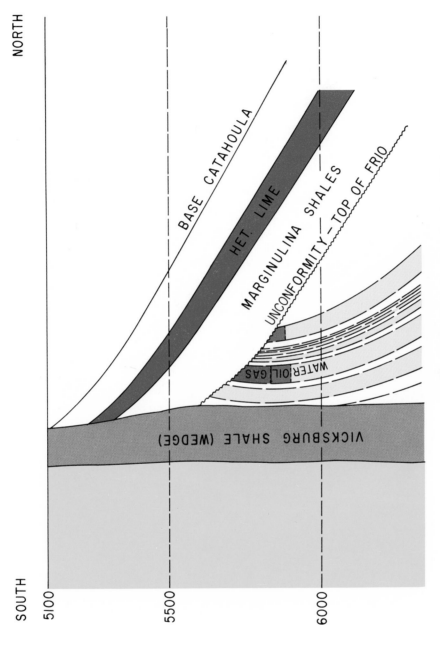

Figure 6-5. Radial cross section, north flank of Nash dome, Fort Bend County, Texas showing Frio (Oligocene) reservoir beneath an unconformity. Because of its vertical attitude the reservoir has a thick oil column; however, the areal extent of the reservoir is relatively small.

98

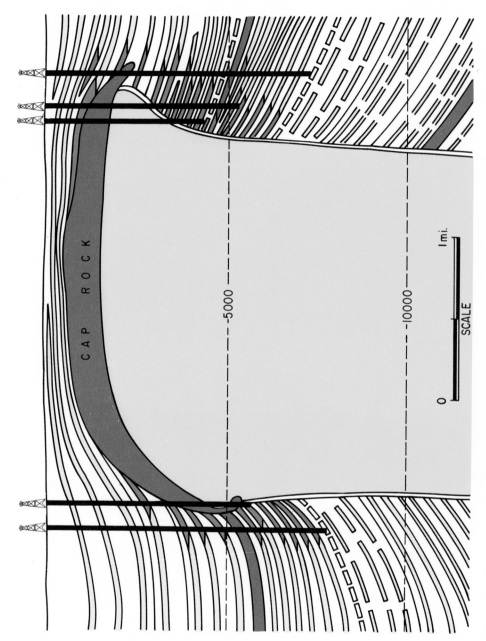

Figure 6-6. Cross section of Barbers Hill dome, Chambers County, Texas showing trap formed in uplifted sands below salt or cap rock overhang. More than 100 million barrels of oil have been produced from sands lying beneath the Barbers Hill overhang.

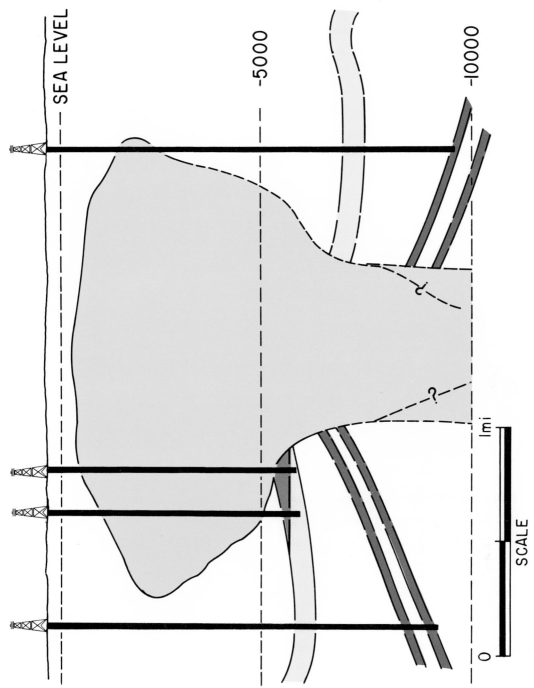

Figure 6-7. Generalized cross section of Bethel dome, Anderson County, Texas showing accumulations below overhang. The possibility of a teardrop shaped salt mass is suggested. The extreme amount of overhang could indicate that the dome is severed from the source bed at depth.

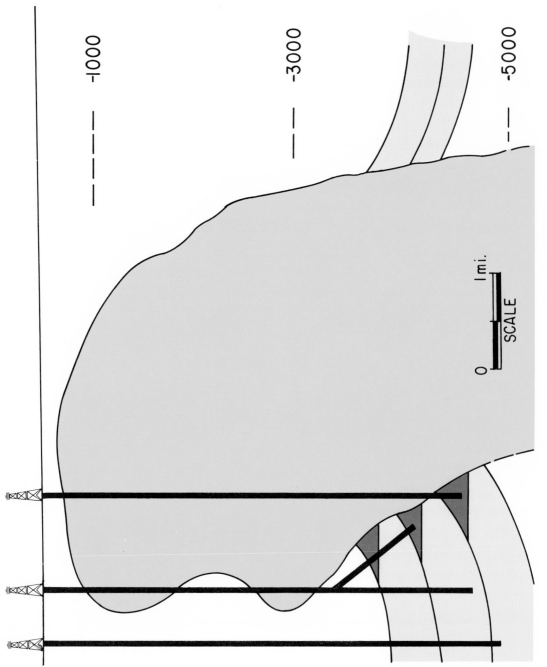

-1000

-3000

-5000

SCALE

0   1 mi.

Figure 6-8. Generalized cross section of Cote Blanche dome, Vermilion Parish, Louisiana showing accumulation below overhang. The irregular shape of the salt mass was proven by wells which encountered part of the salt mass separated by sediments.

Hockley domes). This theory is further supported by the elevation of Upper Eocene (Yegua) strata over the crest of the structure which is at regional normal for this area.

Formations ranging in age from Oligocene (Frio) to Lower Eocene (Wilcox) thin across the Katy structure. The deepest horizon penetrated (Lower Wilcox) thins across Katy as compared to correlative beds adjacent to and pierced by the salt of Hockley and San Felipe domes. This condition is also evident in strata of Upper Eocene age (Jackson-Claiborne). There is no evidence to indicate that the Katy structure was formed contemporaneously with the growth of San Felipe and Hockley domes. To the contrary, it appears that these domes developed rapidly in later geologic time after formation of the Katy structure.

The Katy structure may have formed as a gentle, broad salt uplift along a salt ridge, or it may have remained stable while salt on the flanks of the ridge flowed outward forming local depressions. In either case, the growth of associated salt domes at a later period attests to its classification as a relict salt structure.

High Island Dome

As a possible example of another relict salt structure consider High Island dome, previously discussed as to its possible mode of development. The diagramatic sequence of growth shown in Figure 3-11 depicts what may prove to be a relict salt structure. The Middle Miocene section shows the original salt pillow with peripheral sink development on both sides. If dip reversal is present between the west flank of the present dome and the east flank of the remnant of the original pillow, a relict salt structure, with possible hydrocarbon accumulation, may be present.

Literature Cited

Gahagan, Donald I.: "Dickinson, Gillock, and South Gillock Fields, Galveston County, Texas," *Guidebook,* AAPG-SEPM-SEG Jt. Ann. Mtg., (March, 1953), Houston, Texas, pp. 110-113.

Halbouty, Michel T.: "Geology and Geophysics Showing Cap Rock and Salt Overhang of High Island Dome, Galveston County, Texas," *Bull.,* AAPG (1936), v. 20, no. 5, pp. 560-611; correction p. 818; *Gulf Coast Oil Fields,* AAPG (1936), pp. 909-960; (abs.) *World Pet.,* v. 7, no. 8, p. 404.

Halbouty, Michel T. and Hardin, George C., Jr.: "Types of Hydrocarbon Accumulation and Geology of South Liberty Salt Dome, Liberty County, Texas," *Bull.,* AAPG (1951), v. 35, no. 9, pp. 1939-1977.

McCarter, W. B. and O'Bannon, P. H.: "Sugarland Oil Field, Fort Bend County, Texas," *Bull.,* AAPG (1933), v. 17, no. 11, pp. 1362-1386; *Gulf Coast Oil Fields,* AAPG (1936), pp. 709-733.

Chapter 7

Factors Affecting
Quantity of Accumulation

Throughout the Gulf region cumulative production from approximately 300 known salt structures ranges from a very few barrels to more than 400 million barrels of oil. Gas and gas condensate production from producing salt structures shows a similar wide range. The question arises: "Why this extremely wide variation in quantity of oil and gas accumulation on similar structures?" To a lesser degree, the variation can be ascribed to the fact that many domes with relatively small amounts of past production and small proven reserves have not been adequately tested. Perhaps this explanation is true of newly discovered production from salt structures in offshore Louisiana and Texas. However, it is apparent that even the few test wells drilled on the relatively non-productive salt domes onshore would have been sufficient to find production on the prolific producing

domes such as Hull, West Columbia, Sour Lake, or Spindletop. Every piercement salt dome in the onshore Gulf Coast province has been drilled, but perhaps not adequately explored.

The primary factors affecting the quantity of hydrocarbon accumulation on piercement salt domes are similar in many respects to those conditions governing quantity of accumulation on geologic structures unaffected by salt tectonics.

These factors are:

1. Depositional environment of the host sediments.

2. Rate of growth of the salt uplift.

3. Time of uplift of the salt plug.

Many other contributory factors influence the amount of accumulation on domes. However, examination of these factors will show that they are functions of one or more of the three primary factors.

These subordinate factors include:

1. Area affected by the salt uplift and associated oil-catchment area, or area from which oil could be expected to migrate to the dome.

2. Amount of structural uplift above regional normal of the producing reservoirs penetrated by the salt plug.

3. Structural character of the area within which a dome rises.

4. Shape of the domal mass.

5. Pattern and complexity of faulting around and over the dome.

6. Occurrence and magnitude of unconformities in various stratigraphic sequences in the vicinity of the dome.

7. Dip of the flank beds.

8. Occurrence of cap rock and supradomal accumulations.

The lack or unfavorable nature of any one of the primary factors does not mean that a salt dome will be barren or even sub-commercial. However, a favorable interrelation of these factors is responsible for large accumulations on some structures. As these factors vary both individually and collectively, so do the production and proven reserves of salt structure fields.

Depositional Environment of Host Sediments

The depositional environment of the sediments through which a dome has intruded decidedly affects the quantity of oil accumulation. Environmental conditions and resultant facies are controlled by the geometry of the sedimentary basin, the rate of deposition, physical properties of the waters from which

detrital materials have settled, and chemical properties from which soluble compounds were precipitated. Oil occurrence depends on a compatible relationship of a source facies to a reservoir facies, both of which have many lithologic types. Although source and reservoir rocks are distinctly different, oil occurs most often where there is a close relation of source to reservoir rocks. Reservoir rocks far removed from source rocks are commonly barren of oil and gas. Hedberg (1964) recently presented an excellent summation of the multiple factors which in combination have been the major contributors to genesis and preservation of hydrocarbons. The reader is referred to this for a detailed analysis of favorable depositional environments and the physical, chemical, and biological agents pertaining thereto.

The patterns of oil occurrence in the Gulf region are characteristic of well-defined basins with oil belts or trends concentrically arranged according to age. Oil is found in older sediments on the outer flanks of the basin, while younger occurrences are progressively basinward. Because of varying environments which, in turn, govern facies relations, the abundance of oil varies from one trend to another. As an example, consider the Tertiary trends of the Gulf region. The Miocene, Frio, and Yegua trends have produced much more oil and gas than the Wilcox trend. All other contributing factors being equal, a structure in the Frio trend will produce more hydrocarbons than a Wilcox structure because the facies balance between source rocks and reservoir rocks is more favorable.

Pescadito dome, Webb County Texas, (Figs. 5-12, 5-13) is a large deep-seated salt structure whose past production, reserves, and future potential are far less than geological studies would indicate. The dome has uplifted sediments over a large area and has created a central graben fault system characteristic of other deep domes which produce copious amounts of oil. The dome, uplifted initially during Late Mesozoic time, should have trapped migrating hydrocarbons in various relationships to the salt core. Considering the factors necesary for primary accumulation of hydrocarbons, it is apparent that Pescadito dome is in an area where the depositional environment of the host sediments was less favorable for generation of oil and gas than in other areas of the same geological trend.

Salt structures within the same environmental trends often vary considerably in the quantity of hydrocarbons trapped. Highly productive domes often have different geological characteristics and are difficult to compare on a common basis. The well-documented accumulations at Spindletop, Barbers Hill, and West Columbia are all different. Much of the oil produced at Spindletop has come from cap rock and flank sands, whereas the oil produced at West Columbia is from sands adjacent to the dome. Production at Barbers Hill is largely from beneath the cap rock and salt overhang.

Rate of Growth

Prolific producing domes within favorable environmental trends have experienced a timely growth rate during periods of optimum interplay between the many and varied factors which influence hydrocarbon generation. Conversely, there are minor producing domes within favorable environmental trends where the rate of growth has been too rapid to trap large deposits of oil and gas.

Nash dome (Fig. 6-5) appears to have grown rapidly during Oligocene time just after deposition of the Frio Formation and be-fore deposition of the overlying Anahuac shale. This is evidenced by the fact that there is very little thinning of the Frio Formation adjacent to the dome, but the beds in close proximity to the salt stock are nearly vertical. A local erosional unconformity truncates these upturned Frio beds, and the overlying Anahuac Formation was deposited nonconformably over the truncated edges of the Frio. The near vertical dip of the Frio and attitude (40°) of the overlying Anahuac beds is considered good evidence of rapid movement of the salt plug during a relatively short interval of time after Frio deposition. In marked contrast, the Frio section on the flanks of Spindletop dome (Fig. 7-1) thins gradually toward the dome, indicating a slow but continuous upward movement of the dome during Frio deposition. It is reasonable to conclude from these and other examples that a very rapid growth of the salt plug during a short geologic time interval allows the salt to pierce the overlying sediments with only slight arching and a relatively small amount of structural uplift of the surrounding sediments. On the other hand, slower and more continuous growth of the salt mass results in gently uplifting the sediments to their maximum before the salt plug pierces the strata.

Many domes in the Gulf region have similar structural parameters resulting from amount and rate of growth that offer a means of comparison. These parameters include amount of structural uplift and area affected by the uplift.

Table 7-1 shows the structural uplift of three prolific producing domes in the same geologic trend (Spindletop, Barbers Hill and West Columbia), the subsurface area affected by the uplift, and the cumulative production as compared to comparable parameters at three mediocre producing domes in the same trend (Moss Bluff, Lost Lake and Nash).

TABLE 7-1

Relationship of Amount and Area of Uplift to Production of Selected Domes

Field, County	Approx. Amt. of Uplift on Frio (ft.)	Approx. Area of Uplift (sq. mi.)	Production to 1-1-64 bbls
Spindletop, Jefferson	2,800	50	140,347,494
Barbers Hill, Chambers	1,500	70	114,398,896
West Columbia, Brazoria	3,200	75	141,940,746
Moss Bluff, Liberty	800	23	1,745,648
Lost Lake, Chambers	2,900	16	1,215,933
Nash, Ft. Bend-Brazoria	900	11	3,351,912

Halbouty and Hardin (1955) made a detailed study of the factors controlling quantity of oil accumulation on representative salt domes in the Yegua-Frio trends of the upper Texas Gulf Coast. They concluded that the area of uplift coupled with the associated maximum possible oil-catchment area is one of the most important factors governing the amount of accumulation.

The area of uplift is the area where the surrounding sediments have been uplifted by the rise of a salt plug. Within a favorable environmental trend, highly productive salt domes have large uplift areas. The oil-catchment area of highly productive domes is large because the uplifted area is not closely restricted by a rim syncline lying in close proximity to the salt mass. In contrast, the area of uplift and possible oil-catchment area of relative nonproductive salt domes is smaller and restricted by a well-defined rim syncline.

Piercement salt domes and salt-controlled anticlinal structures in the Gulf region have

synclines on the updip side of the structure where the dip of the strata reverses and normal regional dip (southeastward) is resumed. Also, practically all of the uplifted structures have modified synclines on their strike flanks. Rim synclines that restrict hydrocarbon accumulation must also be present on the downdip as well as on the updip and strike flanks of the uplifted area. Examination of three closely aligned domes at Barbers Hill, Lost Lake, and Moss Bluff (Fig. 4-1) shows the effect of increasing areas of uplift and well-defined rim synclines when compared to cumulative production (Table 7-1). The outline of the salt plug at Barbers Hill dome is slightly smaller than the salt outlines at Lost Lake and Moss Bluff, but the enclosing strata have been uplifted by the dome over an area of approximately 70 square miles. The areas of uplift of the two nearby domes are 21 miles and 28 miles, respectively, or just about one-third that of Barbers Hill. Production from reservoirs surrounding Barbers Hill is more than 30 times that from Lost Lake and Moss Bluff combined.

A salt dome with encircling rim synclines, such as Lost Lake or Moss Bluff, has a limited area from which oil can migrate to the structure after formation of the syncline.

The amount of structural uplift of the reservoir beds above regional normal is another important factor influencing the quantity of oil accumulation. The structural uplift is measured from regional normal and not from the lowest point of a syncline or depression occurring on one or more dome flanks. The development of the syncline, and particularly a rim syncline encircling a dome, is generally the result of a negative movement, or actual sinking of the sediments. Consequently, it is the amount of structural uplift above regional normal that actually influences the quantity of oil accumulation on a dome. The presence of flanking synclines increases the apparent structural closure on the dome.

The amount of structural uplift above regional normal increases with depth on the flanks of domes due to thinning of the sediments nearer the salt plug. For comparison purposes the amount of uplift can be considered on comparable horizons at comparable depths.

When an objective bed on a dome flank reaches an elevation which is higher than regional normal and becomes saturated with petroleum, it is quite possible that oil accumulation in this bed may be great enough to extend the oil column far downflank and below the normal regional position of the productive zone. This situation, for example, occurs on the northwest flank of High Island dome, Galveston County, where the oil column in a basal Miocene sand about 15 to 30 feet thick approximates at least 2,500 feet.

The uplift of objective beds above regional normal in the Texas Gulf Coast ranges from several hundred to several thousand feet and averages about 2,000 feet. The above-regional uplift on the Yegua Formation at Sour Lake, Hardin County, Texas, for example, is about 6,000 feet. Not considered are those instances where formational units are ruptured by the rising domal mass carrying a block of the unit upward over the crest of the dome and separating it from the main body of the unit, which remains on the dome flanks. Position above-regional is considered applicable to beds which may be found to be continuous, except where broken by faults, from the lower to upper flanks, or to the top of the dome.

It can readily be seen that the longer the domal flank and the higher the objective bed is carried onto the upper reaches of the dome, the greater will be the acre-feet of a particular

reservoir rock available to trap and contain hydrocarbons on a dome.

The proximity of the salt or cap rock of a dome to the present surface of the ground bears little relationship to the amount of structural uplift of the surrounding sediments. The top of the domal material at Nash is about 529 feet beneath the present ground surface, and the structural uplift above regional normal measured on top of the Frio Formation is approximately 900 feet. In comparison, the top of the dome material at Spindletop is 700 feet beneath the surface, but the structural uplift measured on top of the Frio is 2,800 feet.

Amount of structural uplift is governed by:

1. The cross-sectional shape of the salt plug.
2. Thickness of salt source bed available for dome growth.
3. Thickness and distribution of overlying sediments.

The amount of sedimentary overburden and thickness of the mother salt bed have been previously discussed as elements necessary for initiating, continuing, or halting actual growth of the salt intrusion. Obviously these factors must influence the amount of structural uplift in the adjacent sediments because they have influenced growth of the dome itself.

Considering the wide variation in quality of oil accumulation in relation to area and amount of structural uplift, Halbouty and Hardin (1955) derived an *area-uplift factor.* This compares production from various domes in the Gulf region to reasonably predict the approximate amount of oil a dome is ultimately expected to produce.

The area-uplift factor was determined by multiplying the average amount of structural uplift of the surrounding sediments, in feet, by the area affected by the uplift, in square miles, and dividing the product by 100. For example, the area-uplift factor for Spindletop field is:

$$\frac{\left(\begin{array}{c} 2800 \text{ feet of} \\ \text{uplift on Frio} \end{array}\right)\left(\begin{array}{c} 50 \text{ sq. mi.} \\ \text{uplift} \end{array}\right)}{100} = 1400$$

Applying the area-uplift factor to selected domes in the Frio and Yegua trends of the upper Texas Gulf Coast, these authors were able to make pertinent general conclusions in comparing salt domes in the same trend where the stratigraphic section penetrated by domes is comparable. If two salt domes that have penetrated the same section have the same area-uplift factors, the ultimate oil production from the two domes should be comparable. Relatively nonproductive domes studied by Halbouty and Hardin had area-uplift factors of less than 400; the area-uplift factors for highly productive domes ranged from 1,400 to 1,700; and some had factors exceeding 4,000.

Time of Uplift of the Salt Plug

The time of uplift of the salt plug coupled with speed of movement is the third primary factor controlling the amount of hydrocarbon accumulation. The importance of time of uplift is certainly not restricted to salt uplifts. Time of uplift is recognized as a most important factor governing structural accumulation of oil or gas in sedimentary basins throughout the world. The relationship of migration to the time of formation of a suitable trap is a recognized maximum in worldwide search for petroleum.

There are numerous examples of piercement domes in the Gulf region where migration of oil and gas preceded growth of the salt structure. Practically barren San Felipe and Hockley domes, as described earlier, are late-occurring movements which took place after oil and gas had migrated into sediments overlying the deep-seated salt mass at Katy.

Wilcox and younger formations dip gently to moderately away from Katy into a rim syncline that encircles San Felipe directly adjacent to the salt plug (Fig. 6-12). Reversal of dip strata influenced by the rising salt mass takes place close to the dome. The steeply upturned and pierced beds (Fig. 5-18) indicated that the dome grew very rapidly. Both Yegua and Wilcox beds thicken from east to west (left to right), moving off the flank of Katy across San Felipe into a local depositional "low." Correlative Yegua horizons are actually thicker on the west side of the dome than on the east side. These stratigraphic and structural relationships of Yegua and older Eocene formations are conclusive evidence that the San Felipe dome grew after deposition of the Yegua and after migration of oil and gas into the Yegua sands at Katy.

Calcasieu Lake dome (Fig. 3-6) is another example of a larger, piercement salt structure located at a highly productive trend where rapid uplift occurred after migration of oil and gas into earlier structures. The present subsurface structure of the Calcasieu Lake area is quite similar to that of the Spindletop area (Fig. 3-5). The arrangement of domes and salt structures around Calcasieu Lake dome suggests analogy to the master dome-secondary dome concept.

If Calcasieu Lake dome growth had preceded the growth of the concentrically arranged salt structures (*i.e.* West Hackberry, etc.) a vast quantity of hydrocarbons should have been trapped. The stratigraphic section and facies associated with the surrounding producing structures are essentially the same at barren Calcasieu Lake dome. The area of uplift and amount of uplift of sediments affected by the dome are small in comparison to nearby domes. These factors, in addition to the late-occurring growth of the dome, are responsible for the lack of hydrocarbon accumulation.

Other classic examples of large barren piercement domes in the Gulf region include Hainesville dome, Wood County, Texas, an oddity in the East Texas basin; and Vermilion Bay dome, Iberia Parish, Louisiana, a uniquely barren structure in the prolific South Louisiana salt dome region. Surrounding structural features associated with Hainesville, Calcasieu Lake, Vermilion Bay, and San Felipe domes are similar. All of these domes rise from well-defined local basins and are more or less centered in their respective depression. These local downwarps are the result of rapid and thick deposition in restricted areas. The increased overburden has initiated the growth of the domes from the approximate center of the local basin. Both the local basins and their barren domes are late-occurring events which developed after hydrocarbon migration took place.

The time of growth of a highly productive dome, while a dominant factor in influencing quantity of accumulation, may be affected by local structural features which cannot be definitely ascribed to salt tectonics.

Domes rising along local structural nosings within basinal segments of the greater Texas-Louisiana coastal basin are often the most prolific producing structures within that particular basinal segment. This is not to be confused with regional positive elements (San Marcos arch, Sabine uplift, etc.) where salt structures are not present.

A generalized structural contour map (Frio) of the Jefferson-Orange counties area (Fig. 3-5) shows that Spindletop dome lies along a well-defined north-south trending nose.

If a dome grows in proximity to an older structural nose, it may destroy a potential trap which preceded dome growth. A rising dome may disturb the attitude of the beds comprising the trap, a flank of the trap becoming a flank of the dome. The oil associated with the original structure relocates itself around or over the salt stock. Thus the dome robs predome traps of hydrocarbons and possibly collects additional petroleum which later migrates into the domal flanks.

A dome which rises within an otherwise structureless area would not disrupt previous traps except for stratigraphic accumulations. Its hydrocarbon reservoirs, therefore, must be primary accumulations. The dome's uplifting effects on objective beds, therefore, must precede or be contemporaneous with oil migration.

Domes which rise within local well-defined synclinal areas usually are completely surrounded by the rim syncline which prevents migration of oil into the dome's flanks from areas beyond the center of the rim syncline. Commonly these salt domes have very short flanks. In fact, with a cylindrical shape it is possible for a dome located near the center of a synclinal area to be surrounded on one or more flanks by sediments which dip toward instead of away from the salt mass (*e.g.,* San Felipe Dome). The original synclinal dips were not reversed by the upthrust of the salt. On such flanks objective beds adjacent to the salt would be found dipping toward the plug, possibly below regional structural positions. Although these domes generally produce only minor amounts of hydrocarbons, it is possible for sizeable accumulations to be present on domes surrounded by rim synclines if the flanks are broad, thus expanding the area from which hydrocarbons migrate (Fig. 7-2). Characteristically, the better producing structures have rim synclines on one or more flanks but at least one flank is a continuation of regional dip. This offers no mystery, since the area of migrating hydrocarbons is enormous compared to those domes with encircling rim synclines (Fig. 7-2).

The amount of oil and gas accumulation controlled by salt domes bears little relation to the size of the salt mass or the height of the salt stock above the mother salt bed. San Felipe (Figs. 5-18, 6-12), a giant piercement dome more than five miles in diameter, produced a meager 1,500 barrels of oil before abandonment in 1951. Efforts to establish production on the flanks of San Felipe have been unsuccessful. In contrast, the shallow salt core at Spindletop dome, Jefferson County, Texas, is little more than one mile in diameter but the structure has produced more than 100 million barrels of oil. In addition, hundreds of flank tests away from the Spindletop salt plug have produced great quantities of oil and gas.

Although salt-dome size does not affect the amount of accumulation, shape of the domal mass is important in petroleum exploration. The geographic and geologic location of potential traps depends on the configuration of the salt mass.

Some domes are vertically cylindrical, others triangular; still others are a combination of the two, that is, one or more flanks may be vertical while other flanks may slant at various angles from the top. Some domes have overhangs, others do not.

Near-flank accumulations in multiple reservoirs around cylindrical domes are usually stacked one above the other, and may all be penetrated by a single well. Near-flank accumulations around triangular domes extend outward from the dome with depth.

A single well on a cylindrically-shaped dome might penetrate many or all objective beds, whereas on a triangular-shaped dome, only a few of the objective beds would be encountered unless it were possible to drill parallel to the flank of the salt core.

Literature Cited

Halbouty, Michel T. and Hardin, George C., Jr.: "Factors Affecting Quantity of Oil Accumulation Around Some Texas Gulf Coast Piercement Type Salt Domes," *Bull.*, AAPG (1955), v. 39, no. 5, pp. 697-711.

Hedberg, Hollis D.: "Geologic Aspects of Origin of Petroleum," *Bull.*, AAPG (1964), v. 48, no. 11, pp. 1775-1803.

Chapter 8

Economic Significance of Salt Structures

The economic significance of salt structures as geologic features controlling the accumulation of vast quantities of hydrocarbons can be described in terms of occurrence and distribution, accessibility, productivity, and other fundamental economic factors. A comprehensive treatment of salt dome economics would comprise a volume in itself and is not within the scope of this book. However, this chapter highlights the most important economic factors associated with salt structures.

Specifically salt domes are economically important for hydrocarbons and other minerals which are either produced directly from the cap rock or salt mass or from host rocks affected by the salt upthrust. In recent years artificial caverns have been dissolved in the salt providing excellent and safe storage for a wide variety of volatile materials. This chapter briefly discusses the production of hydrocar-

bons from salt domes in the Gulf region, the mining of salt, sulphur, and other minerals, the quarrying of limestone from cap rock, and the storage uses of domal cavities. Oil well drilling practices which pertain to salt dome exploration are described in Chapter 9.

Historically, salt structures, particularly the salt dome, have been prolific hydrocarbon producers since the early days of the oil industry; therefore, the economics of salt structures is also part of the economics of oil and gas. Oil and gas as mineral fuels generate the bulk of the world's energy requirements and have contributed greatly to the economic development of the United States and other industrial nations of the world.

Salt domes and salt structures are perhaps the easiest subsurface structural anomalies to locate and recognize, but are undoubtedly among the most complicated of structural features. Multiple traps associated with salt domes are much more elusive to exploratory methods than the simple anticline, faulted anticline, or faulted monoclines. As a result there are undiscovered oil and gas pools around some of the most intensely explored domes.

A review of the production from the several hundred Gulf region domes shows that the bulk of the oil and gas found is concentrated in a circular area up to 3,000 feet outward from the perimeter of the salt mass. The maximum circumference of the potential producing area around the largest salt domes, therefore, would be less than 25 square miles. The areal extent of most salt dome oil and gas fields is less than 6,000 acres. Although the areal extent of production is relatively small, the reservoir characteristics of the producing formations and the thickness of the oil column resulting from attitudes of the beds makes for unusually high yields per acre.

Spindletop dome, Texas, for example, has produced 142,974,000 barrels of oil (Table 8-1) from a total productive area of approximately 500 acres. Discovered in 1901, this first great oil field produced only from cap rock until 1925, when new reservoirs were found in nearflank shallow sands. Total cumulative cap rock production of approximately 55 million barrels—more than 48 million barrels in the 1901-1925 period and an estimated 7 million barrels in the 1925-1964 interval—has been recovered from approximately 250 acres, an average of 220,000 barrels an acre. Flank production, also limited to approximately 250 acres, has totaled about 80 million barrels, or approximately 352,000 barrels an acre. Several small flank tracts have produced in excess of a million barrels an acre. The area of flank production is less

than 1,500 feet outward from the periphery of the salt stock.

Per acre recoveries of this magnitude are common to several Gulf Coast domes. Good examples include: Barbers Hill, Chambers County, Texas (2,000 surface acres—115,-641,000 bbls); Humble, Harris County, Texas (4,000 surface acres—149,399,000 bbls); Jennings, Acadia Parish, Louisiana (3,400 acres—107,698,000 bbls); Weeks Island, Iberia Parish, Louisiana (4,500 acres—113,769,000 bbls).

The history of exploration and development at Spindletop, where persistent wildcatting over years of time has uncovered previously elusive oil traps, is reflected in annual production statistics shown in Table 8-1. The production peaks reflect (1) discovery of cap rock production in 1901, (2) discovery of flank sand production in November, 1925, and (3) the recent discovery and development of production on the previously unproductive northwest flank.

The history of exploration on many highly productive domes of the Gulf region shows that early efforts were often unrewarding. The large reserves of Bay Marchand dome, Lafourche Parish, Louisiana, were not realized until many dry holes and marginal wells were drilled around the north flank of the dome. High Island dome, Galveston County, Texas, was originally believed to be almost barren until accumulation beneath the cap rock overhang was discovered many years after production was first established. Based on the exploration history of these domes it is reasonable to predict that some of the barren or marginal producing domes may yet reveal large undiscovered reserves.

The productive possibilities of salt domes in different exploratory trends of the Gulf region (Miocene, Frio, Yegua, Wilcox, etc.)

TABLE 8-1

Oil Production at Spindletop Dome, Texas, 1901 - 1964

Year	Barrels	Year	Barrels
1901	3,593,113	1934	1,149,625
1902	17,120,949	1935	942,913
1903	8,600,905	1936	841,800
1904	3,433,842	1937	901,303
1905	1,600,379	1938	820,228
1906	1,075,755	1939	772,619
1907	1,615,513	1940	602,265
1908	1,747,537	1941	501,653
1909	1,388,170	1942	419,082
1910	1,182,436	1943	372,706
1911	965,939	1944	337,115
1912	822,916	1945	271,740
1913	716,374	1946	220,907
1914	580,130	1947	284,219
1915	388,266	1948	398,737
1916	340,441	1949	491,650
1917	308,039	1950	1,080,899
1918	502,265	1951	516.899
1919	458,680	1952	450,499
1920	323,995	1953	431,259
1921	321,080	1954	615,107
1922	295,015	1955	506,272
1923	309,315	1956	370,993
1924	359,000	1957	401,073
1925	412,000	1958	560,699
1926	15,040,667	1959	582,824
1927	21,079,573	1960	648,365
1928	14,332,357	1961	820,654
1929	10,183,684	1962	918,738
1930	5,997,913	1963	2,201,419
1931	3,205,994	1964	2,626,608
1932	1,442,560		
1933	1,168,432	Total	142,974,104 barrels

vary considerably because the source-reservoir rock characterized different depositional environments. Viewed economically, it is possible to make some generalized comparisons and conclusions on the probabilities for production and relative merit of new reserves within different producing trends.

Most salt domes within the prolific Frio and Yegua trends of the upper Texas Gulf Coast provide excellent production, whereas the onshore Miocene trend has only one large producing dome, High Island. In contrast, the Miocene trend in South Louisiana is the habitat of many large producing domes.

Basic production data, including the principal geologic trend of production, from all known domes in the Gulf region are listed in Tables 8-3 through 8-8. Oil production for the latest year available (1964) shows current producing capabilities relative to cumulative production.

Sulphur Occurrence and Production

Sulphur and sulphur compounds are important commodities in industrialized nations.

Much sulphur production is associated with salt domes and salt controlled structures. The manufacturing process of sulphuric acid and fertilizer is by far the greatest single use of sulphur today. However, sulphur and products derived directly from sulphur are also important in the manufacture of foodstuffs and countless items of personal and industrial use.

Sulphur is obtained by three major processes: (1) mining, (2) by-products associated with crude oil and natural gas, and (3) reduction of sulphide ores. Mined sulphur is referred to as elemental sulphur, much of which is produced from cap rock of salt domes by the Frasch process. Developed by a German-born American chemist, Herman Frasch, the process utilizes superheated steam to melt the sulphur in cap rock. The casing and tubing design of sulphur wells, which are drilled by conventional methods, consists of a concentric arrangement of various diameter pipes. Steam is injected into the sulphur-bearing zone through one of the inner tubing strings. Compressed air is injected through the innermost tubing string which forces water and molten sulphur to rise in the large diameter outer pipes. The molten sulphur then flows through heated pipe lines to settling tanks. Sulphur produced by the Frasch process is very pure, as much as 99.5 percent sulphur.

An equipment flow sheet of a modern sulphur mine at Orchard dome, Fort Bend County, Texas, is shown in Fig. 8-1.

Two to four wells are usually required to deplete the sulphur bearing cap rock underlying one surface acre; therefore, sulphur mining by the Frasch process requires drilling many wells on a single dome. The productive life of a sulphur well ranges from a few weeks to several years, which creates a correspondingly wide economic range for sulphur operations. In addition to primary sulphur wells, other wells are usually necessary to dispose of excess water and to concentrate the high temperature steam in areas of the cap rock where it will be most effective. In the latter situation, mud wells are drilled and mud is forced into the cap rock to plug large fissures and prevent rapid migration of steam and hot water away from the sulphur zones before reaching the molten stage.

The void created by the extraction of sulphur eventually causes collaspe of portions of the cap rock and overlying sediments. Although collapse of the sulphur-depleted rock fills the void created by the removal of the sulphur and thereby reduces the volume of steam necessary to mine the remaining sulphur, there are problems of surface subsidence which must eventually be corrected.

Although sulphur is commonly associated with cap rock of many domes, only a few have produced Frasch process sulphur in commercial quantities. Twenty-nine salt domes have produced commercial amounts of sulphur in the Gulf region since the first sulphur production began at Sulphur Mines dome, Louisiana, in 1894. In 1966 ten sulphur producing domes were located in the Texas-Louisiana portion of the Gulf region, and four in the Isthmus of Tehuantepec region, Mexico (Fig. 8-2). The remaining fifteen domes have been abandoned but the great demand for sulphur has evoked plans for new operations on some of the old sulphur bearing domes. Table 8-9 lists the producing and abandoned sulphur domes of the Gulf region including Mexico.

The cumulative production of Frasch sulphur from mines in the Gulf region is approximately 170 million long tons. Netzeband, *et al.,* (1964) estimate that the proved Frasch sulphur reserves are about 50 to 70 million long tons (as of 1960). No new large sulphur reserves associated with salt domes have been found since Freeport Sulphur Company began operations at Grand Isle, Louisiana, in 1960. However, recent exploration on abandoned sulphur producing domes indicates new commercial deposits may be developed.

According to Hawkins and Jirik (1966) some sulphur companies have recently drilled wells at Sulphur Mines, Louisiana, and Gulf Hill, Texas, which were sites of early sulphur operations. The new wells are drilled deeper into the cap rock than previous wells.

As sulphur demand increases and presently known Frasch reserves are depleted, the cap rock of shallow domes in the offshore Louisiana area will undoubtedly be a prime exploratory objective. At the present time, it is only conjectural as to the number of possible commercial sulphur-bearing domes in offshore Louisiana or the amount of sulphur reserves that may ultimately be discovered. It is reasonable to predict that the future of the Frasch sulphur industry in the Gulf region depends largely on the success of offshore salt dome exploration.

Sulphur as a by-product is obtained from hydrogen sulphide gas associated with sour crude and gas. This source of sulphur is referred to as *recovered sulphur* and comprises about 2.5% of the total annual sulphur production in the Gulf region. The major sour gas production and recovered sulphur is from the Smackover (Upper Jurassic) fields in East Texas and South Arkansas. Inasmuch as many of the fields located within the Smackover trend produce from apparent salt controlled structures, the sulphur obtained is indirectly related to salt tectonics.

Table 8-2 lists the most important fields in East Texas that produce a high percentage

of hydrogen sulphide with rich gas condensate yields.

TABLE 8-2

Representative Recovered Sulphur Producing Fields, East Texas Basin

Field, County	Recovery/Acre	Approx. Value/Acre
Como, Hopkins Co.	404 LT	$ 7,676
Edgewood, Van Zandt Co.	421 LT	8,189
West Yantis, Wood Co.	131 LT	2,489
Bryans Mill, Cass Co.	297 LT	5,643

Salt Production

Common salt is a basic raw material used by many industries, but even more important it is a compound absolutely essential for human and animal existence. Industrially and domestically consumed pure sodium chloride is obtained from:

1. Bedded salt deposits
2. Evaporated sea water
3. Salt lakes
4. Salt brines
5. Salt domes

Salt is extracted from domes by: (1) conventional underground mining and, (2) solution mining. Mining operations are presently conducted in eight domes in the Texas-Louisiana coastal region. Solution mining is carried on in 16 domes (see Tables 8-3 through 8-8).

The salt mines of the Gulf region are room-and-pillar operations in which the salt is removed in a checkerboard pattern, leaving pillars for roof support. Roof heights vary but some mines have rooms with ceilings over ninety feet high. Drilling, blasting, loading, and hauling rock salt are not standardized. Both old and new techniques are in use because of the different periods in which salt operations started and the reluctance of some mine operators to convert to modernized methods. In recent years, however, salt demand has increased and the profitability of future salt mining may depend on the conversion to modern and more efficient methods.

The two techniques of mining salt are roof extraction and floor mining. Early mining by roof extraction adopted many techniques used in coal mining. Roof mining may be conducted by the reverse bench method or by means of a jumbo rig (Fig. 8-3). In the reverse bench method, drill set-ups are made with an "A" frame assembly, positioned on a muck pile. Large reserves of muck (previously blasted salt) are necessary for this type of operation. The high-roof jumbo rig set-up is a telescoping platform where the entire face from the low roof ceiling to the high roof ceiling is drilled and shot as one face. The face is drilled and loaded from the top down.

Floor mining is gradually replacing roof extraction because of its greater efficiency and economy. Floor mining may be started in two ways—either by sloping up to a high roof ceiling and starting a low roof face operation mining downward to the floor level, or by maintaining the low roof ceiling as the roof and bench mining to a new lower floor level (Fig. 8-4).

Various methods are used to load and haul salt. Some of the more automated mines use belt conveyors to transport salt from the face to the crushers; others use front-end loaders and dump trucks. Salt recovery by room and pillar mining methods ranges from 57 to 75% depending on the strength of the salt.

In the solution mining process, the salt is dissolved in the dome by controlled circulation of fresh water and subsequent evaporation of saturated brines which are pumped or flowed to the surface. Solution mining provides large quantities of near pure commercial salt; however, this process is equally important in the manufacture of chlorine-caustic soda in which the brine from solution salt mining is the raw material.

Solution mining operations are similar to Frasch sulphur mining in that a concentric arrangement of different diameter casing is used to extract the product. A typical flow diagram of a solution mining operation is shown in Fig. 8-5. Fresh water is injected through the middle casing string under several hundred pounds of pressure. The salt in the dome is dissolved, producing brine of a specific gravity of approximately 1.2 which, because of its density, settles to the bottom of the cavity where it flows or is pumped to the surface. Anhydrite and other insoluble impurities remain at the bottom, sometimes plugging the casing if the pressure of the injected water is not maintained above the hydrostatic weight of the brine column in the outflow casing. The brine is removed from the cavity through the inner and smallest casing. To prevent fresh water from dissolving the salt around the casing seat, an inert blanket of gasoline or oil is often maintained at the top of the cavity. An inhibitor may be added to the gasoline to protect against sulphur corrosion.

The location of a salt dome is an important economic factor for salt or brine production because transportation costs are a large part of the final cost of the product and consequently of the profitability of the operations. Many salt or brine producing domes are located near water transportation in areas of dense population. This relationship has been particularly influential in the growth of the Gulf Coast chemical industry.

The potential supply of salt from domes in the Gulf region is almost unlimited. The volume of salt from 156 shallow domes in the Texas-Louisiana coastal salt-dome basin is estimated to be 569 cubic miles (Perkins and Lonsdale, 1955). This estimate includes the volume of salt to a maximum of 2 miles below the surface. Hawkins (1966) states that the production of salt in the United States during 1964 was 0.003 cubic miles (about 32 million short tons). At this rate of production, the volume of salt in the shallow onshore domes would supply the demand for more than 170,000 years with a one percent increase in demand each year.

Underground Storage in Salt Solution Cavities

The use of solution-created cavities in salt domes for underground storage of hydrocarbon products and radioactive waste materials has become an increasingly important function of salt stocks in recent years. Solution cavity storage was first used in Canada during World War II, and during the past decade this type of storage has been used considerably in the United States.

The materials being stored in salt solution cavities fall into four categories:

1. LPG—low pressure liquid gases such as butane and propane (Fig. 8-6).
2. High pressure volatiles such as ethylene.
3. Liquid petroleum products such as gasoline, fuel oil, and crude oil.
4. Radioactive waste materials.

Using cavities for storing natural gas, oxygen, or hydrogen is in the early stages but undoubtedly more use will be made of these safe, practical, and low-cost containers in the future.

Bays (1963, p. 564) described the requirements for underground storage of materials in salt cavities which are particularly adaptable to domal salt. These include:

1. Salt section of sufficient thickness and purity that can be rendered impermeable by the solution process.
2. Satisfactory roof or caprock conditions.
3. Sufficient depth to permit confinement and suitable section between the cavity and the surface to insure effective well completion.
4. Adequate surface provisions and resources for water supply, disposal, and storage.

Man-made solution cavities require careful geological and engineering practices but the process in the broadest sense involves simply the process of dissolving.

The process of creating salt solution cavities as described by Bays (1963, pp. 573, 574) is as follows:

Most effective solution of salt to make a storage cavity can be done by creating a predictable circulation pattern in the cavity, using low-pressure jetting techniques, widely used for mixing in the petroleum industry . . . Such low-pressure jets can cause the discharged brine to have been circulated and received its salt content by movement as well as by diffusion.

In salt where natural layers are present which will cause constrictions or shelf-failure to shear off tubing, some preparatory measures are desirable. Frequently such beds can be suitably enlarged by jetting with high-pressure jet guns, using water or acid, as needed. In some cases either explosive shattering or shooting with shaped charges in open hole have proven useful in eliminating the adverse effects of such beds.

Steel tubing lost in a solution cavity can frequently cause a serious problem. To avoid this possibility it is a good practice to doubly suspend the tubing string used for washing at the surface and to use drillable tubing materials below the casing-shoe area of the well. Various

117

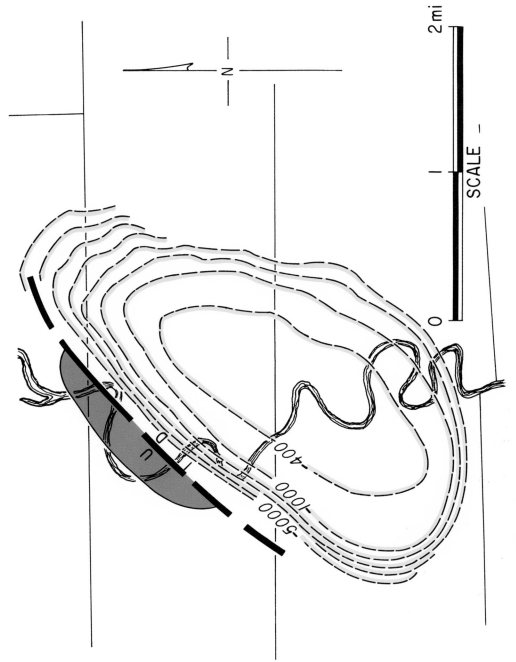

Figure 6-9. Simplified structure contour map of South Liberty dome, Liberty County, Texas showing relation of peripheral fault to salt mass. Accumulation is on upthrown side of fault away from dome. Contours are on top of salt (after Halbouty and Hardin, 1951).

118

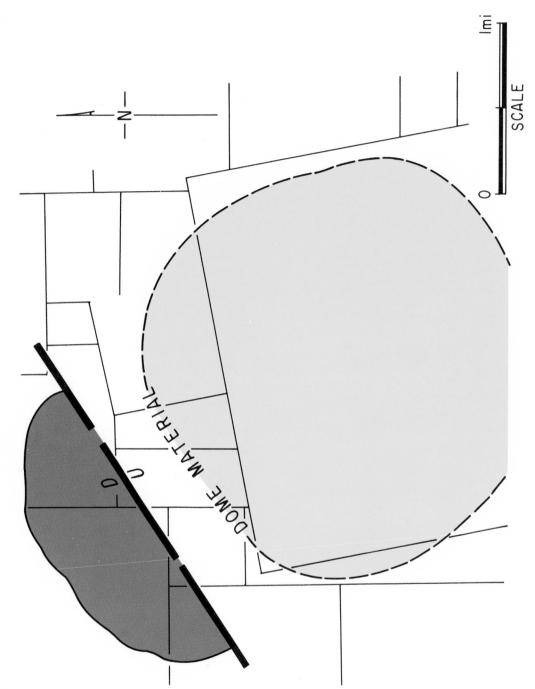

Figure 6-10. Map of Hull dome, Liberty County, Texas showing relationship of tangential fault to salt dome. Accumulation is on down-thrown side of fault away from dome.

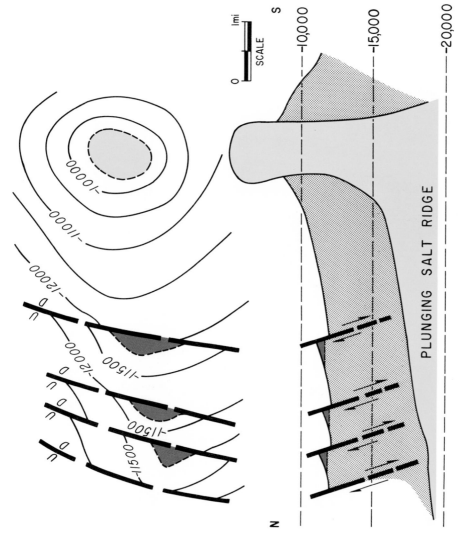

Figure 6-11. Structure contour map and idealized cross section of Bryan Mound salt dome and ridge, Brazoria County, Texas. Bryan Mound is believed to rise from a deeply buried salt ridge. On the north flank a series of normal down-to-the-coast parallel strike faults extend along the upland side of the ridge. Hydrocarbon traps are formed on the upthrown side of the faults. Lateral closure is provided by faults intercepting the north plunging nose. Regional dip in the Gulf Coastal province of Texas is southeastward. However, north dip on deep horizons is quite common and may be influenced by deep salt ridges. Some recent oil and gas discoveries in the Gulf Coast have resulted from identifying areas where normal regional dip is reversed at depth.

120

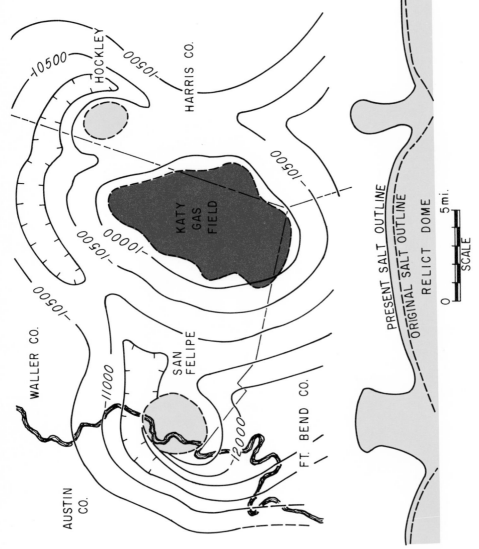

Figure 6-12. Structure contour map and idealized section of the San Felipe-Katy-Hockley area, Waller and Harris Counties, Texas. Katy is postulated as a relict salt mass, a primary uplift in which the locus or path of growth has shifted and ceased to develop into a diapiric structure. From the synclinal area (peripheral sink?) adjacent to Katy, San Felipe and Hockley domes grew rapidly after Katy became stable. The oil and gas at Katy had already migrated and been trapped before Hockley and San Felipe reached their present stage of uplift. This may explain why these shallow piercement domes are virtually barren of oil and gas accumulation.

121

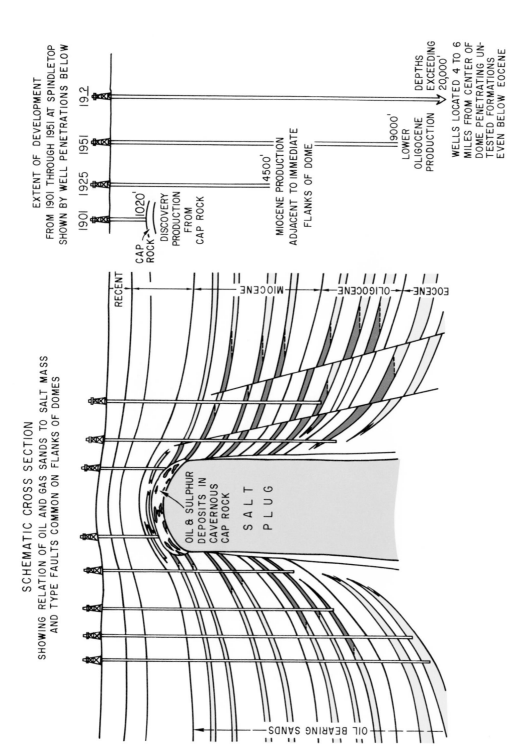

Figure 7-1. Schematic cross section of Spindletop dome, Jefferson County, Texas showing relation of oil and gas sands to salt mass. Note the thinning of Tertiary strata, particularly Frio (Oligocene) beds, toward the dome. This indicates slow, nearly continuous movement of the dome occurred during deposition of the surrounding sediments. The different periods of exploration are depicted in the column on the right.

122

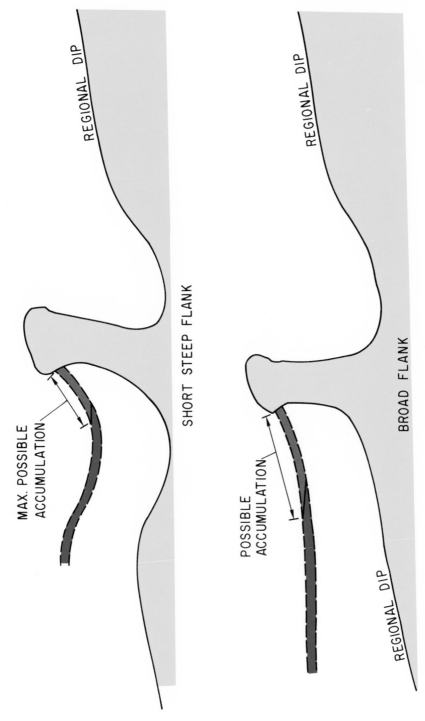

Figure 7-2. Diagrammatic section of two domes comparing the structural attitude and lateral extent of flank sands to the amount of possible hydrocarbon accumulation. All other factors governing accumulation are assumed to be comparable. The maximum possible accumulation in a sand adjacent to a dome with short, steep flanks and encircling rim syncline is governed by the lateral distance from the dome to the axis or mid-point of the rim syncline. The maximum possible accumulation in a comparable sand adjacent to a broad flank dome is greater.

123

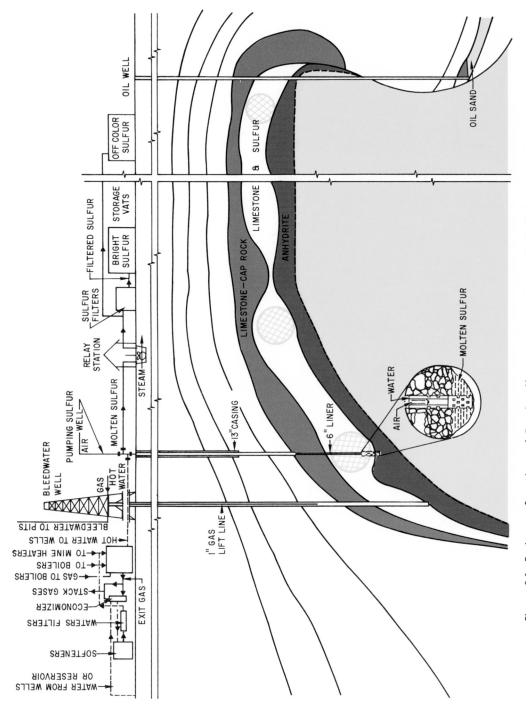

Figure 8-1. Equipment flow sheet of Frasch sulfur mining operations at Orchard dome, Fort Bend County, Texas (after Hawkins and Jirik, 1966).

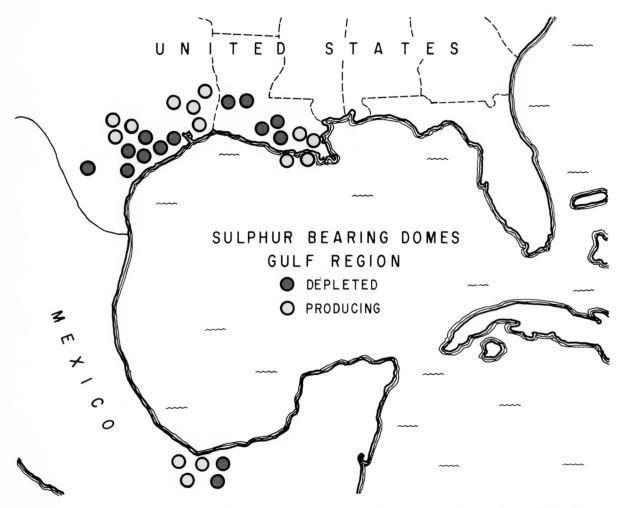

Figure 8-2. Map showing location of sulphur bearing domes of the Gulf region (revised from Myers, 1964). Also see maps in pocket.

TABLE 8-3

Pertinent Data on Piercement Domes in Rio Grande Basin

Dome	County	Geologic Trend	Top Cap (ft.)	Top Salt (ft.)	Date Discovered Dome	Date Discovered Prod.	Vol. Salt* (cu. mi.)	1964 Oil Prod. (1000 bbls)	Cumulative Oil Prod. to 1-1-65 (1000 bbls)	Cumulative Cond. Prod. to 1-1-65 (1000 bbls)	Cumulative Gas Prod. to 1-1-65 (MMCF)	Remarks
Dilworth Ranch	McMullen	Wilcox	-	7,654	1950	1959	0.4	0	38	6	22,086	Production abnd. 1954.
Gyp Hill	Brooks	Frio	Surf.	1,140	1911	1946	2.3	0	337	N.A.	N.A.	
Moca	Webb	Wilcox	-	6,366	1932	1932	1.2	33	2,533	N.A.	N.A.	
Palangana	Duval	Yegua	389	500	1916	1928	3.6	0	9	N.A.	N.A.	Oil and sulfur** prod. abnd.; brine prod.
Pescadito	Webb	Wilcox	-	14,400	1936	1958	-	0	2	28	1,891	Oil prod. abnd.
Piedras Pintas	Duval	Yegua	556	1,205	1900	1905	2.6	39	5,370	N.A.	N.A.	

*Salt volume estimated from top of salt to a depth of 10,560 feet
**In the interest of space, the alternate spelling of sulphur is used throughout these tables

TABLE 8-4
Pertinent Data on Piercement Domes in Texas Portion of the Texas-Louisiana Coastal Basin

Dome	County	Geologic Trend	Top Cap (ft.)	Top Salt (ft.)	Date Discovered Dome	Date Discovered Prod.	Vol. Salt* (cu. mi.)	1964 Oil Prod. (1000 bbls)	Cumulative Oil Prod. to 1-1-65 (1000 bbls)	Cumulative Cond. Prod. to 1-1-65 (1000 bbls)	Cumulative Gas Prod. to 1-1-65. (MMCF)	Remarks
Allen	Brazoria	Mio.	760	1,324	1924	1927	0.8	10	147	N.A.	N.A.	Salt overhang
Arriola	Hardin	Yegua	-	3,929	1928	1932	1.0	140	4,332	N.A.	N.A.	Miocene production
Barbers Hill	Chambers	Frio	350	1,000	1901	1916	5.1	1,243	115,641	N.A.	N.A.	Underground storage (LPG); brine prod. 1st important prod. below salt overhang.
Batson	Hardin	Yegua	1,080	2,050	1903	1903	3.2	615	50,286	N.A.	N.A.	
Big Creek	Ft. Bend	Frio	450	635	1922	1922	1.8	184	13,587	N.A.	N.A.	
Big Hill	Jefferson	Frio	200	1,300	1901	1923	2.6	410	8,727	N.A.	N.A.	Underground storage (LPG).
Block 144	Galveston	Mio.	1,620	1,741	1948	-	-	0	0	0	0	
Blue Ridge	Ft. Bend	Frio.	143	230	1903	1919	1.3	356	22,122	N.A.	N.A.	Underground storage (LPG); brine prod.
Boling	Wharton-Ft. Bend	Frio	383	975	1922	1925	31.3	593	31,292	N.A.	N.A.	Sulfur productive
Brenham	Washington-Austin	Wilcox	800	1,150	1915	1915	1.3	9	415	N.A.	N.A.	
Bryan Mound	Brazoria	Mio.	680	1,136	1901	1949	1.5	7	17	N.A.	N.A.	Brine prod.; sulfur prod. abnd.
Cedar Point	Chambers	Frio	10,226	10,231	1938	1938	-	308	14,475	N.A.	N.A.	
Clam Lake	Jefferson	Mio.	-	8,173	1937	1937	0.4	915	10,267	N.A.	N.A.	Control depression in cap.
Clay Creek	Washington	Wilcox	1,800	2,400	1926	1928	2.2	176	9,685	N.A.	N.A.	Underground storage (LPG); sulfur prod. abnd.
Clemens	Brazoria	Frio	530	1,380	1925	1950	1.9	0	0	29	2,977	Sulfur prod. abnd.
Damon Mound	Brazoria	Frio	Surf.	529	1901	1915	4.3	467	17,900	N.A.	N.A.	
Danbury	Brazoria	Frio	-	4,948	1929	1930	1.9	716	14,911	N.A.	N.A.	Prod. abnd. April 1962
Davis Hill	Liberty	Yegua	800	1,200	1905	1955	5.5	0	24	0	0	Abnd. July 1958; underground storage (LPG).
Day	Madison	Wilcox	2,780	3,167	-	1948	-	1	32	0	0	Oil abnd. Sept. 1958; gas abnd. Feb. 1961
Esperson	Liberty	Yegua	-	6,170	1928	1929	0.8	706	31,841	N.A.	N.A.	Sulfur prod.; underground storage (LPG).
Fannett	Jefferson	Frio	741	2,080	1925	1927	1.0	948	37,782	N.A.	N.A.	
Ferguson Crossing	Brazos-Grimes	Wilcox	3,500±	3,757	1933	1960	0.8	3	11	0	0	
Gulf	Matagorda	Mio.	825	1,100	1902	1502	0.7	0	211	N.A.	N.A.	Sulfur prod. abnd.; oil prod. abnd.
Hankamer	Liberty	Frio	7,535	7,582	1928	1929	0.9	1,299	23,551	N.A.	N.A.	
Hawkinsville	Matagorda	Mio.	95	450	1925	1936	4.4	0	2	N.A.	N.A.	Oil prod. abnd.
High Island	Galveston	Mio.	150	1,228	1901	1922	2.1	9,837	92,891	N.A.	N.A.	Overhang.
Hockley	Harris	Yegua	76	1,010	1905	1923	5.9	13	654	N.A.	N.A.	Salt mine.
Hoskins Md.	Brazoria	Mio.	574	1,100	1904	1905	0.8	0	32	N.A.	N.A.	Sulfur prod. abnd.; oil prod. abnd.
Hull	Liberty	Yegua	260	595	1908	1918	2.6	3,619	156,830	N.A.	N.A.	Underground storage (LPG).
Humble	Harris	Yegua	700	1,214	1903	1905	9.8	794	138,639	N.A.	N.A.	Large broad-topped dome.
Long Point	Ft. Bend	Frio.	550	868	1924	1950	2.8	0	45	N.A.	N.A.	Sulfur productive; first dome discovered by torsion balance.
Lost Lake	Chambers	Frio	3,275	5,430	1925	1929	1.5	21	1,237	N.A.	N.A.	Reportedly has thickest cap rock of any Gulf Coast salt dome.

*Salt volume estimated from top of salt to a depth of 10,560 feet

TABLE 8-4 (CONT.)

Pertinent Data on Piercement Domes in Texas Portion of the Texas-Louisiana Coastal Basin

Dome	County	Geologic Trend	Top Cap (ft.)	Top Salt (ft.)	Date Discovered Dome	Date Discovered Prod.	Vol. Salt* (cu.mi.)	1964 Oil Prod. (1000 bbls)	Cumulative Oil Prod. to 1-1-65 (1000 bbls)	Cumulative Cond. Prod. to 1-1-65 (1000 bbls)	Cumulative Gas Prod. to 1-1-65 (MMCF)	Remarks
Manvel	Brazoria	Frio	1,380	11,274	1929	1931	–	995	64,540	N.A.	N.A.	
Markham	Matagorda	Frio		1,417	1908	1908	1.9	1,159	41,404	N.A.	N.A.	Underground storage (LPG).
McFaddin Beach	Jefferson	Mio.	1,355	2,605	1938	–	2.4	N.A.	133	N.A.	N.A.	
Millican	Brazos	Wilcox	4,890	5,170	–	1942	0.6	0	0	0	N.A.	
Moss Bluff	Liberty	Frio	591	1,077	1926	1926	11.2	37	1,782	N.A.	N.A.	Sulfur productive
Mykawa	Harris	Frio		7,100	1928	1929	0.5	80	7,120	N.A.	N.A.	
Nash	Ft. Bend	Frio	620	950	1924	1926	2.0	53	3,405	N.A.	N.A.	First important oil discovery by torsion balance in U.S.; sulfur. prod. abnd.
North Dayton	Liberty	Yegua	580	800	1900	1905	1.7	298	9,561	N.A.	N.A.	Overhang
Orange	Orange	Frio		7,120	1913	1913	2.0	693	55,155	N.A.	N.A.	
Orchard	Ft. Bend	Yegua	285	369	1924	1926	1.2	593	13,311	N.A.	N.A.	Sulfur productive; 1st salt dome on Gulf Coast disc. by refraction seismograph.
Pierce Junction	Harris	Frio	630	860	1901	1921	1.3	1,474	90,588	N.A.	N.A.	Underground storage (LPG); brine prod.
Port Neches	Orange	Frio		6,948	1928	1929	0.9	496·	24,611	N.A.	N.A.	Prolific middle Frio prod. below unconformity on north flank
Raccoon Bend	Austin	Yegua		11,004	1926	1928	–	1,566	70,857	N.A.	N.A.	Salt contact may represent salt ridge instead of dome
Red Fish Reef	Chambers	Frio		15,228	–	1940	–	1,240	17,155	N.A.	N.A.	
San Felipe	Austin-Waller	Yegua	3,218	4,755	1927	1934	5.2	0	2	0	N.A.	Flat-topped dome with overhang; oil prod. abnd. 1951.
San Luis Pass	Brazoria-Galveston	Mio.	149	358	1955	–	–	0	0	0	0	
Saratoga	Hardin	Yegua	1,500	1,900	1901	1901	2.1	581	51,465	N.A.	N.A.	
Sour Lake	Hardin	Yegua	660	719	1901	1902	1.8	1,341	107,466	N.A.	N.A.	Underground storage (LPG); site of 1st Texas oil refinery – 1896.
South Liberty	Liberty	Yegua	275	480	1901	1925	5.4	2,354	68,632	N.A.	N.A.	
South Houston	Harris	Frio(Mio.†)		4,386	1934	1935	1.0	699	34,494	N.A.	N.A.	
Spindletop	Jefferson	Frio	700	1,200	1901	1901	1.8	2,627	142,974	N.A.	N.A.	Sulfur productive; 1st. major oil prod. from a salt dome in Texas.
Stewart Beach	Galveston	Mio.	1,531	2,640	1957	–	–	0	0	0	0	
Stratton Ridge	Brazoria	Mio.	850	1,250	1913	1922	9.6	97	2,937	N.A.	N.A.	Underground storage (LPG); brine prod.
Sugarland	Ft. Bend	Frio	3,500	4,280	1926	1928	1.9	508	57,413	N.A.	N.A.	Discovered by refraction seismograph.
Thompson	Ft. Bend	Frio		9,320	1925	1931	0.4	5,370·	269,623	N.A.	N.A.	
Webster	Harris	Frio		10,430	1934	1937	–	5,765·	274,028	N.A.	N.A.	
W. Columbia	Brazoria	Frio	650	768	1901	1904	0.8	1,974·	143,814	N.A.	N.A.	Most oil productive salt dome in U.S.

*Salt volume estimated from top of salt to a depth of 10,560 feet
†Primary producing sands

TABLE 8-5
Pertinent Data on Piercement Domes in East Texas Basin

Dome	County	Geologic Trend	Top Cap (ft.)	Top Salt (ft.)	Date Discovered Dome	Date Discovered Prod.	Vol. Salt* (cu. mi.)	1964 Oil Prod. (1000 bbls)	Cumulative Oil Prod. to 1-1-65 (1000 bbls)	Cumulative Cond. Prod. to 1-1-65 (1000 bbls)	Cumulative Gas Prod. to 1-1-65 (MMCF)	Remarks
Bethel	Anderson	Cret.	1,440	1,660	1927	1956	8.0	58	1,017	N.A.	N.A.	First interior salt dome to be oil productive.
Boggy Creek	Anderson-Cherokee	Cret.	–	1,829	1925	1927	11.0	24	5,945	N.A.	N.A.	
Brooks	Smith	Cret.	200	220	1865	1961	5.5	0	1	N.A.	N.A.	Prod. abnd.
Brushy Creek	Anderson	Cret.	3,522	3,570	–	1962	3.1	30	41	N.A.	N.A.	
Bullard	Smith	Cret.	–	527	1927	–	3.0	0	0	0	0	
Butler	Freestone	Cret.	–	312	1957	1957	1.5	0	0	5	1,467	Underground storage (LPG); rock quarry
Concord	Anderson	Cret.	–	6,002	1942	1942	1.3	118	755	N.A.	N.A.	
East Tyler	Smith	Cret.	800	890	1942	1959	4.3	16	55	0	0	Underground storage (LPG).
Elkhart	Anderson	Cret.	–	10,165	1937	1938	–	0	11	.021	1.4	Oil abnd. Sept. 1958.
Grand Saline	Van Zandt	Cret.	171	212	1845	1961	7.6	14	23	0	0	Salt mine and brine prod.
Hainesville	Wood	Cret.	–	1,155	–	1956	8.3	0	33	138	2,123	Prod. abnd.; underground storage (LPG); largest interior dome in Texas.
Keechi	Anderson	Cret.	–	2,162	1891	–	1.1	0	0	0	0	
Kittrell	Houston	Wilcox	2,988	3,855	1933	1934	2.0	65	4,312	N.A.	N.A.	
LaRue	Henderson	Cret.	–	4,450	–	1944	5.4	0	0	0	0	
Mount Sylvan	Smith	Cret.	–	613	1927	1946	2.9	30	0	0	0	
Oakwood	Leon-Freestone	Cret.	703	800	1928	1939	2.9	267	1,877	N.A.	N.A.	
Palestine	Anderson	Cret.	120	122	1891	–	3.1	0	0	0	0	Salt produced from brine commercially-abnd.
Steen	Smith	Cret.	75	300	1866	–	1.9	0	0	0	0	Salt produced from brine wells during Civil War.
Whitehouse	Smith	Cret.	485	2,000	1927	–	2.5	0	0	0	0	

*Salt volume estimated from top of salt to a depth of 10,560 feet

Pertinent Data on Piercement Domes in Louisiana Portion of the Texas-Louisiana Coastal Basin

Dome	Parish	Geologic Trend	Top Cap (ft.)	Top Salt (ft.)	Date Discovered Dome	Date Discovered Prod.	Vol. Salt* (cu. mi.)	1964 Oil Prod. (1000 bbls)	Cumulative Oil Prod. to 1-1-65 (1000 bbls)	Cumulative Cond. Prod. to 1-1-65 (1000 bbls)	Cumulative Gas Prod. to 1-1-65 (MMCF)	Remarks
Anse La Butte	St. Martin-Lafayette	Mio.	–	137	1901	1902	3.1	1,250	49,212	124	34,678	Underground storage (LPG); brine production
Avery Island	Iberia	Mio.	–	8	1862	1942	4.0	2,527	53,054	19	44,396	Salt mine; first discovery of rock salt deposits in Gulf Coast.
Barataria	Jefferson	Mio.	–	7,730	1937	1939	–	428	24,784	65	27,390	
Bay de Chene	Jefferson-Lafourche	Mio.	–	7,950	–	1941	–	2,648	27,400	336	43,798	Found by reflection seismic.
Bay Junop	Terrebonne	Mio.	4,247	4,678	1927	1948	2.8	138	644	90	9,329	
Bay Marchand	Lafourche (Offshore)	Mio.	2,109	2,114	1927	1949	20.3	24,930	132,488	399	112,280	Part of salt massif.
Bay St. Elaine	Terrebonne	Mio.	710	1,407	1927	1929	6.7	7,707	71,584	244	110,559	Sulfur operations abnd.
Bayou Blue	Iberville	Mio.	2,793	2,801	1926	1929	4.6	810	20,806	7	7,725	Found by surface indications.
Bayou Bouillion	St. Martin	Mio.	1,030	1,261	1902	1902	4.5	55	2,081	232	12,292	
Bayou Choctaw	Iberville	Mio.	237	629	1926	1931	1.3	1,111	20,820	36	17,524	Underground storage (LPG); brine prod.
Bayou Couba	St. Charles	Mio.	–	6,160	–	1942	1.3	588	11,372	266	13,227	Found by reflection seismic.
Bayou des Allemands	St. Charles	Mio.	7,552	7,560	1936	1937	0.6	922	14,933	316	26,590	Found by reflection seismic.
Bayou des Glaise	Iberville	Mio.	–	3,219	1926	1940	1.5	1,164	9,863	88	18,228	Found by refraction seismic.
Belle Isle	St. Mary	Mio.	110	135	1896	1941	1.9	1,031	10,316	2,182	141,391	Salt mine.
Big Lake	Cameron	Mio.	–	12,910	1934	1935	–	260	6,170	1,050	46,853	Found by reflection seismic.
Black Bayou	Cameron	Mio.	881	1,035	1927	1929	2.8	1,071	26,140	27	17,095	Surface indications led to initial interest
Bosco	Acadia	Frio (Mio.†)	–	13,742	1929	1934	–	606	39,956	409	90,446	Found by torsion balance and refraction seismic.
Bully Camp	Lafourche	Mio.‡	1,256	1,296	–	1942	2.7	1,607	22,143	468	64,289	Found by refraction seismic.
Caillou Isle	Terrebonne	Mio.	2,500±	2,740	1928	1930	2.3	21,668	239,449	2,296	333,132	Part of salt massif.
Calcasieu Lake	Cameron	Mio.	1,490	2,369	1927	1958	3.1	4	39	0	30	Found by refraction seismic.
Cameron Meadows	Cameron	Mio.	–	4,770	1929	1939	2.7	118	14,056	2,318	84,048	Gas seeps in marshes initiated interest.
Chacahoula	Lafourche	Mio.	875	1,100	1926	1938	9.1	520	18,475	3,119	249,034	Brine prod; sulfur operations abnd.
Charenton	St. Mary	Mio.	–	10,002	1935	1936	–.	1,379	38,662	190	21,062	Found by reflection seismic.
Cheneyville	Rapides	Yegua	6,563.	6,741	1934	1935	.04	37	7,747	19	22,521	Found by reflection seismic.
Clovelly	Lafourche	Mio.	389	1,168	–	1951	0.6	1,603	14,690	533	58,491	Found by gravity and reflection seismic.
Coon Point	Terrebonne (Offshore)	Mio.	–	4,945	–	1957	3.4	0	0	0	0	SI†† Gas abnd.May, 1963

†† SI Shut-in

TABLE 8-6 (CONT.)

Pertinent Data on Piercement Domes in Louisiana Portion of the Texas-Louisiana Coastal Basin

Dome	Parish	Geologic Trend	Top Cap (ft.)	Top Salt (ft.)	Date Discovered Dome	Date Discovered Prod.	Vol. Salt* (cu. mi.)	1964 Oil Prod. (1000 bbls)	Cumulative Oil Prod. to 1-1-65 (1000 bbls)	Cumulative Cond. Prod. to 1-1-65 (1000 bbls)	Cumulative Gas Prod. to 1-1-65 (MMCF)	Remarks
Cote Blanche Island	St. Mary	Mio.	257	298	1921	1948	6.8	3,441	18,109	192	26,274	Salt mine.
Creole	Cameron (Offshore)	Mio.	–	11,965	1936	1938	–	181	5,126	4.6	5,982	Found by reflection seismic.
Crowley	Acadia	Frio (Mio.†)‡	–	14,892	–	1945	–	312	4,421	328	35,768	
Cut Off	Lafourche	Mio.	–	9,708	1945	1953	.03	947	4,185	183	11,407	Found by first reflection seismic work done in the Gulf Coast; brine prod.
Darrow	Ascension	Mio.	–	4,595	1927	1932	1.6	300	9,922	206	15,481	Found by reflection seismic.
Delta Duck Club	Plaquemines	Mio.	–	9,214	–	1941	.06	2,556	22,155	107	47,583	Found by reflection seismic.
Dog Lake	Terrebonne	Mio.	1,423	1,574	1927	1929	–	621	20,316	348	25,541	Found by reflection seismic.
East Cameron Block 115	Cameron (Offshore)	Mio.	338	378	–	–	–	0	0	0	0	Found by reflection seismic.
Block 118	"	Mio.	–	2,930	–	–	–	0	0	0	0	
Block 126	"	Mio.	–	7,677	–	1957	2.7	0	0	0	0	SI†† Gas; found by reflection seismic.
Block 139	"	Mio.	–	9,244	1964	1966	–	0	0	0	0	SI Gas
Block 151	"	Mio.	–	5,830	1964	–	–	0	0	0	0	
Block 152	"	Mio.	–	11,700	1964	–	–	0	0	0	0	
Block 155	"	Mio.	–	11,712	–	–	–	0	0	0	0	
Block 160	"	Mio.	–	11,400	–	1956	–	0	.175	0	3	SI-Gas-Dist.
Block 187	"	Mio.	–	6,946	1963	1966	–	0	0	0	0	SI-Oil
Block 189	"	Mio.	–	<7,450	1963	1966	–	0	0	0	0	SI-Gas
East Hackberry	Cameron	Mio.	2,934	3,330	1926	1927	4.7	4,186	63,720	60	31,527	Underground storage (LPG)
Edgerly	Calcasieu	Frio.	3,800	3,898	1906	1912	1.5	221	12,087	418	23,721	Salt not found until 1927.
Eugene Island Block 32	St. Mary (Offshore)	Mio.	–	16,850	–	1950	–	769	5,617	4,339	468,466	
Block 77	"	Mio.	–	1,685	–	1956	5.2	0	0	0	0	SI-Gas
Block 110	"	Mio.	–	2,610	–	1949	17.1	218	1,394	380	19,104	
Block 126	"	Mio.	–	275	–	1959	3.0	4,568	36,161	102	33,851	
Block 128	"	Mio.	–	3,656	–	1955	5.3	2,187	15,000	312	30,102	
Block 175	"	Mio.	–	201	–	1956	–	197	1,606	218	2,633	
Block 184	"	Mio.	–	1,156	–	1956	3.2	0	34	337	13,980	
Block 188	"	Mio.	–	2,180	–	1956	13.4	1,230	5,723	243	6,303	
Block 205	"	Mio.	–	7,140	1961	–	–	0	0	0	0	SI-Gas-Dist.
Block 208	"	Mio.	–	3,948	–	1958	1.9	992	5,501	10	3,846	
Block 231	"	Mio.	–	8,900	–	–	–	0	0	0	0	

*Salt volume estimated from top of salt to a depth of 10,560 feet

.††SI Shut-in

Pertinent Data on Piercement Domes in Louisiana Portion of the Texas-Louisiana Coastal Basin

Dome	Parish	Geologic Trend	Top Cap (ft.)	Top Salt (ft.)	Date Discovered Dome	Date Discovered Prod.	Vol. Salt* (cu. mi.)	1964 Oil Prod. (1000 bbls)	Cumulative Oil Prod. to 1-1-65 (1000 bbls)	Cumulative Cond. Prod. to 1-1-65 (1000 bbls)	Cumulative Gas Prod. to 1-1-65 (MMCF)	Remarks
Eugene Island												
Block 238	St. Mary	Mio.	—	12,825	1964	—	—	16	16	0	10	SI††-Gas
Block 272	(Offshore)	Mio.	—	8,913	—	1963	—	0	0	0	0	SI-Oil
Block 276	"	Mio.	—	12,230	—	1964	—	0	0	0	0	SI-Gas
Block 292	"	Mio.	—	12,126	1964	—	—	0	0	0	0	
Fausse Point	Iberia, St. Martin	Mio.	792	823	1926	1926	7.9	1,389	19,610	539	32,027	Found by refraction seismic.
Four Isle	Terrebonne	Mio.	498	980	1927	1935	3.1	27	1,975	4,204	130,923	Found by refraction seismic.
Franklin	St. Mary	Mio.	—	16,910	—	1953	—	583	6,391	230	22,470	Found by refraction seismic.
Garden Island Bay	Plaquemines	Mio.	1,350±	1,658±	1928	1936	6.3	5,736	49,319	12	34,202	Sulfur productive.
Golden Meadow	Lafourche	Mio.	—	15,344	1936	1938	—	2,706	85,436	568	76,941	Found by reflection seismic.
Good Hope	St. Charles	Mio.	—	9,580	—	1944	—	1,245	30,004	169	33,036	
Grand Isle												
Block 16	Jefferson (Offshore)	Mio.	1,952 (not on top)	1,780	—	1948	11.6	10,395	41,076	78	33,698	Part of salt massif.
Block 18	"	Mio.	1,773	2,265	—	1948	4.7	1,713	20,224	0	11,985	
Block 72	"	Mio.	(not on top)	6,188	—	—	—	0	0	0	0	
Gueydan	Vermilion-Acadia	Mio.	4,458	4,653	1929	1932	0.8	549	27,262	409	35,175	Found by refraction seismic.
Hester	St. James	Mio.	—	6,780	1935	1938	1.6	0	3.5	560	61,348	Found by torsion balance and refraction seismic.
Iberia	Iberia	Mio.	1,078 (not on top)	805	1917	1917	2.1	854	54,925	60	15,545	
Iowa	Jefferson Davis-Calcasieu	Frio (Mio.†)	—	7,902	1929	1931	0.5	756	83,766	12,268	396,591	
Jeannerette	St. Mary	Mio.	—	10,315	1935	1935	—	970	35,994	1,706	145,683	Found by reflection seismic.
Jefferson Island	Iberia	Mio.	530	31	1895	1931	2.4	102	4,503	85	21,379	Salt mine; sulfur prod. abnd.
Jennings	Acadia	Frio.	2,000 (not on top)	2,400	1901	1901	1.5	563	108,260	97	43,518	Sulfur indications led to discovery.
Lafitte	Jefferson	Mio.	—	13,947	1934	1935	—	5,824	120,045	15	135,750	First field in world to produce below 10,000 feet.
Lake Barre	Terrebonne	Mio.	721	753	1928	1929	1.3	11,498	75,384	671	130,253	Found by refraction seismic.
Lake Chicot	St. Martin	Mio.	—	12,780	—	1941	—	1,301	21,598	169	21,548	Found by reflection seismic.
Lake Hermitage	Plaquemines	Mio.	904	1,400	1928	1934	0.9	211	2,475	308	14,087	Initially drilled for sulfur.
Lake Mongoulois	St. Martin	Mio. (Frio.†)	—	6,915	1933	1938	0.5	659	12,931	324	27,790	Dome first defined by reflection seismic.

*Salt volume estimated from top of salt to a depth of 10,560 feet
†Primary producing sands
††SI Shut-in

TABLE 8-6 (CONT.)

Pertinent Data on Piercement Domes in Louisiana Portion of the Texas-Louisiana Coastal Basin

Dome	Parish	Geologic Trend	Top Cap (ft.)	Top Salt (ft.)	Date Discovered Dome	Date Discovered Prod.	Vol. Salt* (cu. mi.)	1964 Oil Prod. (1000 bbls)	Cumulative Oil Prod. to 1-1-65 (1000 bbls)	Cumulative Cond. Prod. to 1-1-65 (1000 bbls)	Cumulative Gas Prod. to 1-1-65 (MMCF)	Remarks
Lake Pelto	Terrebonne	Mio.	1,487	1,982	1928	1929	1.7	4,334	59,328	78	84,037	Sulfur productive.
Lake Salvador	St. Charles	Mio.	–	11,270	–	1940	–	2,863	42,492	361	58,208	Found by reflection seismic.
Lake Washington	Plaquemines	Mio.	1,094	1,565	1928	1931	14.5	9,386	101,269	4,369	183,710	Sulfur productive.
Lawson	Acadia	Frio	–	16,850	–	1963	–	0	0	86	6,461	
Leeville	Lafourche	Mio.	3,789	3,899	1928	1931	1.3	3,674	87,176	440	111,379	Found by refraction seismic.
Lockport	Calcasieu	Frio	–	8,160	1922	1924	0.6	469	26,761	584	28,097	Gas seeps in edge of marsh led to discovery.
Main Pass Block 46	Plaquemines (Offshore)	Mio.	–	10,168	1956	1956	–	245	1,407	646	10,794	
Napoleonville	Assumption	Mio.	415	657	1926	1942	7.7	592	8,875	1,296	63,855	Brine production.
North Crowley	Acadia	Frio (Mio.†)	–	14,856	1933	1937	–	647	33,132	4,207	185,950	Found by gravity and reflection seismic.
North Mallard Bay	Cameron	Mio.	–	15,754	1964	–	–	0	0	0	0	
North Starks	Calcasieu	Yegua	–	9,031	–	1952	–	36	150	206	6,938	Found by reflection seismic and subsurf. geology.
Paradis	St. Charles	Mio.	–	13,538	1938	1939	–	1,651	70,536	3,424	286,952	Found by reflection seismic.
Pine Prairie	Evangeline	Yegua	Surf.	346	1908	1912	2.9	429	23,911	37	53,174	Underground storage (LPG); limestone quarrying abnd.
Plumb Bob	St. Martin	Frio	–	8,586	1933	1939	0.2	796	7,940	9,938	6,024	Found by reflection seismic.
Port Barre	St. Landry	Frio	3,551	3,642	1926	1928	6.5	836	34,475	627	27,897	Underground storage (LPG).
Potash	Plaquemines	Mio.	519	1,065	1929	1937	1.0	465	12,578	331	38,182	Found by refraction seismic.
Rabbit Island	Iberia (Offshore)	Mio.	–	15	–	1942	.	232	2,045	13	2,262	Found by reflection seismic.
Raceland	Lafourche	Mio.	–	8,170	1936	1938	.03	615	14,912	1,334	100,406	Found by reflection seismic.
Roanoke	Jefferson Davis	Frio (Mio.†)	–	11,585	1928	1934	–	327	20,943	566	72,535	Found by torsion balance and refraction seismic.
St. Gabriel	Iberville	Mio.	–	11,230	1938	1941	–	519	28,225	1,312	62,139	
St. Martinville	St. Martin	Mio.	–	11,205	1935	1935	–	533	6,564	883	89,659	
Section 28	St. Martin	Frio (Mio.†)	730	1,181	1917	1940	2.3	1,252	20,691	665	74,052	
Ship Shoal Block 32	Terrebonne (Offshore)	Mio.	2,375	2,538	–	1947	4.6	28	813	203	5,223	
Block 72	"	Mio.	–	7,545	–	1948	0.3	195	3,135	189	16,088	
Block 113	"	Mio.	–	8,207	–	1955	1.0	152	413	53	3,896	
Block 154	"	Mio.	–	2,916	–	1955	13.8	1,137	11,785	0	5,550	
Block 208	"	Mio.	–	3,320	–	1962	–	2,177	2,739	0	2,123	
Block 230	"	Mio.	–	9,135	–	1962	–	0	0	0	0	SI††-Gas
Block 239	"	Mio.	–	14,380	–	1964	–	0	0	0	0	SI-Gas
Block 274	"	Mio.	.	6,707	–	1965	–	0	0	0	0	SI-Oil and Gas

*Salt volume estimated from top of salt to a depth of 10,560 feet
†Primary producing sands
††SI Shut-in

TABLE 8-6 (CONT.)

Pertinent Data on Piercement Domes in Louisiana Portion of the Texas-Louisiana Coastal Basin

Dome	Parish	Geologic Trend	Top Cap (ft.)	Top Salt (ft.)	Date Discovered Dome	Date Discovered Prod.	Vol. Salt* (cu. mi.)	1964 Oil Prod. (1000 bbls)	Cumulative Oil Prod. to 1-1-65 (1000 bbls)	Cumulative Cond. Prod. to 1-1-65 (1000 bbls)	Cumulative Gas Prod. to 1-1-65 (MMCF)	Remarks
Sorrento	Ascension	Mio.	1,568	1,717	1926	1928	5.1	114	2,595	72	8,758	Underground storage (LPG); brine prod.
South Marsh Island												
Block 6	Iberia	Mio.	—	6,050	1962	1962	—	603	603	0	567	
Block 7	(Offshore)	Mio.	—	8,070	—	—	—	N.A.	N.A.	N.A.	N.A.	Production included with S. Marsh Island Blk. 6
Block 8	"	Mio.	—	6,281	1964	.1965	—	0	0	0	0	SI††
Block 38	"	Mio.	—	2,278	—	1963	—	0	0	0	0	SI-Gas-Dist.
Block 41	"	Mio.	—	9,180	—	1963	—	0	0	0	0	SI-Gas-Dist.
Block 48	"	Mio.	—	8,010	—	1961	—	0	0	0	0	SI-Gas-Dist.
Block 57	"	Mio.	—	11,670	1964	—	—	N.A.	N.A.	N.A.	N.A.	Production included with S. Marsh Island Blk. 73
Block 66	"	Mio.	—	9,870	—	1963	—	0	0	0	0	SI - Gas-Dist.
Block 73	"	Mio.	—	3,565	—	—	—	25	25	0	6	
Block 79	"	Mio.	—	<14,000	1963	—	—	0	0	0	0	SI – Gas-Dist.
South Pass	Plaquemines											
Block 27	(Offshore)	Mio.	—	9,390	1947	1954	—	16,446	72,563	203	153,758	
South Pelto	Terrebonne											
Block 20	(Offshore)	Mio.	—	549	—	1950	3.5	906	2,931	58	11,176	Production included with Section 28; found by reflection seismic.
South Section 28	St. Martin	Mio.	—	14,061	—	.1955	—	N.A.	N.A.	N.A.	N.A.	Found by reflection seismic.
South Tigre Lagoon	Iberia	Mio.	—	14,200	—	1949	—	0	0	250	15,147	
S. Timbalier												
Block 54	Lafourche	Mio.	—	11,380	—	1955	—	355	1,582	1,015	22,837	
Block 86	(Offshore)	Mio.	—	4,100	—	1956	2.1	66	1,036	10	2,238	
Block 131	"	Mio.	—	6,635	—	1958	—	2,300	6,304	0	4,594	
Block 135	"	Mio.	—	5,300	—	1956	6.6	4,888	9,925	0	12,745	
Block 176	"	Mio.	—	<8,784	—	1963	—	194	194	0	385	
Starks	Calcasieu	Frio (Mio.†)	1,157	1,538	1925	1927	2.2	165	7,412	70	20,930	Brine prod.; sulfur prod. abnd.
Stella	Plaquemines	Mio.	—	13,190	1938	1940	—	377	7,295	536	17,695	
Sulphur Mines	Calcasieu	Frio	390	1,460	1868	1926	1.1	137	27,432	0	3,235	Underground storage (LPG); brine prod.; sulfur prod. abnd.; Frasch process proved here.
Sweet Lake	Cameron	Mio.	—	8,560	1925	1926	—	825	17,978	.5	5,314	
Timbalier Bay	Lafourche	Mio.	—	6,430	1936	1938	4.0	12,003	111,576	263	137,556	Part of salt massif.
Valentine	Lafourche	Mio.	—	6,575	1932	1936	1.2	995	20,989	8,038	309,577	
Venice	Plaquemines	Mio.	—	1,328	1928	1937	3.7	4,533	102,258	1,048	141,523	

*Salt volume estimated from top of salt to a depth of 10,560 feet
†Primary producing sands
††SI Shut-in

TABLE 8-6 (CONCLUDED)

Pertinent Data on Piercement Domes in Louisiana Portion of the Texas-Louisiana Coastal Basin

Dome	Parish	Geologic Trend	Top Cap (ft.)	Top Salt (ft.)	Date Discovered Dome	Date Discovered Prod.	Vol. Salt* (cu. mi.)	1964 Oil Prod. (1000 bbls)	Cumulative Oil Prod. to 1-1-65 (1000 bbls)	Cumulative Cond. Prod. to 1-1-65 (1000 bbls)	Cumulative Gas Prod. to 1-1-65 (MMCF)	Remarks
Vermilion												
Block 102	Vermilion	Mio.	—	6,820	—	1956	—	0	0	0	0	SI†† - Gas
Block 111	(Offshore)	Mio.	—	12,420	—	—	—	0	0	0	0	0
Block 120	"	Mio.	—	3,084	—	1957	2.2	285	2,403	0	2,597	SI - Gas
Block 162	"	Mio.	—	2,990	—	1962	—	0	0	0	0	
Block 164	"	Mio.	—	573	—	1957	9.4	52	298	0	38	SI - Gas
Block 193	"	Mio.	—	8,043	—	1964	—	0	0	0	0	SI - Gas
Block 226	"	Mio.	—	3,530	—	—	—	0	0	0	0	
Block 245	"	Mio.	—	10,070	—	1962	—	0	0	0	0	SI - Gas
Block 271	"	Mio.	—	5,190	—	1964	—	0	0	0	0	SI - Oil and Gas
Block 289	"	Mio.	—	7,355	—	1964	—	0	0	0	0	SI - Gas
Block 305	"	Mio.	—	4,500	—	—	—	0	0	0	0	
Vermilion Bay	Iberia	Mio.	—	265	1927	1938	2.9	0	1,332	177	27,276	Found by refraction seismic
Vinton	Calcasieu	Frio	384	700	1902	1910	—	1,725	99,581	87	28,018	Found by surf. geology; salt mined since 1902.
Weeks Island	Iberia	Mio.	Surf.	43	1897	1945	6.1	5,412	119,181	7,969	277,377	Topographic elev. and gas seeps led to discovery
Welsh	Jefferson Davis	Frio	—	6,315	1902	1903	—	320	3,327	919	63,641	
West Bay	Plaquemines	Mio. (Mio.,†)	—	8,280	—	1940	0.1	8,255	79,231	801	162,981	
West Cameron												
Block 306	Cameron	Mio.	—	2,700	—	—	—	0	0	0	0	
Block 383	(Offshore)	Mio.	—	5,000	—	—	—	0	0	0	0	
Block 386	"	Mio.	—	800	1963	—	—	0	0	0	0	
West Cote Blanche Bay	St. Mary	Mio.	—	7,545	1939	1940	0.2	4,120	45,807	211	53,881	Found by reflection seismic.
West Delta												
Block 30	Plaquemines	Mio.	—	2,778	—	1949	10.6	19,558	79,648	28	72,232	Part of salt massif.
Block 133	(Offshore)	Mio.	—	8,496	1962	1966	—	0	0	0	0	SI - Oil
West Hackberry	Cameron	Mio.	1,200	1,790	1902	1928	11.5	3,800	79,872	53	51,821	Brine production.
White Castle	Iberville	Mio.	1,693	2,313	1926	1925	1.3	2,590	35,022	14	17,935	Found by refraction seismic.
Woodlawn	Jefferson Davis	Frio (Mio.,†)	—	10,726	1934	1938	—	0	9,447	1,020	70,412	Found by torsion balance and refraction seismic.

*Salt volume estimated from top of salt to a depth of 10,560 feet
†Primary producing sands
††SI Shut-in

TABLE 8-7

Pertinent Data on Piercement Domes in North Louisiana Basin

Dome	Parish	Geologic Trend	Top Cap (ft.)	Top Salt (ft.)	Date Discovered Dome	Date Discovered Prod.	Vol. Salt* (cu.mi.)	1964 Oil Prod. (1000 bbls)	Cumulative Oil Prod. to 1-1-65 (1000 bbls)	Cumulative Cond. Prod. to 1-1-65 (1000 bbls)	Cumulative Gas Prod. to 1-1-65 (MMCF)	Remarks
Arcadia	Bienville	Cret.	1,282	1,400	1922	–	–	0	0	0	0	Underground storage (LPG).
Bistineau	Webster	Cret.	1,375	1,500	1913	–	–	0	0	0	0	Salt produced from brine wells during Civil War
Cedar Creek	Winn	Cret.	500	750	1907	–	–	0	0	0	0	
Chestnut	Natchitoches	Cret.	–	2,450	1927	–	–	0	0	0	0	
Coochie Brake	Winn	Cret.	2,088	2,338±	1899	–	–	0	0	0	0	Salt produced from brine wells during Civil War
Drakes	Winn	Cret.	200	850	1865	–	–	0	0	0	0	Underground storage (LPG).
Gibsland	Bienville	Cret.	612	885	1926	–	–	0	0	0	0	Salt produced from brine wells during Civil War
King's	Bienville	Cret.	161	172	1914	–	–	0	0	0	0	
Lonnie	Winn	Cret.	4,350	4,840	1944	–	–	0	0	0	0	
Milam	Winn	Cret.	4,147	4,430	–	–	–	0	0	0	0	
Minden	Webster	Cret.	1,190	1,912	1933	1957	–	275	1,084	642	26,645	First commercial prod. from interior dome.
Packton	Winn	Cret.	6,266	6,425	1947	–	–	0	0	0	0	Salt produced from brine wells during Civil War.
Price's	Winn	Cret.	–	700±	1859	–	–	0	0	0	0	
Protho	Bienville	Cret.	–	600±	1922	–	–	0	0	0	0	Salt produced from brine wells during Civil War.
Rayburn's	Bienville	Cret.	Surf.	115	1923	–	–	0	0	0	0	
Sikes	Winn	Cret.	4,435	4,931	1928	–	–	0	0	0	0	
Vacherie	Bienville-Webster	Cret.	658	777	1922	–	–	0	0	0	0	
Winnfield	Winn	Cret.	Surf.	200	1860	–	–	0	0	0	0	Salt mine and limestone quarry

*Salt volume estimated from top of salt to a depth of 10,560 feet

TABLE 8-8

Pertinent Data on Piercement Domes in East Central Louisiana-Mississippi Interior Basin

Dome	Parish or County	Geologic Trend	Top Cap (ft.)	Top Salt (ft.)	Date Discovered Dome	Date Discovered Prod.	Vol. Salt* (cu. mi.)	1964 Oil Prod. (1000 bbls)	Cumulative Oil Prod. to 1-1-65 (1000 bbls)	Cumulative Cond. Prod. to 1-1-65 (1000 bbls)	Cumulative Gas Prod. to 1-1-65 (MMCF)	Remarks
Allen	Copiah	Cret.	2,447	2,774	1944	–	–	0	0	0	0	
Arm	Lawrence	Cret.	1,412	1,930	1945	–	–	0	0	0	0	
Ashwood (La.)	Tensas	Wilcox	3,994	4,073	1942	–	–	0	0	0	0	
Brownsville	Hinds	Cret.	4,512	4,689	1947	–	–	0	0	0	0	
Bruinsburg	Claiborne	Cret. (Yegua†)	1,629	2,016	1944	1944	–	0	0	0	113	Salt mine in initial stage of development.
Burns	Smith	Cret.	–	<11,310	1960	–	–	0	0	0	0	
Byrd	Greene	Cret.	1,440	2,058	1943	–	–	0	0	0	0	
Camichael	Hinds	Cret.	2,700	2,966	1949	1960	–	69	154	0	1.5	
Carson	Jefferson Davis	Cret.	2,318	3,086	1943	–	–	0	0	0	0	
Caseyville	Lincoln	Cret.	–	3,035	–	–	–	0	0	0	0	
Centerville	Jones	Cret.	2,032	2,400	1949	–	–	0	0	0	0	
Coleman (La.)	Madison	Cret.	3,352	3,400±	1942	–	–	0	0	0	0	
County Line	Greene	Cret.	1,288	<1,343	1948	–	–	0	0	0	0	
Crowville (La.)	Franklin	Cret.	572	800±	1946	–	–	0	0	0	0	
D'Lo	Simpson	Cret.	2,090	2,250±	1942	–	–	0	0	0	0	
Dont	Covington	Cret.	2,032	2,200±	–	–	–	0	0	0	0	
Dry Creek	Covington	Cret.	1,986	2,100±	1946	–	–	0	0	0	0	
Duck Port (La.)	Madison	Cret.	–	5,345	1960	–	–	0	0	0	0	
Eagle Bend	Warren	Cret.	4,241	4,425	1947	–	–	0	0	0	0	
Edwards	Hinds	Cret.	2,775	3,026	1937	–	–	0	0	0	0	
Ellisville	Jones	Cret.	13,928	14,075	1962	–	–	0	0	0	0	
Eminence	Covington	Cret.	1,964	2,440	1947	–	–	0	0	0	0	
Eucutta	Wayne	Cret.	11,796	11,804	1943	1943	–	1,164	33,813	0	2,359	First salt dome in Mississippi to be commercially oil productive.
Foules (La.)	Catahoula	Cret.	5,900	6,013	1947	–	–	0	0	0	0	
Galloway	Claiborne	Cret.	4,348	4,432	1945	–	–	0	0	0	0	
Gilbert (La.)	Franklin	Cret.	1,424	1,778	1939	–	–	0	0	0	0	
Glass	Warren	Cret.	3,992	4,030	1940	–	–	0	0	0	0	
Glazier	Perry	Cret.	7,476	7,685	1951	1951	–	52	454	0	10	
Grange	Jefferson Davis	Cret.	–	15,274	1959	1959	–	0	0	20	2,710	
Gwinville	Jefferson Davis	Cret.	–	>10,000	1955	1955	–	0	245	4,833	1,062,585	
Halifax	Hinds	Cret.	3,912	4,000	1941	–	–	0	0	0	0	
Hazelhurst	Copiah	Cret.	1,430	1,850±	1946	–	–	0	0	0	0	

*Salt volume estimated from top of salt to a depth of 10,560 feet
†Primary producing sands

TABLE 8-8 (CONT.)

Pertinent Data on Piercement Domes in East Central Louisiana-Mississippi Interior Basin

Dome	Parish or County	Geologic Trend	Top Cap (ft.)	Top Salt (ft.)	Date Discovered Dome	Date Discovered Prod.	Vol. Salt* (cu. mi.)	1964 Oil Prod. (1000 bbls)	Cumulative Oil Prod. to 1-1-65 (1000 bbls)	Cumulative Cond. Prod. to 1-1-65 (1000 bbls)	Cumulative Gas Prod. to 1-1-65 (MMCF)	Remarks
Heidelburg	Jasper	Cret.	9,325	9,390	1944	1944	–	3,547	73,271	0	7,084	
Hervey	Claiborne	Cret.	3,326	3,547	1945	–	–	0	0	0	0	
Hiwanee	Wayne	Cret.	–	13,598	1952	1952	–	246	2,309	0	85	Gas prod. abnd. 1949
King's	Warren	Cret. (Cane River†)	3,593	3,845	1941	1946	–	0	0	0	58	
Kola	Covington	Cret.	2,218	3,048	1948	–	–	0	0	0	0	
Lampton	Marion	Cret.	1,365	1,647	1943	–	–	0	0	0	0	
Laurel	Jones	Cret.	–	12,304	1959	1959	–	56	309	0	0	
Learned	Hinds	Cret.	4,430	4,437	1949	–	–	0	0	0	0	
Leedo	Jefferson	Cret.	1,428	2,065	1943	–	–	0	0	0	0	
McBride	Jefferson	Cret. (Yegua†)	1,905	2,205	1947	1947	–	0	0	0	0.4	SI††-Gas
McIntosh (Ala.)	Washington	Cret.	270	400	1948	–	†	0	0	0.	0	Brine prod.
McLaurin	Forrest	Cret.	1,708	1,933	1948	–	–	0	0	0	0	First proven salt dome in Mississippi.
Midway	Lamar	Cret.	1,328	2,205	1937	–	–	0	0	0	0	
Monticello	Lawrence	Cret.	2,253	2,757	1943	–	–	0	0	0	0	
Moselle	Jones	Cret.	2,120	2,200±	1943	†	–	0	0	0	0	
Newellton	Tensas	Cret.	3,968	4,123	1939	–	–	0	0	0	0	
New Home	Smith	Cret.	1,832	2,595	1943	–	–	0	0	0	0	
Newman (La.)	Warren	Cret.	5,055	5,108	1940	–	–	0	0	0	0	
North Tal-lulah (La.)	Madison	Cret.	4,372	4,537	1950	–	–	0	0	0	0	
Oakley	Hinds	Cret. (Wilcox †)	2,615	2,634	1949	1954	–	0	4	0	0	Field abnd. December 1963.
Oak Ridge	Warren	Cret.	–	5,062	1955	–	–	0	0	0	0	
Oakvale	Jefferson Davis	Cret.	1,836	2,696	1940	–	–	0	0	0	0	
Ovette	Jones	Cret.	–	13,156	1948	1948	–	288	2,008	0	53	Underground storage (LPG).
Petal	Forrest	Cret.	1,235	1,739	–	–	–	0	0	0	0	
Prentiss	Jefferson Davis	Cret.	2,548	2,800±	1943	–	–	0	0	0	0	
Raleigh	Smith	Cret.	1,490	2,140	1964	1964	–	1,507	11,315	0	27,455.	
Richmond	Covington	Cret.	1,610	1,954	1944	–	–	0	0	0	0	
Richton	Perry	Cret.	497	722	1944	–	–	0	0	0	0	Largest known salt dome in Mississippi.
Rufus	Rankin	Cret.	–	12,485	1960	–	–	0	0	0	0	
Ruth	Lincoln	Cret.	2,208	2,700	1942	–	–	0	0	0	0	
Sardis Church	Copiah	Cret.	1,441	2,000±	1943	–	–	0	0	0	0	

*Salt volume estimated from top of salt to a depth of 10,560 feet
†Primary producing sands
††SI Shut-in

TABLE 8-8 (CONCLUDED)

Pertinent Data on Piercement Domes in East Central Louisiana-Mississippi Interior Basin

Dome	Parish or County	Geologic Trend	Top Cap (ft.)	Top Salt (ft.)	Date Discovered Dome	Date Discovered Prod.	Vol. Salt* (cu. mi.)	1964 Oil Prod. (1000 bbls)	Cumulative Oil Prod. to 1-1-65 (1000 bbls)	Cumulative Cond. Prod. to 1-1-65 (1000 bbls)	Cumulative Gas Prod. to 1-1-65 (MMCF)	Remarks
Singer (La.)	Madison	Cret.	3,950	4,197	1938	–	–	0	0	0	0	
Snake Bayou (La.)	Tensas	Cret.	–	5,989	1963	–	–	0	0	0	0	
South Carlton	Clarke	Cret.	–	11,176	1952	1952	–	177	1,932	0	0	Only oil productive salt dome in Alabama.
South Tal-lulah (La.)	Madison	Cret.	–	3,023	1942	–	–	0	0	0	0	
Sunrise	Forrest	Cret.	5,610	5,940	–	–	–	0	0	0	0	
Tatum	Lamar	Cret.	.967	1,516	1940	–	–	0	0	0	0	Underground atomic test site.
Utica	Copiah	Cret.	2,630	3,135	1946	–	–	0	0	0	0	
Valley Park	Issaquena-Sharkey	Cret.	–	12,424	1955	1956	–	0	6	0	0	Field abnd. December 1960.
Vicksburg	Warren	Cret.	4,356	4,386	–	–	–	0	0	0	0	
Walnut Bayou (La.)	Madison	Cret.	2,660	2,740	1953	–	–	0	0	0	0	
Wesson	Copiah	Cret.	3,394	3,550	1956	–	–	0	0	0	0	
Yellow Creek	Wayne	Cret.	–	11,422	–	1952	–	1,259	23,182	0	1,187	

*Salt volume estimated from top of salt to a depth of 10,560 feet

†Primary producing sands

TABLE 8-9

Frasch Sulphur Production

Dome	County, Parish or State	Years Operated	Cumulative Production (long tons) as of (date)	
Texas (Operating)				
Boling (New Gulf)	Wharton	1929—	58,582,400	(1/65)
Fannet...........................	Jefferson	1958—	1,493,027	(1/65)
Gulf.............................	Matagorda	1919—1936 1965—	12,350,000	(8/36)
Long Point.......................	Fort Bend	1946—	3,970,000	(1/65)
Moss Bluff.......................	Liberty	1949—	4,543,950	(1/65)
Orchard..........................	Fort Bend	1938—	4,915,520	(1/65)
Spindletop.......................	Jefferson	1952—	5,161,829	(1/65)
Texas (Abandoned)				
Big Creek........................	Fort Bend	1925—1926	1,710	(2/26)
Bryan Mound.....................	Brazoria	1912—1935	5,001,000	(12/35)
Clemens..........................	Brazoria	1937—1960	2,985,500	(12/60)
Damon Mound....................	Brazoria	1953—1957	139,618	(4/57)
High Island......................	Galveston	1960—1962	27,751	(1/62)
Hoskins Mound...................	Brazoria	1923—1955	10,895,090	(5/55)
Nash............................	Fort Bend	1954—1956	153,115	(11/56)
Palangana........................	Duval	1928—1935	237,607	(12/35)
Louisiana (Operating)				
Bully Camp.......................	Lafourche	1966—	(facilities planned)	
Garden Island Bay................	Plaquemines	1953—	5,497,000	(1/65)
Grand Isle Blk. 16.................	Offshore	1966—	(facilities planned)	
Grand Isle Blk. 18.................	Offshore	1960—	1,973,000	(1/65)
Lake Pelto.......................	Terrebonne	1960—	1,330,000	(1/65)
Lake Washington..................	Plaquemines	1933—	28,365,000	(1/65)
Louisiana (Abandoned)				
Bay St. Elaine....................	Terrebonne	1952—1959	1,131,204	(12/59)
Chacahoula......................	Lafourche	1955—1962	1,199,015	(12/61)
Jefferson Island..................	Iberia	1932—1936	425,902	(6/36)
Starks...........................	Calcasieu	1951—1960	840,293	(12/60)
Sulphur Mines....................	Calcasieu	1903—1924	9,412,165	(12/24)
Mexico (Operating)				
Amezquite (Salinas, Mesquital)......	Veracruz	1956—	2,004,644	(1/64)
Jaltipan (Potrerillos)..............	Veracruz	1954—	7,495,716	(1/64)
Mexico (Abandoned)				
Nopalapa.........................	Veracruz	1957—1960	322,343	(2/64)
San Cristobal.....................	Veracruz	1953—1957	152,167	(5/57)
Texistepec.......................	Veracruz	1959—1962	56,571	(11/62)

types of materials such as plastics, cement-asbestos pipe, and readily drillable metal alloys have been used for the lower portion of such tubing strings. Where lighter plastic materials are used, some weighting is necessary to make this portion of the string heavier than the brine.

With the use of a low-pressure jet system to attain a circulation pattern for a desirable cavity shape, it is evident that tubing injection must be used and production of brine will be from the annulus. Casing injection, with attendant widespread upper cavity, should not be considered for storage cavities.

During the entire solution operation careful volumetric and collateral records are required. These should include:

1. Metering of injection
2. Temperature of injection fluid.
3. Metering of production.
4. Temperature of produced fluid.
5. Gravity of produced fluid.
6. Resistivity and periodic chemical analyses of produced fluid.
7. Continuous pressure records.

If other data do not indicate whether tubing is intact during dissolving, frequent steel line measurements of the length of tubing are desirable.

If a cavity is to be carried to a maximum span, where roof support might become inadequate, radioactivity logging inside the tubing after considerable solution has been done will provide useful information.

The volume of salt removed from a cavity can be computed if adequate records are available. This figure often has little significance as to the volume and shape of the cavity because of the role of the impurities present and tubing strings in such solution cavities often are not maintained continuously intact to the designed bottom of the cavity. The non-homogeneities and impurities of most salt require that cavities can be relatively small in diameter to insure a stable roof and minimize the hazards of failure. Some plastic shrinkage or contraction is also to be expected as a part of the process. Such

shrinkage will, in turn, aid the sealing of the cavity wells. Size of cavity to be developed for storage depends on judgment and the data collected in the solution process, but is inherently dependent first on the vertical thickness of salt present.

The cost of dissolving storage cavities in salt domes depends on drilling costs related to depth, brine disposal problems, and varying capital equipment costs. Reidel (1952) states that the average cost of a 100,000 barrel cavity at a depth between 2,000 and 4,000 feet ranges from $.75 to $1.00 a barrel. At present the cost of underground storage in Gulf region domes averages less than $1.00 a barrel. This is less than one-half the cost of equivalent conventionally mined storage, and about one-twentieth the cost of storage in above ground steel tanks.

A recent application of underground storage in salt solution cavities is the disposal of radioactive waste material. According to Struxness (1963), storage of such hazardous material in salt cavities has the following advantages:

1. Salt is impervious to the passage of water because of its plasticity and crystalline structure so that the cavity is very dry.
2. Salt has a sufficiently high melting point and a comparatively high thermal conductivity so that the heat generated in radioactive wastes can be dissipated in the salt without exceeding predetermined temperature rises if care is taken to design the size, shape, and spacing of waste containers.
3. Salt dome storage caverns are relatively easy to construct and are lower in cost than other containers of comparable size.

Underground storage in salt cavities has multiple applications other than those just described. An investigation on the feasibility

141

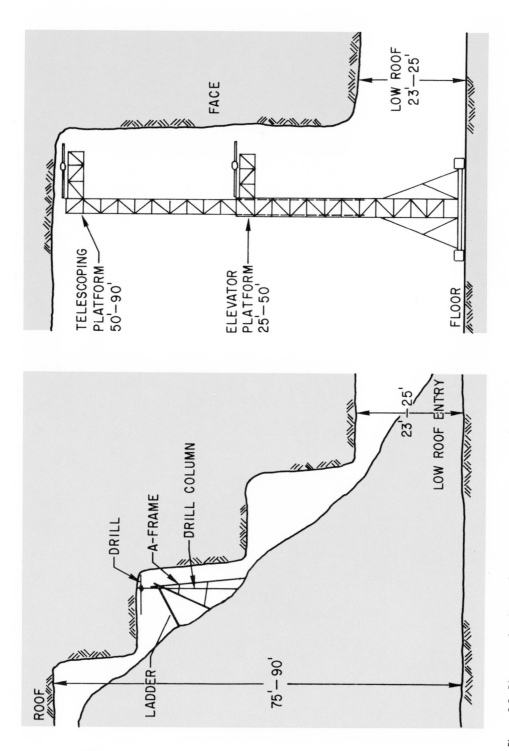

Figure 8-3. Diagrams showing roof extraction methods for mining salt. A.—Roof extraction, reverse bench method. B.—High roof jumbo rig method (after Nicola, 1963).

142

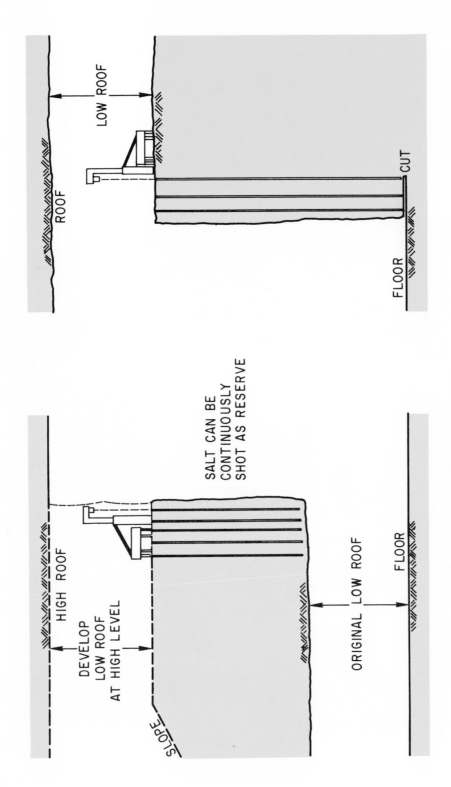

Figure 8-4. Diagrams showing floor mining techniques for salt mining. These are the methods in general use today. A.—Low roof face operation followed by floor mining to the floor level. B.—Low roof method of floor mining to whatever depth is practical (after Nicola, 1963).

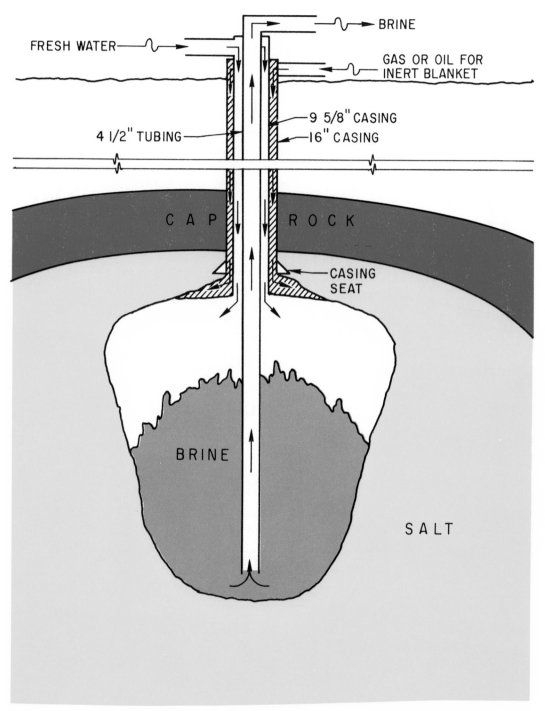

Figure 8-5. Typical well completion and flow diagram of a solution-mining operation (after Hawkins and Jirik, 1966).

144

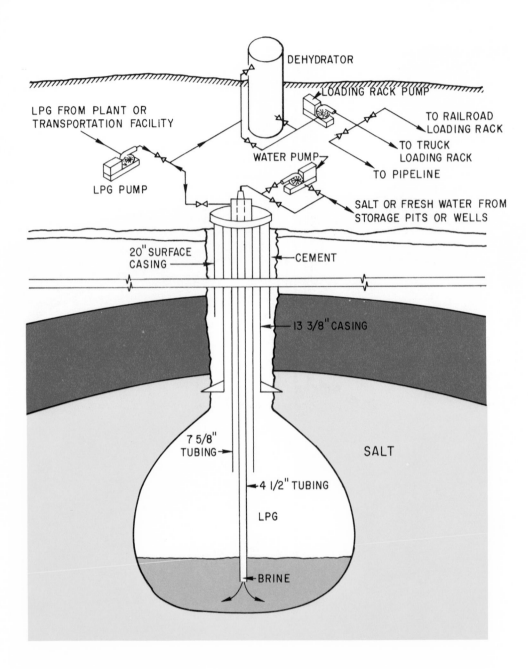

Figure 8-6. Schematic diagram of an LPG storage operation in a salt dome (after Hawkins and Jirik, 1966).

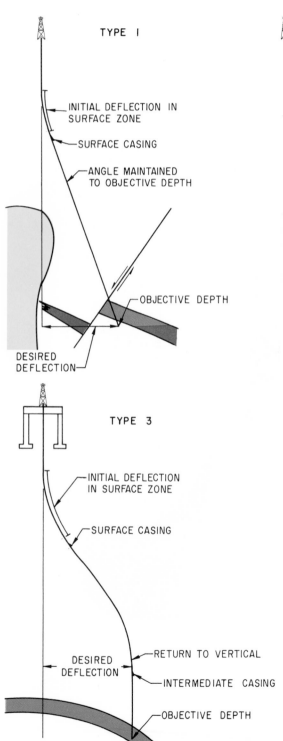

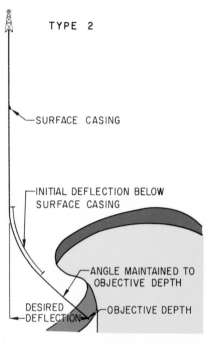

Figure 9-1. Diagrams showing major types of directional drilling methods. Type 1—Initial deflection in the surface zone with the deviation angle maintained to the objective depth. Used in shallow to moderately deep wells where small lateral displacement is required and where intermediate casing is not anticipated. Type 2—Initial deflection below surface casing. Used for short deflections in multi-pay fields where multiple completions are not desired and to determine the extent and structural attitude of the reservoir. Type 3—Initial deflection in surface zone and reduction of the angle of deflection to near vertical after desired horizontal deflection is achieved. Used in wells where intermediate casing is set to protect against problem zones and to achieve uniform bottomhole spacing (modified after Cook, 1957).

146

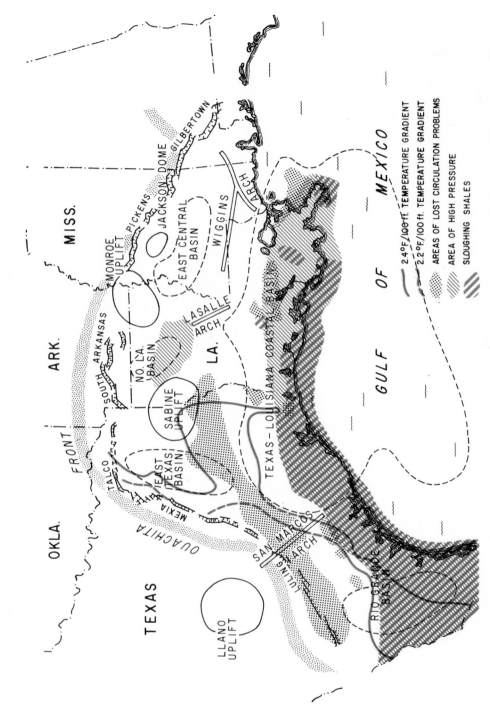

Figure 9-2. Map of Gulf Coastal province showing known areas where drilling problems may be anticipated. Indicated on the map are areas where high pressure, high temperature, sloughing-shale, and lost circulation may be encountered in drilling (modified after Harper and Ruhe, 1963).

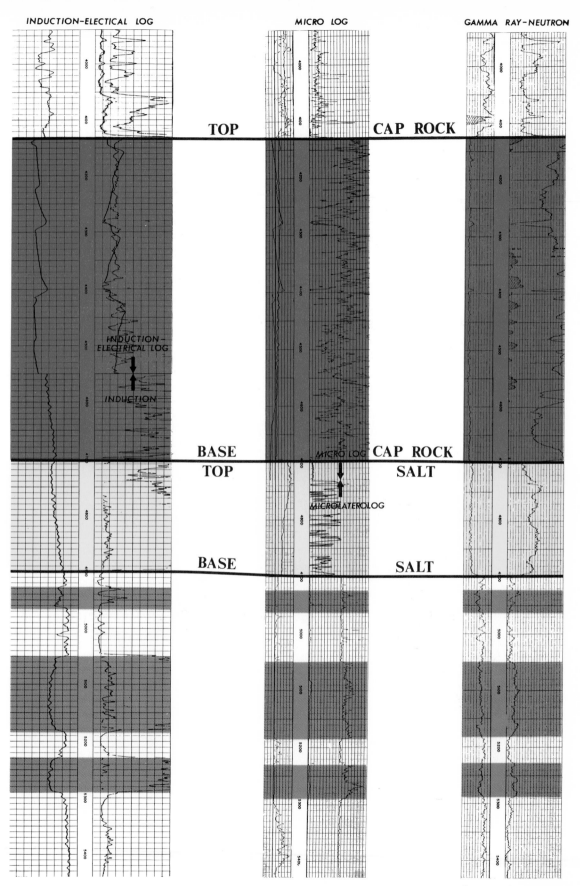

Figure 9-3. Composite panel of logs in well drilled through salt overhang showing characteristic curves of different logging devices. Top of cap rock at 4127 feet and base of salt overhang at 4896 feet is easily identified by all curves; the boundary between cap rock and salt at 4696 feet is apparent on the neutron curve.

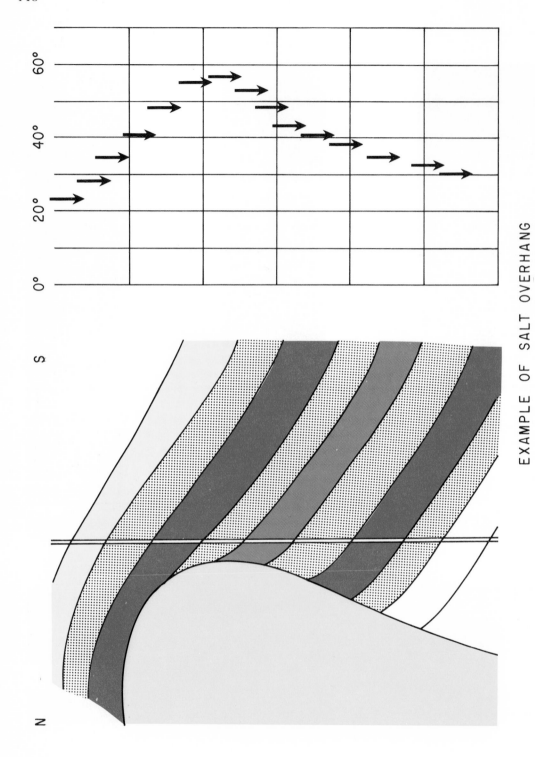

EXAMPLE OF SALT OVERHANG

Figure 9-4. Schematic section and dipmeter plot showing application of continuous dipmeter to determine proximity to salt stock or salt over-hang (courtesy Schlumberger Well Surveying Corporation).

of storing important records, vital to the national security, has been made by Underground Vaults and Storage, Inc., an organization founded to study available underground storage areas in which to establish a Records Security facility.

The most recent application of salt domes was made by the Atomic Energy Commission who used a salt mass to house a nuclear explosion to study peaceful applications of nuclear energy.

Domes with underground storage facilities now in operation are listed in the remarks section of Tables 8-2 through 8-7. In addition to the current storage domes, most shallow domes are good future storage sites. It is estimated that as inventories of hydrocarbon products increase, much more use will be made of underground storage in salt domes.

Rock Quarrying

Quarrying gypsum and limestone from cap rock zones of domes is very minor at the present time. The only domes considered for quarrying operations are those with the cap rock lying but a few feet below the surface.

The only significant limestone quarry in operation is Winnfield dome, Winn Parish, Louisiana. Quarries have been operated in the past in Louisiana at Rayburns dome, Bienville Parish, and Pine Prairie, Evangeline Parish; and in Texas at Gyp Hill, Brooks County, and Hockley, Harris County.

Rock quarries have generally been operated in conjunction with salt mining operations. Although increased limestone quarrying from domes is not foreseen in the near future, this source of a quality building material may eventually become more important.

Literature Cited

Bays, Carl A.: "Use of Salt Solution Cavities for Underground Storage," *Symposium on Salt* (1963), Northern Ohio Geol. Soc., Inc., pp. 564-578.

Hawkins, Murphy E. and Jirik, C. J.: "Salt Domes in Texas, Louisiana, Mississippi, Alabama and Offshore Tidelands: A Survey," *Information Circular*, U. S. Dept. of the Interior, Bur. of Mines (in press, 1966).

Myers, John C.: "Sulphur: Its Occurrence, Production and Economics," *Bull. 4*, Society of Independent Professional Earth Scientists (July 22, 1964), Houston, Texas.

Netzeband, F. F., Early, Thomas R., Ryan, J. P. and Miller, W. C.: "Sulfur Resources and Production in Texas, Louisiana, Missouri, Oklahoma, Arkansas and Mississippi, and Markets for the Sulfur," *Information Circular 8222*, U. S. Dept. of the Interior, Bur. of Mines (1964).

Nicola, Nicholas J.: "Dome Mining: Floor vs. Roof Extraction," *Symposium on Salt*, Northern Ohio Geol. Soc., Inc. (1963), Cleveland, Ohio, pp. 390-398.

Perkins, J. M. and Lonsdale, J. T.: *Mineral Resources of the Texas Coastal Plain*, Bur. Econ. Geol. (1955), Tex. U., Min. Res. *Circ. 38*, 49 pp.

Reidel, John C.: "L. P. G. Goes Underground for Summer," *Oil and Gas Jour.* (1952), v. 41, no. 12, p. 302.

Struxness, E. G.: "Storage of Radioactive Waste in Mine Cavities," (abs.), *Symposium on Salt* (1963), Northern Ohio Geol. Soc., Inc., p. 412.

Chapter 9

Salt Dome Drilling and Production Problems

The twentieth century was quite young when the Lucas gusher at Spindletop dome near Beaumont, Texas, roared in heralding the birth of the modern petroleum industry. This spectacular and oft described oil well is perhaps the most significant well ever drilled in the United States. Although the discovery is better known for its contribution to the growth of the industry as a whole (many of the largest oil companies date their origin to the initial production at Spindletop) there were also many "firsts" accomplished during actual drilling operations on the Lucas well.

Rotary drilling methods were proven to be more effective than cable-tool operations in drilling the shallow unconsolidated sands of the Gulf region. Increasing the "muddiness" of the drilling fluid helped to prevent shallow water-saturated sands from sloughing into the borehole. Tough wall-cake formed by low-

filtrate loss muds were unknown; however, a herd of cattle driven into the slush pit mixed a mud, in unique manner, with crude wall-cake properties.

At a depth of 160 feet in the Lucas well, a coarse sand and gravel caused lost circulation. The drilling contractors, Al and Curt Hamill, soon to be renowned in the industry, ingeniously devised a drive-head assembly, similar to a pile-driver, to force eight-inch diameter pipe through the lost circulation zone while circulating through an inner four-inch diameter pipe. This procedure was the forerunner of protection casing strings.

At a depth of 445 feet, a gas pocket was penetrated which caused the mud to return more rapidly than it was being injected, and eventually to spout halfway up the derrick—the first stage of a blowout. Drilling with continuous circulation was carried on only during the daylight hours. The morning tour was responsible for keeping up steam for the day and evening tour to drill. After this small blowout it became obvious that continuous circulation was necessary throughout the 24-hour period.

At a depth of approximately 800 feet, sand flowed into the hole and rose several hundred feet into the drill pipe. To avoid the problem of sand entering the bottom of the drill pipe on connections, Captain Lucas designed and constructed the first float or check valve. The valve was made from a piece of pine board, perforated in the center and attached on the underside to a rubber belt. When the device was inserted between casing couplings, flow-back was virtually eliminated.

Spindletop dome is referred to in many chapters of this book primarily because it is the dome most symbolic of salt dome geology. All of the drilling problems that first happened at Spindletop recurred many times on subsequently drilled domes. However, new and different problems, which were not part of the Spindletop saga, were encountered in drilling other domes—the different problems being attributable to changes in geological characteristics.

In general, problems that occur in drilling salt domes are not necessarily unique because the same problems are found on other types of geologic structures. Drilling on and around salt domes began early in the life of the industry; therefore, many of the problems which formerly occurred have been virtually eliminated in today's drilling operations.

Drilling on salt domes can be classified into three broad phases, each being characteristic of a particular period of time. The first salt dome drilling efforts were on crests of shallow domes. The available drilling equipment could function properly only to shallow depths.

The second drilling phase extended drilling capabilities to medium depths on the flanks of shallow, piercement domes. This phase was brought about by technological advances in drilling equipment which not only permitted operators to drill deeper on the flanks of domes but to drill through salt overhang. The third phase was drilling deep salt structures, both domal and anticlinal. This phase is characteristic of present drilling operations and has many more potential complications and problems. Included in the third phase are shallow offshore domes which, irrespective of depth, are more difficult to explore than shallow onshore domes.

Progress in design of drilling equipment and associated services has brought about new drilling techniques which are generally applicable to drilling domes or other types of prospects. For example, mud problems associated with drilling salt formations were encountered in some salt basins before the same problems were found in salt dome basins. Control of borehole deviation through the use of directional drilling tools was used for many years on the coast of California to develop offshore reservoirs.

It can be safely stated, however, that no other particular type of drilling has as many potential problems or combination of problems as salt dome exploration. Because of surface relief, many domes on the Texas-Louisiana Gulf Coast were selected by early settlers for home sites, and many of the early settlements grew into towns and cities. From the beginning, therefore, salt dome drilling has been plagued with problems associated with town lot or small tract operations.

Drilling salt domes requires meticulous geological and directional drilling control because the steeply dipping beds, complexly faulted into separate reservoirs, must be pene-

trated at a precise bottom hole location to produce the maximum recoverable oil in place.

To drill thick evaporite sections requires a
special mud system which is more costly to
prepare and maintain than normal mud systems. Standard logging parameters are adversely affected by muds used to drill evaporites. This necessitates the use of different
types of logs which will permit satisfactory
quantitative interpretation but which often
complicate geological correlation. Compaction near salt-sand interfaces in conjunction
with unusual mineral deposits may result in
excessive wear on the drilling bit as well as
causing deviation problems. Heavily weighted
muds are required to drill most deep salt
structures. Heavy muds commonly create lost
circulation problems in shallow beds requiring
expensive protection casing strings.

The many technical problems and geological complexities encountered in salt dome
drilling result in:

1. Difficulty in completely exploring a productive dome.

2. Increased risks which may result in
greater financial loss as compared to drilling
non-salt prospects.

If we attempt to illustrate all of the problems which might befall an operator in drilling a salt dome prospect, it could hardly be
more catastrophic than the true example of
a well drilled at Pierce Junction dome,
Harris County, Texas.

The objective sand was steeply upturned
below a prominent salt overhang. To produce at its optimum attitude the sand should
have been penetrated near its pinch out. The
operator hoped to penetrate the sand at its
optimum position without encountering salt,
thus saving the cost of converting the mud

system. The following sequence of events
occurred during the course of drilling:

The drillsite was located on a small tract
of land with a homestead in the immediate
vicinity. Rig equipment and mud pits were
crowded into less than desired space. A fresh-
water canal that could not be contaminated
with mud or other drilling waste bordered
the drillsite. The well encountered high pressure shallow sands, blew out, and caught fire.
The blowout stuck the drill pipe. After controlling the well at considerable expense and
delay, the well penetrated a cavernous section
immediately causing lost circulation. Many
days of futile efforts were expended in an
attempt to regain circulation.

Finally, the hole was "blind" drilled and
a liner set through the lost circulation zone.
Salt was encountered, contaminating the mud
system and requiring an expensive conversion
treatment. The well was directionally drilled
from the surface in order to bottom at the
planned optimum position. Upon reaching
the proposed depth and target area the well
was still drilling in salt which necessitated
plugging back and setting a whipstock. A
dog-leg developed in the sidetracked hole
which created a key seat and stuck the drill
pipe. Happily, the sand was eventually located
and a successful completion made.

Refinement and improvement in all phases
of drilling, drilling services, and equipment
have made possible the efficient development
and production of tremendous quantities of
oil from salt dome accumulations. Refinements and changes were made in a number
of drilling practices for each succeeding phase
of salt dome exploration. One of the most
effective and useful tools developed for salt
dome drilling is directional drilling equipment.
During the second phase of salt dome development, on flanks of domes, it was found that

geologic interpretation was highly inaccurate because of lack of bottom-hole control. Without proper equipment for measuring hole deviation, it was necessary to assume that each well was drilled approximately straight. After development of reliable directional surveying equipment, it was found that the bottom-hole location of many of the original wells deviated from the surface location. Large reserves of recoverable oil had been by-passed.

The development of accurate directional measurement equipment and methods for deviating holes at desired angles and directions brought about a new era of exploration and development on many domes that were nearly depleted in the original reservoirs. Together with directional drilling methods, knowledge of reservoir mechanics was expanded and refined. These two factors helped to stage carefully planned drilling programs which emphasized more efficient drainage, higher recoveries, and lower development costs.

Directional Drilling Methods

Directional drilling is the practice of controlling angle-deviation from vertical in any borehole. A directionally drilled well is not a crooked hole, but is a directed well wherein the bends are controlled to stay within predetermined, safe limits. The control of the angle of the well bore is accomplished by specialty tools which induce the deviation, followed by survey instruments which record the amount of deviation from vertical and the direction of deviation.

The device used to effect deviation is known as a whipstock—a tapered steel wedge with a concave groove on its inclined face, which guides the bit away from the previous course of the well toward the direction in which the inclined groove faces. There are two general types of whipstocks, removable and fixed. The removable tools are used in open hole, whereas the fixed device is used in cased holes to permit the cutting of a "window" in the casing. The operating principle of modern whipstocks is the same as earlier tools; however, refinements are constantly being made, as in all other specialized equipment. One of the most recent advances in whipstock design is the circulating whipstock which permits positive circulation to the bottom of the tool until it has been diverted and the pin sheared for drilling-off operations.

The earliest whipstocks were no more than logs or other objects lowered into the hole to sidetrack lost tools. If a driller considered junk in the hole irretrievable, a tapered log was forced down the hole until it lodged on top of the fish. He then would go back in the hole with the drill pipe and drill alongside the log until the fish was by-passed. This method, crude by today's standards, was effective in drilling past stuck equipment but the direction of the hole was uncontrolled.

Directional drilling on salt domes utilizing modern whipstocks and surveying instruments may be grouped into three basic deflection patterns (Fig. 9-1) depending on the geologic factors, economics, and the desired final results.

The first type of deflection pattern maintains a relatively constant deviation from the surface hole to the objective depth. Surface casing is set and cemented after attaining the desired angle of deviation. The main reason for deflecting the surface hole is that surface casing, set in a deviated hole, minimizes the danger of keyseating the drill string. Rubber protectors are positioned on the drill pipe working inside the angled surface casing during subsequent drilling. Directional drilling using this deviation pattern is normally used in holes of shallow to moderate depth where a considerable amount of horizontal displacement is not required and where intermediate casing strings are not anticipated.

The second type of deflection pattern utilizes directional drilling tools in a straight hole some depth below the surface casing or subsequent casing strings, which are set in a vertical hole. This method is used for short distance deflection after drilling a straight hole to determine the reservoir's geologic extent and attitude. It is also commonly deployed in dry holes where the objective sand is absent due to faulting or where the vertical hole bottomed on the wrong side of a fault.

The third type of deflection pattern involves an initial deflection in the surface zone. The angle of deflection is gradually reduced until the desired lateral displacement is achieved whereupon the hole is vertically drilled to the objective depth. This method is obviously more difficult and costly. The straightening procedure in the deeper portion of the well is often a slow process. This pattern is used in deep wells in areas where intermediate casing is set to protect against high pressure gas pockets, water flows, or lost circulation zones above the producing horizon. This technique also permits more uniform bottomhole spacing in multipay areas for purposes of more efficient drainage and more accurate geologic correlation. This procedure may also be used in areas where protection casing strings are not required. One advantage of the third pattern is that the directional control is effected at relatively shallow depths where drilling time per foot is fast and where the cost of frequent round trips to deviate the hole is not excessive.

Sticking of the drill string is the greatest hazard in slant-hole drilling operations. In addition to key-seating due to sharp bends in the hole, differential- or wall-sticking of the pipe is always a possible danger whenever the drill string is motionless and circulation is stopped while taking survey readings. Another significant problem in directional drilling is the high cost of round trips necessary to set the directional equipment.

Before deciding on any one of the directional drilling techniques described, other factors must be carefully considered, which, in the final analysis, may necessitate something less than the optimum method. The productive characteristics of the sands have a distinct bearing on the well completion method. For example, suppose that under a given set of geological conditions, an operator prefers the first method of directional drilling (Fig. 9-1). However, it is known before drilling that the well will probably require pumping to produce. Anticipating this, he might elect to use the second of the three methods which causes the least amount of wear on rods and tubing.

The decision to drill directionally should also take into consideration the compaction characteristics of the geologic section. Heaving shales and unconsolidated water-bearing sands may be extremely difficult to control in a slant hole. In addition, casing-collapse problems caused by shifting of steeply dipping sands may require modification of planned casing strings. Surface subsidence problems must be considered in setting the casing string.

Directional drilling tools are extensively used to drill offshore salt domes. Permanent drilling platforms are designed for drilling many wells (up to 48) from a single surface location. Directional drilling programs in these cases are highly complex and various modifications of the three basic deviation patterns may be required to complete a development program on a permanent platform.

Mud Systems in Salt Dome Drilling

A carefully planned drilling mud program with strict adherence to constant control of the drilling fluids is universally recognized as an integral part of any successful drilling venture. A complete technological cycle in mud engineering has been made since Stroud (1921) introduced weighted drilling fluids to control blowouts. In the years that followed Stroud's first controlled drilling fluid, mud systems became increasingly complex. Many organic and inorganic additives were added to gel muds to maintain the desired mud qualities under varying conditions. At one time, not many years ago, deep drilling programs utilized muds composed of several different additives to maintain high pH, low filtrate loss, low gel strength, moderate viscosity, and other properties of closely controlled drilling fluids. Recently, however, there has been a tendency to return to simpler mud systems which accomplish all of the desired effects of former complex muds with fewer additives. The completion of the mud technology cycle was made possible by new additives which work satisfactorily under many different conditions.

The functions and properties of drilling fluids and the various classifications of mud systems are contained in many publications and technical manuals. The most complete text on oil well drilling muds was compiled by Rogers (1963), to which the reader is referred for details of the history, nature, chemistry, and use of drilling fluids.

There are two basic types of mud programs—one designed for drilling shallow domes, the other for deep salt structures. The use of shallow or deep drilling mud systems is, of course, predicated on drilling salt at some stage before reaching the objective depth.

If salt is to be drilled at very shallow depths a saturated salt-water mud may be mixed in the surface system and utilized as a spud mud. If, however, the dome is several thousand feet deep (but still in the shallow or intermediate depth range) it is generally advantageous to maintain a fresh-water mud system until the cap rock or salt is penetrated, then convert to a saturated salt mud. Both native or gel mud fresh-water systems may require addition of: caustic soda (sodium hydroxide) to develop proper alkaline values which promote hydration and dispersion of shales drilled; quebracho-type thinners to maintain the desired viscosity; and phosphate to provide adequate gel strength reducing properties. The use of different chemical additives depends on the nature of the geologic section overlying the salt, which is normally not an unknown factor in Gulf Coast drilling.

Salt-water muds are muds with salt concentrations above 10,000 ppm or one percent salt. Normal fresh-water muds with either high or low pH values maintain good physical properties up to this salt concentration. When this salt concentration is exceeded, the physical properties of fresh-water muds are drastically upset so that salt-water muds are almost a necessity. If a salt-water mud system is made up initially, the usual procedure is to add saturated brine or common salt to fresh-water. To reach a salt concentration of about 315,000 ppm, a barrel of fresh-water requires the addition of about 125 pounds. The commonly used fresh-water clays (gels) are adversely affected by high salt concentration; therefore, a special salt-water clay (attapulgite) must be used. Salt-water clays will impart viscosity but do not provide adequate fluid loss control. To maintain low filtration rates, pregelatinized starch is added to the salt-water system. Preservatives are not required for the starch in high salt concentration. Sodium carboxymethylcellulose, the organic colloid used for filtration control in fresh-water systems, is not effective in salt-water muds.

Saturated salt-water muds are characterized by high gel strength. The common organic thinning agents are not satisfactory in reducing gel strengths in salt-water muds. Saturated salt-water is usually added to the system if abnormal viscosity and high gel strength create a problem.

If a fresh-water mud is converted to a salt mud immediately upon penetrating the salt, the usual procedure is to discard one-third to one-half of the fresh-water mud and add salt to saturate the remaining fresh mud. The addition of salt immediately causes the mud to thicken, but by adding water at the same time the salt is introduced, a pumpable mud can usually be maintained. Some operators prefer to saturate a fresh-water mud by drilling domal salt. This practice was common in the past and is still used to some extent today. Although operations may be successfully concluded using domal salt to saturate the mud, the probability of encountering difficulty is greatly increased. While this procedure saves purchasing salt or brine, it produces excessive hole enlargement. Casing failures due to poor cement jobs are common in washed-out boreholes. Also a "fish" lost in the hole may be impossible to locate if the washout is quite large.

In offshore drilling operations it is more economical to use sea water as the base fluid for the salt-mud system. In an emergency (*e.g.,* lost circulation) the availability in quantity of the base fluid is important. Seawater mud is effective in drilling shallow offshore domes; however, contamination from calcium and magnesium ions may necessitate additional treating agents to develop the de-

sired mud properties. Filtration rates are affected by high concentrations of these metallic ions, and starch itself may be of no value unless these contaminants are first treated out.

Foaming of saturated salt-muds is quite common. Increasing the P-filtrate (Phenolthaline alkalinity) by adding caustic soda may successfully decrease the degree of foaming. If foaming persists, a defoaming agent may be required.

Depending on the geologic conditions it may be necessary to set protective casing to the top of the salt, convert the mud system, and drill ahead. If only a few hundred feet of salt is anticipated, and up-hole problems do not occur, the salt may be drilled without setting casing. The cost of setting an expensive protective casing string can be avoided in many cases if the drilling program involves a carefully planned and executed mud program.

Drilling shallow domes presents far fewer potential problems than drilling deep structures. Nonetheless, many problems can arise in drilling the shallowest domes. In general, there is more likelihood of encountering difficulties in drilling shallow salt than in wells where no salt section is penetrated. One of the most common problems in drilling shallow domes is lost circulation. Lost circulation almost always occurs in drilling highly cavernous cap rock over most shallow domes.

Where formations above a cavernous zone must be protected, a floating mud-cap may be used. Gray, *et al.,* (1956) describe the methods of combating lost circulation in shallow cavernous zones at Pierce Junction salt dome, Harris County, Texas, where a floating mud-cap has been used. When circulation is lost at depths of 1,100 to 2,600 feet, water is pumped through the drill pipe and mud weighing about nine ppg is pumped through the annulus. After the lost circulation zone is drilled, casing is set before resuming normal drilling.

Another method of effectively drilling shallow lost circulation zones at Barbers Hill dome is accomplished by using aerated salt water instead of mud. The lost circulation zone occurs at 1,300 feet. A surfactant is added to the salt-water and the mixture is aerated and injected into the pump discharge in the ratio of 2½ cubic feet of air per cubic foot of water. By reducing the hydrostatic weight of the drilling fluid, circulation can be restored and casing set after drilling through the zone.

Drilling deep salt structures naturally involves greater risks than shallow drilling; therefore, specialized mud systems must be programmed to insure the best chance for successful operations. Attendant with the drilling of many deep salt structures are the following problems:

1. Lost circulation
2. Heaving shale
3. Salt water flows
4. Abnormally high pressure zones
5. High temperature.

The incidence of these problems is characteristic of certain general localities in the Gulf region. The map (Fig. 9-2), modified after Harper and Ruhe (1963), indicates potential problem areas which include, but are not limited to, salt domes.

Lost circulation common to shallow salt-dome wells is also a problem in deep drilling, regardless of whether salt is penetrated. Lost circulation can occur at any depth where the total pressure against the formation, due to the weight of the mud column, exceeds the total fluid pressure in the formation, and the openings in the formations (pore space) are

about three times as large as the largest particles in quantity making up the mud system.

Most deep wells require high mud weights to protect against possible high pressure zones. As the weight is increased mud will almost invariably be lost to shallower formations. Therefore, deep drilling usually cannot be accomplished without setting a protective casing string or strings. In addition to lost circulation zones inherent in the geologic section drilled, fluid may be lost to induced fractures caused by poor drilling techniques. Pressure surges developed by rapid running or spudding drill pipe, and constriction of the annulus due to balling the bit, may break down or fracture the formation. Once a fracture has been created, mud lost into the formation will rapidly wash out and widen the fracture. Even with the most careful and gentle drilling techniques, heaving shale may cause a restriction in the annulus which can quickly result in formation fracturing and lost circulation.

Heaving shale problems, recognized early in the history of salt dome exploration (Halbouty, 1936), other than directly influencing lost circulation, can also be a problem in viscosity control or in pipe sticking. Hydration of low gravity shale and clay from and adjacent to the borehole aggravates the problem of proper viscosity control. Upon hydration the shale forming the wall of the borehole may disintegrate and fall into the hole, sticking the drill pipe. In the case of non-hydratable shales, heaving shale may still be a problem due to brecciation, fracturing of the formation by mud or filtrate, or hydrostatic pressure differentials which may force the shale into the hole.

High pressure salt-water flows are occasionally encountered in deep wells above salt structures. If a fresh-water mud system is being used, contamination effects of a salt-water flow are similar to contamination from drilling solid salt. Remedial action must be taken.

Bottom-hole pressures in excess of the normal gradient (0.465 pound per foot) are commonplace in deep well drilling in the Gulf region. The mud weights used in drilling normal pressures rarely exceed 9.5 pounds a gallon, which affords an ample safety factor against possible blowouts. An abnormal pressure well is generally considered to require mud weights exceeding 12 ppg. To drill many of the deep salt structures in the Gulf region mud weights over 18 ppg have been necessary.

Heavy muds have a high content of suspended solids which directly affect the viscosity. As in the case of hydratable shales, the control of viscosity by dilution requires the addition of large quantities of barite which can run the cost of a mud program to extremes. Cannan and Sullins (1947, p. 29) discuss abnormal pressure situations in the drilling of deep salt structures in the Gulf region. They state:

> The most credible theory as to the cause for abnormally high pressures over deep-seated domes is the incompetence of formations to bear the overburden without compaction, coupled with a complete or partial seal of the formation. The packing of the formation results in a reduction of volume of fluids carried in the pore spaces and if there is no escape, there is a consequent increase in pressure. The seal against escape of this pressure may be caused either by deposition or by faulting. The conclusion that there must be a seal to trap high pressure seems inescapable; otherwise, the pressure would be dissipated to the outcrop or into zones of normal pressure and thence to the outcrop.

According to Dickinson (1953) abnormal pressures in the Texas-Louisiana Gulf Coast often occur in thick shale sections below major sand units, and are not necessarily a function of depth alone. The pressure is a result of the transfer of overburden weight from the fluid being squeezed from the compacting shale to the fluid in the permeable sand body. Abnormal pressures may be found a few feet below a zone of normal hydrostatic pressure. Abnormal pressures may be accentuated if hydrocarbon gases are trapped in a long column subject to overburden pressure. This occurs because the pressure at the top of the column is equivalent to the abnormal pressure gradient at that point plus additional pressure due to the difference in density of the fluid in the confined column and the abnormal pressure down to the water contact of the confined hydrocarbons.

High temperatures found in drilling many deep salt structures have a detrimental effect on drilling fluids. The downhole temperature of some deep salt-dome wells has exceeded 425° F (Pescadito dome, Webb County, Texas). Organic dispersing agents and filtration reducing additives break down, alkalies react with clays, and the result is a high viscosity, high water-loss mud unless a continuous program of treatment is carried out.

To combat many of the potential problems of drilling deep salt structures and provide satisfactory drilling fluid properties, calcium-treated muds have been widely used for many years. Calcium treated (lime mud) drilling fluid permits the use of maximum weight muds with viscosities well within workable limits. Lime muds, however, have many disadvantages. They are corrosive, hard to handle, and expensive to maintain. Moreover, they are unstable at high temperatures.

Recent development and widespread acceptance of a particular new thinner and dispersant, a modified chrom-lignosulphonate, has nearly revolutionized mud systems in deep wells drilled in the Gulf region. The lignosulphonate, a by-product of paper manufacturing by the sulphite process, is a highly effective thinner and filtrate reducing agent in low pH, gyp, lime, or salt muds. It is soluble in fresh or salt water. With lignosulphonate mud systems the concentration of the ingredients can be varied for the anticipated drilling conditions by simple addition of the basic materials, thus eliminating the need for costly conversion of mud systems.

A lignosulphonate system can withstand all types of contamination at high temperatures and is more economical than a comparable calcium-treated system. So called calcium "embrittlement" of clay results from high temperature reacting on lime muds. Heaving shale problems accompany calcium "embrittlement."

The lignosulphonate system is an inert, inhibitive mud (one which prevents hydration and swelling of clays and shales), does not appreciably alter the formation being drilled, and prevents dispersion of drilled cuttings (won't "make" mud). In all aspects it undoubtedly comes closer to the perfect mud than any other type of fluid, including invert oil emulsions.

Realizing all of the potential problems of deep salt-dome drilling, the prudent operator today usually drills with a lignosulphonate mud and, upon penetrating the top of the salt, adds salt to saturate the system. After drilling through the salt, casing is usually set before drilling ahead.

An alternative mud system is occasionally used in drilling deep salt domes where the operator wishes to avoid, if possible, setting protective casing unless the well penetrates potentially productive zones. Oil base or invert oil emulsion muds have been used with success in many deep salt dome wells where protective casing was not set. The operator gambles that the initial high cost of the mud system will be substantially less than setting protective casing.

If the well is successfully drilled without the need of protective casing, and no other serious problems such as lost circulation occur, the payout of costs attributable to drilling will be much more rapid and greater profits realized.

The uses and qualities of an oil mud are many. The primary disadvantages are high initial cost of the system and possible adverse effect on conventional mud analyses equipment. Formerly, electric logging devices were greatly influenced or rendered ineffective by non-conductive drilling fluids. This is no longer a problem due to the development of new logging equipment. In fact, most of the formation evaluation methods used routinely in water-base muds can be used with equal, or in some instances greater, effectiveness in oil muds. Rogers (1963) summarizes the application and qualities of oil-mud as follows (p. 564):

> Application of oil-base and invert emulsions revolve around their use for drilling in or recompleting wells subject to reduced productivity if completed with water-base muds; for drilling shales subject to sloughing in water-clay muds; and for drilling deep, hot wells having attendant difficulties and high costs for keeping water-clay muds in good condition. Their lack of solidification under high temperatures; the inertness of clays and shales in oil, as well as the noncontaminating effects of salt, gypsum or cement; their low fluid loss; and the higher viscosity of the fluid phase as compared to water, all give rise to beneficial properties which cannot yet be met by water-clay muds.

Well Logging

Well logging in salt mud (conductive) or oil mud (nonconductive) used to drill salt domes can be accomplished with satisfactory results, although some of the common formation evaluation devices and methods are complicated or adversely affected.

Salt muds affect the self potential (SP) and resistivity curves on electrical logs. The SP appearance is controlled by the relative salinity of the mud and formation water. With a highly conductive fluid in the borehole the SP tends to flatten out or may even reverse. The traces of normal resistivity and induction curves are depressed by conductive borehole fluids. The lateral trace, conversely, increases in value under the same conditions. Those curves which are most influenced by invasion of mud filtrate are most affected. The induction curve which measures further into the formation is least affected.

In nonconductive muds (oil base or invert emulsion) the SP and conventional resistivity curves (excluding the induction-conductivity curves) are totally ineffective. However, loss of these curves is no sacrifice, because other formation evaluation methods, designed to provide necessary qualitative and quantitative parameters, are often more effective due to the superior condition of the borehole (gaged hole, negligible invasion). For example, the acoustic-velocity, density, and neutron logs are adversely influenced by a washed-out, erratic borehole, common to wells drilled with aqueous muds. Table 9-1 summarizes the effectiveness of electrical logging devices in holes drilled with salt-water, oil-base, or invert emulsion muds.

By far the greatest number of salt dome wells were logged with the conventional electrical log which was of little use in formation evaluation if salt had been penetrated before the log was run. As different logging devices were developed it became the practice to run a combination of logs omitting normal and

TABLE 9-1

Effect of Mud System on Logging Devices

Log	Salt-Water	Oil or Invert Emulsion
SP	Poor	Useless
Normal Resist.	Depressed	Useless
Micro-Resist.	Poor-Qualitative Value Only	Useless
Induction/Dual Induction	Good	Good
Lateral/Laterolog	Good	Useless
Acoustic-Velocity	Good if gauged hole	Good
Density	Good if gauged hole	Good
Gamma Ray	Good	Good
Neutron	Good if gauged hole	Good
Nuclear Magnetism	Good	Good
Dipmeter	Good	Good

micro-resistivity curves after salt was drilled (Fig. 9-3). Focus resistivity curves were commonly used for bed definition after drilling through a salt section.

A complete suite of logs that might be run in a salt dome well drilled with salt-water mud (a lignosulphonate system) and the results obtained are as follows:

1. The induction or dual induction log for determination of true resistivity.

2. The density log for effective porosity. The ρB curve on the density log usually correlates with the SP log made in fresh-water muds so that it may be an aid to correlation between wells which penetrate salt and those that do not. A caliper log is always run simultaneously with the density log.

3. The gamma-ray log for lithology determination, correlation and bed determination. The gamma-ray can be run in cased hole if necessary.

4. Acoustic-velocity log for apparent porosity. This log is usually run simultaneously

with a gamma-ray. The combination of the acoustic-velocity and density logs may be used as a replacement for the SP but, more important, provides one of the best methods for true porosity determinations.

5. Dipmeter log for true bed thickness, geologic control and stratigraphic environmental analysis. A continuous plot of true dips recorded by the dipmeter may indicate the proximity to an overhang in a flank well. (Fig. 9-4). Subsequent wells may then be programmed with accuracy whether or not the flank well is commercially productive.

In the example shown in Fig. 9-4 the beds increase in dip to a maximum nearest the position of the overhang and then gradually decrease as the borehole moves farther from the salt stock. If the well in the example is a dry hole or has a defined water level in a producing sand, a later well could be carefully programmed with the dipmeter plot to penetrate the objective bed at a more optimum structural position.

Conventional mud logging can be carried out without difficulty in salt-water mud systems. Problems do arise, however, when using oil base or invert emulsions. Of the two oil systems, the invert emulsion is somewhat less a problem. The main difficulty is in the identification of true fluorescence in sample cuttings. The oils in the mud system may fluoresce, depending on their composition, and overshadow formation oil in the cuttings. Detergents have been used in washing the samples but only with limited success. Standard gas detection equipment (hot-wire and chromatography) may operate effectively in oil muds unless the filaments become oversaturated with the oil in the mud. If a background level can be controlled, any appreciable increase in gas will be indicated on the recording mechanism. In a few cases the heavy ends of formation gases (pentane, hexane, etc.) are detected in oil muds; however, this has occurred in very few cases.

Literature Cited

Cannan, G. E. and Sullins, R. S.: "Problems Encountered in Drilling Abnormal Pressure Formations," *Drilling & Production Practice 1946,* API (1947), N. Y., pp. 29-33; *Drilling* (June 1946), pp. 48-50; (abs.) *Oil Weekly* (May 20, 1946), p. 31.

Cook, W. H.: "Offshore Directional Drilling Practices Today and Tomorrow," *Preprint,* presented Chicago Chapter of AIME (November, 1957), Chicago, Illinois; presented Annual Meeting AIME (February, 1957), New Orleans.

Dickinson, George: "Geological Aspects of Abnormal Reservoir Pressures in Gulf Coast Louisiana," *Bull.,* AAPG (1953), v. 37, no. 2, pp. 410-432; *Proc.,* Third World Pet. Cong., (1951), The Hague, Holland.

Gray, Dr. George R., Allen, G. C. and Tschirley, N. K.: "Gulf Coast Drilling Mud Practices Demand Attention to Special Problems," *World Oil* (1956), v. 142, no. 7, pp. 155-160.

Halbouty, Michel T.: "Mud Treatment for Heaving Shales," *World Petroleum* (May, 1936), pp. 268-273.

Harper, Douglas C. and Ruhe, Robert W., Jr.: "Maps Predict Problem Formations," *Oil and Gas Jour.* (April 29, 1963).

Rogers, Walter F.: *Composition and Properties of Oil Well Drilling Fluids,* Gulf Publishing Co., (1963), Houston, Texas, 818 pp.

Stroud, B. K.: "Use of Barytes as a Mud-Laden Fluid," *Oil World* (June 5, 1925), p. 29.

Appendix

Eleven structure maps contoured on top of the salt and the corresponding field data sheets are presented in this appendix. The maps of domes located in Texas are from the author's own files; the maps of Louisiana salt domes were reprinted through the courtesy of the New Orleans Geological Society.

The eleven domes selected, which are listed alphabetically, are representative of the several hundred piercement domes in the Gulf region, as to size, shape or configuration in plan view, and production of hydrocarbons. Due to the abundance of salt datums for structural control, all of the domes illustrated in this Appendix are located in the Texas-Louisiana coastal basin. Individual and distinctive domal outlines influenced the selection of the domes. No other specific importance of the selection is implied.

The comparative sizes of the eleven domes are shown collectively at the end of the appendix.

NAME OF DOME: Avery Island   COUNTY/PARISH: Iberia, La.

LOCATION: Township 13 south, range 5 east, and township 13 south, range 6 east; 10 miles SW of New Iberia townsite.

TYPE OF DOME: Piercement, with pronounced overhang on northeast and north flanks.

MEANS OF DISCOVERY: Surface indications - mound, gas seeps, brine springs and salt (8' below surface).

DISCOVERY WELLS: Salt - found in hand-dug well 8' below surface, 1862; Humble Oil and Refining #2 Petit Anse, oil production, 1942.

SHALLOWEST CAP ENCOUNTERED:

SHALLOWEST SALT ENCOUNTERED: 8'

PRODUCTIVE ZONES: Miocene, Anahuac

LOCATION OF PRODUCTION: Flanks; also north-northeast flank under overhang.

AREAL EXTENT OF DOMAL MASS: 9000' x 7000' at 1000' salt level.

CUMULATIVE OIL PRODUCTION AS OF 1-1-65   53,054,000   BBLS.

REMARKS: Salt has been mined with interruptions since 1862. Salt previously had been obtained from brine springs in area (since 1812). Dome almost entirely surrounded by marshland.

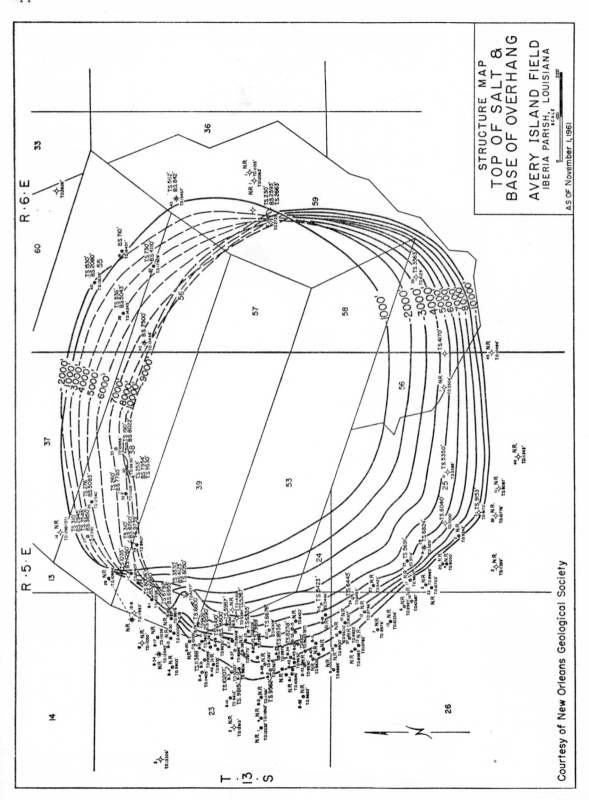

STRUCTURE MAP
TOP OF SALT &
BASE OF OVERHANG
AVERY ISLAND FIELD
IBERIA PARISH, LOUISIANA

AS OF November 1, 1961

Courtesy of New Orleans Geological Society

NAME OF DOME:_Boling_____COUNTY/PARISH:_Ft. Bend-Whart
                                                                                  Texas

LOCATION:_Approx. 7 miles SE Wharton townsite in Stephen F. Austin Survey, A-2._

TYPE OF DOME:_Piercement. No definite overhang drilled._____

MEANS OF DISCOVERY:_Surface indications - sulphur water in water wells, 1922.___

DISCOVERY WELLS:_Caprock, 1923; sulphur, 1927; Texas Co. #3 Taylor, oil_____

__production, 1925._____

SHALLOWEST CAP ENCOUNTERED:___383'_____

SHALLOWEST SALT ENCOUNTERED:__975'_____

PRODUCTIVE ZONES:__Miocene, Frio_____

LOCATION OF PRODUCTION:__Supercap, near flanks, far south flank._____

AREAL EXTENT OF DOMAL MASS:_Approx. 5-1/2 x 3-1/2 miles at 3000' domal_____

__material level; elongated NW-SE._____

CUMULATIVE OIL PRODUCTION AS OF 1-1-65_____31,292,000_____BBLS.

REMARKS:_Boling has the largest horizontal extent of any Texas salt dome. One of

__the very few Texas Coast thrust faults occurs on south flank. Frasch method

__sulphur mining initiated in 1929; production to 1964 - 57,279,327 tons. Boling has

__been the largest source for American sulphur production. Also known as Newgulf

Dome.

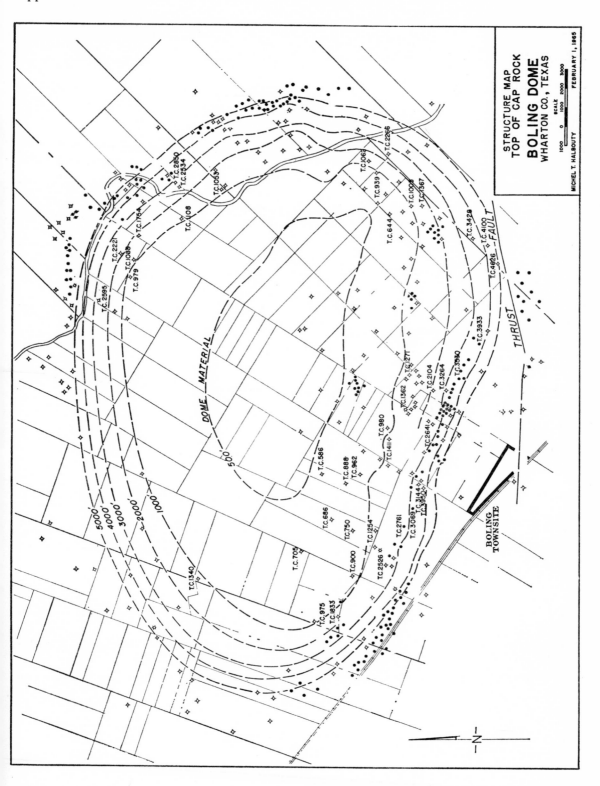

STRUCTURE MAP
TOP OF CAP ROCK
BOLING DOME
WHARTON CO., TEXAS

MICHEL T. HALBOUTY   FEBRUARY 1, 1965

NAME OF DOME:__Calcasieu Lake_____ ~~COUNTY~~/PARISH:__Cameron, La.__

LOCATION:__SE portion of Calcasieu Lake in township 13 south, range 9 west_____

TYPE OF DOME:__Piercement, with a pronounced overhang._____

MEANS OF DISCOVERY:__Refraction seismograph survey, 1927._____

DISCOVERY WELLS:__Louisiana Land & Expl. - Texas Co. #1 State, salt, 1928;____

____Hunt #2 SL 2402, oil production, 1958._____

SHALLOWEST CAP ENCOUNTERED:__1490'_____

SHALLOWEST SALT ENCOUNTERED:__2369'_____

PRODUCTIVE ZONES:__Miocene_____

LOCATION OF PRODUCTION:__East flank below overhang._____

AREAL EXTENT OF DOMAL MASS:__6500' x 5000' at 3000' salt leve; 12,500' x 11,500'__

____at 8000' salt. Roughly circular with slight elongation to north_____

CUMULATIVE OIL PRODUCTION AS OF 1-1-65_____39,000_____BBLS.

REMARKS:__27 dry tests drilled previous to discovery of production._____

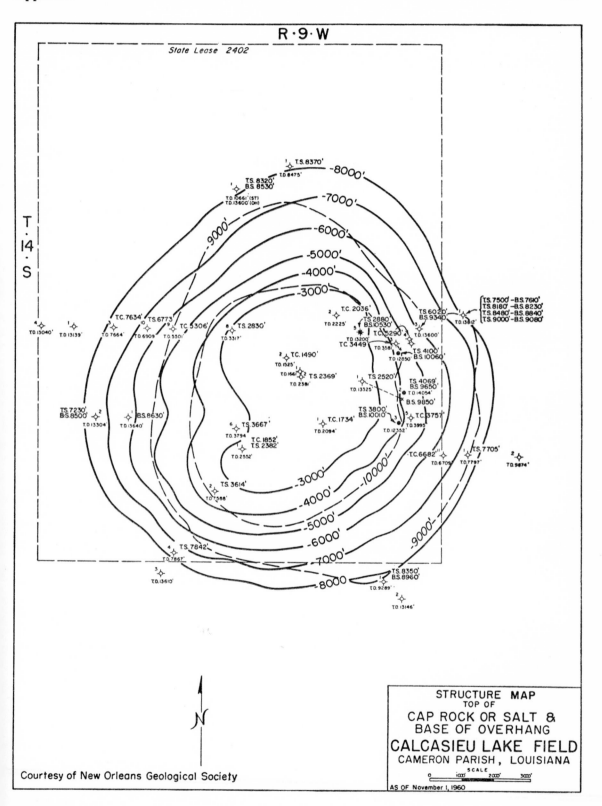

R·9·W

State Lease 2402

T·14·S

—8000'
—7000'
—6000'
—5000'
—4000'
—3000'
—9000'

T.S.8370'
T.D.8475'

T.S.8320'
B.S.8530'
T.D.1066'(ST)
T.D.13600'(OH)

T.C.7634'
T.S.6773'
T.C.5306'
T.S.2830'

T.D.13040'
T.D.13139'
T.D.7664'
T.D.6909'
T.D.5501'
T.D.3317'

T.C.2036'
T.D.2225'
T.S.2880'
B.S.10530'
T.C.5290'
T.D.13600'

T.S.602.0'
B.S.934.0'
T.D.13112'

T.S.7500'—B.S.7610'
T.S.8180'—B.S.8230'
T.S.8480'—B.S.8840'
T.S.9000'—B.S.9080'

T.C.3449'
T.D.13200'
T.D.3581'

T.S.4100'
B.S.10060'
T.D.12850'

T.C.1490'
T.D.1525'
T.D.1661'
T.S.2369'
T.D.2381'

T.S.2520'
T.D.13325'

T.S.4069'
B.S.9650'
T.D.14054'
B.S.9850'

T.S.7230'
B.S.8500'
T.D.13304'
B.S.8630'
T.D.13640'

T.S.3667'
T.D.3794'
T.C.1852'
T.S.2382'
T.D.2552'

T.C.1734'
T.D.2094'
T.S.3800'
B.S.10010'
T.D.12352'
T.C.3757'
T.D.3995'

T.C.6682'
T.D.6709'
T.S.7705'
T.D.7797'
T.D.9874'

T.S.3614'
T.D.7588'
—3000'
—4000'
—10000'

—5000'
—6000'

T.S.7842'
T.D.7867'
—7000'
—9000'

T.D.13610'
—8000'
T.S.8350'
B.S.8960'
T.D.9289'

T.D.13146'

N

Courtesy of New Orleans Geological Society

STRUCTURE MAP
TOP OF
CAP ROCK OR SALT &
BASE OF OVERHANG
CALCASIEU LAKE FIELD
CAMERON PARISH, LOUISIANA

SCALE
0   1000   2000'   3000'

AS OF November 1, 1960

NAME OF DOME:___Fausse Point_____ XXIXXX/PARISH: Iberia-St. Martin,
                                                            La.

LOCATION: Township 11 south, range 8 east, centers near Section 26.

TYPE OF DOME: Piercement

MEANS OF DISCOVERY: Refraction seismograph survey, 1926.

DISCOVERY WELLS: Union Sulphur #1 Shaw Fee, salt and oil production, 1926.

SHALLOWEST CAP ENCOUNTERED:_____792'

SHALLOWEST SALT ENCOUNTERED:_____823'

PRODUCTIVE ZONES: Miocene, Anahuac.

LOCATION OF PRODUCTION: Supercap, cap, flanks.

AREAL EXTENT OF DOMAL MASS: 14,000' x 6000' at 3000' salt level; 28,000'

___x 10,500' at 10,000' salt level.

CUMULATIVE OIL PRODUCTION AS OF 1-1-65____19,610,000_____BBLS.

REMARKS: Dome unusually elongated, in east-west direction.

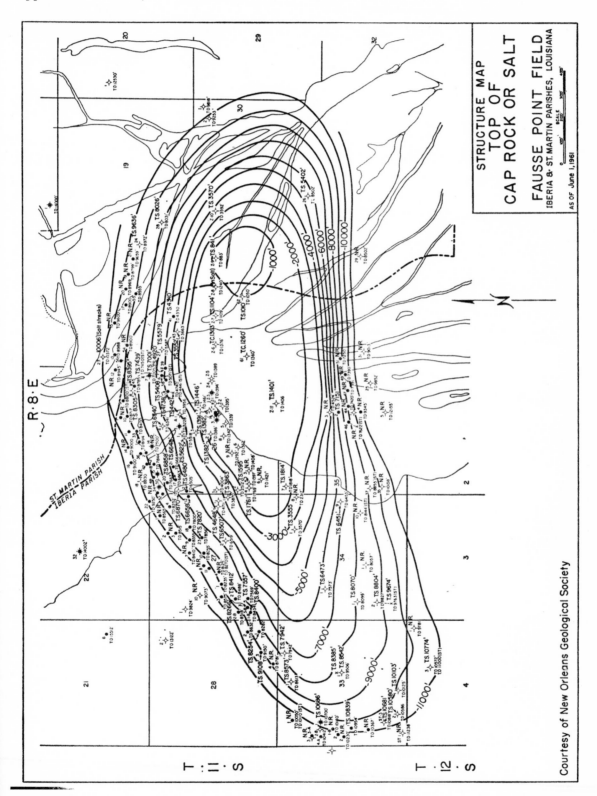

STRUCTURE MAP
TOP OF
CAP ROCK OR SALT

FAUSSE POINT FIELD
IBERIA & ST. MARTIN PARISHES, LOUISIANA

AS OF June 1, 1961

Courtesy of New Orleans Geological Society

NAME OF DOME:___Hockley_____COUNTY/~~PARISH~~: _Harris, Texas_

LOCATION:_3 miles due south Hockley townsite, approx. 31 miles northwest of____

___Houston. Centers on west line Thos. Goghill Survey, A-203._____

TYPE OF DOME:_Piercement, with overhang._____

MEANS OF DISCOVERY:_Surface indications - gas seeps, sour water, paraffin____

___dirt, 1905._____

DISCOVERY WELLS:___Patillo Higgins, caprock, 1906; first oil production, 1923;___

___Magnolia #2 Warren Ranch, first commercial oil production, 1945._____

SHALLOWEST CAP ENCOUNTERED:____76'_____

SHALLOWEST SALT ENCOUNTERED:_1010'_____

PRODUCTIVE ZONES:_Yegua; Frio and Miocene have provided very minor production.

LOCATION OF PRODUCTION:_Southwest and west flanks, beneath overhang. Minor___

___production on NW and NE flanks._____

AREAL EXTENT OF DOMAL MASS:__Approx. 16,000' x 11,000' at 3000' domal_____

___material level; dome elongated NW-SE._____

CUMULATIVE OIL PRODUCTION AS OF 1-1-65____654,000_____BBLS.

REMARKS:_No oil production in super dome area; salt has been mined since 1930.___

___Hockley is one of the large domes of the Gulf Coast. Sulphur shows have_____

___been found in cap._____

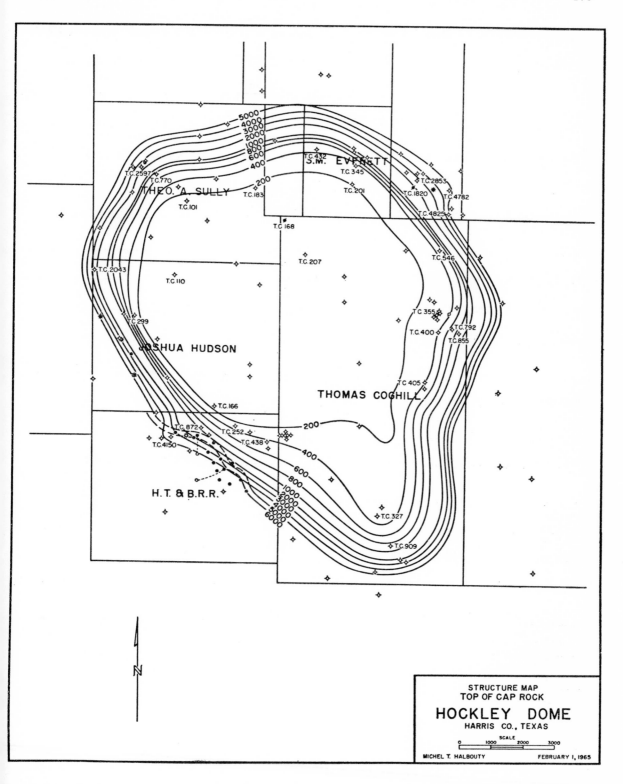

STRUCTURE MAP
TOP OF CAP ROCK

HOCKLEY DOME

HARRIS CO., TEXAS

SCALE

MICHEL T. HALBOUTY   FEBRUARY 1, 1965

NAME OF DOME: Jennings   COUNTY/PARISH: Acadia, La.

LOCATION: 4 miles NE Jennings, Louisiana in township 9 south, range 2 west.

TYPE OF DOME: Piercement; cap overhang indicated on SE flank.

MEANS OF DISCOVERY: Surface indications; mound, gas seeps, 1901.

DISCOVERY WELLS: Salt, 1926; Jennings Oil Co. #1 Clement, oil production, 1901.

SHALLOWEST CAP ENCOUNTERED: 2000'

SHALLOWEST SALT ENCOUNTERED: 2400'

PRODUCTIVE ZONES: Pliocene, Fleming, Anahuac, Frio.

LOCATION OF PRODUCTION: Supercap, flanks.

AREAL EXTENT OF DOMAL MASS: 7500' x 7000' at 7000' salt level; roughly circular.

CUMULATIVE OIL PRODUCTION AS OF 1-1-65   108,260,000   BBLS.

REMARKS: One of the prolific Gulf Coast domes. Bass and Benkenstein #2 Wilkens, early well, produced 1,000,000 bbls. oil in 82 days and a total of 2-1/2 million barrels during its productive life.

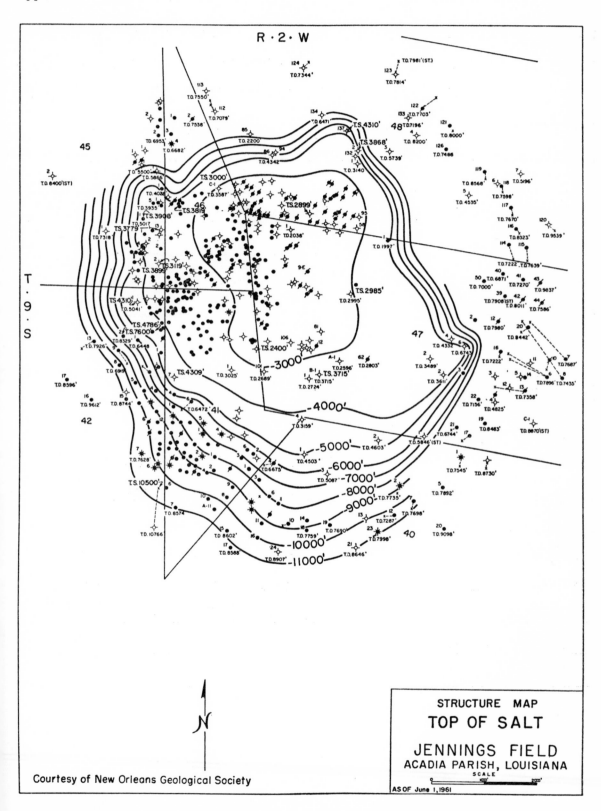

STRUCTURE MAP
TOP OF SALT
JENNINGS FIELD
ACADIA PARISH, LOUISIANA
SCALE
AS OF June 1, 1961

Courtesy of New Orleans Geological Society

NAME OF DOME: Lake Washington   ~~COUNTY~~/PARISH: Plaquemines, La

LOCATION: Townships 19 and 20 south, ranges 26 and 27 east, and township 21 south, range 26 east. Centers in Section 24, township 20 south, range 26 east.

TYPE OF DOME: Piercement.

MEANS OF DISCOVERY: Refraction seismograph survey, 1928.

DISCOVERY WELLS: Humble et al #1 Cockrell-Moran, salt, 1930; Humble et al #4 Cockrell-Moran, oil production, 1931.

SHALLOWEST CAP ENCOUNTERED: 1094'

SHALLOWEST SALT ENCOUNTERED: 1565'

PRODUCTIVE ZONES: Miocene

LOCATION OF PRODUCTION: Cap, flanks

AREAL EXTENT OF DOMAL MASS: 11,000' x 9,000' at 3000' salt level; elongated NE-SW. 30,000' x 25,000' at 10,000' salt level, elongated NW-SE.

CUMULATIVE OIL PRODUCTION AS OF 1-1-65   101,269,000   BBLS.

REMARKS: One of the largest domes in Gulf Coast. Surrounded by marshes. Has been a major producer of sulphur since 1933 - 27,085,701 tons to date. Dome also known as Grand Ecaille.

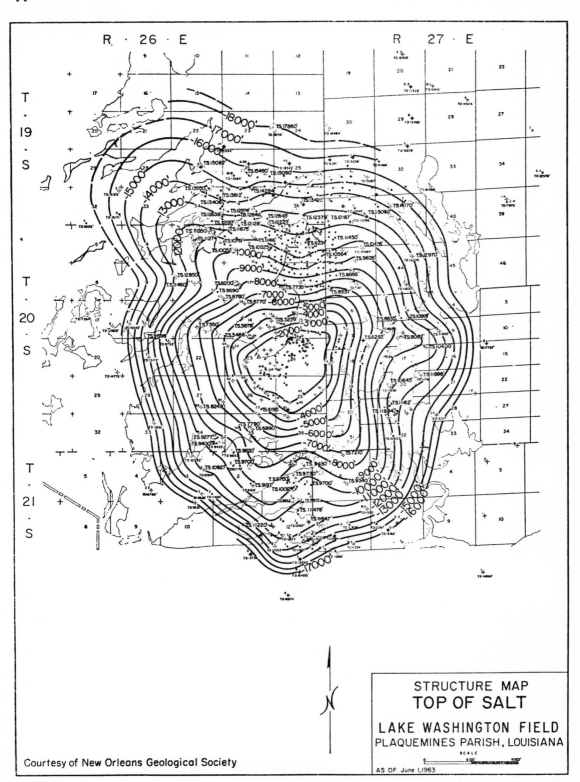

STRUCTURE MAP
TOP OF SALT

LAKE WASHINGTON FIELD
PLAQUEMINES PARISH, LOUISIANA

SCALE

AS OF June 1,1963

Courtesy of New Orleans Geological Society

NAME OF DOME:___Nash_____COUNTY/~~PARISH~~: Ft. Bend, Texas

LOCATION:_H. N. Cleveland Survey, A-150 and Thos. Allsberry Survey, A-2, on_

___south line of county._____

TYPE OF DOME:__Piercement. Cap overhang drilled on northeast flank._____

MEANS OF DISCOVERY:__Torsion balance, surface indications (sulphur waters),____

___1924._____

DISCOVERY WELLS:__Salt, 1924; Rycade Oil Co. #5 W. R. Nash, oil production, 1926.

SHALLOWEST CAP ENCOUNTERED:____620'_____

SHALLOWEST SALT ENCOUNTERED:___950'_____

PRODUCTIVE ZONES:__Miocene, Frio_____

LOCATION OF PRODUCTION:__Flanks._____

AREAL EXTENT OF DOMAL MASS:__16,000' x 14,000' at 5000' cap level; roughly_____

___circular, with slight elongation in a north-south direction._____

CUMULATIVE OIL PRODUCTION AS OF 1-1-65_____3,405,000_____BBLS.

REMARKS:__Most of production is from several lower Miocene sands between_____

___3500' - 5000'; small amount Frio production located on north flank. Some_____

___sulphur (153,115 tons) has been produced, but Frasch mining operations have___

___been closed since 1956._____

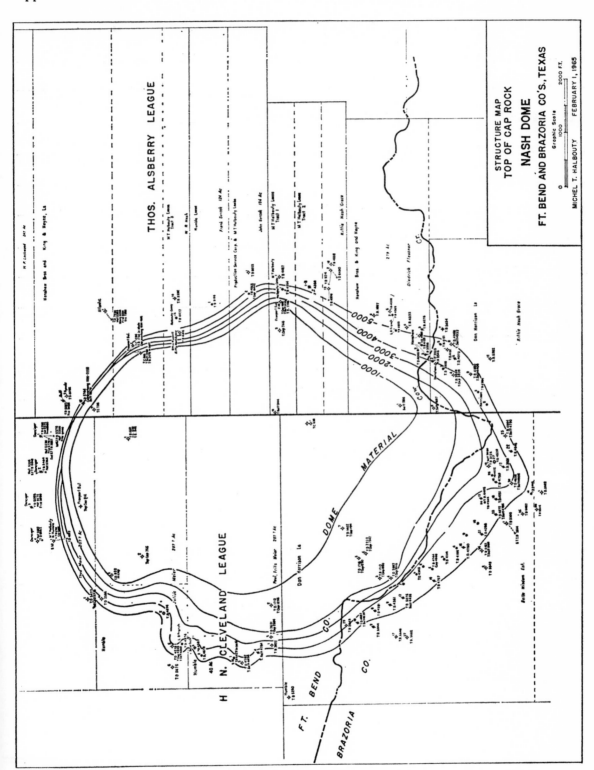

STRUCTURE MAP
TOP OF CAP ROCK
NASH DOME
FT. BEND AND BRAZORIA CO'S., TEXAS

Graphic Scale

MICHEL T. HALBOUTY   FEBRUARY 1, 1965

NAME OF DOME:__South Liberty_____COUNTY/PARISH:_Liberty, Texas

LOCATION:_Immediately south of Liberty townsite; centers near juncture of

__E. Munson, Wm. Duncan, M. G. White and David Minchey Surveys.

TYPE OF DOME:__Piercement; no overhang drilled.

MEANS OF DISCOVERY:__Surface indications - sulphur springs, gas and oil

__seeps, 1901.

DISCOVERY WELLS:_Sulphur Springs Oil Co. #2, caprock, 1905; Winfree Trustee

__#1 Pickett, oil production, 1925.

SHALLOWEST CAP ENCOUNTERED:_____275'

SHALLOWEST SALT ENCOUNTERED:_____480'

PRODUCTIVE ZONES:__Cook Mountain, Yegua, Frio.

LOCATION OF PRODUCTION:__Main production on northwest, west, southwest,

__northeast and east flanks.

AREAL EXTENT OF DOMAL MASS:_16,500' x 9000' at 3000' salt level; elongated

__northeast-southwest.

CUMULATIVE OIL PRODUCTION AS OF 1-1-65___68,632,000_____BBLS.

REMARKS:_Production controlled by sand pinch-outs, fault traps, and sand

__truncation by salt. Production steps outward with depth. Discovery of Yegua

__production on NE flank in 1947 initiated a surge of flank drilling on other domes

__which resulted in several important Yegua discoveries.

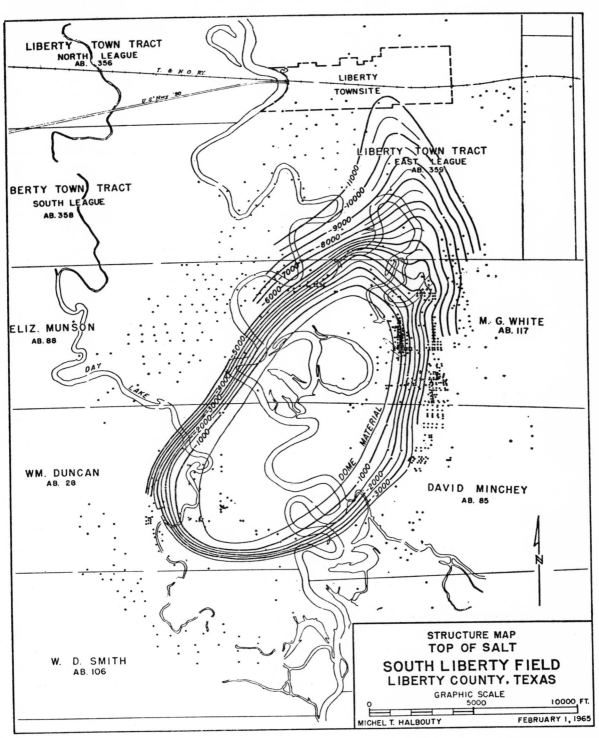

STRUCTURE MAP
TOP OF SALT
SOUTH LIBERTY FIELD
LIBERTY COUNTY, TEXAS
GRAPHIC SCALE
0   5000   10000 FT.
MICHEL T. HALBOUTY   FEBRUARY 1, 1965

NAME OF DOME: <u>South Timbalier Block 86</u>   ~~COUNTY/PARISH~~ Offshore Louisiana

LOCATION: <u>Centers in Block 86 and extends into Blocks 87 and 63,</u>
<u>South Timbalier offshore area.</u>

TYPE OF DOME: <u>Intermediate, with salt overhang.</u>

MEANS OF DISCOVERY: <u>Reflection seismic survey.</u>

DISCOVERY WELLS: <u>Sinclair A-3, OCS 0605, salt, 1957; Sinclair A-1, OCS 0605,</u>
<u>oil production, 1956.</u>

SHALLOWEST CAP ENCOUNTERED: _____

SHALLOWEST SALT ENCOUNTERED: <u>-4100'</u>

PRODUCTIVE ZONES: <u>Upper Miocene</u>

LOCATION OF PRODUCTION: <u>Southwest and northeast flanks.</u>

AREAL EXTENT OF DOMAL MASS: <u>7500' x 6500' at 5000' salt level; 13,000' x 7500'</u>
<u>at 10,000' salt level.</u>

CUMULATIVE OIL PRODUCTION AS OF 1-1-65 <u>1,582,000</u> BBLS.

REMARKS: <u>Dome apparently roughly circular at approx. 5000' level and elongated</u>
<u>NW-SE increasingly with depth.</u>

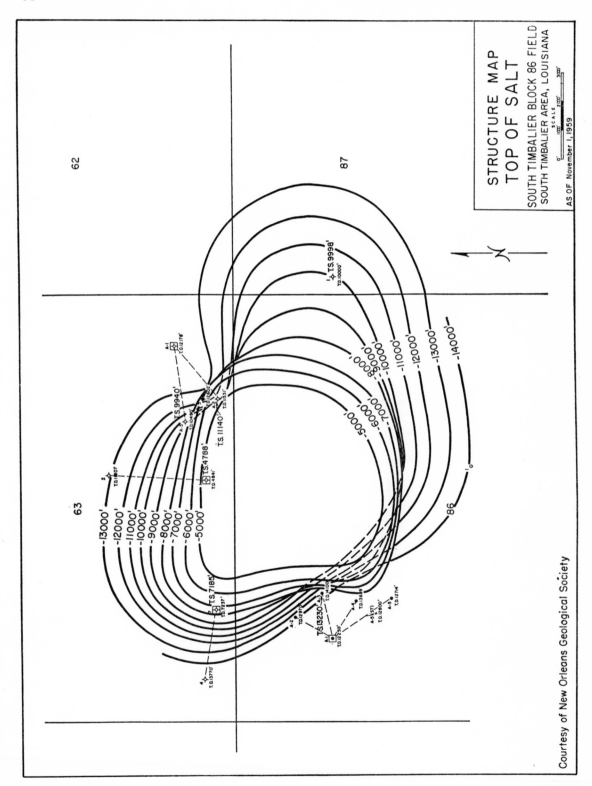

STRUCTURE MAP
TOP OF SALT

SOUTH TIMBALIER BLOCK 86 FIELD
SOUTH TIMBALIER AREA, LOUISIANA

AS OF November 1, 1959

Courtesy of New Orleans Geological Society

NAME OF DOME:___Spindletop_____COUNTY/PARISH:__Jefferson, Texas

LOCATION:__J. A. Veatch and P. Humphrey Leagues, approx. 2 miles south

___of Beaumont._____

TYPE OF DOME:__Piercement; suspected minor overhang._____

MEANS OF DISCOVERY:___Surface indications - mound, gas seeps, sour waters, 1901.

_____

DISCOVERY WELLS:___Lucas Gusher, caprock and oil production, Jan. 10, 1901;___

___Yount-Lee #2 McFaddin, flank oil production, 1926._____

SHALLOWEST CAP ENCOUNTERED:_____700'_____

SHALLOWEST SALT ENCOUNTERED:___1200'_____

PRODUCTIVE ZONES:___Caprock, Miocene, Frio_____

_____

LOCATION OF PRODUCTION:___Cap; near north, south and west flank; far north flank.

_____

AREAL EXTENT OF DOMAL MASS:___Approx. 6000' in diameter at 2000' salt level.___

___Configuration of dome is generally circular._____

_____

CUMULATIVE OIL PRODUCTION AS OF 1-1-65___142,974,000_____BBLS.

REMARKS:___Texas Gulf Sulphur initiated Frasch method production in 1952; sulphur___

___production through 1963 - 4,629,968 tons. Oil production of 140,000,000 bbls.

___has been obtained from an area of approximately 500 acres. First of the great

___oil fields._____

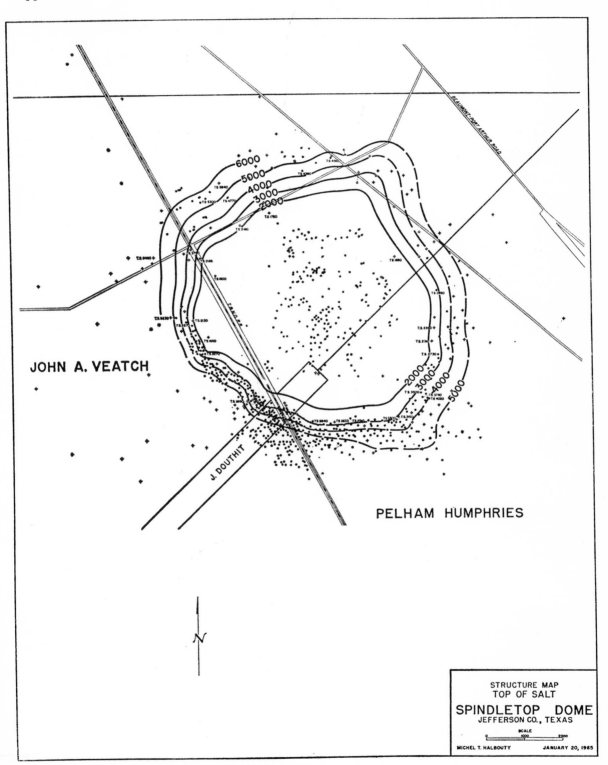

JOHN A. VEATCH

PELHAM HUMPHRIES

J. DOUTHIT

N

STRUCTURE MAP
TOP OF SALT

SPINDLETOP DOME
JEFFERSON CO., TEXAS

SCALE

MICHEL T. HALBOUTY   JANUARY 20, 1965

Comparative Sizes of Domes

All eleven domes have been drawn according to the same scale. All datums shown are subsea and the numbers of barrels represent cumulative production through 1964.

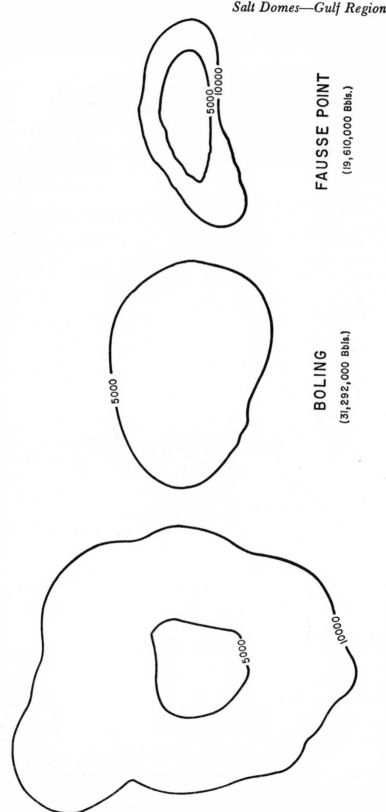

FAUSSE POINT

(19,610,000 Bbls.)

BOLING

(31,292,000 Bbls.)

LAKE WASHINGTON

(101,269,000 Bbls.)

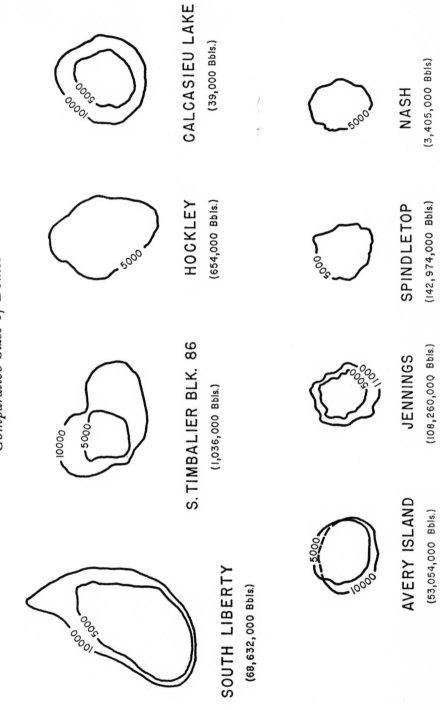

Comparative Sizes of Domes

SOUTH LIBERTY
(68,632,000 Bbls.)

S. TIMBALIER BLK. 86
(1,036,000 Bbls.)

HOCKLEY
(654,000 Bbls.)

CALCASIEU LAKE
(39,000 Bbls.)

AVERY ISLAND
(53,054,000 Bbls.)

JENNINGS
(108,260,000 Bbls.)

SPINDLETOP
(142,974,000 Bbls.)

NASH
(3,405,000 Bbls.)

Bibliographies and Salt Dome Indices

Introduction to Bibliographies and Salt Dome Indices

This is the most comprehensive and usable Index and Bibliography ever published on the known Salt Domes of the Gulf Region of the United States and Mexico. References used in this compilation include those most likely to be readily available to the reader.

Important Note: To insure the completeness of this bibliographic material, research work continued even after the publisher started setting type for the book, and continued until just prior to the actual printing. This additional material has been treated in the form of Addenda to the Bibliography Arranged According to Author, Bibliography Arranged According to Subject Matter, and Salt Dome Indices. These are found beginning on page 385.

To facilitate using this publication please note the following:

Bibliography Arranged According to Author

The name or names of authors of papers are listed alphabetically, followed by the name of the paper, the name of the publication in which it may be found, the date of the publication and, when possible, the exact placement of the paper in the publication.

In the case of co-authors, each author may be found listed first alphabetically. For example: Adams, Emmett R. and Davis, David C.: "Developments in Southeastern States in 1961," *Bull.,* AAPG (1962), v. 46, no. 6, pp. 953-958. This will appear twice in the Bibliography, once as written above and again as Davis, David C. and Adams, Emmett R. The reason for this is that in instances of co-authorship a person researching a subject may perhaps only remember the name of one of the authors.

Bibliography Arranged According to Subject Matter

In this portion of the reference section, the entire title of the paper is used, but the subject has been repositioned so that it appears as the first word in the title. For example, a paper written by M. I. Goldman is entitled "Origin of Anhydrite Cap Rock." This paper in the *Bibliography by Subject* is written "Anhydrite Cap Rock, Origin of."

In many instances one paper may appear in the *Bibliography by Subject* more than one time.

In the case of such a paper as "Aerial Photomosaic of Barbers Hill Area, Chambers County, Texas," the title actually has only one subject, but suggests another important subject matter. For the person doing research on "aerial photomosaics" the title appears in the *Bibliography by Subject* as written above. However, for the person researching "Barbers Hill," this paper appears again written as "Barbers Hill Area, Chambers County, Texas, Aerial Photomosaics of."

In the paper entitled "Frio and Anahuac Sediments in Louisiana," there are two subjects, "Frio" and "Anahuac," and still another subject matter, "Louisiana," which may be of prime importance to some readers. This paper, therefore, appears in the *Bibliography by Subject* three times written as "Anahuac and Frio Sediments in Louisiana," "Frio and Anahuac Sediments in Louisiana," and "Louisiana, Frio and Anauhuac Sediments in."

Of course, the *Bibliography by Subject* gives all of the other important reference data such as the author and where the paper may be found. A typical entry in the *Bibliography by Subject* is "Anse la Butte Dome, St. Martin Parish, Louisiana": Bates, F. W. and Wharton, J. B., Jr., *Bull.*, AAPG (1943), v. 27, no. 8, pp. 1123-1156.

The *Bibliography by Subject* is arranged alphabetically by subject, and numbered consecutively where possible. This number is the "reference number." Of prime importance is the fact that each individual paper has only one reference number even though it may appear in the *Bibliography by Subject* several

times. For this reason, the numerical sequence of the reference numbers will be broken in instances. As an example, the paper entitled "Frio and Anahuac Sediments in Louisiana" first occurs in the *Bibliography by Subject* as "Anahuac and Frio . . .," which is the seventh entry alphabetically. This paper's reference number is therefore 7. Number 7 will appear twice more in the *Bibliography by Subject* because of this paper's title being rearranged as "Frio and Anahuac . . ." and "Louisiana, Frio and Anahuac . . ." In instances such as this, the reference number will appear out of numerical sequence. The reference numbers will be used in conjunction with the Salt Dome Indices, and their use will be further explained in the next section.

Salt Dome Indices

This section includes *Salt Dome Indices* for Texas, Louisiana, Mississippi, Alabama and Mexico. Each Index is arranged alphabetically by the name of each salt dome. Under the name of each dome, there is an abbreviated list of publications such as EGP, (Early Geophysical Papers), which contain references to that particular dome (see *List of Abbreviations* which follows). Positioned to the left of each reference in the *Salt Dome Indices* is the reference number, which was previously discussed. For example, in the Index to Texas Salt Domes, the first dome listed is

Allen, Brazoria County—the first reference under Allen is

923. *Bull.*, v. 17, no. 10, p. 1206; *GC*, p. 263.

The reader may quickly determine whether or not this particular reference is of interest to him. Turning to the *Bibliography by Sub-*

ject and finding number 923, it will be noted that this is a paper written by D. C. Barton entitled "Surface Fracture System of South Texas." If the reader wishes to pursue this reference, he may find this specific reference to Allen dome in the *AAPG Bulletin,* volume 17, number 10, page 1206; or in the book *Gulf Coast Oil Fields,* on page 263.

You will notice that some of the reference numbers are followed by a small letter (the first of these are 6a and 6b on page 241). These references have no additional significance. They are merely late additions to the list after the initial references had already been numbered.

Abbreviations Used in Bibliography

BMIC	Bureau of Mines Information Circular
Bol.	Boletin de la Asociacion Mexicana de Geologos Petroleros
Bull.	Bulletin of The American Association of Petroleum Geologists
Chron. Hist.	The Chronological History of the Petroleum and Natural Gas Industries (James A. Clark, 1963)
EGP	Early Geophysical Papers
GAGC	Geology of the Atlantic and Gulf Coastal Province of North America (Grover E. Murray, 1961)

GAS	Geology of Natural Gas (AAPG, 1935)
GC	Gulf Coast Oil Fields (AAPG, 1936)
GCAGS	Gulf Coast Association of Geological Societies
GCH	Geophysical Case Histories
GSA	Geological Society of America
HGS	Houston Geological Society
JPT	Journal of Petroleum Technology
NOGS	Salt Domes of South Louisiana (New Orleans Geological Society, 1960, 1962, 1963)
OFNA	Oil Fields in North America (W. A. Ver Wiebe, 1949)
OGJ	Oil and Gas Journal
OW	Oil Weekly
Pet. Geol.	Petroleum Geology (John Wiley and Sons, 1951)
Pet. Inter.	Petroleo Interamericano
Proc.	Proceedings
PROB.	Problems of Petroleum Geology (AAPG, 1942)
SBP	Source Beds of Petroleum (AAPG, 1942)
SD	Geology of Salt Dome Oil Fields (AAPG, 1926)
SOS	Symposium on Salt (Northern Ohio Geological Society, Inc., 1963)
STR	Structure of Typical American Oil Fields (AAPG, 1929)
Trans.	Transactions
WO	World Oil
WP	World Petroleum

Bibliography Arranged According to Author

Adams, Emmett R. and Davis, David C.: "Developments in Southeastern States in 1961," *Bull.,* AAPG (1962), v. 46, no. 6, pp. 953-958.

Adams, G. I.: "Oil and Gas Fields of the Upper Cretaceous and Tertitary Formations of the West Gulf Coast," *Bull.,* USGS (1901), pp. 37-62.

Adams, J. E.: "Upper Permian Ochoa Series of Delaware Basin, West Texas and Southeastern New Mexico," *Bull.,* AAPG (1944), v. 28, no. 11, pp. 1598-1625.

Adams, J. E. and Rhodes, M. L.: "Dolomitization by Seepage Refluxion," *Bull.,* AAPG (1960), v. 44, no. 12, pp. 1912-1920.

Adkins, W. S., Plummer, F. B. and Sellards, E. H.: "The Geology of Texas; Volume 1, Stratigraphy," *Bull. 3232,* Tex. U. (1933), Bur. Econ. Geol., 1007 pp.

Albertson, M.: "Isostatic Adjustments on a Minor Scale, in Their Relation to Oil Domes," *Trans.,* AIME (1931), v. 65, pp. 418-420; (abs.) *Mining and Metallurgy,* no. 170, pp. 38-39.

Alexander, C. I.: "Concord Salt Dome, Anderson County, Texas," *Bull.,* AAPG (1944), v. 28, no. 10, pp. 1537-1538.

Alexander, C. I. and Burnett, T. J., Jr.: "Developments in East Texas in 1943," *Bull.,* AAPG (1944), v. 28, no. 6, pp. 841-852.

Alexander, C. W.: "Developments in Southeastern States in 1945," *Bull.,* AAPG (1946), v. 30, no. 6, pp. 1020-1050; (abs.) *Trans.,* AAPG-SEPM-SEG Jt. Ann. Mtg. (1946), Los Angeles, Calif., pp. 37-38.

Alexander, C. W., Morgan, C. L. and Norman, M. E.: "Developments in Southeastern States in 1944," *Bull.,* AAPG (1945), v. 29, no. 6, pp. 815-835.

Allen, Edwin R. and Shead, W. C.: "Is a Salt Dome's North Flank Its Best Prospect?" *World Oil* (1956), v. 142, no. 5, pp. 158-160.

Allen, G. G., Tschirley, N. K. and Gray, Dr. George R.: "Gulf Coast Drilling Mud Practices Demand Attention to Special Problems," *World Oil* (1956), v. 142, no. 7, pp. 155-160.

Allen, H. H.: "Development in Upper Gulf Coast District of Texas in 1950," *Bull.,* AAPG (1951), v. 35, no. 6, pp. 1322-1337.

Allen, W. E., Caillouet, H. J. and Stanley, L.: "Gravity Investigations in the Hockley Salt Dome, Harris County, Texas," *Geophysics* (1936), v. 20, no. 4, pp. 829-840.

Allen, W. H.: "Developments in Southeastern States in 1953," *Bull.,* AAPG (1954), v. 38, no. 6, pp. 1242-1251.

Allison, A. P. and Claypool, C. B.: "Developments in the Upper Gulf Coast of Texas in 1946," *Bull.,* AAPG (1947), v. 31, no. 6, pp. 1071-1077.

Allison, A. P., Beckelhymer, R. L., Benson, Don G., Hutchins, R. M., Jr., Lake, C. L., Lewis, Ray C., O'Bannon, P. H., Self, S. R. and Warner, C. A.: "Geology of Katy Field, Waller, Harris and Fort Bend Counties, Texas," *Bull.,* AAPG (1946), v. 30, no. 2, pp. 157-180.

Alvarez, Manuel, Jr.: "Tectonics of Mexico," *Bull.,* AAPG (1949), v. 33, no. 8, pp. 1319-1335; *Bol.,* Soc. Geol. Mex. (1949), Tomo 14.

Alvarez, Manuel, Jr.: "Sintesis Geologico de la Cuenca Salina del Istmo de Tehuantepec," *Bol.,* Asoc. Mex. Geol. Petrol. (1950), v. 2, no. 7, pp. 445-452.

Alvarez, M., Diaz, T., Imlay, R. W. and Cepeda, E.: "Stratigraphic Relations of Certain Jurassic Formations in Eastern Mexico," *Bull.,* AAPG (1948), v. 32, no. 9, pp. 1750-1761.

Ames, E. R.: "Southern Louisiana Domes Reviewed," *Oil and Gas Jour.* (1930), v. 28, no. 45, pp. 42, 159-160.

Ames, E. R.: "Present Activities Among Southern Louisiana Salt Domes," (abs.) *Pan Am. Geologist,* v. 53, no. 3, pp. 220-221.

Anderson, E. G.: "Correlation Problem—Minden Dome (Palentologic Interpretation)," *Guidebook,* 1960 Spring Field Trip, Shreveport Geol. Soc., pp. 27-28.

Andrau, E. W. K. and Deussen, Alexander: "Orange, Texas Oil Field," *Bull.,* AAPG (1936),

v. 20, no. 5, pp. 531-559; *Problems of Petroleum Geology,* AAPG (1934), pp. 880-908.

Andrews, Donald I.: "The Louann Salt and Its Relationship to Gulf Coast Salt Domes," *Trans.,* GCAGS (1960), v. 10, pp. 215-240.

Anonymous: "Oil and Sulphur Development in the Texas and Louisiana Gulf Coast Salt Dome Region," *Bull.* 1, Tex. Gulf Coast Scouts Assoc. and South La. Oil Scouts Assoc. (1930), 128 pp.

Anonymous: "Strategic Location of Wells in Flank Sands on Piercement-type Salt Domes," *Oil Weekly* (1942), v. 104, no. 10, pp. 17-20.

Anonymous: "Earth Cycling Operation (Louisiana Gas Field)," *Oil and Gas Jour.* (1945), v. 43, no. 45, pp. 65-88.

Applin, E. R. and Weinzierl, L. L. L.: "The Claiborne Formation on the Coastal Domes," *Jour. Paleontology* (1929), v. 3, pp. 384-410.

Applin, P. L.: "The Stratton Ridge Salt Dome, Brazoria County, Texas," *Bull.,* AAPG (1925), v. 9, no. 1, pp. 1-34; *Geology of Salt Dome Oil Fields, AAPG* (1926), pp. 644-677.

Arrhenius, Sv.: "Zur Physik der Salzlagerstatten," *Meddelanden fran K. Vetenskabsakademiens Nobelinstitut,* v. 2, no. 20.

Arrhenius, Sv. and Lachmann, R.: "Die Phys.-chem. Bedingungen Beider Bildungen der Salzlager und ihre Anwendung auf Geologische Probleme," *Geol. Rundshau,* v. 3, no. 139.

Atwater, Gordon: "The Geology of the Five Islands, Iberia and St Mary Parishes, Louisiana," *Trans.,* GCAGS, First Ann. Mtg. (Nov., 1951), New Orleans, La., p. 212.

Atwater, Gordon: "Geology and Petroleum Development of the Continental Shelf of the Gulf of Mexico," *Preprint,* Fifth World Pet. Cong.; *Trans.,* GCAGS (1959), v. 9, pp. 131-145.

Atwater, Gordon: "Highly Complex Dome Yields Many Secrets," *Oil and Gas Jour.* (1959), v. 57, no. 31, pp. 250-252.

Atwater, Gordon and Forman, McLain J.: "Nature and Growth of Southern Louisiana Salt Domes and Its Effect on Petroleum Accumulation," *Bull.,* AAPG (1959), v. 43, no. 11, pp. 2592-2622; (abs.) *Trans.,* GCAGS (1958), v. 8, pp. 20-21.

Aulick, Burton, Hopkins, H. F., Saye, Frank and Hower, Wayne, "Improved Production by Chemical Treatment in Gulf Coast Areas," *Jour. of Pet. Tech.* (1952), v. 4, no. 9, pp. 13-16.

Aymé, J. M.: "The Senegal Salt Basin," *Salt*

Basins Around Africa (1965), The Institute of Petroleum, London, pp. 83-90.

Babisak, Julius and Pyle, G. T.: "Structure of the Woodlawn Field, Jefferson Davis Parish, Louisiana," *Trans.,* GCAGS (1951), pp. 200-210.

Baird, James A.: "New Life for an Old Dome," *Oil and Gas Jour.* (1962), v. 60, no. 40, pp. 113-114.

Baker, C. L. and Sellards, E. H.: "The Geology of Texas; Volume 2, Structural and Economic Geology," *Bull. 3401,* Tex. U. (1934), Bur. Econ. Geol., 884 pp.

Balk, Robert: "Structure Elements of Domes," *Bull.,* AAPG (1936), v. 20, no. 1, pp. 51-67; (abs.) v. 19, no. 1, p. 136; *World Pet.,* v. 7, no. 3, p. 150.

Balk, Robert: "Salt Dome Structure (Preliminary Notice)," *Bull.,* AAPG (1947), v. 31, no. 7, pp. 1295-1299.

Balk, Robert: "Structure of Grand Saline Salt Dome, Van Zandt County, Texas," *Bull.,* AAPG (1949), v. 33, no. 11, pp. 1791-1829.

Balk, Robert: "Salt Structure of Jefferson Island Salt Dome, Iberia and Vermilion Parishes, Louisiana," *Bull.,* AAPG (1953), v. 37, no. 11, pp. 2455-2474.

Ballard, Eva O.: "Limestone in the Heterostegina Zone (Oligocene-Miocene) on Damon Mound Salt Dome, Brazoria County, Texas," *Trans.,* GCAGS (1961), v. 11, pp. 213-223.

Ballard, J. L.: "Developments in Upper Gulf Coast of Texas in 1949," *Bull.,* AAPG (1950), v. 34, no. 6, pp. 1179-1190.

Barber, Thomas D. and Halbouty, Michel T.: "Port Acres and Port Arthur Fields, Jefferson County, Texas," *Trans.,* GCAGS (1961), v. 11, pp. 225-234.

Barksdale, Jelks: "Possible Salt Deposits in the Vicinity of the Jackson Fault, Alabama," *Circ. 10,* Ala. Geol. Svy. (1929), 22 pp.

Barnes, Kenneth B. and McCaslin, Leigh S., Jr.: "Spectacular Gulf of Mexico Discovery," *Oil and Gas Jour.* (1948), v. 46, no. 46, pp. 96-99, 113-114.

Barnes, V. E.: "Metallic Minerals in Caprock, Winnfield Salt Dome, Louisiana," *Am. Mineralogist* (1933), v. 18, pp. 335-340.

Barret, Wm. M.: "Relation of Geophysics to Salt Dome Structure (with discussion by J. B. Eby and R. P. Clark)," *Bull.,* AAPG (1935), v. 19, no. 7, pp. 1069-1073.

Barret, Wm. M.: "Note on the Radio Transmission Demonstration at Grand Saline, Texas," *Geophysics* (1952), v. 17, no. 3, pp. 544-549.

Barrington, Jonathan and Kerr, P. F.: "Clays of Deep Shale Zone, Caillou Island, Louisiana," *Bull.*, AAPG (1961), v. 45, no. 10, pp. 1697-1712.

Barton, D. C.: "The Palangana Salt Dome, Duval County, Texas," *Econ. Geol.* (1920), v. 6, pp. 497-510.

Barton, D. C.: "The West Columbia Oil Field, Brazoria County, Texas," *Bull.*, AAPG (1921), v. 5, no. 2, pp. 212-251.

Barton, D. C.: "Occurrence of Gypsum in Gulf Coast Salt Domes," *Econ. Geol.* (1922), v. 17, no. 2, pp. 141-143.

Barton, D. C.: "Salt Dome Sulphur Deposits of Texas Gulf Coast," *Pan Am. Geologist* (1925), v. 44, no. 1, pp. 59-60.

Barton, D. C.: "Pine Prairie Salt Dome," *Bull.*, AAPG (1925), v. 9, no. 4, pp. 738-755; *Geology of Salt Dome Oil Fields*, AAPG (1926), pp. 419-436.

Barton, D. C.: "The American Salt Dome Problems in the Light of the Rumanian and German Salt Domes," *Bull.*, AAPG (1925), v. 9, no. 9, pp. 1227-1268; *Geology of Salt Dome Oil Fields*, AAPG (1926), pp. 167-208.

Barton, D. C.: "The Salt Domes of South Texas," *Bull.*, AAPG (1925), v. 9, no. 3, pp. 536-589; *Geology of Salt Dome Oil Fields*, AAPG (1926), pp. 718-771.

Barton, D. C.: (Discussion) "Moss Bluff Salt Dome Discovery," *Bull.*, AAPG (1927), v. 11, no. 3, p. 308.

Barton, D. C.: "The Economic Importance of Salt Domes," *Bull. 2801*, Tex. U. (1928), pp. 7-53.

Barton, D. C.: "The Eotvos Torsion Balance Method of Mapping Geologic Structure," *Tech. Pub. 50*, AIME (1928), 51 pp; *Trans.*, v. 81, pp. 416-479; (abs.) *Mining and Metallurgy*, v. 9, no. 254, p. 83.

Barton, D. C.: "Torsion Balance Survey of Esperson Salt Dome, Liberty County Texas," *Bull.*, AAPG (1930), v. 14, no. 9, pp. 1129-1143.

Barton, D. C.: "Petrographic Study of Salt Dome Cap Rock," *Bull.*, AAPG (1930), v. 14, no. 12, pp. 1573-1574.

Barton, D. C.: "Torsion Balance Survey at Esperson," *Oil and Gas Jour.* (1930), v. 28, no. 46, pp. 38, 141.

Barton, D. C.: "Geophysical Prospecting for Petroleum on Gulf Coast," *Oil and Gas Jour.* (1930), v. 28, no. 50, pp. 70, 142-143.

Barton, D. C.: "Belle Isle Torsion Balance Survey, St. Mary Parish, Louisiana," *Bull.*, AAPG (1931), v. 15, no. 11, pp. 1335-1350; *Trans.*, Soc. Pet. Geophys. (1931), v. 1, pp. 29-44; *Early Geophysical Papers*, SEG (1947), pp. 53-68.

Barton, D. C.: "Effect of Salt Domes on the Accumulation of Petroleum," *Bull.*, AAPG (1931), v. 15, no. 1, pp. 61-66.

Barton, D. C.: "Iberian Structural Axis, Louisiana," *Jour. Geol.* (1932), v. 41, no. 3, pp. 225-242; (abs.) *Bull.*, GSA, v. 43, p. 248.

Barton, D. C.: "Torsion Balance Surveys in Southwest Louisiana and Southeast Texas," *Trans.*, Am. Geophys. Union, 13th Ann. Mtg. (1932), pp. 40-42.

Barton, D. C.: "Mechanics of Formation of Salt Domes with Special Reference to Gulf Coast Salt Domes of Texas and Louisiana," *Bull.*, AAPG (1933), v. 17, no. 9, pp. 1025-1083; *Gulf Coast Oil Fields*, AAPG (1936), pp. 20-78.

Barton, D. C.: "Surface Fracture System of South Texas," *Bull.*, AAPG (1933), v. 17, no. 10, pp. 1194-1212; *Gulf Coast Oil Fields*, AAPG (1936), pp. 251-269.

Barton, D. C.: "Foreword to Variation in Physical Properties," *Problems of Petroleum Geology*, AAPG (1934), pp. 97-99.

Barton, D. C.: "Natural History of the Gulf Coast Crude Oil," *Problems of Petroleum Geology*, AAPG (1934), pp. 109-156.

Barton, D. C.: "Prediction of Overhang at Barbers Hill, Chambers County, Texas; A Study in Quantitative Calculations from Torsion Balance Data," *Bull.*, AAPG (1935), v. 19, no. 1, pp. 25-36; *Trans.*, Soc. Pet. Geophy. (1935), v. 5, pp. 25-36; *Early Geophysical Papers*, SEG (1947), pp. 685-696.

Barton, D. C.: "Variation and Migration of Crude Oil at Spindletop, Jefferson County, Texas;" *Bull.*, AAPG (1935) v. 19, no. 5, pp. 618-643: *Gulf Coast Oil Fields*, AAPG (1936), pp. 309-334.

Barton, D. C.: "Belle Isle Salt Dome, St. Mary Parish, Louisiana," *Bull.*, AAPG (1935), v. 19, no. 5, pp. 644-650; *Gulf Coast Oil Fields*, AAPG (1936), pp. 1033-1039; *Trans.*, SEG, v. 1, p. 29.

Barton, D. C.: "Current Geophysical Activity in Louisiana and Texas," *Trans.*, Am. Geophys. Union, 17th Ann. Mtg. (1936), pt. 1, pp. 76-77; *Earthquake Notes*, no. 8, p. 76.

Barton, D. C.: "Late Recent History of Cote Blanche Salt Dome, St. Mary Parish, Louisiana," *Bull.*, AAPG (1936), v. 20, no. 2, pp. 179-185;

Gulf Coast Oil Fields, AAPG (1936), pp. 1026-1032; (abs.) *World Pet.,* v. 7, p. 278.

Barton, D. C.: "Reading the Aerial Photomosaic of Barbers Hill Area, Chambers County, Texas," *Gulf Coast Oil Fields,* AAPG (1936), pp. 15-22.

Barton, D. C.: "Evolution of Gulf Coast Crude Oil," *Bull.,* AAPG (1937), v. 21, no. 7, pp. 914-946.

Barton, D. C.: "Gravity Anomalies of Nash and Damon Mounds, Fort Bend and Brazoria Counties, Texas," *Tech. Pub. 1760,* AIME (1944); *Jour. of Pet. Tech.* (1944), v. 7, no. 6, pp. 2-9; *Geophysical Case Histories,* SEG (1948), v. 1, pp. 35-42.

Barton, D. C.: "Gravity Minimum at Tepetate on Very Deep Salt Dome, Acadia Parish, Louisiana," *Geophysical Case Histories,* SEG (1948), v. 1, pp. 175-183; *Tech. Pub. 1760,* AIME; *Pet. Tech.,* AIME (1944), v. 7, no. 6, pp. 15-22.

Barton, D. C.: "Quantitative Calculations of Geologic Structure from Gravimetric Data," *Geophysical Case Histories,* SEG (1948), v. 1, pp. 251-280; *Tech. Pub. 1760,* AIME; *Pet. Tech.* (1944), v. 7, no. 6, pp. 22-49.

Barton, D. C. and Goodrich, R. H.: "The Jennings Oil Field, Acadia Parish, Louisiana," *Bull.,* AAPG (1926), v. 10, no. 1, pp. 72-92; *Geology of Salt Dome Oil Fields,* AAPG (1926), pp. 398-418.

Barton, D. C. and Hickey, Maude: "The Continental Margin at Texas-Louisiana Gulf Coast," *Trans.,* Am. Geophys. Union, 14th Ann. Mtg. (1933), pp. 16-20.

Barton, D. C. and Mason, S. L.: "Further Notes on Barite Pisolites from the Batson and Saratoga Oil Fields," *Bull.,* AAPG (1925), v. 9, no. 9 pp. 1294-1295.

Barton, D. C. and Paxson, R. B.: "The Spindletop Salt Dome and Oil Field, Jefferson County, Texas," *Bull.,* AAPG (1925), v. 9, no. 3, pp. 594-612; *Geology of Salt Dome Oil Fields,* AAPG (1926), pp. 478-496.

Barton, D. C. and Sawtelle, George (ed.): *Gulf Coast Oil Fields,* American Association of Petroleum Geologists (1936), Tulsa, Oklahoma, 1070 pp.

Barton, D. C., Ritz, C. H. and Hickey, Maude: "Gulf Coast Geosyncline," *Bull.,* AAPG (1933), v. 17, no. 12, pp. 1446-1458; *Gulf Coast Oil Fields,* AAPG (1936), pp. 192-204, (abs.) *Pan. Am. Geologist,* v. 59, p. 230.

Bastin, Edson S.: "The Problem of the Natural Reduction of Sulfates," *Bull.,* AAPG (1926), v. 10, no. 12, pp. 1270-1299.

Basurto Garcia Jesus, and Islas Leal, Juventino: "El Metodo Sismologico de Refraccion en la Cuenca Salina del Istmo," *Bol. Asoc. Mex. Geol. Petrol.* (1950), v. 2, no. 7, pp. 461-472.

Bateman, Alan M.: *Economic Mineral Deposits,* 2nd Edition, Wiley and Sons (1950), New York, N. Y.

Bates, F. W. and Bornhauser, Max: "Geology of Tepetate Oil Field, Acadia Parish, Louisiana," *Bull.,* AAPG (1940), v. 22, no. 3, pp. 285-305.

Bates, F. W. and Wharton, J. B., Jr.: "Anse La Butte Dome, St. Martin Parish, Louisiana," *Bull.,* AAPG (1943), v. 27, no. 8, pp. 1123-1156.

Bates, F. W. and Wharton, J. B., Jr.: "Developments in Louisiana Gulf Coast in 1945," *Bull.,* AAPG (1946), v. 30, no. 6, pp. 999-1006.

Bates, F. W., Copeland, R. R., Jr. and Dixon, K. P.: "Geology of Avery Island Salt Dome, Iberia Parish, Louisiana," *Bull.,* AAPG (1959), v. 43, no. 5, pp. 944-957.

Battan, F. P. and Koonce, G. K.: "Developments in East Texas in 1958," *Bull.,* AAPG (1959), v. 43, no. 6, pp. 1293-1303.

Battle, J. C. and Judson, Sidney A.: "Special Methods Required to Drill Through Overhanging Cap Rock and Salt," *Oil Weekly* (1933), v. 69, no. 1, pp 59-60, 62.

Bauernschmidt, A. J., Jr.: "Sulphur Dome, Calcasieu Parish, Louisiana," *Bull.,* AAPG (1930), v. 14, no. 8, pp. 1079-1086.

Bauernschmidt, A. J., Jr.: "East Hackberry Salt Dome, Cameron Parish, Louisiana," *Bull.,* AAPG (1931), v. 15, no. 3, pp. 247-256.

Bays, Carl A.: "Use of Salt Solution Cavities for Underground Storage," *Symposium on Salt,* Northern Ohio Geol. Soc., Inc. (1963), pp. 564-578.

Beautelspacher, S. R. and Del Castillo, G. L.: *Levantamiento Sismologico de Refraccion en el Area de Chinameca, Ver.,* Del Castillo, G. L. and Beutelspacher, S. R., Inedito, Archivo Consejo de Recursos Naturales no Renovables (1961).

Beckelhymer, R. L.: "New Development in Orange Field, Orange County, Texas," *Bull.,* AAPG (1939), v. 23, no. 4, pp. 602-603.

Beckelhymer, R. L.: "Stratigraphy of Waller and Harris Counties, Texas," *Bull.,* AAPG (1946), v. 30, no. 1, 52-62.

Beckelhymer, R. L., Benson, Don G., Hutchins, R. M., Jr., Lake, C. L., Lewis, Ray C., O'Bannon,

P. H., Self, S. R., Warner, C. A., and Allison, A. P.: "Geology of Katy Field, Waller, Harris and Fort Bend Counties, Texas," *Bull., AAPG* (1946), v. 30, no. 2, pp. 157-180.

Bediz, P. I.: "Salt Core Structures and Their Importance in Petroleum Geology," *Mines Mag.* (1942), v. 32, no. 5, pp. 215-217, 255, 265; no. 6, pp. 287-289.

Behrman, R. G., Jr.: "Thompson Field, Fort Bend County, Texas," *Guidebook,* AAPG-SEPM-SEG Jt. Ann. Mtg., (March, 1953), Houston, Texas, pp. 157-160.

Beilharz, C. F. and Davis, D. M.: "Developments in Upper Gulf Coast of Texas in 1945," *Bull., AAPG* (1946), v. 30, no. 6, pp. 991-998.

Belchic, Harriet Cameron: "The Winnfield Salt Dome, Winn Parish, Louisiana," *Guidebook,* 1960 Spring Field Trip, Shreveport Geol. Soc., pp. 29-47.

Bell, J. S., Wendlandt, E. A. and Shelby, T. H., Jr.: "Hawkins Field, Wood County, Texas," *Bull., AAPG* (1946), v. 30, no. 6, pp. 1830-1856.

Bell, Olin G.: "Friendswood Field, Harris County, Texas," *Bull., AAPG* (1938), v. 22, no. 11, pp. 1602-1603.

Belmonte, Y., Hirtz, P. and Wenger, R.: "The Salt Basins of the Gabon and the Congo (Brazzaville): A Tentative Paleogeographic Interpretation," *Salt Basins Around Africa,* The Institute of Petroleum (1965), London, pp. 55-78.

Belt, B. C.: "Chapeno Salt Dome, Tamaulipas, Mexico," *Bull., AAPG* (1925), v. 9, no. 1, pp. 134-135; *Geology of Salt Dome Oil Fields,* AAPG (1926), pp. 772-773.

Benavides, G. Luis: "Notas Sobre la Geologia Petrolera de Mexico," Simposium, *Sobre Yacimientos de Petroleo y Gas,* Tomo III, America del Norte, 20 Congreso Geologico Internacional, Mexico, 1956.

Benson, Don G., Hutchins, R. M., Jr., Lake, C. L., Lewis, Ray C., O'Bannnon, P. H., Self, S. R., Warner, C. A., Allison, A. P. and Beckelhymer, R. L.: "Geology of Katy Field, Waller, Harris and Fort Bend Counties, Texas," *Bull., AAPG* (1946), v. 30, no. 2, pp. 157-180.

Bernatchez, Gerry: "A Neglected Objective," *World Oil* (1957), v. 144, no. 7, pp. 179-181.

Bersticker, A. C. (ed.): *Symposium on Salt,* Northern Ohio Geol. Soc., Inc. (1963), Cleveland, Ohio, 661 pp.

Beu, R. D. and Waters, K. M.: "Developments in Louisiana Gulf Coast in 1956," *Bull., AAPG* (1957), v. 41, no. 6, 1190-1200.

Bevier, G. M.: "The Damon Mound Oil Field, Texas," *Bull., AAPG* (1925), v. 9, no. 3, pp. 505-535; *Geology of Salt Dome Oil Fields,* AAPG (1926), pp. 613-643.

Bevier, G. M.: "The Barbers Hill Field, Chambers County, Texas," *Bull., AAPG* (1925), v. 9, no. 6, pp. 958-973; *Geology of Salt Dome Oil Fields,* AAPG (1926), pp. 530-545.

Bianchi, J. C., Jr., Briggs, K. S. and Miller, C. D.: "Developments in South Texas in 1952," *Bull., AAPG* (1953), v. 37, no. 6, pp. 1405-1415.

Bianchi, J. C., Jr., Janosky, R. A. and Grayson, R. W.: "Developments in South Texas in 1953," *Bull., AAPG* (1954), v. 38, no. 6, pp. 1184-1195.

Bignell, L. G. E.: "Wild Gas Well, Rice Land and Heavy Rains Test Man's Ingenuity in a Struggle for Control," *Oil and Gas Jour.* (1933), v. 32, no. 13, p. 12.

Bignell, L. G. E.: "Fourth Well Drilled on Coastal Louisiana Salt Dome Finds Oil," *Oil and Gas Jour.* (1937), v. 35, no. 38, pp. 17-18.

Bignell, L. G. E.: "Geological Structures," *Oil and Gas Jour.* (1938), v. 37, no. 20, pp. 60, 62.

Billings, M. P.: *Structural Geology,* Second Edition, Prentice-Hall (1954), New York, 514 pp.

Blanpied, B. W.: "Tabulation of North Louisiana Salt Domes," *Guidebook,* 1960 Spring Field Trip, Shreveport Geol. Soc., pp. 57-60.

Blanpied, B. W. and Hazzard, R. T.: "Developments in North Louisiana and South Arkansas in 1941," *Bull., AAPG* (1942), v. 26, no. 6, pp. 1250-1276.

Blanpied, B. W. and Hazzard, R. T.: "Interesting Wildcat Wells Drilled in North Louisiana in 1942," *Bull., AAPG* (1944), v. 28, no. 4, pp. 554-561.

Blanpied, B. W. and Hazzard, R. T.: "Salt Dome Discoveries in North Louisiana in 1942," *Bull., AAPG* (1944), v. 28, no. 4, pp. 561-562.

Blanpied, B. W., Spooner, W. C. and Hazzard, R. T.: "Notes on Correlations of the Cretaceous of East Texas, South Arkansas, North Louisiana, Mississippi, and Alabama," *1945 Ref. Rept.,* Shreveport Geol. Soc. (1947), v. 2, pp. 472-481.

Blanpied, B. W., Hazzard, R. T. and Spooner, W. C.: "Notes on the Stratigraphy of Formations Which Underlie the Smackover Limestone in South Arkansas, Northeast Texas, and North Louisiana," *1945 Ref. Rept.*, Shreveport Geol. Soc. (1947), v. 2, pp. 483-503.

Blanton, S. A. and Champion, W. L.: "Developments in Arkansas-North Louisiana in 1958," *Bull.*, AAPG (1959), v. 43, no. 6, pp. 1322-1330.

Blanton, Sankey L. and Duschatko, R. W.: "Developments in Arkansas and North Louisiana in 1959," *Bull.*, AAPG (1960), v. 44, no. 6, pp. 834-841.

Bleakley, W. B.: "New Tools, New Completion Methods Salvage an Old Oil Field," *Oil and Gas Jour.* (1962), v. 60, no. 24, pp. 140-141.

Boissonas, Eric and Leonardon, E. G.: "Geophysical Exploration by Telluric Currents, with Special Reference to a Survey of the Haynesville Salt Dome, Wood County, Texas," *Geophysics* (1948), v. 13, no. 3, pp. 387-403.

Bolton, H. C.: "Notes on the Great Salt Deposits of Petite Anse, Louisiana," *Trans.*, New York Acad. Sci. (1888), v. 7, pp. 122-127; *Sci. Am. Supp.*, v. 26, pp. 10,475-10,476.

Born, W. T.: (review) "Model Studies of Salt Dome Tectonics by A. N. McDowell and T. J. Parker." *Geophysics* (1955), v. 21, no. 4, p. 1121.

Bornhauser, Max: "Gulf Coast Tectonics," *Bull.*, AAPG (1958), v. 42, no. 2, pp. 339-370.

Bornhauser, Max and Bates, F. W.: "Geology of Tepetate Oil Field, Acadia Parish, Louisiana," *Bull.*, AAPG (1940), v. 22, no. 3, pp. 285-305.

Bornhauser, Max, and Marshall, L. R.: "Three New Interior Salt Domes in Northeast Louisiana," *Bull.*, AAPG (1940), v. 24, no. 3, pp. 483-486.

Bose, E.: "Resena Acerca de la Geologia de Chiapas y Tabasco," *Bol.*, Inst. Geol. Mexico, num. 20, 116 pp., 9 lams.

Bowman, W. F.: "The South Dayton Salt Dome, Liberty County, Texas," *Bull.*, AAPG (1925), v. 9, no. 3, pp. 655-666; *Geology of Salt Dome Oil Fields*, AAPG (1926), pp. 558-569.

Bowman, W. F.: "Pierce Junction Salt Dome, Harris County, Texas," *Oil Weekly* (1927), v. 46, no. 11, pp. 95-98.

Brace, O. L.: "Hardin Dome, Liberty County, Texas," *Bull.*, AAPG (1936), v. 20, no. 8, pp. 1122-1123.

Brace, O. L.: "Gulf Coastal Developments in 1936," *Bull.*, AAPG (1937), v. 21, no. 8, pp. 1050-1062.

Brace, O. L.: "Interrelationship of Geology and Geophysics," *Bull.*, AAPG (1937), v. 21, no. 2, pp.

197-211; Review of by E. E. Rosaire, *Geophysics* (1937), v. 2, no. 1, pp. 63-67.

Brace, O. L.: "Gulf Coastal Developments in 1937," *Bull.*, AAPG (1938), v. 22, no. 6, 736-749; (abs.) *Oil and Gas Jour.* (1938), v. 36, no. 44, p. 56.

Brace, O. L.: "Review of Developments in 1938, Gulf Coast of Southeast Texas and Louisiana," *Bull.*, AAPG (1939), v. 23, no. 6, pp. 871-888.

Brace, O. L.: "Review of Developments in 1939, Gulf Coast of Upper Texas and Louisiana." *Bull.*, AAPG (1940), v. 24, no. 6, pp. 1079-1091.

Brace, O. L.: "Review of Developments in 1940, Gulf Coast of Upper Texas and Louisiana," *Bull.*, AAPG (1941), v. 25, no. 6, pp. 1004-1015.

Brace, O. L.: "Review of Developments in 1941, Gulf Coast of Upper Texas and Louisiana," *Bull.*, AAPG (1942), v. 26, no. 6, pp. 983-990; (abs.) v. 26, no. 6, pp. 905-906.

Bradley, D.: Rhythm May Determine Gulf Coast Dome Production," *Oil Trade Jour.* (1921), v. 12, p. 32.

Bradley, Virginia: "The Petroleum Industry of the Gulf Coast Salt Dome Area," *Econ. Geol.* (1939), v. 15, no. 4, pp. 395-407.

Branson, E. B.: "Origin of Thick Gypsum and Salt Deposits," *Bull.*, GSA (1915), v. 26, no. 6, pp. 231-242; (abs.) pp. 103-104.

Braunstein, Jules: "Habitat of Oil in Eastern Gulf Coast," *Habitat of Oil*, AAPG (1958), pp. 511-522.

Bray, E. E. and Nelson, H. F.: "Radiocarbon Age Determination of Recent Pleistocene Contact in Block 126 Field, Eugene Island, Gulf of Mexico," *Bull.*, AAPG (1956), v. 40, no. 1, pp. 173-177.

Briggs, K. S., Miller, C. C. and Bianchi, J. C., Jr.; "Developments in South Texas in 1952," *Bull.*, AAPG (1953), v. 37, no. 6, pp. 1405-1415.

Brixey, A. D., Jr. and Yust, M. R.: "Developments in Upper Gulf Coast of Texas in 1958," *Bull.*, AAPG (1959), v. 43, no. 6, pp. 1304-1311.

Brown, K. E. and Jessen, F. W.: "Effect of Pressure and Temperature on Cavities in Salt," *Trans.*, AIME (1959), v. 216, pp. 341-345; *Jour. of Pet. Tech.* (1959), v. 11, no. 12.

Brown, L. S.: "Cap Rock Petrography," *Bull.*, AAPG (1931), v. 15, no. 5, pp. 509-529.

Brown, L. S.: "Petrography and Paragenesis of Gulf Coast Salt Dome Cap Rock Minerals," *Bull.*, GSA (1931), v. 42, pp. 228-229; (abs.) *Pan Am. Geologist*, v. 55, p. 314.

Brown, L. S.: "Age of Gulf Border Salt Deposits," *Bull.*, AAPG (1934), v. 18, no. 10, pp. 1227-1296.

Brown, R. V.: "Salt Domes," *Jour Inst. Pet.* (1934), v. 20, pp. 73-93.

Bryan, C. L.: "Regional Geology and Geophysics of the Ark-La-Tex Area," *Geophysics* (1951), v. 16, no. 3, pp. 401-415.

Bryan, C. L. and Hamilton, W. F.: "Crow-ville Dome, Franklin Parish, Louisiana," *Bull.*, AAPG (1947), v. 31, no. 11, pp. 2049-2050.

Buchanan, G. S.: "Discovery of Valentine (La Rose) Dome, Louisiana by Reflection Seismograph," *Bull.*, AAPG (1934), v. 18, no. 4, p. 543; *Gulf Coast Oil Fields,* AAPG (1936), p. 1040.

Buck, C. E. and Goessmann, C. A.: "On the Rock Salt Deposit of Petite Anse, Louisiana Rock Salt Company," *Rept.*, Amer. Bur. of Mines (1867), 35 pp.

Burford, S. O.: "Structural Features of Brenham Salt Dome, Washington and Austin Counties, Texas," *Bull.*, AAPG (1935), v. 19, no. 9, pp. 1330-1338; *Gulf Coast Oil Fields,* AAPG (1936), pp. 780-788; *Bull.*, Houston Geol. Soc., pp. 28-29.

Burford, S. O.: "Brenham Field, Washington and Austin Counties, Texas," *Typical Oil and Gas Fields of Southeast Texas,* Houston Geol. Soc. (1962), pp. 28-29.

Burgess, Curtis W., Jr. and Tague, Glenn C.: "Developments in Upper Gulf Coast of Texas in 1960," *Bull.*, AAPG (1961), v. 45, no. 6, pp. 868-878.

Burke, R. A.: "Summary of Oil Occurrence in Anahuac and Frio Formations of Texas and Louisiana," *Bull.*, AAPG (1958), v. 42, no. 12, pp. 2935-2950.

Burnett, T. J., Jr. and Alexander, C. I.: "Developments in East Texas in 1943," *Bull.*, AAPG (1944), v. 28, no. 6, pp. 841-852.

Burnett, T. J., Jr. and Trowbridge, R. M.: "Developments in East Texas in 1942," *Bull.*, AAPG (1943), v. 27, no. 6, pp. 782-789.

Burtchaell, E. P. and Smith, E. R.: "Pressure Control by Water Injection-A Resume of Case Histories," *Jour. of Pet. Tech.* (1952), v. 4, no. 7, pp. 15-18.

Bustillos, S. Gonzalo: "El Azufre en la Cuenca Salina del Istmo de Tehuantepec," *Tesis Profesional* (1959).

Butler, E. Ann and Jones, Douglas E.: "Cretaceous Ostracoda of Protho and Rayburn's Salt Domes,

Bienville Parish, Louisiana," *Bull. 32*, La. Geol. Svy. (1957), Dept. of Conserv., 65 pp.

Cadman, W. H.: "The Origin of Hydrogen Sulphide in Persian Natural Gas and a Method of Preparing Unsaturated Hydrocarbons," *Jour. Inst. Pet.* (1925), v. 2, pp. 487-489.

Caillouet, H. J., Stanley, L. and Allen, W. E.: "Gravity Investigations in the Hockley Salt Dome, Harris County, Texas," *Geophysics* (1936), v. 20, no. 4, pp. 829-840.

Calderon Garcia, Alejandro; "Condiciones Estatigraficos de las Formaciones Miocenicas de la Cuenca Salina del Istmo de Tehuantepec," *Bol.*, Asoc. Mex. Geol. Petrol. (1951), v. 3, nos. 3, 7-8, pp. 229-259.

Campbell, F. F.: "Deep Correlation Reflections Near Hoskins Mound Salt Dome Texas," *Geophysics* (1941), v. 6, no. 3, pp. 259-263.

Campbell, M. R.: "Historical Review of Theories Advanced by American Geologists to Account for the Origin and Accumulation of Oil," *Econ. Geol.* (1911), v. 6, pp. 363-395.

Canada, W. R.: "Hockley Field, Harris County, Texas," *Guidebook*, AAPG-SEPM-SEG Jt. Ann. Mtg. (1953), Houston, Texas, pp. 125-128, *Typical Oil and Gas Fields in Southeast Texas,* Houston Geol. Soc. (1962), pp. 76-79.

Cannan, G. E. and Sullins, R. S.: "Problems Encountered in Drilling Abnormal Pressure Formations," *Drilling and Production Practice 1946,* API (1947), N. Y., pp. 29-33; *Drilling* (June, 1946), pp. 48-50; (abs.) *Oil Weekly* (May 20, 1946), p. 31.

Cantrell, R. B.: "Boling Field, Fort Bend and Wharton Counties, Texas," *Guidebook*, AAPG-SEPM-SEG Jt. Ann. Mtg. (1953), Houston, Texas, pp. 87-96.

Cantrell, R. B. and Hagen, Cecil: "Development Trends in Salt Dome Exploration (U. S. Gulf Coast)," *Oil Weekly* (1946), v. 123, no. 3, pp. 87-88.

Cantrell, R. B., Montgomery, J. C. and Woodard, A. E.: "Heterostegina Reef on Nash and Other Piercement Salt Domes in Northwestern Brazoria County, Texas," *Trans.*, GCAGS (1959), v. 9, pp. 59-62.

Carlton, D. P.: "West Columbia Salt Dome and Oil Field, Brazoria County, Texas," *Structure of Typical American Oil Fields*, AAPG (1929), v. 2, pp. 451-469.

Carroll, Don L.: "Outer Rings of Production Should Surround Salt Domes," *Oil Weekly* (1943), v. 111, no. 9, p. 14.

Carroll, Don L.: "Frio Discovery in Old Salt Dome Field is Major Strike," *Oil Weekly* (1943), v. 112, no. 1, pp. 12-13.

Carsey, J. B.: "Basic Geology of Gulf Coastal Area and the Continental Shelf," *Oil and Gas Jour.* (1948), v. 47, no. 8, pp. 246-251, 266-267; (abs.) no. 25, p. 129; *Bull.,* AAPG (1948), v. 32, no. 12, p. 2315.

Carsey, J. B.: "Geology of Gulf Coastal Area and Continental Shelf," *Bull.,* AAPG (1950), v. 34, no. 3, pp. 361-385.

Cash, T. C. and Loetterle, G. J.: "Developments in East Texas During 1946," *Bull.,* AAPG (1947), v. 31, no. 6, pp. 1059-1070.

Castillo Tejero, Carlos: "Bosquejo Estratigrafico de la Cuenca Salina del Istmo de Tehuantepec," *Bol., Asoc. Mex. Geol. Petrol.* (1955), v. 7, nos. 5-6, p. 173.

Castillon, B. M.: "Salt Deposits of the Isthmus of Tehuantepec," *Symposium on Salt,* Northern Ohio Geol. Soc., Inc. (1963), Cleveland, Ohio, pp. 263-280.

Castillon, B. M. and Contreras, Hugo: "Morfologia y Origen de los Domos Salinos del Istmo de Tehuantepec," *Bol., Asoc. Mex. Geol. Petrol.* (1960), v. 12, nos. 7 and 8, pp. 221-242.

Cepeda, E., Alvarez, M., Diaz, T. and Imlay, R. W.: "Stratigraphic Relations of Certain Jurassic Formations in Eastern Mexico," *Bull.,* AAPG (1948), v. 32, no. 9, pp. 1750-1761.

Champion, W. L. and Blanton, S. A.: "Developments in Arkansas-North Louisiana in 1958," *Bull.,* AAPG (1959), v. 43, no. 6, pp. 1322-1330.

Champion, W. L. and Morrow, Ernest H.: "Developments in Arkansas and North Louisiana in 1957," *Bull.,* AAPG (1958), v. 42, no. 6, pp. 1319-1326.

Chapman, L. C.: "The Hockley Salt Dome," *Bull.,* AAPG (1923), v. 7, no. 3, pp. 297-299.

Cheney, C. A.: "Salt Domes of Northeastern Texas," *Oil and Gas Jour.* (1922), v. 20, no. 32, pp. 82-83.

Clabaugh, Patricia S., Hightower, Maxwell L. and Muehlberger, William R.: "Palestine and Grand Saline Salt Domes," *Field Excursion No. 6, Geol. of the Gulf Coast and Central Texas and Guidebook of Excursions,* Houston Geol. Soc. (1962), Houston, Tex., pp. 266-277.

Clapp, F. G.: "Role of Geologic Structure in the Accumulation of Petroleum," *Structure of Typical American Oil Fields,* AAPG (1929), v. 2, pp. 667-716.

Clapp, F. G.: "Salt Domes of Texas and Louisiana Gulf Coast," *Jour. Inst. Pet.* (1931), v. 17, pp. 281-299.

Clark, Frank R.: "Origin and Accumulation of Oil," *Problems of Petroleum Geology,* AAPG (1934), pp. 309-345.

Clark, G. C.: "Developments in East Texas in 1948," *Bull.,* AAPG (1949), v. 33, no. 6, pp. 956-965.

Clark, G. C.: (abs.) "Interior Salt Domes of East Texas," *Bull.,* AAPG (1949), v. 33, no. 12, pp. 2067-2068; *Oil and Gas Jour.* (1948), v. 48, no. 25, p. 87.

Clark, G. C.: "Interior Salt Domes of Texas, Louisiana and Mississippi," *Guidebook,* 1960 Spring Field Trip, Shreveport Geol. Soc., pp. 3-16; (abs.) *Bull.,* AAPG (1959), v. 43, no. 7, pp. 1776-1777.

Clark, James A.: *The Chronological History of the Petroleum and Natural Gas Industries,* Clark Book Co. (1963), Houston, Texas, 317 pp.

Clark, James A. and Halbouty, Michel T.: *Spindletop,* Random House, Inc. (1952), New York, 306 pp.

Clark, James A. and Halbouty, Michel T.: "Spindletop's Second Fifty Years," *The Texas Preview* (Jan., 1953), pp. 26-28.

Clark, P. H.: "Developments in Upper Gulf Coast of Texas in 1947," *Bull.,* AAPG (1948) v. 32, no. 6, pp. 1024-1031.

Clark, R. P.: "Changing Conception of Structural Features in the Gulf Coast Area," *Oil and Gas Jour.* (1937), v. 35, no. 48, pp. 87-88; (abs.) *World Pet.,* v. 8, p. 106.

Clark, R. P. and Eby, J. B.: "Relation of Geophysics to Salt Dome Structure," *Bull.,* AAPG (1935), v. 19, no. 3, pp. 356-377; *Gulf Coast Oil Fields,* AAPG (1936), pp. 170-191.

Claudet, A. P.: "New Method of Correlation by Resistivity Values of Electrical Logs," *Bull.,* AAPG (1949), v. 34, no. 10, pp. 2027-2060.

Claypool, C. B. and Allison, A. P.: "Developments in the Upper Gulf Coast of Texas in 1946," *Bull.,* AAPG (1947), v. 31, no. 6, pp. 1071-1077.

Clendenin, W. W.: "A Preliminary Report Upon the Florida Parishes of East Louisiana and the Bluff, Prairie, Hill Lands of S. W. Louisiana, Louisiana State Experimental Station," *Geology and Agriculture* (1896), v. 3, pp. 236-240.

Cockerham, K. L., Jr.: "Developments in Upper Gulf Coast in 1956," *Bull.*, AAPG (1957), v. 41, no. 6, pp. 1181-1189.

Cockerham, K. L., Jr.: "Developments in Upper Gulf Coast of Texas in 1957," *Bull.*, AAPG (1958), v. 42, no. 6, pp. 1299-1307.

Cockerham, K. L., Jr., Rotan, R. A., Jr. and Stout, E. D.: "Developments in Upper Gulf Coast of Texas in 1955," *Bull.*, AAPG (1956), v. 40, no. 6, pp. 1239-1252.

Collier, L. D.: "Development in Arkansas and North Louisiana in 1950." *Bull.*, AAPG (1951), v. 35, no. 6, pp. 1345-1351.

Contreras, Hugo: "Posibilidades del Alto Salino de Moloacan-Ixhuatlan," *Bol.*, Asoc. Mex. Geol. Petrol. (1950), v. 2, no. 7, pp. 473-485.

Contreras, Hugo and Castillon, B. M.: "Morfologia y Origen de los Domos Salinos del Istmo de Tehuantepec," *Bol.*, Asoc. Mex. Geol. Petrol. (1960) v. 12, nos. 7 and 8, pp. 221-242.

Contreras, Hugo and Sansores, Enrique: "Geologia del Domo Salino de 'El Rosario' en el Estado de Tabasco y sus Posibilidades Petroliferas," *Bol.*, Asoc. Mex. Geol. Petrol. (1953), v. 5, nos. 1-2, pp. 57-74.

Cook, C. E.: "Darrow Salt Dome, Ascension Parish, Louisiana," *Bull.*, AAPG (1938), v. 22, no. 10, pp. 1412-1422; *Oil and Gas Jour.* (1938), v. 36, no. 44, pp. 51, 53; *World Pet.*, v. 9, no. 13, p. 54.

Cook, W. H.: "Offshore Directional Drilling Practices Today and Tomorrow," *Preprint*, Presented Chicago Chapter of AIME (Nov., 1957), Chicago, Illinois; Presented Ann. Meeting AIME (Feb., 1957), New Orleans, La.

Cooke, C. W., Gardner, J. A. and Stephenson, L. W.: "The Atlantic and Gulf Coastal Plain," in Erich Krenkel (ed.), *Geologie der Erde, Nord Amerika*, Berlin, Gebruder Borntraeger, v. 1, pp. 519-578.

Cooke, W. F., Jr.: "Developments in Upper Gulf Coast of Texas in 1952," *Bull.*, AAPG (1953), v. 37, no. 6, pp. 1431-1442.

Coon, L. A.: "Tertiary-Cretaceous Growth of the East Texas Basin," *Trans.*, GCAGS (1956), v. 6, pp. 85-90.

Copeland, R. R., Jr., Dixon, K. P. and Bates, F. W.: "Geology of Avery Island Salt Dome, Iberia Parish, Louisiana," *Bull.*, AAPG (1959), v. 43, no. 5, pp. 944-957.

Corbin, M. W.: "Developments in Arkansas and North Louisiana in 1949," *Bull.*, AAPG (1950), v. 34, no. 6, pp. 1199-1211.

Cornejo Toledo, Alfonso and Hernandez Osuna, Alfonso: "Las Anomalias Gravimetricas en la Cuenca Salina del Istmo, Planicie Costera de Tabasco, Campeche and Peninsula de Yucatan", *Bol.*, Asoc. Mex. Geol. Petrol. (1950), v. 2, no. 7, pp. 453-460.

Coste, Eugene: "The Volcanic Origin of Natural Gas & Petroleum," *Canadian Min. Inst. Jour.* (1903), v. 6, pp. 73-123.

Coste, E. and Matteson, W. G.: "Secondary Intrusive Origin of Gulf Coastal Plain Salt Domes," *Trans.*, AIME (1921), v. 65, pp. 295-334; preprints, nos. 1048, 1073, 1088; (abs.) *Mining and Metallurgy*, no. 170, p. 37.

Cozad, D. J.: "Design Development of Underground Storage Caverns at Texas Eastern's Mont Belvieu, Texas, Terminal," *Symposium on Salt*, Northern Ohio Geol Soc., Inc. (1963), Cleveland, Ohio, pp. 634-661.

Craft, B. C.: "Mineral Development," *Bull. 6*, La. Geol. Svy. (1935), pp. 181-186.

Craft, B. C., Hawkins, Murray F., Jr. and Rayne, John R.: "The Reservoir Mechanism of Sulphur Recovery," *Trans.*, AIME (1956), v. 207, pp. 246-251; *Tech. Paper 4385*, AIME; *Jour. of Pet. Tech.* (1956), v. 8, no. 11, pp. 246-251.

Craft, B. C., Stephenson, M. B., Howe, H. V., Russell, R. J. and McGuirt, J. H.: "Reports on the Geology of Cameron and Vermilion Parishes," *Bull. 6*, La. Geol. Svy. (1935), 242 pp.

Crain, H. F.: "Stratigraphy and the Geology of the Port Barre Salt Dome," *Thesis*, Kan. U. (1947), Dept. of Geol.

Crain, H. F.: "Developments in Louisiana Gulf Coast in 1953," *Bull.*, AAPG (1954), v. 38, no. 6, pp. 1221-1232.

Cram, Ira H.: "Deep Hunting Grounds," *Bull.*, AAPG (1963), v. 47, no. 12, pp. 2009-2014.

Critz, James S.: "Highlights of Gulf Coast Development," *Oil Weekly* (1946), v. 123, no. 3, pp. 81-86, 88.

Critz, James S.: "Gulf Coast Oil Fields, Geological Data, Development History," *Oil Weekly* (1946), v. 123, no. 3, pp. 110-159.

Critz, James S. and Sholl, Vinton H.: "Developments in Upper Gulf Coast of Texas in 1961," *Bull.*, AAPG (1962), v. 46, no. 6, pp. 921-928.

Crouch, Robert W.: "Inspissation of Post-Oligocene Sediments in Southern Louisiana,"

Bull., GSA (1959), v. 70, pp. 1283-1292.

Crum, H. E. and Prommel, H. W. C.: "Salt Domes of Permian and Pennsylvanian Age in Southeastern Utah and Their Influence on Oil Accumulation," *Bull.*, AAPG (1927), v. 11, no. 4, pp. 373-393.

Cserna, Zoltan de: *Tectonica de la Sierra Madre Oriental de Mexico, entre Torreon y Monterrey*, 20th Congreso Geologico Internacional (1956).

Culbertson, J. A., Eby, J. B. and Thompson, W. C.: "Guidebook for Field Trips," *Guidebook*, AAPG, 26th Ann. Mtg. (1941), Houston, Texas, 28 pp.

Culligan, L. B. and Powell, L. C.: "Developments in Southeastern States in 1954," *Bull.*, AAPG (1955), v. 39, no. 6, pp. 1004-1014.

Currie, J. B.: "Three Dimensional Method for Solution of Oil Field Structures," *Bull.*, AAPG (1952), v. 36, no. 5, pp. 889-890.

Currie, J. B.: "Role of Concurrent Deposition and Deformation of Sediments in Development of Salt Dome Graben Structures," *Bull.*, AAPG (1956), v. 40, no. 1, pp. 1-16.

Davies, W. J.: "Brookshire (San Felipe) Field, Waller County, Texas," *Guidebook*, AAPG, SEPM, SEG, Jt. Ann. Mtg. (March, 1953), Houston, Texas, pp. 97-99.

Davis, David C. and Adams, Emmett R.: "Developments in Southeastern States in 1961," *Bull.*, AAPG (1962), v. 46, no. 6, pp. 953-958.

Davis, David C. and Kargos, Harold E. :"Developments in Southeastern States in 1962," *Bull.*, AAPG (1963), v. 47, no. 6, pp. 1109-1115.

Davis, D. M. and Beilharz, C. F.: "Developments in Upper Gulf Coast of Texas in 1945," *Bull.*, AAPG (1946), v. 30, no. 6, pp. 991-998.

Davis, Morgan J.: "Geophysics—Full Partner," *Geophysics* (1956), v. 22, no. 2, pp. 225-232.

Davis, R. A.: "Manvel Field, Brazoria County, Texas," *Guidebook*, AAPG-SEPM-SEG Jt. Ann. Mtg. (March, 1953), Houston, Texas, pp. 136-137.

Davis, Wallace: "Big Creek Can Increase Production When Oil is Wanted," *Oil Weekly* (1927), v. 45, no. 8, p. 39.

Day, W. L. and Thompson, Wallace C.: "Geophysics and Geology of the Discovery and Development of Esperson Dome, Texas." *Geophysical Case Histories*, SEG (1948), v. 1, pp. 48-65.

DeBlieux, Charles: "Photogeology in Gulf Coast Exploration," *Bull.*, AAPG (1949), v. 33, no. 7, pp. 1251-1259.

DeBlieux, Charles: "Photogeology in Louisiana Coastal Marsh and Swamp," *Trans.*, GCAGS (1962), v. 12, pp. 231-241.

DeGolyer, E. L.: "Origin of the Cap Rock of the Gulf Coast Salt Domes," (discussion), *Econ. Geol.* (1918), v. 13, pp. 616-620.

DeGolyer, E. L.: "The Theory of Volcanic Origin of Salt Domes," *Bull. 137*, AIME (1918), pp. 987-1000.

DeGolyer, E. L.: "The West Point, Texas Salt Dome, Freestone County," *Jour. Geol.* (1919), v. 27, no. 8, pp. 647-663.

DeGolyer, E. L.: (abs.) "Notes on the Salt Domes of North America," *Bull.*, GSA (1923), v. 34, p. 66.

DeGolyer, E. L.: (abs.) "Discovery by Geophysical Methods of a New Salt Dome in the Gulf Coast," *Bull.*, GSA (1925), v. 36, p. 161; *Pan Am. Geologist*, v. 43, no. 2.

DeGolyer, E. L.: "Discovery of Potash Salts and Fossil Algae in Texas Salt Dome," *Bull.*, AAPG (1925), v. 9, no. 2, pp. 348-349; *Geology of Salt Dome Oil Fields*, AAPG (1926), pp. 781-782.

DeGolyer, E. L.: "Origin of North American Salt Domes," *Bull.*, AAPG (1925), v. 9, no. 5, pp. 831-874; *Geology of Salt Dome Oil Fields*, AAPG (1926), pp. 1-44.

DeGolyer, E. L.: "Origin of the Salt Domes of the Gulf Coastal Plain of the United States," *Jour. Inst. Pet.* (1931), v. 17, pp. 331-333.

DeGolyer, E. L.: "Notes on the Early History of Applied Geophysics in the Petroleum Industry," *Geophysics* (1935), v. 6, no. 1, pp. 1-10; *Early Geophysical Papers*, SEG (1957), pp. 245-255.

DeHart, B. H. and Wallace, W. E., Jr.: "Calcasieu Lake Salt Dome, Cameron Parish, Louisiana," *Trans.*, GCAGS (1953), v. 3, pp. 71-81.

Del Castillo, G. L. and Beautelspacher, S. R.: *Levantamiento Sismologico de Refraccion en el Area de Chinameca, Ver.*, Inedito, Archivo Consejo de Recursos Naturales no Renovables (1961).

Demaison, G. J.: "The Triassic Salt in the Algerian Sahara," *Salt Basins Around Africa*, The Institute of Petroleum (1965), London, pp. 91-100.

Denham, R. L. (ed.): *Typical Oil and Gas Fields of Southeast Texas*, Houston Geol. Soc. (1962), 243 pp.

Denton, F. R.: "Developments in East Texas during 1941," *Bull.*, AAPG (1942), v. 26, no. 6, pp. 1050-1057; (abs.), v. 26, no. 6, p. 905.

Denton, F. R. and Trowbridge, R. M.: "Developments in East Texas During 1940," *Bull.*, AAPG (1941), v. 25, no. 6, pp. 1081-1089.

Desjardins, Louis: "Aerial Photos of Multiple Surface Faults May Locate Deep Seated Salt Domes," *Oil and Gas Jour.* (1952), v. 51, no. 13, pp. 82-84.

Deussen, Alexander: "Salt Domes of Texas and Louisiana," *Oil Weekly* (1922), v. 24, no. 4, pp. 11, 16, 18.

Deussen, Alexander: "Oil Reserves of the Gulf Coast," *Oil Weekly* (1933), v. 69, no. 1, pp. 16-18.

Deussen, Alexander: "Oil Producing Horizons of Gulf Coast in Texas and Louisiana," *Bull.*, AAPG (1934), v. 18, no. 4, pp. 500-518; *Gulf Coast Oil Fields*, AAPG (1936), pp. 1-19.

Deussen, Alexander: "Thirty-five Years of Progress in the Knowledge of the Geology of Texas," *Bull. 3501*, Tex. U. (1935), pp. 37-57.

Deussen, Alexander: "Discoveries," *Geophysics* (1938), v. 3, no. 3, pp. 177-197.

Deussen, Alexander and Andrau, E. W. K. "Orange, Texas Oil Field, *Bull.*, AAPG (1936), v. 20, no. 5, pp. 531-559; *Problems of Petroleum Geology*, AAPG (1934), pp. 880-908.

Deussen, Alexander and Lane, L. L.: "Hockley Salt Dome, Harris County, Texas," *Bull.*, AAPG (1926), v. 9, no. 7, pp. 1031-1060; *Geology of Salt Dome Oil Fields*, AAPG (1926), pp. 570-599.

Diaz, T., Imlay, R. W., Cepeda, E. and Alvarez, M.: "Stratigraphic Relations of Certain Jurassic Formations in Eastern Mexico," *Bull.*, AAPG (1948), v. 32, no. 9, pp. 1750-1761.

Diaz Gonzalez, T. E. and Humphrey, W. E.: "Secuencia Mesozoica. Anticlinal de las Grutas de Garcia en la Sierra del Fraile, a 30 Kilometros al NW de la Ciudad de Monterrey," *Congreso Geologico Internacional* (1958), pp. 26-31.

Diaz Gonzalez, T. E. and Humphrey, W. E.: "Secuencia Mesozoica en la Arroyo de San Rogue, Cerro de la Silla, Nuevo Leon, Approximadamente a 15 Kilometros al SE de la Ciudad de Monterrey, Nuevo Leon," *Congreso Geologico Internacional* (1958), pp. 18-23.

Diaz Gonzalez, T. E. and Humphrey, W. E.: "Secuencia Mesozoica. Portal de la Muralla, Sierra de la Gavia, Coahuila," *Congreso Geologico Internacional* (1958), pp. 41-45.

Diaz, Teodoro, Mixon, R. B. and Murray, G. E.: "Age and Correlation of Huizachal Group (Mesozoic), State of Tamaulipas, Mexico," *Bull.*, AAPG (1959), v. 43, no. 4, pp. 757-771; (addendum), v. 43, pp. 2499.

Dickinson, George: "Geological Aspects of Abnormal Reservoir Pressures in Gulf Coast Louisiana," *Bull.*, AAPG (1953), v. 37, no. 2, pp. 410-432; *Proc.*, Third World Pet. Cong. (1951), The Hague, Holland.

Dixon, K. P., Bates, F. W. and Copeland, R. R., Jr.: "Geology of Avery Island Salt Dome, Iberia Parish, Louisiana," *Bull.*, AAPG (1959), v. 43, no. 5, pp. 944-957.

Dobbins, W. D., Morren, J. H. and Hendy, W. J.: "Developments in South Texas in 1957," *Bull.*, AAPG (1958), v. 42, no. 6, pp. 1279-1288.

Dobrin, M. B.: "Some Quantitative Experiments on a Fluid Salt Dome Model and Their Geological Implications," *Trans.*, Am. Geophys. Union, 22nd Ann. Mtg. (1941), pt. 2, pp. 528-542.

Doering, John: "Post-Fleming Surface Formations of Coastal Southeast Texas and South Louisiana," *Bull.*, AAPG (1935), v. 19, no. 5, pp. 651-688; *Gulf Coast Oil Fields*, AAPG (1936), pp. 432-469.

Donoghue, D.: "The Bayou Bouillon Salt Dome, St. Martin Parish, Louisiana," *Bull.*, AAPG (1925), v. 9, no. 9, pp. 1283-1289; *Geology of Salt Dome Oil Fields*, AAPG (1926), pp. 345-351.

Donoghue, D.: "Section 28 Salt Dome, St. Martin Parish, Louisiana," *Bull.*, AAPG (1925), v. 9, no. 9, pp. 1290-1293; *Geology of Salt Dome Oil Fields*, AAPG (1926), pp. 352-355.

Dugan, Albert F. and Peters, Jack W.: "Gravity and Magnetic Investigations at the Grand Saline Salt Dome, Van Zandt County, Texas," *Geophysics* (1945), v. 10, no. 3, pp. 376-393; *Geophysical Case Histories*, SEG (1948), v. 1, pp. 105-120.

Dumble, E. T.: *First Annual Report of the Geological Survey of Texas* (1889), 410 pp.

Dumble, E. T.: "Origin of the Texas Domes," *Bull.*, AIME (1918), v. 142, pp. 1629-1636.

Dumble, E. T.: "The Geology of East Texas," *Bull. 1869*, Tex. U. (1918), 388 pp.

Duncan, Donald R. and Love, Donald W.: "Developments in Louisiana Gulf Coast in 1959," *Bull.*, AAPG (1960), v. 44, no. 6, pp. 827-833.

Duncan, R. L. and Waters, K. M.: "Developments in Louisiana Gulf Coast in 1955," *Bull.*, AAPG (1956), v. 40, no. 6, pp. 1253-1262.

Dunham, R. L. (ed.): *Typical Oil and Gas Fields of Southeast Texas*, Houston Geol. Soc. (1962), 243 pp.

Durham, C. O., Jr. and White, W. S., Jr.: "A Guided Geological Tour Through North and Central Louisiana," *Guidebook,* 1960 Spring Field Trip, Shreveport Geol. Soc., pp. 83-147.

Durschner, H.: "Einige Physikalische Uberlegungen zum Problem der Halokinese," *Zeits. Deutsch. Geol. Ges.* (1957), v. 109, pp. 152-158.

Duschatko, R. W. and Blanton, Sankey L.: "Developments in Arkansas and North Louisiana in 1959," *Bull.,* AAPG (1960), v. 44, no. 6, pp. 834-841.

Eardley, A. J.: *Structural Geology of North America,* Harper (1951), New York, 624 pp.

Early, Thomas R., Ryan, J. P., Miller, W. C. and Netzeband, F. F.: "Sulfur Resources and Production in Texas, Louisiana, Missouri, Oklahoma, Arkansas and Mississippi, and Markets for the Sulfur," *Inf. Circ. 8222,* U. S. Dept. of the Interior, Bur. of Mines, (1964), 77 pp.

East Texas Geological Society; "Developments in East Texas in 1944," *Bull.,* AAPG (1945), v. 29, no. 6, pp. 766-776.

Easton, H. D., Jr.: "North Louisiana Surface Structure Evidence is Small," *Oil Weekly* (1935), v. 77, no. 2, pp. 35-38.

Eaton, R. W.: "Boggy Creek Field, Anderson and Cherokee Counties, Texas," *Pub. 5116,* Tex. U. (1951), pp. 29-34.

Eaton, R. W.: "Developments in East Texas in 1952," *Bull.,* AAPG (1953), v. 37, no. 6, pp. 1416-1430.

Eaton, R. W.: "Resume of Subsurface Geology of Northeast Texas with Emphasis on Salt Structures," *Trans.,* GCAGS (1956), v. 6, pp. 79-84.

Eby, J. B.: "Geophysical History of the Iowa Field, Calcasieu and Jefferson Davis Parishes, Louisiana," *Geophysics* (1943), v. 8, no. 4, pp. 348-355; *Geophysical Case Histories,* SEG (1948), v. 1, pp. 153-160.

Eby, J. B.: "Geophysical History of South Houston Salt Dome and Oil Field, Harris County, Texas," *Bull.,* AAPG (1945), v. 29, no. 2, pp. 210-214; *Geophysical Case Histories,* SEG (1948), v. 1, pp. 43-47.

Eby, J. B.: "Salt Dome Interest Centers on Gulf Coast," *World Oil* (1956), v. 143, no. 5, pp. 143-150; *Proc.,* International Geol. Cong. (1956).

Eby, J. B. and Clark, R. P.: "Relation of Geophysics to Salt Dome Structure," *Bull.,* AAPG (1935), v. 19, no. 3, pp. 356-377; *Gulf Coast Oil Fields,* AAPG (1936), pp. 170-191.

Eby, J. B. and Halbouty, Michel T.: "Geology and Economic Significance of Anahuac (Oil Field), Texas," *World Pet.* (1937), v. 8, no. 4, pp. 46-55.

Eby, J. B. and Halbouty, Michel T.: "Spindletop Oil Field, Jefferson County, Texas," *Bull.,* AAPG (1937), v. 21. no. 4, pp. 475-490.

Eby, J. B. and Harkins, T. I.: "Geophysical History of Darrow Dome, Ascension Parish, Louisiana," *Tech. Pub. 1495,* AIME (1942); *Trans.,* AIME, v. 151, pp. 253-260; *Geophysical Case Histories,* SEG (1948), v. 1, pp. 144-152.

Eby, J. B., Thompson, W. C. and Culbertson, J. A.: "Guide for Field Trips," *Guidebook,* AAPG 26th Ann. Mtg. (1941), Houston, Texas, 28 pp.

Echols, D. A. J. and Malkin, D. S.: "Wilcox (Eocene) Stratigraphy, a Key to Production (of oil and gas)," *Bull.,* AAPG (1948), v. 32, no. 1, pp. 11-33; corrections, p. 310.

Eckhardt, E. A.: "A Brief History of the Gravity Method of Prospecting for Oil," *Geophysics* (1940), v. 5, no. 3, pp. 231-242; *Geophysical Case Histories,* SEG (1948), v. 1, pp. 21-32.

Eichelberger, O. H. and Thompson, S. A.: "Vinton Salt Dome, Louisiana," *Bull.,* AAPG (1928), v. 12, no. 4, pp. 385-394.

Eisenhardt, Wm. C. and Stanley, Herbert M., Jr.: "Developments in East Texas in 1960," *Bull.,* AAPG (1961), v. 45, no. 6, pp. 861-867.

Elkins, T. A. and Nettleton, L. L.: "Geologic Models from Powdered Materials," *Trans.,* Amer. Geophysical Union (1947), v. 28, no. 3, pp. 451-466.

Ellison, R. F., Garwick, R. W., and Krisle, Jack E.: "Esperson Dome Field, Liberty and Harris Counties, Texas," *Guidebook,* AAPG-SEPM-SEG Jt. Ann. Mtg., Houston, Texas (March, 1953), pp. 115-116.

Ellisor, A. C.: "Jackson Group of Formations in Texas with Notes on Frio and Vicksburg," *Bull.,* AAPG (1933), v. 17, no. 11, pp. 1293-1350; *Gulf Coast Oil Fields,* AAPG (1936), pp. 470-527.

Enright, Robert J.: "Drillers Eye Texas 'Dry' Domes," *Oil and Gas Jour.* (1963), v. 61, no. 52, pp. 210-214.

Erwin, Walter and Vernon, R. O.: "Developments in Southeastern States in 1955," *Bull.,* AAPG (1956), v. 40, no. 6, pp. 1272-1282.

Escher, B. G. and Kuehner, P. H.: "Experiments in Connection with Salt Domes," *Leidsche Geol. Mededeel.* (1929), Afl. 3, pp. 151-182.

Euwer, M. L.; "Salt Water Injection for Pressure Maintenance in East Hackberry Field, Louisiana," *Oil and Gas Jour.* (1945), v. 44, no. 21, pp. 100-102, 131.

Euwer, M. L.: "Pressure Maintenance of East Hackberry," *Oil Weekly* (1945), v. 119, no. 6, pp. 46, 49-51.

Evans, G. L. and Sellards, E. H.: "Index to Mineral Resources of Texas by Counties," *Min. Res. Circ. 29,* Tex. U. (1944), 21 pp.

Ewing, J. M. and Woodhams, R. L.: "Developments in East Texas in 1962," *Bull.,* AAPG (1963), v. 47, no. 6, pp. 1073-1080.

Ewing, M., et al: "Geophysical and Geological Investigations in the Gulf of Mexico," *Geophysics* (1955), v. 20, pp. 1-18.

Feely, H. W. and Kulp, J. L.: "Origin of Gulf Coast Salt Dome Sulphur Deposits," *Bull.,* AAPG (1957), v. 41, no. 8, pp. 1802-1853.

Ferguson, W. B., Heath, F. E. and Waters, J. A.: "Clay Creek Salt Dome, Washington County, Texas," *Bull.,* AAPG (1931), v. 15, no. 1, pp. 43-60; *Pan Am Geologist* (1930), v. 53, no. 3, p. 226.

Ferguson, W. B. and Minton, J. W.: "Clay Creek Salt Dome, Washington County, Texas," *Bull.,* AAPG (1936), v. 20, no. 1, pp. 68-90; *Gulf Coast Oil Fields,* AAPG (1936), pp. 757-779; (abs.) *World Pet.,* v. 7, no. 3, p. 150.

Ferrando, Al and Richardson, H. T.: "Barataria Field, Jefferson Parish, Louisiana," *Bull.,* AAPG (1941), v. 25, no. 2, pp. 322-323.

Fietz, R. P., Scott, K. R. and Hayes, W. E.: "Geology of the Eagle Mills Formation," *Trans.,* GCAGS (1961), v. 11, pp. 1-14.

Finfrock, L. J.: "Development in Southeastern States in 1951," *Bull.,* AAPG (1952), v. 36, no. 6, pp. 1228-1237.

Finfrock, L. J. and Morton, R. B.: "Developments in Southeastern States in 1952," *Bull.,* AAPG (1953), v. 37, no. 6, pp. 1460-1474.

Finley, J. C., McGee, D. A. and Seale, Tom: "Oil in the Gulf of Mexico," (abs.) *Proc.,* Oklahoma Acad. Sci., v. 29, pp. 60-61.

Fisk, Harold N.: "Geology of Avoyelles and Rapides Parishes, Louisiana," *Bull. 18,* La. Geol. Svy. (1940), 240 pp.

Fisk, Harold N. and McClelland, Bramlette: "Geology of Continental Shelf Off Louisiana: Its Influence on Offshore Foundation Design," *Bull.,* GSA (1959), v. 70, pp. 1369-1394.

Flawn, P. T., Goldstein, A., Jr., King, P. B. and Weaver, C. E.: "The Ouachita System," *Pub. 6120,* Tex. U. (1961), 399 pp.

Foose, R. M., O'Neill, B. J., Jr. and Hoy, R. B.: "Structure of Winnfield Salt Dome, Winn Parish, Louisiana," *Bull.,* AAPG (1962), v. 46, no. 8, pp. 1444-1459.

Forgotson, J. M., Jr.: "A Correlation and Regional Stratigraphic Analysis of the Formation of the Trinity Group of the Comanchan Cretaceous of the Gulf Coastal Plain; and the Genesis and Petrography of the Ferry Lake Anhydrite," *Trans.,* GCAGS (1956), v. 6, pp. 91-105.

Forman, McLain J.: "The Heterostegina Zone at Anse la Butte, Lafayette and St. Martin Parishes, Louisiana: A Study in Gulf Coast Tertiary Reefs," *Trans.,* GCAGS (1955), v. 5, pp. 65-72.

Forman, McLain J. and Atwater, Gordon: "Nature of Growth of Southern Louisiana Salt Domes and Its Effect on Petroleum Accumulation;" *Bull.,* AAPG (1959), v. 43, no. 11, pp. 2592-2622; (abs.) *Trans.,* GCAGS (1958), v. 8, pp. 20-21.

Fox, Bruce W. and Patrick, Thomas B.: "Developments in East Texas in 1959," *Bull.,* AAPG (1960), v. 44, no. 6, pp. 810-818.

Fralich, E. E. and Torrey, P. D.: "An Experimental Study of the Origin of Salt Domes," *Jour. Geol.* (1926), v. 34, no. 3, pp. 224-234; (abs.) *Oil and Gas Jour.* (1925), v. 23, no. 45, p. 133.

Franco, Alvaro: "Gulf Lures Mexicans," *Oil and Gas Jour.* (1964), v. 62, no. 38, p. 102.

Fuellhart, Donald E.: "Subsurface Disposal of Oil Field Brines in Southern Louisiana," *Oil and Gas Jour.* (1938), v. 36, no. 34, pp. 46, 48-50.

Gahagan, Donald I.: "Dickinson, Gillock, and Oil Field Brines in Southern Louisiana," *Oil and Gas Jour.* (1938), v. 36, no. 34, pp. 46, 48-50.

Gahagan, Donald I.: "Dickinson, Gillock, and South Gillock Fields, Galveston County, Texas," *Guidebook,* AAPG-SEPM-SEG Jt. Ann. Mtg., (March, 1953), Houston, Texas, pp. 110-113.

Garcia, Tijerina N.: "Bosquejo Geologico del Istmo de Tehuantepec," *Bol.,* Asoc. Mex. Geol. Petrol. (1950), v. 2, no. 7, pp. 435-444.

Gardner, Frank J.: "Salt Domes, A Geological Enigma," *Oil and Gas Jour.* (1955), v. 54, no. 14, p. 155.

Gardner, Frank J.: "Another Salt Barrier Falls," *Oil and Gas Jour.* (1957), v. 55, no. 22, p. 167.

Gardner, Frank J.: "Pescadito—It's Texas' Deepest Salt Dome," *Oil and Gas Jour.* (1957), v. 55, no. 26, p. 189.

Gardner, Frank J.: "Calcasieu Lake Finally Pays Off After 31 Years of Probing," *Oil and Gas Jour.* (1958), v. 56, no. 30, p. 263.

Gardner, Frank J.: "Sixth 'Dry' Dome Yields

Oil in East Texas," *Oil and Gas Jour.* (1960), v. 58, no. 7, p. 157.

Gardner, Frank J.: "Mississippi Offers Domal Prospects," *Oil and Gas Jour.* (1962), v. 60, no. 29, p. 131.

Gardner, G. D. and Mabra, D. A.: "Developments in East Texas in 1957," *Bull.,* AAPG (1958), v. 42, no. 6, pp. 1289-1298.

Gardner, J. A., Stephenson, L. W. and Cooke, C. W.: "The Atlantic and Gulf Coastal Plain," in Erich Krenkel (ed.), *Geologie der Erde, Nord Amerika,* Berlin, Gebruder Borntraeger (1938), v. 1, pp. 519-578.

Gardner, L. W.: "Seismograph Determination of Salt Dome Boundary Using Well Detector Deep on Dome Flank," *Geophysics* (1949), v. 14, no. 1, p. 29-38; (abs.) *Oil and Gas Jour.* (1948), v. 46, no. 52, p. 115.

Garwick, R. W., Krisle, Jack E. and Ellison, R. F.: "Esperson Dome Field, Liberty and Harris Counties, Texas," *Guidebook,* AAPG-SEPM-SEG Jt. Ann. Mtg., (March, 1953), Houston, Texas, pp. 115-116.

Gatling, Leroy: "El Campo Petrolero de Rabon Grande, Sureste del Estado de Veracruz, Mexico," *Bol.,* Asoc. Mex. Geol. Petrol. (1954), v. 6, nos. 3-4 pp. 139-151.

Getzendaner, F. M.: "Problem of Pre-Trinity Deposits in South Texas," *Bull.,* AAPG (1943), v. 27, no. 9, pp. 1228-1244; (abs.) v. 26, no. 5, pp. 904-905.

Gibson, B. Juan: *Sintesis de la Morfologia de las Masas de Sal del Istmo de Tehuantepec en Relacion con los Yacimientos de Azufre,* Inedito, Archivo Consejo de Recursos Naturales no Renovables (1957).

Gibson, D. T.: "Developments in East Texas in 1949," *Bull.,* AAPG (1950), v. 34, no. 6, pp. 1170-1178.

Gill, W. D.: "The Mediterranean Basin," *Salt Basins Around Africa,* The Institute of Petroleum (1965), London, pp. 101-111.

Glass, Charles N.: "Pierce Junction Field, Harris County, Texas," *Guidebook,* AAPG-SEPM-SEG Jt. Ann. Mtg., Houston, Texas (March, 1953), pp. 147-150.

Goessmann, C. A. and Buck, C. E.: "On the Rock Salt Deposit of Petite Anse, Louisiana Rock Salt Company," *Rept.,* Amer. Bur. of Mines (1867), 35 pp.

Goheen, H. C.: "Sedimentation and Structure of the Planulina-Abbeville Trend, South Louisiana," *Trans.,* GCAGS (1959), v. 9, pp. 91-103.

Goldman, M. I.: "Petrography of Salt Dome Cap Rock," *Bull.,* AAPG (1925), v. 9, no. 1, pp. 42-78; *Geology of Salt Dome Oil Fields,* AAPG (1926), pp. 50-86.

Goldman, M. I.: (abs.) "Features of Gypsum-Anhydrite Salt Dome Cap Rock," *Bull.,* GSA (1929), v. 40, pp. 99-100.

Goldman, M. I.: "Bearing of Cap Rock on Subsidence on Clay Creek Salt Dome, Washington County, Texas and Chestnut Dome, Natchitoches Parish, Louisiana," *Bull.,* AAPG (1931), v. 15, no. 9, pp. 1105-1113.

Goldman, M. I.: "Origin of the Anhydrite Cap Rock of American Salt Domes," *Prof. Paper 175,* USGS (1933), pp. 83-114; Review of by Marcus A. Hanna, *Econ. Geol.* (1936), v. 31, no. 6, pp. 642-644.

Goldman, M. I.: "Origin of Anhydrite Cap Rock," *Econ. Geol.* (1936), v. 31, no. 8, p. 881.

Goldman, M. I.: "Deformation, Metamorphism, and Mineralization in Gypsum-Anhydrite Cap Rock, Sulphur Salt Dome, Louisiana," *Memoir 50,* GSA (1952), 169 pp.

Goldstein, A., Jr., King, P. B., Weaver, C. E. and Flawn, P. T.: "The Ouachita System," *Pub. 6120,* Tex. U. (1961), 399 pp.

Goldston, W. L. and Stevens, G. D.: "Esperson Dome, Liberty County, Texas," *Bull.,* AAPG (1934), v. 18, no. 12, pp. 1632-1654; *Gulf Coast Oil Fields,* AAPG (1936), pp. 857-879.

Goodrich, R. H. and Barton, D. C.: "The Jennings Oil Field, Acadia Parish, Louisiana," *Bull.,* AAPG (1926), v. 10, no. 1, pp. 72-92; *Geology of Salt Dome Oil Fields,* AAPG (1926), pp. 398-418.

Goodwyn, J. T., Jr. and Smith, Fred L., Jr.: "Batson Field, Hardin County, Texas," *Typical Oil and Gas Fields of Southeast Texas,* Houston Geol. Soc. (1962), pp. 8-13.

Gould, H. R. and Morgan, J. P.: "Coastal Louisiana Swamps and Marshlands," *Field Trip No. 9,* Geology of the Gulf Coast and Central Texas and Guidebook of Excursions, Houston Geol. Soc., (1962), pp. 287-341.

Gray, Dr. George R., Allen, G. G. and Tschirley, N. K.: "Gulf Coast Drilling Mud Practices Demand Attention to Special Problems," *World Oil* (1956), v. 142, no. 7, pp. 155-160.

Gray, Helen, Musgrove, A. W. and Woolley, W.

C.: "Outlining of Salt Masses by Refraction Methods," *Geophysics* (1960), v. 25, no. 1, p. 141-167.

Grayson, R. W., Bianchi, J. C., Jr. and Janosky, R. A.: "Developments in South Texas in 1953," *Bull.*, AAPG (1954), v. 38, no. 6, pp. 1184-1195.

Grinstead, Fred E.: "Sugarland Field, Fort Bend County, Texas," *Typical Oil and Gas Fields of Southeast Texas*, Houston Geol. Soc. (1962), pp. 219-220.

Gussow, W. C.: (abs.) "Energy Source of Intrusive Masses," *Bull.*, AAPG (1965), v. 49, no. 3, p. 343.

Gutierrez, Gil R.: "Yacimientos Petroliferos en la Region de Macuspano, Tabasco," *Bol.*, Asoc. Mex. Geol. Petrol. (1950), v. 2, no. 8, pp. 499-510.

Gutierrez, Gil R. and Yzaguierre, Lauro A.: "A Look at the Isthmus of Tehuantepec," *Oil and Gas Jour.* (1960), v. 58, no. 7, pp. 159-163.

Gutierrez, Gil R. and Yzaguierre, Lauro A.: "Tehuantepec Oil Domes May Mark Potential Oil Territory for Mexico," *Oil and Gas Jour.* (1960), v. 58, no. 8, pp. 150-161.

Guyod, H. C.: "Temperature Well Logging: Part I, Heat Conductions," *Oil Weekly* (1946), v. 123, no. 8, pp. 35-39; "Part II, Salt Intrusions," no. 9, pp. 33-42; "Part III, Temperature Distribution in the Ground," no. 10, pp. 32-39; "Part IV, Wells in Thermal Equilibrium," no. 11, pp. 50-53; "Part V, Wells Not in Thermal Equilibrium; A, Rotary Holes," (1947), v. 124, no. 1, pp. 26-30, 32-34; "Part VI," no. 2, pp. 36-40; "Part VII, Conclusion," no. 3, pp. 38-40.

Guzman, Eduardo J., Juarez, C. Rodolfo and Lopez Ramos, Ernesto: "Geologia Petrolera de Mexico," *Bol.*, Asoc. Mex. Geol. Petrol. (1955), v. 7, pp. 137-171.

Hackbarth, R. E.: "West Columbia Field, Brazoria County, Texas," *Guidebook*, AAPG-SEPM-SEG Jt. Ann. Mtg. (March, 1953), Houston, Texas, pp. 161-162.

Hackford, J. E.: "The Origin of the Cap Rock of Salt Domes," *Oil Eng. and Finance* (1924), v. 5, no. 101, p. 512.

Hagen, Cecil: "Predict Discovery of Much Oil from Known Domes," *Oil and Gas Jour.* (1941), v. 39, no. 49, pp. 82-86, 97-98.

Hagen, Cecil and Cantrell, R. B.: "Development Trends in Salt Dome Exploration (U.S. Gulf Coast)," *Oil Weekly* (1946), v. 123, no. 3, pp. 87-88.

Hager, D. S. and Stiles, S.: "The Blue Ridge Salt Dome, Fort Bend County, Texas," *Bull.*, AAPG

(1925), v. 9, no. 2, pp. 304-316; *Geology of Salt Dome Oil Fields*, AAPG (1926), pp. 600-612.

Hager, Lee: "The Mounds of the Southern Oil Fields," *Eng. and Mining Jour.* (1904), v. 78, pp. 137-139, 180-183.

Hahn, F. F.: "The Form of Salt Deposits," *Econ. Geol.* (1912), v. 7, pp. 120-135.

Halbouty, James J. and Halbouty, Michel T.: "Oil and Gas Development in South Texas During 1941," *Trans.*, AIME, Petroleum Development and Technology (1942), v. 146, pp. 475-508.

Halbouty, Michel T.: "High Island Dome, Galveston County, Texas," *Bull.*, AAPG (1932), v. 16, 7, pp. 701-702.

Halbouty, Michel T.: "Vicksburg Formation in Deep Test, Acadia Parish, Louisiana," *Bull.*, AAPG (1932), v. 16, no. 6, pp. 609-610.

Halbouty, Michel T.: "Geology and Geophysics of Southeast Flank of Jennings Dome, Acadia Parish, Louisiana, With Special Reference to Overhang," *Bull.*, AAPG (1935), v. 19, no. 9, pp. 1308-1329; *Gulf Coast Oil Fields*, AAPG (1936), pp. 961-982.

Halbouty, Michel T.: "Geology and Geophysics Showing Cap Rock and Salt Overhang of High Island Dome, Galveston County, Texas," *Bull.*, AAPG (1936), v. 20, no. 5, pp. 560-611; correction, p. 818; *Gulf Coast Oil Fields*, AAPG, (1936), pp. 909-960; (abs.) *World Pet.*, v. 7, no. 8, p. 404.

Halbouty, Michel T.: "Mud Treatment for Heaving Shales," *World Pet.* (May, 1936), pp. 268-273.

Halbouty, Michel T.: *Petrographic and Physical Characteristics of Sands from Seven Gulf Coast Producing Horizons*, Gulf Publishing Company (1937), Houston, Texas, 106 pp.

Halbouty, Michel T.: "Geology and Economic Significance of Hastings Field, Brazoria County, Texas," *World Pet.* (Sept., 1937), pp. 36-51.

Halbouty, Michel T.: "Lafitte—World's Deepest Major Field," *World Pet.* (May, 1938), pp. 44-48.

Halbouty, Michel T.: "Oil and Gas Development of South Texas During 1937," *Trans.*, AIME, Petroleum Development and Technology (1938), v. 127, pp. 552-579.

Halbouty, Michel T.: "Probably Undiscovered Stratigraphic Traps on Gulf Coast," *World Pet.* (1938), v. 9, no. 6, pp. 27-39.

Halbouty, Michel T.: "Geology and Economic Significance of Barbers Hill Dome, Texas," *World Pet.* (1939), v. 10, no. 1, pp. 40-55.

Halbouty, Michel T.: "Oil and Gas Development of South Texas During 1938", *Trans.,* AIME, Petroleum Development and Technology (1939), v. 132, pp. 453-493.

Halbouty, Michel T.: "Temperature Effects on Oil Well Drilling, Part I," *Oil Weekly* (1939), v. 96, no. 2, pp. 10-16; "Temperature Affecting Crude Oil Producing, Part II," (1939), v. 96, no. 3, pp. 15-19.

Halbouty, Michel T.: "Temperature as Affecting Oil Well Drilling and Production," *Symposium on Temperatures,* Am. Inst. of Physics (1940), New York, pp. 1039-1057.

Halbouty, Michel T.: "Oil and Gas Development of South Texas During 1939," *Trans.,* AIME, Petroleum Development and Technology (1940), v. 136, pp. 458-498.

Halbouty, Michel T.: "Oil and Gas Development of South Texas During 1940," *Trans.,* AIME, Petroleum Development and Technology (1941), v. 142, pp. 476-504.

Halbouty, Michel T.: "Hawkins Field—Valuable Addition to Nation's Reserves," *World Pet.* (Feb., 1941), pp. 24-26.

Halbouty, Michel T.: "Geological and Engineering Thinking in the Gulf Coast of Texas and Louisiana—Past, Present and Future," *Jour. of Pet Tech.* (May, 1957), v. 9, no. 5, pp. 19-20; *Texas Oil Jour.,* pp. 18-19, 26; *The Independent Petroleum Association of America Monthly,* pp. 30-32, 39.

Halbouty, Michel T.: "Geological Prospects for Discoveries Brighter Than Ever," (Editorial) *World Oil,* Gulf Coast Issue (1958), v. 146, no. 7, pp. 102-103, 127-128.

Halbouty, Michel T.: "A Review of Geological Concepts and Economic Significance of Salt Domes in the Gulf Coast Region," *Bull.,* Houston Geol. Soc. (1959), v. 2, no. 2.

Halbouty, Michel T.: "South Liberty Field, Liberty County, Texas," *Typical Oil and Gas Fields of Southeast Texas,* Houston Geol. Soc. (1962), pp. 200-206.

Halbouty, Michel T.: "If They Had No Fear, Why Should We?," *Jour. of Pet. Tech.* (1962), v. 14, no. 8, pp. 821-824.

Halbouty, Michel T.: "Stratigraphic-Trap Possibilities in Upper Jurassic Rocks, San Marcos Arch, Texas," *Bull.,* AAPG (1966), v. 50, no. 1, pp. 3-24.

Halbouty, Michel T. and Barber, Thomas D.: "Port Acres and Port Arthur Fields, Jefferson County, Texas," *Trans., GCAGS* (1961), v. 11, pp. 225-234.

Halbouty, Michel T. and Clark, James A.: *Spin-*
dletop, Random House, Inc., (1952), New York, 306 pp.

Halbouty, Michel T. and Clark, James A.: "Spindletop's Second Fifty Years," *The Texas Preview* (Jan., 1953), pp. 26-28.

Halbouty, Michel T. and Eby, J. B.: "Spindletop Oil Field, Jefferson County, Texas," *Bull.,* AAPG (1937), v. 21, no. 4, pp. 475-490.

Halbouty, Michel T. and Eby, J. B.: "Geology and Economic Significance of Anahuac (Oil Field), Texas," *World Pet.* (1937), v. 8, no. 4, pp. 46-55.

Halbouty, Michel T. and Halbouty, James J.: "Oil and Gas Development in South Texas During 1941," *Trans.,* AIME, Petroleum Development and Technology (1942), v. 146, pp. 475-508.

Halbouty, Michel T. and Hardin, George C., Jr.: "Petroleum Geology of the Gulf Coast (United States)," *Oil and Gas Jour.* (1947), v. 46, no. 4, pp. 136-141.

Halbouty, Michel T. and Hardin, George C., Jr.: "Types of Hydrocarbon Accumulation and Geology of South Liberty Salt Dome, Liberty County, Texas," *Bull.,* AAPG (1951), v. 35, no. 9, pp. 1939-1977.

Halbouty, Michel T. and Hardin, George C., Jr.: "Salt Dome Geology May Enter New Phase," *Oil and Gas Jour.* (1954), v. 53, no. 26, pp. 93-98.

Halbouty, Michel T. and Hardin, George C., Jr.: "New Exploration Possibilities on Piercement Type Salt Domes Established by Thrust Fault at Boling Salt Dome, Wharton County, Texas," *Bull.,* AAPG (1954), v. 38, no. 8, pp. 1725-1740.

Halbouty, Michel T. and Hardin, George C., Jr.: "Reply to Thrust Faults on Salt Domes," *Bull.,* AAPG (1954), v. 38, no. 12, p. 2566.

Halbouty, Michel T. and Hardin, George C., Jr.: "New Geological Studies Result in Discoveries of Large Gas and Oil Reserves from Salt Dome Structures in the Texas-Louisiana Gulf Coast," *Proc.,* Fourth World Pet. Cong. (1955), Rome, Italy, sec. 1, pp. 83-101.

Halbouty, Michel T. and Hardin, George C., Jr.: "Factors Affecting Quantity of Oil Accumulation Around Some Texas Gulf Coast Piercement Type Salt Domes," *Bull.,* AAPG (1955), v. 39, no. 5, pp. 697-711.

Halbouty, Michel T. and Hardin, George C., Jr.: "Significance of Salt Dome Geology in Past and Future Oil Exploration," *The Oil Forum,* Special Oil Finders' Issue (April, 1955), pp. 129-131, 152.

Halbouty, Michel T. and Hardin, George C., Jr.:

"64 Chances to Find New Gulf Coast Oil," *Oil and Gas Jour.* (1955), v. 54, no. 23, pp. 321-324.

Halbouty, Michel T. and Hardin, George C., Jr.: "Genesis of Salt Domes of Gulf Coastal Plain," *Bull.,* AAPG (1956), v. 40, no. 4, pp. 737-746.

Halbouty, Michel T. and Hardin, George C., Jr.: "Exploration Techniques on Salt Domes of the Gulf Region of the U. S.," *Oil and Gas Jour.* (1959), v. 57, no. 24, pp. 134-137.

Halbouty, Michel T. and Hardin, George C., Jr.: "A Geological Appraisal of Present and Future Exploration Techniques on Salt Domes of the Gulf Region of the United States," *Paper 5,* Fifth World Pet. Cong. (1959), sec. 1, pp. 1-13; *Oil* (1959), v. 19, no. 8, pp. 33-42.

Halbouty, Michel T. and Hardin, George C., Jr.: "Nash Salt Dome, Fort Bend and Brazoria Counties, Texas," *Typical Oil and Gas Fields of Southeast Texas,* Houston Geol. Soc. (1962), pp. 134-137.

Halbouty, Michel T. and Kaldenbach, N. A.: "Characteristics, Methods of Combating, and Economic Importance of Heaving Shales," *Oil Weekly* (1938), v. 91, no. 7, pp. 17-26; no. 8, pp. 42-54.

Hallam, A. H.: "Salt Domes and Anticlines," *Oil Eng. and Finance* (1923), v. 3, p. 119.

Hamilton, W. F. and Bryan, C. L.: "Crowville Dome, Franklin Parish, Louisiana," *Bull.,* AAPG (1947), v. 31, no. 11, pp. 2049-2050.

Hammer, Sigmund: "The Salt Volume of Gulf Coast Salt Domes," AAPG-SEPM-SEG Jt. Ann. Mtg. (1953), Houston, Texas, p. 9, unpublished ms. (Courtesy Sigmund Hammer and Gulf Research and Development Company).

Hanna, Marcus A.: "Galena and Sphalerite in the Fayette at Orchard Salt Dome, Fort Bend County, Texas," *Bull.,* AAPG (1929), v. 13, no. 4, pp. 384-385.

Hanna, Marcus A.: "Secondary Salt Dome Materials of Coastal Plain of Texas and Louisiana," *Bull.,* AAPG (1930), v. 14, no. 11, pp. 1469-1475.

Hanna, Marcus A.: "Salt Domes of the United States," *Bull.,* GSA (1932), v. 43, p. 160; *Pan Am. Geologist,* v. 57, no. 1, pp. 75-76.

Hanna, Marcus A.: (Review) "Origin of the Anhydrite Cap Rock of American Salt Domes, by M. I. Goldman," *Econ. Geol.* (1933), v. 31, no. 6, pp. 642-644.

Hanna, Marcus A.: "Geology of the Gulf Coast Salt Domes," *Problems of Petroleum Geology,* AAPG (1934), pp. 629-678.

Hanna, Marcus A.: "Evidence of Erosion of Salt Stock in Gulf Coast Salt Plug in Late Oligocene," *Bull.,* AAPG (1939), v. 23, no. 4, pp. 604-607; corrections, p. 1576; v. 27, no. 1, pp. 85-86.

Hanna, Marcus A.: "Salt Domes of the Gulf Coast Region," *Oil* (1944), v. 4, no. 4, pp. 29-30.

Hanna, Marcus A.: (abs.) "Salt Dome Configuration," *Bull.,* AAPG (1948), v. 33, no. 1, pp. 109; *Oil and Gas Jour.* (1948), v. 47, no. 32, p. 104.

Hanna, Marcus A.: "Tectonics of Gulf Coast Salt Domes," (abs.) *Trans.,* GCAGS (1958), v. 8, p. 100.

Hanna, Marcus A.: "Salt Domes; Favorite Home for Oil," *Oil and Gas Jour.* (1959), v. 57, no. 6, pp. 138-142.

Hanna, Marcus A. and Parker, W. G.: "Notes on an Occurrence of Galena at Pierce Junction Salt Dome, Harris County, Texas," *Bull.,* AAPG (1933), v. 17, no. 4, pp. 438-439.

Hanna, Marcus A. and Wolf, A. G.: "Texas and Louisiana Salt Dome Cap Rock Minerals," *Bull.,* AAPG (1934), v. 18, no. 2, pp. 212-225; *Gulf Coast Oil Fields,* AAPG (1936), pp. 119-132.

Hanna, Marcus A. and Wolf, A. G.: "Aragonite in Texas and Louisiana Salt Dome Cap Rocks," *Bull.,* AAPG (1938), v. 22, no. 2, pp. 217-220.

Hanna, Marcus A. and Wolf, A. G.: "Gold, Silver and Other Elements in Salt Dome Cap Rocks," *Bull.,* AAPG (1941), v. 25, no. 4, pp. 750-752.

Harbort, E.: "Zur Frage der Aufpressungsvorgelange und des Alters der Nordwestdeutschen Salzvorkommen," *Kali* (1913), Heft 5, p. 112.

Harbort, E.: "Zur Geologie der Nordhannoverschen Salzhorste," *Monatsber. d. Deutsch. Geol. Ges.,* 62 (1910), p. 326.

Hardin, Frank R. and Hardin, George C., Jr.: "Contemporaneous Normal Faults of Gulf Coast and Their Relation to Flexures," *Bull.,* AAPG (1961), v. 45, no. 2, pp. 238-248.

Hardin, George C., Jr.: "Economic Factors in the Geological Appraisal of Wildcat Prospects," *Trans.,* GCAGS (1958), v. 8, pp. 14-19; *World Oil,* Part I (1959), v. 148, no. 4, pp. 119-120; Part II (1959), v. 148, no. 5, pp. 138-141.

Hardin, George C., Jr. and Halbouty, Michel T.: "Petroleum Geology of the Gulf Coast (United States)," *Oil and Gas Jour.* (1947), v. 46, no. 4, pp. 136-141, 194-196.

Hardin, George C., Jr. and Halbouty, Michel T.: "Types of Hydrocarbon Accumulation and Geology of South Liberty Salt Dome, Liberty County,

Texas," *Bull.,* AAPG (1951), v. 35, no. 9, pp. 1939-1977.

Hardin, George C., Jr. and Halbouty, Michel T.: "New Exploration Possibilities on Piercement Type Salt Domes Established by Thrust Fault at Boling Salt Dome, Wharton County, Texas," *Bull.,* AAPG (1954), v. 38, no. 8, pp. 1725-1740.

Hardin, George C., Jr. and Halbouty, Michel T.: "Reply to Thrust Faults on Salt Domes," *Bull.,* AAPG (1954), v. 38, no. 12, p. 2566.

Hardin, George C., Jr. and Halbouty, Michel T.: "Salt Dome Geology May Enter New Phase," *Oil and Gas Jour.* (1954), v. 53, no. 26, pp. 93-98.

Hardin, George C., Jr. and Halbouty, Michel T.: "Factors Affecting Quantity of Oil Accumulation Around Some Texas Gulf Coast Piercement Type Salt Domes," *Bull.,* AAPG (1955), v. 39, no. 5, pp. 697-711.

Hardin, George C., Jr. and Halbouty, Michel T.: "New Geological Studies Result in Discoveries of Large Gas and Oil Reserves from Salt Dome Structures in the Texas-Louisiana Gulf Coast," *Proc., Fourth World Pet. Cong.* (1955), Rome, sec. 1, pp. 83-101.

Hardin, George C., Jr. and Halbouty, Michel T.: "Significance of Salt Dome Geology in Past and Future Oil Exploration," *The Oil Forum,* Special Oil Finders' Issue (April, 1955), pp. 129-131, 152.

Hardin, George C., Jr. and Halbouty, Michel T.: "64 Chances to Find New Gulf Coast Oil," *Oil and Gas Jour.* (1955), v. 54, no. 23, pp. 321-324.

Hardin, George C., Jr. and Halbouty, Michel T.: "Genesis of Salt Domes of Gulf Coastal Plain," *Bull.,* AAPG (1956), v. 40, no. 4, pp. 737-746.

Hardin, George C., Jr. and Halbouty, Michel T.: "A Geological Appraisal of Present and Future Exploration Techniques on Salt Domes of the Gulf Region of the United States," *Paper 5,* Fifth World Pet. Cong (1959), sec. 1, pp. 1-13; *Oil* (1959), v. 19, no. 8, pp. 33-42.

Hardin, George C., Jr. and Halbouty, Michel T.: "Exploration Techniques on Salt Domes of the Gulf Region of the United States," *Oil and Gas Jour.* (1959), v. 57, no. 24, pp. 134-137.

Hardin, George C., Jr. and Halbouty, Michel T.: "Nash Salt Dome, Fort Bend and Brazoria Counties, Texas," *Typical Oil and Gas Fields of Southeast Texas,* Houston Geol. Soc. (1962), pp. 134-137.

Hardin, George C., Jr. and Hardin, Frank R.: "Contemporaneous Normal Faults of Gulf Coast and Their Relation to Flexures," *Bull.,* AAPG (1960), v. 45, no. 2, pp. 238-248.

Hare, J. E.: "Salt Domes of the Gulf Coast and Their Relation to Petroleum," *MS Thesis,* Yale U. (1922), Dept. of Geol.

Harkins, T. I. and Eby, J. B.: "Geophysical History of Darrow Dome, Ascension Parish, Louisiana," *Tech. Pub. 1495,* AIME (1942); *Trans.,* AIME, v. 151, pp. 253-260; *Geophysical Case Histories,* SEG (1948), v. 1, pp. 144-152.

Harper, Douglas C. and Ruhe, Robert W., Jr.: "Maps Predict Problem Formations," *Oil and Gas Jour.* (April 29, 1963).

Harrell, David C. and Lynch, William D.: "Developments in Southeastern States in 1960," *Bull.,* AAPG (1961), v. 45, no. 6, pp. 903-909.

Harris, G. D.: "Notes on the Geology of the Winnfield Sheet," *Rept. of 1907,* Geol. Svy. of La. (1907), Bull. 5.

Harris, G. D.: "Rock Salt," *Rept. of 1907,* La. Geol. Svy. (1908), Bull. 7.

Harris, G. D.: "Salt in Louisiana, with Special Reference to Its Geologic Occurrence," *Bull.,* La. Geol. Svy. (1908), v. 7, pp. 5-59.

Harris, G. D.: "The Salt Domes of Louisiana and Texas," *Science* (1908), new ser., v. 27, pp. 347-348.

Harris, G. D.: "The Geological Occurrence of Rock Salt in Louisiana and East Texas," *Econ. Geol.* (1909), v. 4, pp. 12-34.

Harris, G. D.: "Dome Theories Applied to Gulf Coast Geology," *Science* (1912), new ser., v. 36, pp. 173-174.

Harris, G. D.: "Oil Concentration About Salt Domes," *Science* (1912), new ser. v. 35, pp. 546-547.

Harris, G. D.: "Immense Salt Concretions," *Pop. Sci. Monthly* (1913), v. 82, pp. 187-191.

Harris, G. D., Maurey, F. J. and Reinecke, L.: "Rock Salt, Its Origin, Geological Occurrence and Economic Importance in the State of Louisiana, Together with Brief Notes and References to all Known Salt Deposits and Industries of the World," *Bull.,* La. Geol. Svy. (1908), v. 7, 259 pp.

Harris, G. D. and Veatch, A. C.: "A Preliminary Report on the Geological Survey of Louisiana," *Rept. for 1899,* La. Geol. Svy. (1899), pp. 9-138.

Harris, R. M. and Payne, W. M.: "Developments in Southeastern States in 1946 and 1947," *Bull.,* AAPG (1948), v. 32, no. 6, pp. 1065-1076.

Harris, R. M. and Payne, W.: "Developments in Southeastern States in 1948," *Bull.,* AAPG (1949), v. 33, no. 6, pp. 1002-1010.

Harrison, J. V.: "Salt Domes in Persia," *Jour.*

Inst. Pet. (1931), v. 17, pp. 300-320.

Harrison, T. S.: "Colorado-Utah Salt Domes," *Bull.*, AAPG (1927), v. 11, no. 2, pp. 111-133.

Hawkins, A. C.: "Minerals of the Saline Domes of the Texas-Louisiana Coastal Plain," *Am. Mineralogist* (1918), v. 3, pp. 189-192.

Hawkins, Murphy E. and Jirik, C. J.: "Salt Domes in Texas, Louisiana, Mississippi, Alabama, and Offshore Tidelands: A Survey," *Inf. Circ.*, U.S. Dept. of the Interior, Bur. of Mines (in press, 1966).

Hawkins, Murray F., Jr., Rayne, John R. and Craft, B. C.: "The Reservoir Mechanism of Sulphur Recovery," *Trans.*, AIME (1956), v. 207, pp. 246-251; *Tech. Paper 4385*, AIME; *Jour. of Pet. Tech.* (1956), v. 8, no. 11, pp. 246-251.

Hayes, Mack, Jr.: "Developments in East Texas in 1950," *Bull.*, AAPG (1951), v. 35, no. 6, pp. 1313-1321.

Hayes, W. E., Fietz, R. P. and Scott, K. R.: "Geology of the Eagle Mills Formation," *Trans.*, GCAGS (1961), v. 11, pp. 1-14.

Hazelhurst, J. N.: "A Piece of Difficult Shaft Sinking in Developing the Salt Mines of Grand Cote Island," *Eng. News* (Nov. 7, 1901).

Hazzard, R. T. and Blanpied, B. W.: "Developments in North Louisiana and South Arkansas in 1941," *Bull.*, AAPG (1942), v. 26, no. 6, pp. 1250-1276.

Hazzard, R. T. and Blanpied, B. W.: "Interesting Wildcat Wells Drilled in North Louisiana in 1942," *Bull.*, AAPG (1944), v. 28, no. 4, pp. 554-561.

Hazzard, R. T. and Blanpied, B. W.: "Salt Dome Discoveries in North Louisiana in 1942," *Bull.*, AAPG (1944), v. 28, no. 4, pp. 561-562.

Hazzard, R. T., Blanpied, B. W., and Spooner, W. C.: "Notes on Correlations of the Cretaceous of East Texas, South Arkansas, North Louisiana, Mississippi and Alabama," *1945 Ref. Rept.*, Shreveport Geol. Soc. (1947), v. 2, pp. 472-481.

Hazzard, R. T., Spooner, W. C. and Blanpied, B. W.: "Notes on the Stratigraphy of Formations Which Underlie the Smackover Limestone in South Arkansas, Northeast Texas and North Louisiana," *1945 Ref. Rept.*, Shreveport Geol. Soc. (1947), v. 2, pp. 483-503.

Heald, K. C.: "Sandstone Inclusion in Salt in Mine on Avery's Island," *Bull.*, AAPG (1924), v. 8, no. 5, pp. 674-676.

Heald, K. C.: "Highlights of Domestic Development in 1946," *Bull.*, AAPG (1947), v. 31, no. 7, pp. 1125-1134.

Heath, F. E., Waters, J. A. and Ferguson, W. B.: "Clay Creek Salt Dome, Washington County, Texas," *Bull.*, AAPG (1931), v. 15, no. 1, pp. 43-60; (abs.) *Pan Am. Geologist*, v. 53, no. 3, p. 226.

Hedberg, Hollis D.: "Geologic Aspects of Origin of Petroleum," *Bull.*, AAPG (1964), v. 48, no. 11, pp. 1775-1803.

Hendricks, L. C. and Sellards, E. H.: "Occurrence of Oil and Gas in Texas," *Pub. 4301*, Tex. U. (1946), pp. 179-190.

Hendricks, L. C. and Sellards, E. H.: *Structural Map of Texas*, Third Ed., Tex. U., Bur. Econ. Geol.

Hendy, W. J., Dobbins, W. D. and Morren, J. H.: "Developments in South Texas in 1957," *Bull.*, AAPG (1958), v. 42, no. 6, pp. 1279-1288.

Henley, A. S.: "The Big Hill Salt Dome, Jefferson County, Texas," *Bull.*, AAPG (1925), v. 9, no. 3, pp. 590-593; *Geology of Salt Dome Oil Fields*, AAPG (1926), pp. 497-500.

Henninger, W. F.: "Occurrence of Sulphur Waters in the Gulf Coast of Texas and Louisiana, and Their Significance in Locating New Domes," *Bull.*, AAPG (1925), v. 9, no. 1, pp. 35-37; *Geology of Salt Dome Oil Fields*, AAPG (1926), pp. 774-776.

Herald, F. A. (ed.): "Occurrence of Oil and Gas in Northeast Texas," *Pub. 5116*, Tex. U. (1951), 449 pp.

Hernandez, Osuna Alfonso and Cornejo, Toledo Alfonso: "Las Anomalias Gravimetricas en la Cuenca Salina del Istmo, Planicie Costera de Tabasco, Campeche, Peninsula de Yucatan," *Bol.*, Asoc. Mex. Geol. Petrol. (1950), v. 2, no. 7, pp. 453-460.

Herold, C. L. and Wendlandt, E. A.: "Resume of Developments in East Texas During 1937," *Bull.*, AAPG (1938), v. 22, no. 6, pp. 728-735.

Herring, L. B.: "Developments and Status of Oil Reserves in South Texas, 1939," *Bull.*, AAPG (1940), v. 24, no. 6, pp. 1068-1078.

Herring, L. B.: "Developments in South Texas During 1940," *Bull.*, AAPG (1941), v. 25, no. 6, pp. 1037-1043; (abs.) v. 25, no. 6, pp. 931-932.

Herring, L. B.: "Developments in South Texas During 1941," *Bull.*, AAPG (1942), v. 26, no. 6, pp. 1000-1006.

Hickey, Maude and Barton, D. C.: "The Continental Margin at Texas-Louisiana Gulf Coast," *Trans.*, Amer. Geophys. Union, 14th Ann. Mtg. (1933), pp. 16-20.

Hickey, Maude, Barton, D. C. and Ritz, C. H.: "Gulf Coast Geosyncline," *Bull.*, AAPG (1933), v. 17, no. 12, pp. 1446-1458; *Gulf Coast Oil Fields,* AAPG (1936), pp. 192-204; (abs.) *Pan Am. Geologist,* v. 59, p. 230.

Hightower, Maxwell L., Muehlberger, William R. and Clabaugh, Patricia S.: "Palestine and Grand Saline Salt Domes," *Field Excursion No. 6,* Geology of the Gulf Coast and Central Texas and Guidebook of Excursions, Houston Geol. Soc. (1962), Houston, Texas, pp. 266-277.

Hilgard, E. W.: "On the Geology of Lower Louisiana and the Rock Salt Deposit of Petite Anse," *Am. Jour. Sci.* (1869), ser. 2, v. 47, pp. 77-88.

Hilgard, E. W.: "Preliminary Report of a Geological Reconnaissance of Louisiana," *DeBow's New Orleans Monthly Rev.* (1869), v. 37-38, pp. 754-769.

Hilgard, E. W.: "On the Geology of the Delta, and the Mudlumps of the Passes of the Mississippi," *Am. Jour. Sci.* (1871), ser. 3, v. 1, pp. 238-246, 356-368, 425-434.

Hilgard, E. W.: "On the Geological History of the Gulf of Mexico," *Am. Jour. Sci.* (1871), ser. 3, v. 2, pp. 391-404; *Proc.*, Am. Assoc. Adv. Sci., v. 20, pp. 222-236; *Sup. Ann. Rept.,* LSU (1872), pp. 207-222; *Am. Naturalist,* v. 5, pp. 514-518.

Hilgard, E. W.: "Remarks on the Age of the Rock Salt Deposits of Petite Anse," *Am. Naturalist* (1871), v. 5, p. 523.

Hilgard, E. W.: "On the Geology of Lower Louisiana and Salt Deposit on Petite Anse Island," *Art. 3,* Smithsonian Contr. Knowledge (1872), no. 248, 34 pp.

Hill, R. T.: "The Gulf Coast Salt Domes," *Econ. Geol.* (1919), v. 14, no. 8, pp. 643-644.

Hillyer, L. D.: "A Study of Intersecting Faults and Their Effects on Accumulation in the Clam Lake Field, Jefferson County, Texas," *Trans.*, GCAGS, 1st Ann. Mtg. (Nov., 1951) New Orleans, La., p. 76.

Hines, E. R., Jr. and Thomas, G. T. : "Developments in Southeastern States in 1957," *Bull.*, AAPG (1958), v. 42, no. 6, pp. 1327-1338.

Hinson, Hillord: "Blue Ridge Field, Fort Bend County, Texas," *Guidebook*, AAPG-SEPM-SEG Jt. Ann. Mtg. (March, 1953), Houston, Texas, pp. 82-85.

Hirtz, P., Wenger, R. and Belmonte, Y.: "The Salt Basins of the Gabon and the Congo (Brazzaville): A Tentative Palaeographic Interpretation," *Salt Basins Around Africa,* The Institute of Petroleum (1965), London, pp. 55-78.

Hoffmeister, W. S. and Robinson, V. D.: "Developments in South Arkansas and North Louisiana in 1945," *Bull.*, AAPG (1946), v. 30, no. 6, pp. 1007-1009.

Hofman, H. O. and Mostowitsch, W.: "The Reduction of Calcium Sulfate by Carbon Monoxide and the Oxidation of Calcium Sulfide," *Trans.*, AIME (1910), v. 41, pp. 763-783.

Holden, F. T.: "Developments in Southeastern States in 1949," *Bull.*, AAPG (1950), v. 34, no. 6, pp. 1212-1223.

Holden, F. T.: "Developments in Southeastern States in 1950," *Bull.*, AAPG (1951), v. 35, no. 6, pp. 1352-1365.

Hollingsworth, W. E. and Weston, H. C.: "Chacahoula Dome, La Fourche and Terrebonne Parishes, Louisiana, Geophysical History," *Geophysical Case Histories,* SEG (1956), v. 2, pp. 113-129.

Hoot, Carl: "Salt Dome Exploration Picks up in East Texas," *Oil and Gas Jour.* (1958), v. 56, no. 10, pp. 248-250.

Hopkins, F. V.: *First Annual Report of the Louisiana State Geological Survey; Annual Report of Board of Supervisors of the Louisiana State Seminary of Learning and Military Academy for the Year Ending Dec. 31, 1869,* New Orleans (1870), pp. 77-109.

Hopkins, H. F., Saye, Frank, Hower, Wayne and Aulick, Burton: "Improved Production by Chemical Treatment in Gulf Coast Areas," *Jour. of Pet. Tech.* (1952), v. 4, no. 9, pp. 13-16.

Hopkins, O. B.: "The Palestine Salt Dome, Anderson County, Texas," *Bull. 661,* USGS (1917), pp. 253-270; (abs.) *Jour.,* Washington Acad. Sci., v. 8, p. 173.

Hopkins, O. B.: "The Brenham Salt Dome, Washington and Austin Counties, Texas," *Bull. 661,* USGS (1917), pp. 271-280.

Hopkins, O. B. and Powers, Sidney: "The Brooks, Steen and Grand Saline Salt Domes, Smith and Van Zandt Counties, Texas," *Bull. 736,* USGS (1922), pp. 179-239.

Hoppins, Charles: "Pierce Junction is Hottest Spot on Texas Gulf Coast," *World Oil* (1956), v. 142, no. 7, pp. 205-214.

Horton, C. W.: "Salt Diffusion in Woodbine Sand Waters, East Texas," *Bull.*, AAPG (1944), v. 28, no. 11, pp. 1635-1641.

Horvitz, Leo: "On Geochemical Prospecting,"

Geophysics (1939), v. 4, no. 3, pp. 210-228.

Horvitz, Leo: "Recent Developments in Geo-chemical Prospecting for Petroleum," *Geophysics* (1945), v. 10, no. 4, pp. 487-493.

Hough, Leo W., Raggio, David L., Sandberg, Adolph E. and Martin, James L.: "Geology of Webster Parish," *Bull. 29,* La. Geol. Svy. (1954), Dept of Conserv., 252 pp.

Hough, W. H.: "Distribution of Heterostegina Lime, Fannett Field, Jefferson C o u n t y, Texas," (abs.), *Oil and Gas Jour.* (1948), v. 47, no. 30, p. 93.

Houston Geological Society: "An Introduction to Gulf Coast Oil Fields," (1941), Houston, Texas, 22 unnumbered pp.

Howe, H. V.: "The Many Salt Dome, Sabine Parish, Louisiana," *Bull.,* AAPG (1925), v. 9, no. 1, pp. 170-171.

Howe, H. V.: "Review of Tertiary Stratigraphy of Louisiana," *Bull.,* AAPG (1933), v. 17, no. 6, pp. 613-655; *Gulf Coast Oil Fields,* AAPG (1936), pp. 383-424.

Howe, H. V.: "Future Louisiana Oil Fields," *Oil* (1944), v. 4, pp. 22-24.

Howe, H. V. and McGuirt, J. H.: "Salt Domes of Cameron and Vermilion Parishes," *Bull. 6,* La. Geol. Svy. (1935), pp. 73-166.

Howe, H. V. and McGuirt, J. H.: "Salt Domes of Plaquemines and St. Bernard Parishes," *Bull. 8,* La. Geol. Svy. (1936), pp. 200-278.

Howe, H. V. and McGuirt, J. H.: "Salt Domes of Iberville and Ascension Parishes," *Bull. 13,* La. Geol. Svy. (1938), pp. 87-187.

Howe, H. V. and Moresi, C. K.: "Geology of Iberia Parish," *Bull. 1,* La. Geol. Svy. (1931), 187 pp.

Howe, H. V. and Moresi, C. K.: "Geology of Lafayette and St. Martin Parishes, Louisiana," *Bull. 3,* La. Geol. Svy. (1933), 328 pp.

Howe, H. V., Russell, R. J. and McGuirt, J. H.: "Physiography of Coastal Southwest Louisiana," *Bull. 6,* La. Geol. Svy. (1935), pp. 1-68.

Howe, H. V., Russell, R. J., McGuirt, J. H., Craft, B. C. and Stephenson, M. B.: "Reports on the Geology of Cameron and Vermilion Parishes," *Bull. 6,* La. Geol. Svy. (1935), 242 pp.

Howell, J. V. (ed.): *Structure of Typical American Oil Fields,* Vol. III, American Association of Petroleum Geologists (1948), Tulsa, Oklahoma, 516 pp.

Howell, Lynn G. and Kean, C. H.: "Note on

Wave-Guide Propagation Over a Shallow Salt Dome," *Geophysics* (1953), v. 18, no. 2, pp. 338-339.

Hower, Wayne, Aulick, Burton, Hopkins, H. F. and Saye, Frank: "Improved Production by Chemical Treatment in Gulf Coast Areas," *Jour. of Pet. Tech.* (1952), v. 4, no. 9, pp. 13-16.

Hoy, R. B., Foose, R. M. and O'Neill, B. J., Jr.: "Structure of Winnfield Salt Dome, Winn Parish, Louisiana," *Bull.,* AAPG (1962), v. 46, no. 8, pp. 1444-1459.

Hoy, R. B. and Kuhn, Robert: "Structure of Winnfield Salt Dome, Winn Parish, Louisiana," *Bull.,* AAPG (1964), v. 48, no. 3, pp. 360-361.

Hoylman, H. Wayne: "Seismograph Evidence on the Depth of the Salt in Southeast Texas," *Geophysics* (1945), v. 10, no. 3, p. 450.

Hoylman, H. Wayne: "Seismograph Evidence on Depth of Salt Column, Moss Bluff Dome, Texas," *Geophysics* (1946), v. 11, no. 2, pp. 128-134.

Hubbert, M. K.: "Theory of Scale Models as Applied to the Study of Geologic Structures," *PhD Dissertation,* Chicago U. (1937), Dept. of Geol.; *Bull.,* GSA (1937), v. 48, pp. 1459-1519.

Hughes, Dudley J.: "Faulting Associated with Deep Seated Salt Domes in the Northeast Portion of the Mississippi Salt Basin," *Trans.,* GCAGS (1960), v. 10, pp. 154-173.

Hughes, U. B.: "Developments in Mississippi in 1940," *Bull.,* AAPG (1941), v. 25, no. 6, pp. 1015-1023.

Hughes, U. B.: "Developments in Southeastern United States in 1941," *Bull.,* AAPG (1942), v. 26, no. 6, pp. 991-999.

Hughes, U. B.: "Developments in Southeastern United States in 1943," *Bull.,* AAPG (1944), v. 28, no. 6, pp. 801-805.

Hull, J. P. D.: "Prothro Salt Dome, Bienville Parish, Louisiana," *Bull.,* AAPG (1925), v. 9, no. 5, pp. 904-906.

Humphrey, W. E.: *Notes on Geology of Northeast Mexico,* Corpus Christi Geol. Soc. (1956), 41 pp.; *Guidebook,* Laredo to Monterrey Field Trip (Supp.), Corpus Christi Geol. Soc. (1956), pp. 9-11; *Guidebook,* Corpus Christi Geol. Soc., 11th Ann. Field Trip (1961), pp. 6-8.

Humphrey, W. E.: "Tectonic Framework of Northeast Mexico," *Trans.,* GCAGS (1956), v. 6, pp. 25-35.

Humphrey, W. E. and Diaz Gonzalez, T. E.: "Secuencia Mesozoica. Anticlinal de las Grutas de

Garcia en la Sierra del Fraile, a 30 Kilometros al NW de la Ciudad de Monterrey," *Congreso Geologico Internacional* (1958), pp. 26-31.

Humphrey, W. E. and Diaz Gonzalez, T. E.: "Secuencia Mesozoica en el Arroyo de San Rouge, Cerro de la Silla, Nuevo Leon, Aproximadamente a 15 Kilometros al SE de la Ciudad de Monterrey, Nuevo Leon," *Congreso Geologico Internacional* (1958), pp. 18-23.

Humphrey, W. E. and Diaz Gonzalez, T. E.: "Secuencia Mesozoica. Portal de la Muralla, Sierra de la Gavia, Coahuila," *Congreso Geologico Internacional* (1958), pp. 41-45.

Hundley, H. B. and Sevier, Richard P.: "Developments in Arkansas and North Louisiana in 1961," *Bull.*, AAPG (1962), v. 46, no. 6, pp. 938-952.

Hundley, H. B. and Womack, S. A., Jr.; "Developments in Arkansas and North Louisiana in 1951," *Bull.*, AAPG (1952), v. 36, no. 6, pp. 1220-1227.

Huner, John, Jr.: "Geology of Caldwell and Winn Parishes, Louisiana," *Bull. 15*, La. Geol. Svy. (1939), 356 pp.

Hungsberg, Ulrich: "Origen del Azufre en el Casquete de los Domos Salinos de la Cuenca Salina del Istmo de Tehuantepec," *Bol. 51* (1960), Consejo de Recursos Naturales no Renovables, 96 pp.

Hunt, V. G. and O'Connor, J.P., Jr.; "Developments in East Texas in 1953," *Bull.*, AAPG (1954), v. 38, no. 6, pp. 1196-1207.

Hurlbut, C. S., Jr. and Taylor, R. E.: "Hilgardite, a New Mineral Species from Choctaw Salt Dome, Louisiana," *Am. Mineralogist* (1937), v. 22, no. 10, pp. 1052-1057.

Hurlbut, C. S., Jr. and Taylor, R. E.: "Notes on Minerals Associated with Hilgardite," *Am. Mineralogist* (1938), v. 23, no. 12, pt. 1, pp. 898-902.

Hurlbut, E. M., Jr.: (Summary) "Limestone on Damon Mound, Brazoria County, Texas," *Min. Res. Circ. 31*, Tex. U. (1944), 3 pp.

Hutchins, R. M., Jr., Lake, C. L., Lewis, Ray C., O'Bannon, P. H., Self, S. R., Warner, C. A. Allison, A. P., Beckelhymer, R. L. and Benson, Don G.: "Geology of Katy Field, Waller, Harris and Fort Bend Counties, Texas," *Bull.*, AAPG (1946), v. 30, no. 2, pp. 157-180.

Hyer, D. E. and Latshaw, W.: "Developments in Louisiana Gulf Coast in 1958," *Bull.*, AAPG (1959), v. 43, no. 6, pp. 1312-1321.

Iles, G. G.: "Developments in Louisiana Gulf Coast in 1951," *Bull.*, AAPG (1952), v. 36, no. 6, pp. 1211-1219.

Illing, V. C.: "Geology Applied to Petroleum," *Proc.*, Geologists Assoc. (1942), v. 53, pts. 3 and 4, pp. 156-187.

Illing, V. C.: "Geology Applied to Petroleum: Part 1, Petroleum in the Sedimentary Cycle," *Oil Weekly* (1946), v. 122, no. 7, pp. 34-35, 42; "Parts II and III, Types of Regional Structure," no. 13, pp. 30-33, (1947), v. 123, no. 1, pp. 27-29; "Part IV, Oil Recovery and Exploration," no. 2, pp. 39-42, 44; "Part V, Influence of Oil on Geology; no. 3, pp. 174, 176.

Imlay, R. W.: "Lower Cretaceous and Jurassic Formations of Southern Arkansas and their Oil and Gas Possibilities," *Inf. Circ. 12*, Ark. Geol. Svy. (1940), 64 pp.

Imlay, R. W.: (abs.) "Upper Jurassic Formations of the Southern States," *Bull.*, GSA (1942), v. 53, pp. 1803-1804.

Imlay, R. W.: "Jurassic Formations of Gulf Region of North America, including United States, Mexico, and Cuba," *Bull.*, AAPG (1943), v. 27, no. 11, pp. 1407-1533.

Imlay, R. W. and Williams, J. S.: "Late Paleozoic Age of Morehouse Formation of Northeastern Louisiana," *Bull.*, AAPG (1942), v. 26, no. 10, pp. 1672-1673.

Imlay, R. W., Cepeda E., Alvarez, M. and Diaz, T.: "Stratigraphic Relations of Certain Jurassic Formations in Eastern Mexico," *Bull.*, AAPG (1948), v. 32, no. 9, pp. 1750-1761.

Ingalls, Phillip C.: "Salt Domes Still Reign in Gulf Coast," *Oil and Gas Jour.* (1953), v. 52, no. 7, p. 357.

Ingram, Robert: "Spindletop—Its Roar Echoed Around the World," *Oil and Gas Jour.* (1941), v. 39, no. 49, pp. 42-46,

International Oil Scouts Association: *International Oil and Gas Development*, Year Book (1962-1965), Vols. 32-35, Austin, Texas.

International Oil Scouts Association and Society of Petroleum Engineers of AIME: *International Oil and Gas Development*, Year Book (1960-1961), Vols. 30-31, Austin, Texas.

Islas Leal, Juventino and Basurto Garcia, Jesus: "El Metodo Sismologico de Refraccion en la Cuenca Salina del Istmo," *Bol.*, Asoc. Mex. Geol. Petrol. (1950), v. 2, no. 7, pp. 461-472.

Israelsky, M. C.: "Cores From a Deep Well at Rodessa, Caddo Parish, Louisiana," *Bull.*, AAPG (1938), v. 22, no. 6, pp. 764-770.

Ives, G. O.: "Mississippi Becomes a Major Oil Center," *Oil Weekly* (1945), v. 118, no. 4, pp. 33-42.

Jackson, A. and Shaub, H. P.: "The Northwestern Oil Basin of Borneo," *Habitat of Oil,* AAPG (1958), pp. 1330-1336.

Jackson, J. Roy, Jr.: "Unconformity Traps Around Piercement Salt Domes in South Louisiana," (abs.) *Oil and Gas Jour.* (1956), v. 54, no. 53, pp. 142-144.

Jacoby, C. H. and Walden, Wm.: "Exploration by Horizontal Drilling at Avery Island, Louisiana," *Symposium on Salt,* Northern Geol. Soc., Inc. (1963), Cleveland, Ohio, pp. 367-378.

Janosky, R. A., Grayson, R. W. and Bianchi, J. C., Jr.: "Developments in South Texas in 1953," *Bull.,* AAPG (1954), v. 38, no. 6, pp. 1184-1195.

Janssen, R. E.: "(Review of) Origin of the Cap Rock of Louisiana Salt Domes, by R. E. Taylor," *Jour. Geol.* (1939), v. 47, p. 222.

Jenkinson, Lewis F. and Sevier, Richard P.: "Developments in Arkansas and North Louisiana in 1960," *Bull.,* AAPG (1961), v. 45, no. 6, pp. 889-902.

Jenny, W. P.: "Geopyhsicial Prospecting in Gulf Coast District Had to Overcome Many Difficulties," *Oil and Gas Jour.* (1932), v. 31, no. 8, pp. 14, 16.

Jenny, W. P.: "Structural Correlation of Micromagnetic and Reflection Data," *Oil Weekly* (1946), v. 124, no. 3, pp. 32-33.

Jenny, W. P.: "Magnetic Vector Study of Regional and Local Geologic Structure in Principal Oil States," *Early Geophysical Papers,* SEG (1957), pp. 335-363; *Trans.,* SEG (1932), v. 3, pp. 7-33.

Jenswold, Nancy and Scrafford, Bruce: "Developments in South Texas in 1950," *Bull.,* AAPG (1951), v. 35, no. 6, pp. 1300-1312.

Jessen, F. W. and Brown, K. E.: "Effect of Pressure and Temperature on Cavities in Salt," *Trans.,* AIME (1959), v. 216, pp. 341-345; *Jour. of Pet. Tech.* (1959), v. 11, no. 12.

Jirik, C. J. and Hawkins, Murphy E.: "Salt Domes in Texas, Louisiana, Mississippi, Alabama, and Offshore Tidelands: A Survey," *Inf. Circ.,* U. S. Dept. of the Interior, Bur. of Mines (in press, 1966).

Johnson, Thelma, et al: *The Spindletop Oil Field, a History of its Discovery and Development,* Neches Printing Company, (1927) Beaumont, Texas.

Jones, Douglas E. and Butler, E. Ann: "Cretaceous Ostracoda of Prothro and Rayburn's Salt Domes, Bienville Parish, Louisiana," *Bull. 32,* La. Geol. Svy. (1957), Dept. of Conserv., 65 pp.

Jones, F. O.: "Formation and Geology of the Salt Deposits," *Sci. Am.* (1902), v. 87, p. 59.

Jones, R. A.: "Manner of Salt Flowage in Salt Domes," *Oil Weekly* (1932), v. 66, no. 7, pp. 31-32, 35-36.

Jones, W. A.: "Intrusive Origin of the Gulf Coast Salt Domes, Its Bearing on the Accumulation of Oil," *Econ. Geol.* (1918), v. 13, no. 8, pp. 621-622.

Jones, Walter B.: "Alabama's Geology—and Summary of State's Oil and Gas Development," *Oil and Gas Jour.* (1952), v. 51, no. 6, pp. 328-340.

Joynt, K. R. and Massad, A. H.: "Directional Drilling for Salt Dome Oil Production," *World Oil* (1956), v. 142, no. 7, pp. 192, 194, 199, 202.

Juarez, C. Rodolfo, Lopez Ramos, Ernesto and Guzman, Eduardo J.: "Geologia Petrolera de Mexico," *Bol.,* Asoc. Mex. Geol. Petrol. (1955), v. 7, pp. 137-171.

Judson, Sidney A.: "Result of Operations on Gulf Coast," *Oil and Gas Jour.* (1927), v. 25, no. 40, pp. 97, 151-152, 155.

Judson, Sidney A.: "Resume of Discoveries and Developments in Northeastern Texas in 1928," *Bull.* AAPG (1929), v. 13, no. 6, pp. 611-613.

Judson, Sidney A. and Battle, J. C.: "Special Methods Required to Drill Through Overhanging Cap Rock and Salt," *Oil Weekly* (1933), v. 69, no. 1, pp. 59-60, 62.

Judson, Sidney A. and Murphy, P. C.: "Deep Sand Development at Barbers Hill, Chambers County, Texas," *Bull.,* AAPG (1930), v. 14, no. 6, pp. 719-741; (abs.) *Pan Am. Geologist,* v. 53, no. 3, p. 221.

Judson, Sidney A. and Stamey, R. A.: "Overhanging Salt on Domes of Texas and Louisiana," *Bull.,* AAPG (1933), v. 17, no. 12, pp. 1492-1520; *Gulf Coast Oil Fields,* AAPG (1936), pp. 141-169; *Oil Weekly,* v. 71, no. 11, pp. 18-24; no. 12, pp. 18-22; no. 13, pp. 18, 20-24; *Oil and Gas Jour.,* v. 32, no. 21, pp. 16, 30; no. 22, pp. 18, 22; no. 25, pp. 16, 18; no. 27, p. 18; (abs.) *Pan Am. Geologist,* v. 59, no. 3, p. 230.

Judson, Sidney A., Murphy, P. C. and Stamey, R. A.: "Overhanging Cap Rock and Salt at Barbers Hill, Chambers County, Texas," *Bull.,* AAPG (1932), v. 16, no. 5, pp. 469-482.

Jux, Ulrich: "The Palynologic Age of Diapiric and Bedded Salt in the Gulf Coastal Province," *Bull.* 38, La. Geol. Svy. (1961), Dept. of Conserv., 46 pp.; Review of by Hans D. Pflug, *Bull.,* AAPG (1963), v. 47, no. 1, pp. 180-181.

Kaldenbach, N. A. and Halbouty, Michel T.: "Characteristics, Methods of Combating, and Economic Importance of Heaving Shales," *Oil Weekly*

(1938), v. 91, no. 7, pp. 17-26; no. 8, pp. 42-54.

Kannenstine, F. M.: "The Relationship of Geophysics to Geology," *Geophysics* (1939), v. 4, no. 3, pp. 149-154.

Kargos, Harold E. and Davis, David C.: "Developments in Southeastern States in 1962," *Bull.*, AAPG (1963), v. 47, no. 6, pp. 1109-1115.

Kastrop, J. E.: "Fifty-six Years of Gulf Coast Oil," *World Oil* (1950), v. 130, no. 7, pp. 58-59.

Kastrop, J. E.: "Rotary System of Drilling Pioneered at Spindletop," *World Oil* (1951), v. 132, no. 1, pp. 233-234, 238, 240, 244, 246, 248, 252.

Kastrop, J. E.: "Practical Offshore Production Practices at Bay Marchand," *World Oil* (1951), v. 132, no. 7, pp. 167-172, 177.

Kean, C. H. and Howell, Lynn G.: "Note on Wave Guide Propagation Over a Shallow Salt Dome," *Geophysics* (1953), v. 18, no. 2, pp. 338-339.

Keith, B. A.: "Are Salt Domes Genetically Related to Zones of Crustal Megashearing?" *Oil Weekly* (1942), v. 108, no. 3, p. 24.

Kelly, P. K.: "The Sulphur Salt Dome, Louisiana," *Bull.*, AAPG (1925), v. 9, no. 3, pp. 479-496; *Geology of Salt Dome Oil Fields*, AAPG (1926), pp. 452-469.

Kennedy, William: "Coastal Salt Domes," *Bull.*, AAPG (1917), v. 1, no. 1, pp. 34-59; Discussion by E. G. Woodruff, *Bull.*, AAPG (1917), v. 1, no. 1, p. 79.

Kennedy, William: "The Bryan Heights Salt Dome, Brazoria County, Texas," *Bull.*, AAPG (1925), v. 9, no. 3, pp. 613-625; *Geology of Salt Dome Oil Fields*, AAPG (1926), pp. 678-690.

Kennedy, W. Q.: "The Influence of Basement Structure on the Evolution of the Coastal (Mesozoic and Tertiary) Basins," *Salt Basins Around Africa*, The Institute of Petroleum (1965), London, pp. 7-16.

Kent, P. E.: "An Evaporite Basin in Southern Tanzania," *Salt Basins Around Africa*, The Institute of Petroleum (1965), London, pp. 41-54.

Kerlin, M. L. and Meier, D. R.: "Developments in Louisiana Gulf Coast in 1954," *Bull.*, AAPG (1955), v. 39, no. 6, pp. 988-994.

Kerlin, M. L. and Watson, J. G.: "Developments in Louisiana Gulf Coast in 1952," *Bull.*, AAPG (1953), v. 37, no. 6, pp. 1443-1448.

Kern, Charles E.: "Possibility of Oil Structures out in the Gulf of Mexico," *Oil and Gas Jour.* (1927), v. 25, no. 42, pp. 80, 225-226.

Kerr, P. F. and Barrington, Jonathan: "Clays of Deep Shale Zone, Caillou Island, Louisiana," *Bull.*,

AAPG (1961), v. 45, no. 10, pp. 1697-1712.

Kerr, P. F. and Kopp, O. C.: "Salt Dome Breccia," *Bull.*, AAPG (1958), v. 42, no. 3, pp. 548-560.

Keyte, W. Ross and McCoy, Alex W.: "Present Interpretations of the Structural Theory for Oil and Gas Migration and Accumulation," *Problems of Petroleum Geology*, AAPG (1934), p. 276.

Kidd, Gentry: "Petroleum Developments in South Texas 1938-1939," *Bull.*, AAPG (1939), v. 23, no. 6, pp. 860-870.

King, P. B., Weaver, C. E., Flawn, P. T. and Goldstein, A., Jr.: "The Ouachita System," *Pub. 6120,* Tex. U. (1961), 399 pp.

King, R. H.: "Sedimentation in Permian Castile Sea," *Bull.*, AAPG (1947), v. 31, no. 3, pp. 470-477.

Kirkland, R. A., Richey, W. E. and Love, Donald W.: "Developments in East Texas in 1956," *Bull.*, AAPG (1957), v. 41, no. 6, pp. 1171-1180.

Kitchens, Joe C.: "Developments in East Texas in 1954," *Bull.*, AAPG (1955), v. 39, no. 6, pp. 967-975.

Knaffle, L. L.: "Origin, Nature and Character of Salt Dome Cap Rock," *MS Thesis,* Michigan U. (1950), Dept. of Geol.

Knebel, G. M. and Wendlandt, E. A.: "Lower Claiborne of East Texas, with Special Reference to Mount Sylvan Dome and Salt Movements," *Bull.*, AAPG (1929), v. 13, no. 10, pp. 1347-1375.

Knebel, G. M. and Wendlandt, E. A.: "Mount Sylvan Dome, Smith County, Texas," *Gulf Coast Oil Fields*, AAPG (1936), pp. 1041-1049.

Knoy, M. F.: "Salt Domes," *Sci. Am.* (1931), v. 144, p. 308.

Koonce, G. K., and Battan, F. P.: "Developments in East Texas in 1958," *Bull.*, AAPG (1959), v. 43, no. 6, pp. 1293-1303.

Kopp, O. C. and Kerr, P. F.: "Salt Dome Breccia," *Bull.*, AAPG (1958), v. 42, no. 3, pp. 548-560.

Kornfeld, J. A.: "Faulted Structures Play Big Roles in Gulf Coastal Production," *Oil Weekly* (1938), v. 90, no. 13, pp. 17-18.

Kornfeld, J. A.: "Oil Search in Eastern Gulf Region," *Mines Mag.* (1944), v. 34, no. 9, pp. 476-484.

Kornfeld, J. A.: "Moss Bluff Revived," *Oil and Gas Jour.* (1950), v. 49, no. 30, pp. 45-46.

Kornfeld, J. A.: "Blue Ridge Field Stages Comeback," *Oil and Gas Jour.* (1950), v. 49, no. 34, pp. 52-55.

Kornfeld, J. A.: "Oil Found on Ship Shoals

Dome Off Louisiana Coast," *Oil and Gas Jour.* (1951), v. 49, no. 36, p. 58.

Kornfeld, J. A.: "Miocene Gas Strike Spurs Rio Grande Embayment Work," *Oil and Gas Jour.* (1953), v. 52, no. 7, pp. 358, 360.

Kornfeld, M. M.: "Hackberry Foraminiferal Zonation of Starks Field, Calcasieu Parish, Louisiana," *Bull.*, AAPG (1939), v. 23, no. 12, pp. 1835-1836.

Kornfeld, M. M.: "Better Concept of Faulting Patterns Aids Piercement Salt Dome Development," *Oil Weekly* (1941), v. 100, no. 10, pp. 19-20.

Krejci, Karl: "Der Bau der Rumanischen Olgebiete," *Geol. Rundschau Band 16* (1926), Heft 1, S. 1-16; Heft 2, S. 99-127.

Krisle, Jack E., Ellison, R. F. and Garwick, R. W.: "Esperson Dome Field, Liberty and Harris Counties, Texas," *Guidebook,* AAPG-SEPM-SEG Jt. Ann. Mtg., Houston, Texas (March, 1953), pp. 115-116.

Krusekopf, H. H., Jr.: "Salt Domes of East Texas Basin Flavored with Oil," *Oil and Gas Jour.* (1959), v. 57, no. 19, pp. 143-147.

Kuehner, P. H. and Escher, B. G.: "Experiments in Connection with Salt Domes," *Leidsche Geol. Mededeel.* (1929), Deel 3, Afl. 3, pp. 151-182.

Kuhn, Robert and Hoy, Robert B.: "Structure of Winnfield Salt Dome, Winn Parish, Louisiana," *Bull.*, AAPG (1964), v. 48, no. 3, pp. 360-361.

Kulp, J. L. and Feely, H. W.: "Origin of Gulf Coast Salt Dome Sulphur Deposits," *Bull.*, AAPG (1957), v. 41, no. 8, pp. 1802-1853.

Kupfer, Donald H.: "Structure of Morton Salt Company Mine, Weeks Island Salt Dome, Louisiana," *Bull.*, AAPG (1962), v. 46, no. 8, pp. 1460-1467.

Kupfer, Donald H.: "Structure of Salt in Gulf Coast Domes," *Symposium on Salt,* Northern Ohio Geol. Soc., Inc. (1963), Cleveland, Ohio, pp. 104-123.

Lachmann, R.: "Studien Uber den Bau von Salzmassen," *Kali* (1910a), Heft 9, p. 188.

Lachmann, R.: "Uber Autoplaste (Nichttektonische) Formelemente in Bau der Salzgesteine Norddeutschlands," *Monatsber. d. Deutsch. Geol. Ges.*, Bd. 62, (1910b), pp. 113-116.

Lachmann, R.: *Ekzeme und Tektonik,* Zentralbl. f. Min. usw. (1917), 414 pp.

Lachmann, R. and Arrhenius, Sv.: "Die Phys.-chem. Bedingungen Beider Bildungen del Salzlager

and ihre Anwendung auf Geologische Probleme," *Geol. Rundshau,* v. 3, no. 139.

Lahee, F. H.: "Chestnut Dome, Natchitoches Parish, Louisiana," *Bull.*, AAPG (1931), v. 15, no. 3, pp. 277-278.

Lahee, F. H.: "Clay Creek Dome, Washington County, Texas." *Bull.*, AAPG (1931), v. 15, no. 3, pp. 279-283.

Lahee, F. H.: "A Study of the Evidences for Lateral and Vertical Migration of Oil," *Problems of Petroleum Geology,* AAPG (1934), pp. 399-427.

Lahee, F. H. and Wrather, W. E. (ed.): *Problems of Petroleum Geology,* American Association of Petroleum Geologists (1934), Tulsa, Oklahoma, 1073 pp.

Lahee, F. H.: "Wildcat Drilling 1941, with Some Comments on Discovery Rate," *Bull.*, AAPG (1942), v. 26, no. 6, pp. 969-982; (abs.) no. 5, p. 904; *Yearbook,* National Oil Scouts and Landman's Assoc. (1942), pp. 22-28.

Lake, C. L., Lewis, Ray C., O'Bannon, P. H., Self, S. R., Warner, C. A., Allison, A. P., Beckelhymer, R. L., Benson, Don G. and Hutchins, R. M., Jr.: "Geology of Katy Field, Waller, Harris and Fort Bend Counties, Texas," *Bull.*, AAPG (1946), v. 30, no. 2, pp. 157-180.

Lambert, Ernest H., Jr. (ed.). "Interior Salt Domes and Tertiary Stratigraphy of North Louisiana," *Guidebook,* 1960 Spring Field Trip, Shreveport Geol. Soc., 147 pp.

Lambert, Ernest H., Jr.: "Tabulation of Wells Which Have Encountered Salt or Cap Rock in North Louisiana and South Arkansas," *Guidebook,* 1960 Spring Field Trip, Shreveport Geol. Soc., pp. 61-69.

Landes, Kenneth K.: *Petroleum Geology,* John Wiley and Sons (1951), New York, 660 pp.

Lane, L. L. and Deussen, Alexander: "Hockley Salt Dome, Harris County, Texas," *Bull.*, AAPG (1926), v. 9, no. 7, pp. 1031-1060; *Geology of Salt Dome Oil Fields,* AAPG (1926), pp. 570-599.

Lang, Otto: "Deutschlands Kalisalzlanger Chemische Industrie," Berlin (1900), H. Gaertner, H. Heyfelder, v. 23, pp. 153, 159, 169-174, 193-197.

Latshaw, W. and Hyer, D. E.: "Developments in Louisiana Gulf Coast in 1958," *Bull.*, AAPG (1959), v. 43, no. 6, pp. 1312-1321.

Lawrence, Carl: "Santa Ana: Mexico's No. 2 Field?" *Oil and Gas Jour.* (1961), v. 59, no. 35, pp. 80-82.

Leavenworth, P. B.: "Developments in Gulf Coast

of Upper Texas and Louisiana in 1943," *Bull.,* AAPG (1944), v. 28, no. 6, pp. 853-857.

Lees, G. M.: "Salt—Some Depositional and Deformation Problems," *Jour. Inst. Pet.* (1931), v. 17, pp. 259-280.

Leonardon, E. G. and Boissonas, Eric: "Geophysical Exploration by Telluric Currents, with Special Reference to a Survey of the Haynesville Salt Dome, Wood County, Texas," *Geophysics* (1948), v. 13, no. 3, pp. 387-403.

Lester, H. H.: "Developments in East Texas in 1947," *Bull.,* AAPG (1948), v. 32, no. 6, pp. 1009-1023.

Lester, O. C.: "A Suggested Method Of Approach for Determination of Salt Dome Overhang," *Paper 2,* Soc. Pet. Geophy. (1937); *Early Geophysical Papers,* SEG (1947), p. 11.

Lester, O. C. and Rosaire, E. E.: "Seismological Discovery and Partial Detail of Vermilion Bay Salt Dome, Louisiana," *Bull.,* AAPG (1932), v. 16, no. 12, pp. 1221-1229; *Trans.,* Soc. Pet. Geophy. (1933), pp. 51-59; *Early Geophysical Papers,* SEG (1947), p. 381-389; *Geophysical Case Histories,* SEG (1948), v. 1, pp. 135-143.

Levorsen, A. I.: "Relation of Oil and Gas Pools to Unconformities in the Mid-Continent Region," *Problems of Petroleum Geology,* AAPG (1934), 780 pp.

Levorsen, A. I.: "Stratigraphic Versus Structural Accumulation," *Bull.,* AAPG (1936), v. 20, no. 5, pp. 521-530.

Levorsen, A. I.: "Sediments from Gulf of Mexico," *Bull.,* AAPG (1939), v. 23, no. 7, p. 1123.

Lewis, Ray C., O'Bannon, P. H., Self, S. R., Warner, C. A., Allison, A. P., Beckelhymer, R. L., Benson, Don G., Hutchins, R. M., Jr. and Lake, C. L.: "Geology of Katy Field, Waller, Harris and Fort Bend Counties, Texas," *Bull.,* AAPG (1946), v. 30, no. 2, pp. 157-180.

Lewis, Wm. Bradley: "Electrical Surveys of Some Shallow Salt Domes, Texas," *Geophysics* (1948), v. 13, no. 4, pp. 595-599.

Ley, H. A. (ed.): *Geology of Natural Gas,* American Association of Petroleum Geologists (1935), Tulsa, Oklahoma, 1227 pp.

Ley, H. A. and Willson, K. M.: "Gas Fields in Northeast Texas Embayment," *Geology of Natural Gas,* AAPG (1935), pp. 651-682.

Leyendecker, Charles: "Bosco Detailed Subsurface Geological Data are Benefiting Field Operations," *Oil Weekly* (1935), v. 76, no. 11, pp. 66-67.

Leyendecker, Charles: "Gulf Coast Oil Fields, Salt Domes and Prospects—Geological Data and Development History," *Oil Weekly* (1936), pp. 85-164.

Leyendecker, Charles: "Fields in the Gulf Coast Belt of Texas and Louisiana have High Per-Acre Recovery," *Oil Weekly* (1936), v. 82, no. 10, pp. 14-15.

Leyendecker, Charles: "Gulf Coast Oil Fields, Salt Domes and Prospects," *Oil Weekly* (1938), v. 90, no. 7, pp. 143-228.

Limes, Leonard L.: "Developments in Louisiana Gulf Coast in 1957," *Bull.,* AAPG (1958), v. 42, no. 6, pp. 1308-1318.

Limes, Leonard L. and Stipe, Jack C.: "Occurrence of Miocene Oil in South Louisiana," *Trans.,* GCAGS (1959), v. 9, pp. 77-90.

Limes, Leonard L. and Stipe, Jack C.: "Offshore Louisiana: One of the Largest Undrilled Reserves in the World," *Oil and Gas Jour.* (1959), v. 57, no. 48, pp. 126-130.

Lindsey, R. W. and Swartz, C. A.: "Reflected Refractions," *Geophysics* (1942), v. 7, no. 1, pp. 78-91.

Link, T. A.: "Experiments Relating to Salt Dome Structures," *Bull.,* AAPG (1930), v. 14, no. 4, pp. 483-508; (abs.) *Pan Am Geologist,* v. 53, p. 221.

Link, T. A.: "Discussion of Thrust Faults on Salt Domes," *Bull.,* AAPG (1954), v. 38, no. 12, p. 2506.

Link, Walter K.: "Significance of Oil and Gas Seeps in World Oil Exploration," *Bull.,* AAPG (1952), v. 36, no. 8, pp. 1505-1590.

Lipari, C. A.: "An Engineering Challenge—Development of South Louisiana's Giant Timbalier Bay Field," *Jour. of Pet. Tech.* (1963), v. 15, no. 2, pp. 127-132.

Lloyd, J. J.: "The Significance of Salt Domes to Petroleum Occurrence," *Geol. Rev.,* Geol. Soc. Coll. (1944), New York, v. 4, no. 1, pp. 24-28.

Lockett, S. H.: "Report of Topographical Survey of Louisiana," *Rept. of Supt. for 1870,* LSU (1871), pp. 16-26.

Lockwood's, C. D. Oil Report: "Reference Report Texas Upper Gulf Coast 1939," *C. D. Lockwood's Oil Report* (March, 1939), Houston, Texas.

Lockwood's, C. D. Oil Report: "Reference Report Southern Louisiana 1940," *C. D. Lockwood's Oil Report* (Oct., 1940), 343 pp.

Loetterle, G. J. and Cash, T. C.: "Developments in East Texas During 1946," *Bull.,* AAPG (1947), v. 31, no. 6, pp. 1059-1070.

Loetterle, G. J. and Shelby, T. H., Jr.: "Developments in East Texas During 1945," *Bull.,* AAPG (1946), v. 30, no. 6, pp. 980-990.

Logan, Jack: "East Texas Salt Domes and Structures Promise Oil," *Oil Weekly* (Aug. 7, 1931), pp. 17-20.

Logan, Jack: "Iowa Field, High Gravity Oil, Great Depth, Typical of New Era Along Coast," *Oil Weekly* (1933), v. 71, no. 13, pp. 12-13, 16.

Logan, Jack: "Gulf Coast Oil Fields, Salt Domes, and Prospects," *Oil Weekly* (1934), v. 74, no. 5, pp. 67-138.

Logan, L. J.: "Spindletop, First and Among Best of Gulf Coast Fields," *World Oil* (1951), v. 132, no. 1, pp. 228-230.

Logan, L. J. and Smith, Cecil: "Continental Shelf Activity Intensified (Gulf Coast)," *World Oil* (1948), v. 123, no. 3, pp. 37-40.

Longwell, C. R., et al: "Tectonic Map of the United States," AAPG and USGS (1944).

Lonsdale, J. T. and Perkins, J. M.: *Mineral Resources of the Texas Coastal Plain,* Bur. Econ. Geol. (1955), Tex. U., Min. Res. Circ. 38, 49 pp.

Lopez Ramos, Ernesto, Guzman, Eduardo J. and Juarez, C. Rodolfo: "Geologia Petrolera de Mexico," *Bol.,* Asoc. Mex. Geol. Petrol. (1955), v. 7, pp. 137-171.

Louisiana Geological Survey: *Oil and Gas Map of Louisiana* (1959), Dept. of Conserv.

Love, Donald W. and Duncan, Donald R.: "Developments in Louisiana Gulf Coast in 1959," *Bull.,* AAPG (1960), v. 44, no. 6, pp. 827-833.

Love, Donald W., Kirkland, R. A. and Richey, W. E.: "Developments in East Texas in 1956," *Bull.,* AAPG (1957), v. 41, no. 6, pp. 1171-1180.

Lowe, W. O. and Shaffer, H. R.: "Developments in Arkansas and North Louisiana in 1953," *Bull.,* AAPG (1954), v. 38, no. 6, pp. 1233-1241.

Lowman, Shepard W.: "Salt Dome Stratigraphy —Lower Gulf Coast," (abs.) *Oil and Gas Jour.* (1955), v. 53, no. 48, p. 212.

Lucas, A. F.: "The Avery Island Salt Mine and the Joseph Jefferson Salt Deposit, Louisiana," *Eng. and Mining Jour.* (1896), v. 62, pp. 463-464.

Lucas, A. F.: "Rock Salt in Louisiana," *Trans.,* AIME (1900), v. 29, pp. 462-474; (abs.) *Eng. and Mining Jour.,* v. 68, pp. 577-578.

Lucas, A. F.: "Geology of the Sulphur and Sulphur Oil Deposits of the Coastal Plain," *Indus. and Chem. Eng. Jour.* (1912), v. 4, pp. 140-143.

Lucas, A. F.: "The Dome Theory of the Coastal Plain," *Science* (1912), new ser., v. 35, pp. 961-964.

Lucas, A. F.: "A Review of the Exploration at Belle Isle, Louisiana," *Bull. 129,* AIME (1917), pp. 1435-1447; *Trans.,* AIME, v. 57, pp. 1034-1049.

Lundy, W. T.: "Development of the Grand Ecaille Sulphur Deposit," *Tech. Pub. 553,* AIME (1925), pp. 3-18.

Lusk, Tracy W. and St. John, F. B., Jr.: "Developments in Southeastern States in 1959," *Bull.,* AAPG (1960), v. 44, no. 6, pp. 842-850.

Lynch, William D. and Harrell, David C.: "Developments in Southeastern States in 1960," *Bull.,* AAPG (1961), v. 45, no. 6, pp. 903-909.

Lyons, P. L.: "Geology and Geophysics of the Gulf of Mexico," *Trans.,* GCAGS (1957), v. 7, pp. 1-10; (abs.), *Bull.,* AAPG (1965), v. 49, no. 3, p. 348.

Mabra, D. A. and Gardner, G. D.: "Developments in East Texas in 1957," *Bull.,* AAPG (1958) v. 42, no. 6, pp. 1289-1298.

Mac Naughton, Lewis W.: "Recent Developments in the South Mid-Continent," *Bull.,* AAPG (1940), v. 24, no. 6, pp. 1025-1032.

Macelwane, James B.: "Fifteen Years of Geophysics: A Chapter in the Exploration of the United States and Canada, 1924-1939," *Geophysics* (1940), v. 5, no. 3, pp. 250-258.

Macnamara, J., Thode, H. G., Szabo, A. and Tudge, A.: "The Distribution of S34 in Nature and the Sulphur Cycle," *Science* (1950), v. 111, pp. 464-465.

Mais, W. R.: "Peripheral Faulting at Bayou Blue Salt Dome, Iberville Parish, Louisiana," *Bull.,* AAPG (1957), v. 41, no. 9, pp. 1915-1951.

Malkin, D. S. and Echols, D. A. J.: "Wilcox (Eocene) Stratigraphy, a Key to Production (of oil and gas)," *Bull.,* AAPG (1948), v. 32, no. 1, pp. 11-33; corrections, p. 310.

Maricelli, J. J. and Timm, B. C.: "Formation Waters in Southwest Louisiana," *Bull.,* AAPG (1953), v. 37, no. 2, pp. 394-409.

Markley, Leo A.: "Geophysical History of Grand Isle, Block 18, Oil Field, Gulf of Mexico, Louisiana," *Geophysical Case Histories,* SEG (1956), v. 2, pp. 103-112.

Marquez Pineda, Aremos: "Estudio Geologico del Domo Salino de Chinameca, Ver.," *Tesis Profesional* (1962).

Marquez Pineda, Aremos, Viveros Juarez, Manuel and Serna Vigueras, Reyes: "Depositos de Sal y

Azufre en la Cuenca Salina del Istmo, Ver.," *Bol. 64* (1964), Consejo de Recursos Naturales no Renovables, 76 pp.

Marshall, L. R. and Bornhauser, Max.: "Three New Interior Salt Domes in Northeast Louisiana," *Bull.*, AAPG (1940), v. 24, no. 3, pp. 483-486.

Martin, James L., Hough, Leo W., Raggio, David L. and Sandberg, Adolph E.: "Geology of Webster Parish," *Bull. 29,* La. Geol. Svy. (1954), Dept. of Conserv., 252 pp.

Marx, A. H.: "Hoskins Mound Salt Dome, Brazoria County, Texas," *Bull.*, AAPG (1936), v. 20, no. 2, pp. 155-178; *Gulf Coast Oil Fields,* AAPG (1936), pp. 833-856.

Mason, S. L. and Barton, D. C.: "Further Notes on Barite Pisolites from the Batson and Saratoga Oil Fields," *Bull.*, AAPG (1925), v. 9, pp. 1294-1295.

Massad, A. H. and Joynt, K. R.: "Directional Drilling for Salt Dome Oil Production," *World Oil* (1956), v. 142, no. 7, pp. 192, 194, 199, 202.

Matteson, W. G. and Coste, E.: "Secondary Intrusive Origin of Gulf Coastal Plain Salt Domes," *Trans.*, AIME (1921), v. 65, pp. 295-334; preprints, nos. 1048, 1073, 1088; (abs.) *Mining and Metallurgy*, no. 170, p. 37.

Maurey, F. J., Reinecke, L. and Harris, G. D.: "Rock Salt, Its Origin, Geological Occurrence and Economic Importance in the State of Louisiana, Together with Brief Notes and References to All Known Salt Deposits and Industries of the World," *Bull.*, La. Geol. Svy. (1908), v. 7, 259 pp.

May, G. N.: "Developments in Louisiana Gulf Coast in 1949," *Bull.*, AAPG (1950), v. 34, no. 6, pp. 1191-1198.

McBee, W. B. and Orchard, P. J.: "Developments in Louisiana Gulf Coast in 1948," *Bull.*, AAPG (1949), v. 33, no. 6, pp. 979-989.

McBeth, R. S.: "Opening Spindletop with Lucas Gusher; A Lesson in Perserverance," *Nat'l. Pet. News* (1921), v. 13, pp. 51-52.

McCarter, W. B. and O'Bannon, P. H.: "Sugarland Oil Field, Fort Bend County, Texas," *Bull.*, AAPG (1933), v. 17, no. 11, pp. 1362-1386; *Gulf Coast Oil Fields,* AAPG (1936), pp. 709-733.

McCaslin, Leigh S., Jr.: "Seven Discoveries in Gulf of Mexico Drilling Boom," *Oil and Gas Jour.* (1948), v. 47, no. 22, pp. 64-67.

McCaslin, Leigh S., Jr. and Barnes, Kenneth B.: "Spectacular Gulf of Mexico Discovery," *Oil and Gas Jour.* (1948), v. 46, no. 46, pp. 96-99, 113-114.

McClelland, Bramlette and Fisk, Harold N.: "Geology of Continental Shelf Off Louisiana: Its Influence on Offshore Foundation Design," *Bull.*, GSA (1959), v. 70, pp. 1369-1394.

McCollum, E. V.: "Gravity Expression of the Hatchetigbee Anticline," *Geophysics* (1943), v. 8, no. 1, pp. 46-50.

McCoy, Alex. W. and Keyte, W. Ross: "Present Interpretations of the Structural Theory for Oil and Gas Migration and Accumulation," *Problems of Petroleum Geology*, AAPG (1934), p. 276.

McCullough, R. A.: "Geology of the Heidelberg Oil Field, Mississippi," *Oil* (1944), v. 4, no. 8, pp. 8-9.

McDowell, A. N.: "The Origin of the Structural Depression over Gulf Coast Salt Domes, with Particular Reference to Clay Creek Dome, Washington County, Texas," *MS Thesis*, Tex. A & M U. (1951), Dept. of Geol.

McDowell, A. N. and Parker, T. J.: "Notes on the Construction of Geologic Scale Models," *Mines Mag.* (1950), v. 40, no. 10, pp. 75-79.

McDowell, A. N. and Parker, T. J.: "Scale Models as Guide to Interpretation of Salt Dome Faulting," *Bull.*, AAPG (1951), v. 35, no. 9, pp. 2076-2086.

McDowell, A. N. and Parker, T. J.: "Model Studies of Salt Dome Tectonics," *Bull.*, AAPG (1955), v. 39, no. 12, pp. 2384-2470; Review by W. T. Born, *Geophysics* (1955), v. 21, no. 4, p. 1121.

McGee, D. A., Seale, Tom, and Finley, J. C.: "Oil in the Gulf of Mexico," (abs.) *Proc.*, Okla. Acad. Sci. (1950), v. 29, pp. 60-61.

McGlothlin, Tom: "General Geology of Mississippi," *Bull.*, AAPG (1944), v. 28, no. 1, pp. 29-62.

McGreal, P. L.: "Salt and Sulphur Valuable Deposits in Coastal Fields," *Oil and Gas Jour.* (1927), v. 25, no. 35, p. 107.

McGuckin, Glenn M.: "History of the Geophysical Exploration of the Cameron Meadows Dome, Cameron Parish, Louisiana," *Geophysics* (1945), v. 10, no. 1, pp. 1-16; *Geophysical Case Histories*, SEG (1948), v. 1, pp. 161-174; *Oil Weekly*, v. 118, no. 12, pp. 46-52; (abs.) *Dallas Digest* (1948), p. 98.

McGuirt, J. H.: "Geology of Cameron and Vermilion Parishes (Salt Dome Prospects)," *Bull. 6*, La. Geol. Svy. (1935), pp. 167-179.

McGuirt, J. H.: "A Partial List of Maps Dealing with Cameron and Vermilion Parishes," *Bull. 6*, La. Geol. Svy. (1935), pp. 197-203.

McGuirt, J. H.: "Salt Dome Prospects," *Bull. 6,* La. Geol. Svy. (1935), pp. 167-179.

McGuirt, J. H. and Howe, H. V.: "Salt Domes of Cameron and Vermilion Parishes," *Bull. 6,* La. Geol. Svy. (1935), pp. 73-166.

McGuirt, J. H. and Howe, H. V.: "Salt Domes of Plaquemines and St. Bernard Parishes," *Bull. 8,* La. Geol. Svy. (1936), pp. 200-278.

McGuirt, J. H. and Howe, H. V.: "Salt Domes of Iberville and Ascension Parishes," *Bull. 13,* La. Geol. Svy. (1938), pp. 87-187.

McGuirt, J. H., Howe, H. V. and Russell, R. J.: "Physiography of Coastal Southwest Louisiana," *Bull. 6,* La. Geol. Svy. (1935), pp. 1-68.

McGuirt, J. H., Craft, B. C., Stephenson, M. B., Howe, H. V. and Russell, R. J.: "Reports on the Geology of Cameron and Vermilion Parishes," *Bull. 6,* La. Geol. Svy. (1935), 242 pp.

McLellan, H. J.: "Raccoon Bend Salt Dome, Austin County, Texas," *Bull.,* AAPG (1946), v. 30, no. 8, pp. 1306-1307.

McLellan, H. J. and Wendlandt, E. A.: "Developments in East Texas During 1939," *Bull.,* AAPG (1940), v. 24, no. 6, pp. 1062-1068.

McLellan, H. J., Wendlandt, E. A. and Murchison, E. A.: "Boggy Creek Salt Dome, Anderson and Cherokee Counties, Texas," *Bull.,* AAPG (1932), v. 16, no. 6, pp. 584-600; (abs.) *Pan Am. Geologist,* v. 57, no. 4, p. 308.

McLeod, Richard R.: "A Theory for the Formation of Limestone Cap Rock of Salt Domes," *Trans.,* GCAGS (1960), v. 10, pp. 151-153.

McMahan, W. W., Jr.: "Developments in Upper Gulf Coast District of Texas in 1951," *Bull.,* AAPG (1952), v. 36, no. 6, pp. 1201-1210.

Meier, D. R. and Kerlin, M. L.: "Developments in Louisiana Gulf Coast in 1954," *Bull.,* AAPG (1955), v. 39, no. 6, pp. 988-994.

Melchior, L. F.: "The Geophysical Discovery and Development of the Bayou Couba Dome," *Geophysics* (1953), v. 18, no. 2, pp. 371-382; *Geophysical Case Histories,* SEG (1936), v. 2, pp. 130-141.

Mettner, F. E.: "Developments in Upper Gulf Coast of Texas in 1948," *Bull.,* AAPG (1949), v. 33, no. 6, pp. 966-978.

Meyer, W. G.: "Stratigraphy and Historical Geology of Gulf Coastal Plain in Vicinity of Harris County, Texas," *Bull.,* AAPG (1939), v. 23, no. 2, pp. 145-211; *PhD Dissertation,* Cincinnati U. (1941),

Dept. of Geol. and Geography; (abs.) *World Pet.,* v. 10, no. 6, p. 109.

Meyer, W. G.: "Grabens in Gulf Coast Anticline and Their Relation to Other Faulted Troughs," *Bull.,* AAPG (1943), v. 28, no. 4, pp. 541-553.

Miller, C. C., Bianchi, J. C., Jr. and Briggs, K. S.: "Developments in South Texas in 1952," *Bull.,* AAPG (1953), v. 37, no. 6, pp. 1405-1415.

Miller, Charis R. and Teas, L. P.: "Raccoon Bend Oil Field, Austin County, Texas," *Bull.,* AAPG (1933), v. 17, no. 12, pp. 1459-1491; *Gulf Coast Oil Fields,* AAPG (1936), pp. 676-708.

Miller, John C.: "Well Spacing and Production Interference in West Columbia Field, Brazoria County, Texas," *Bull.,* AAPG (1942), v. 26, no. 9, pp. 1441-1466.

Miller, W. C., Netzeband, F. F., Early, Thomas R. and Ryan, J. P.: "Sulfur Resources and Production in Texas, Louisiana, Missouri, Oklahoma, Arkansas and Mississippi, and Markets for the Sulfur," *Information Circular 8222,* U. S. Dept. of the Interior, Bur. of Mines, (1964), 77 pp.

Mills, Brad: "New Coast Discoveries Throw Additional Light on Salt Dome Area as Future Reserve," *Oil Weekly* (1935), v. 78, no. 10, pp. 19-20, 22-23.

Minor, H. E.: "Chemical Relation of Salt Dome Waters," *Bull.,* AAPG (1925), v. 9, no. 1, pp. 38-41; *Geology of Salt Dome Oil Fields,* AAPG (1926), pp. 777-780.

Minor, H. E.: "The Edgerly Oil Field, Louisiana," *Bull.,* AAPG (1925), v. 9, no. 3, pp. 497-504; *Geology of Salt Dome Oil Fields,* AAPG (1926), pp. 470-477.

Minor, H. E.: "Goose Creek Oil Field, Harris County, Texas," *Geology of Salt Dome Oil Fields,* AAPG (1926), pp. 546-557.

Minor, H. E.: "Oil Field Waters of the Gulf Coastal Plain," *Problems of Petroleum Geology,* AAPG (1934), pp. 891-905.

Minton, J. W. and Ferguson, W. B.: "Clay Creek Salt Dome, Washington County, Texas," *Bull.,* AAPG (1936), v. 20, no. 1, pp. 68-90; *Gulf Coast Oil Fields,* AAPG (1936), pp. 757-779; (abs.) *World Pet.,* v. 7, no. 3, p. 150.

Mississippi Geological Society: "Mississippi Oil Field and Salt Dome Names," *Bull.,* AAPG (1944), v. 28, no. 7, pp. 1046-1049.

Mississippi State Oil and Gas Board: *Oil and Gas Bulletins and Annual Reports,* Jackson, Mississippi.

Mixon, R. B.: "Jurassic Formations of the Ciudad Victoria Area, Tamaulipas, Mexico," *MS Thesis,* LSU (1958), Dept. of Geol.

Mixon, R. B., Murray, G. E. and Diaz, Teodoro: "Age and Correlation of Huizachal Group (Mesozoic), State of Tamaulipas, Mexico," *Bull.,* AAPG (1959), v. 43, no. 4, pp. 757-771; (addendum) v. 43, p. 2499.

Montgomery, J. C., Woodard, A. E. and Cantrell, R. B.: "Heterostegina Reef on Nash and Other Piercement Salt Domes in Northwestern Brazoria County, Texas," *Trans.,* GCAGS (1959), v. 9, pp. 59-62.

Moore, E. S.: "Oolitic and Pisolitic Barite from the Saratoga Oil Field, Texas," *Bull., GSA* (1914), v. 25, pp. 77-79.

Moore, Hastings: "Nolan Edward Field, Wood County, Texas," *Pub. 5116,* Tex. U. (1951), pp. 266-268.

Moore, Leslie M., Jr. and Tansil, John T.: "Automatic Custody Transfer System at Lake Pelto, Louisiana," *Jour. of Pet. Tech.* (1960), v. 12, no. 10, pp. 15-19.

Moore, M. L.: "Diamond Alkali Brine Field at Mont Belvieu, Texas," *Symposium on Salt,* Northern Ohio Geol. Soc., Inc. (1963), Cleveland, Ohio, pp. 539-545.

Moore, R. C. (ed.): *Geology of Salt Dome Oil Fields,* American Association of Petroleum Geologists (1926), 797 pp.

Moresi, C. K.: "Louisiana's Sulphur Mines," *Review,* La. Conserv. (1934), v. 4, no. 1, pp. 44-48.

Moresi, C. K.: "Prolific Sands Found in the Chacahoula Field," *Oil* (1941), v. 1, pp. 16-18.

Moresi, C. K. and Howe, H .V.: "Geology of Iberia Parish," *Bull. 1,* La. Geol. Svy. (1931), 187 pp.

Moresi, C. K. and Howe, H. V.: "Geology of Lafayette and St. Martin Parishes, Louisiana," *Bull. 3,* La. Geol. Svy. (1933), 328 pp.

Morgan, Aubrey: "The Van Zandt Dome (Texas)," *Compass* (1940), v. 20, no. 3, pp. 166-170.

Morgan, C. L.: "Tatum Salt Dome, Lamar County Mississippi," *Bull.,* AAPG (1941), v. 25, no. 3, p. 424.

Morgan, C. L., Norman, M. E. and Alexander, C. W.: "Development in Southeastern States in 1944," *Bull.,* AAPG (1945), v. 29, no. 6, pp. 815-835.

Morgan, J. P. and Gould, H. R.: "Coastal Louisiana Swamps and Marshlands," *Field Excursion No.*

6, Geology of the Gulf Coast and Central Texas and Guidebook of Excursions, Houston Geol. Soc. (1962), pp. 287-341.

Morren, J. H., Hendy, W. J. and Dobbins, W. D.: "Developments in South Texas in 1957," *Bull.,* AAPG (1958), v. 42, no. 6, pp. 1279-1288.

Morrisey, Norman S.: "In South Louisiana Old Fields Never Die," *Oil and Gas Jour.* (1956), v. 54 no. 59, pp. 213-214.

Morrison, T. E.: "First Authentic Cretaceous Formation Found on Gulf Coast Salt Domes of Texas," *Bull.,* AAPG (1929), v. 13, no. 8, pp. 1065-1069.

Morrow, Ernest H. and Champion, Wm. L.: "Developments in Arkansas and North Louisiana in 1957," *Bull.,* AAPG (1958), v. 42, no. 6, pp. 1319-1326.

Morrow, Ernest H. and Wise, W. H.: "Developments in Arkansas and North Louisiana in 1956," *Bull.,* AAPG (1957), v. 41, no. 6, pp. 1201-1209.

Morse, W. C.: "Mississippi Oil Resources," *Quarterly Bull.,* Interstate Oil Compact (1944), v. 3, no. 4, pp. 11-16; *Mississippi Oil Rev.,* pp. 3-7; *World Pet.,* v. 16, no. 2, pp. 53-54.

Morton, R. B. and Finfrock, L. J.: "Developments in Southeastern States in 1952," *Bull.,* AAPG (1953), v. 37, no. 6, pp. 1460-1474.

Mossom, D. S.: "Activities in South Texas, 1937-1938," *Bull.,* AAPG (1938), v. 22, no. 6, pp. 750-757; (abs.) *Oil and Gas Jour.* (1938), v. 36,, no. 44, p. 56; v. 37, no. 24, p. 52.

Mostowitsch, W. and Hofman, H. O.: "The Reduction of Calcium Sulfate by Carbon Monoxide and the Oxidation of Calcium Sulfide," *Trans.,* AIME (1910), v. 41, pp. 763-783.

Mount, Tom M. and Wise, W. H.: "Developments in Arkansas and North Louisiana in 1955," *Bull.,* AAPG (1956), v. 40, no. 6, pp. 1263-1271.

Muehlberger, Wm. R.: "Internal Structure of the Grand Saline Salt Dome, Van Zandt County, Texas," *RI 38,* Tex. U. (1959), Bur. Econ. Geol., 24 pp.

Muehlberger, Wm. R., Clabaugh, Patricia S. and Hightower, Maxwell L.: "Palestine and Grand Saline Salt Domes," *Field Excursion No. 6,* Geology of the Gulf Coast and Central Texas and Guidebook of Excursions, Houston Geol. Soc. (1962), Houston, Texas, pp. 266-277.

Munroe, D. J.: "Scanlon or Midway Dome, Lamar County, Mississippi," *Bull., AAPG* (1938), v. 22, no. 7, pp. 816-822; (abs.) *Oil and Gas Jour.,*

(1938), v. 36, no. 44, pp. 58, 62; *World Pet.*, v. 9, no. 10, p. 70.

Murchison, E. A., McLellan, H. J. and Wendlandt, E. A.: "Boggy Creek Salt Dome, Anderson and Cherokee Counties, Texas," *Bull.*, AAPG (1932), v. 16, no. 6, pp. 584-600; (abs.) *Pan Am. Geologist*, v. 57, no. 4, p. 308.

Murchison, E. A., Jr. and Patton, J. L.: "Developments in Louisiana Gulf Coast in 1950," *Bull.*, AAPG (1951), v. 35, no. 6, pp. 1338-1344.

Murphy, P. C. and Judson, S. A. : "Deep Sand Development at Barbers Hill, Chambers County, Texas," *Bull.*, AAPG (1930), v. 14, no. 6, pp. 719-741; (abs.) *Pan Am. Geologist*, v. 53, no. 3, p. 221.

Murphy, P. C., Stamey, R. A. and Judson, S. A.: "Overhanging Cap Rock and Salt at Barbers Hill, Chambers County, Texas," *Bull.*, AAPG (1932), v. 16, no. 5, pp. 469-482.

Murray, G. E.: "Resume of Salt and Sulphur in Louisiana," *Proc.*, Southeastern Mineral Symposium, (1950); *Spec. Pub. 1*, Ky. Geol. Svy. (1953), pp. 48-68.

Murray, G. E.: *Geology of the Atlantic and Gulf Coastal Province of North America*, Harper and Bros. (1961), New York, 692 pp.

Murray, G. E.: "Salt Structures of Mexico Basin —A Review," *Bull.*, AAPG (1966), v. 50, no. 3, pp. 439-478.

Murray, G. E. and Wall, J. R.: "Preliminary Report on Intrusive Gypsum, Sierra del Fraile, State of Nuevo Leon, Mexico," *Guidebook*, 1959 Field Trip, So. Tex. Geol. Soc., pp. D1-D7; *Spanish Trans.* by P. E. Narvarte, pp. D8-D12.

Murray, G. E., Diaz, Teodoro and Mixon, R. B.: "Age and Correlation of Huizachal Group (Mesozoic), State of Tamaulipas, Mexico," *Bull.*, AAPG (1959), v. 43, no. 4, pp. 757-771; (addendum), v. 43, p. 2499.

Murzaiev, P. M.: "Genesis of Some Sulphur Deposits of the U.S.S.R.," *Econ. Geol.* (1937), v. 32, pp. 69-103.

Musgrove, A. W., Woolley, W. C. and Gray, Helen: "Outlining of Salt Masses by Refraction Methods," *Geophysics* (1960), v. 25, no. 1, 141-167.

Musolff, Neale C.: "Caplen Field, Galveston County, Texas," *Typical Oil and Gas Fields of Southeast Texas*, Houston Geol. Soc. (1962), pp. 30-33.

Myers, John C.: "Sulphur: Its Occurrence, Production and Economics," *Bull. 4*, Society of Independent Professional Earth Scientists (July 22, 1964), Houston, Texas, 9 pp.

National Oil Scouts and Landmen's Association: *Oil and Gas Field Development in United States and Canada*, Year Book (1931-1959), Vols. 1-29, Austin, Texas.

Neely, Joseph: "Newman Salt Dome, Warren County, Mississippi," *Bull.*, AAPG (1941), v. 25, no. 3, p. 424.

Neill, W. B.: "Developments in Louisiana Gulf Coast in 1947," *Bull.*, AAPG (1948), v. 32, no. 6, pp. 1032-1039.

Nelson, H. F. and Bray, E. E.: "Radiocarbon Age Determination of Recent-Pleistocene Contact in Block 126 Field, Eugene Island, Gulf of Mexico," *Bull.*, AAPG (1956), v. 40, no. 1, pp. 173-177.

Nettleton, L. L.: "Fluid Mechanics of Salt Domes," *Bull.*, AAPG (1934), v. 18, no. 9, pp. 1175-1204; *Gulf Coast Oil Fields*, AAPG (1936), pp. 79-108.

Nettleton, L. L.: "History of Concepts of Gulf Coast Salt-Dome Formation," *Bull.*, AAPG (1955), v. 39, no. 12, pp. 2373-2383.

Nettleton, L. L.: "Recent Experimental and Geophysical Evidence of Mechanics of Salt Dome Formation," *Bull.*, AAPG (1943), v. 27, no. 1, pp. 51-63; (abs.) v. 26, no. 5, pp. 903-904.

Nettleton, L. L.: "Geophysical History of Typical Mississippi Piercement Salt Domes," *Geophysics* (1947), v. 12, no. 1, pp. 30-42; *Geophysical Case Histories*, SEG (1948), v. 1, pp. 239-250; (abs.) *Geophysics* (1947), v. 11, no. 3, p. 418; *Oil and Gas Jour.*, v. 44, no. 48, p. 98.

Nettleton, L. L. (ed.): *Geophysical Case Histories*, SEG (1948), v. 1, 671 pp.

Nettleton, L. L.: "Geophysical Aspects, Part IV of Sedimentary Volumes in Gulf Coastal Plain of the United States and Mexico," *Bull.*, GSA (1952), v. 63, pp. 1221-1228.

Nettleton, L. L.: "History of Concepts of Gulf Coast Salt Dome Formation," *Bull.*, AAPG (1955), v. 39, no. 12, pp. 2373-2383.

Nettleton, L. L.: "Gravity Determination of Cap Rock, Pine Prairie Dome, Louisiana," *Geophysical Case Histories*, SEG (1956), v. 2, pp. 149-155.

Nettleton, L. L.: "Submarine Gravity Detailing, San Luis Pass Dome, Brazoria County, Texas," *Geophysics* (1957), v. 22, no. 2, pp. 348-358.

Nettleton, L. L.: "Gravity Survey Over a Gulf Coast Continental Shelf Mound," *Geophysics* (1957), v. 22, no. 3, pp. 630-642; (abs.) *Trans.*, GCAGS (1957), v. 7, p. 301.

Nettleton, L. L. and Elkins, T. A.: "Geologic

Models from Powdered Materials," *Trans.*, Am. Geophys. Union (1947), v. 28, no. 3, pp. 451-466.

Netzeband, F. F., Early, Thomas R., Ryan, J. P. and Miller, W. C.: "Sulfur Resources and Production in Texas, Louisiana, Missouri, Oklahoma, Arkansas and Mississippi, and Markets for the Sulfur," *Inf. Circ. 8222*, U.S. Dept. of the Interior, Bur. of Mines, (1964), 77 pp.

New Orleans Geological Society: "Cross Sections Through South Louisiana," *New Orleans Geol. Soc.* (1954).

Nicholson, Gordon B.: "Directional Drilling from Man Made Islands," *Oil Weekly* (1946), v. 121, no. 9, pp. 18-19, 21.

Nicola, Nicholas J.: "Dome Mining: Floor vs. Roof Extraction," *Symposium on Salt,* Northern Ohio Geol. Soc., Inc. (1963), Cleveland, Ohio, pp. 390-398.

Noble, H. A.: "Developments in Upper Gulf Coast of Texas in 1944," *Bull.*, AAPG (1945), v. 29, no. 6, pp. 785-791.

Nolthenius, Tutein, A. B.: *Geological Report No. 191 on the Salt Dome of El Moralar,* Archive Petroleos Mexicanos (1922).

Norman, M. E., Alexander, C. W. and Morgan, C. L.: "Developments in Southeastern States in 1944," *Bull.*, AAPG (1945), v. 29, no. 6, pp. 815-835.

Norman, Stanley: "Homage Paid to Spindletop as Discovery of Petroleum Epoch," *Oil and Gas Jour.* (1941), v. 40, no. 22, pp. 14-15.

Northern Ohio Geological Society: *Symposium on Salt,* (1963), 661 pp.

Norton, E. G.: "The Origin of the Louisiana and East Texas Salines," *Bull.*, AIME (1915), no. 97, pp. 93-102; no. 101, pp. 1120-1122; *Trans.*, AIME (1916), v. 51, pp. 502-513.

Norton, R. G. and Skrivanos, N. C.: "Liquefied Petroleum Gas Storage in Arcadia Salt Dome," *Guidebook,* 1960 Spring Field Trip, Shreveport Geol. Soc., pp. 48-56.

Nuttall, W. L. F.: "Notes on the Stratigraphy of Southeast Mexico," *Geol. Rept. 192,* (March, 1929), (inedito).

Oakes, R. L.: "The Grandison Complex, La-Fourche and Jefferson Parishes, Louisiana," *Trans.,* GCAGS (1959), v. 9, pp. 111-120.

O'Bannon, P. H. and McCarter, W. B.: "Sugarland Oil Field, Fort Bend County, Texas," *Bull.,* AAPG (1933), v. 17, no. 11, pp. 1362-1386; *Gulf Coast Oil Fields,* AAPG (1936), pp. 709-733.

O'Bannon, P. H., Self, S. R., Warner, C. A., Allison, A. P., Beckelhymer, R. L., Benson, Don G., Hutchins, R. M., Jr., Lake, C. L. and Lewis, Ray C.: "Geology of Katy Field, Waller, Harris and Fort Bend Counties, Texas," *Bull.,* AAPG (1946), v. 30, no. 2, pp. 157-180.

O'Brien, C. A. E.: "Salt Diapirism in South Persia," *Geologie en Mijnbouw Niewve Serie,* 19e Jaargang (1957), pp. 357-376.

Ocamb, Rayburn D.: "Growth Faults of South Louisiana," *Trans.,* GCAGS (1961), v. 11, pp. 139-175.

Ochsenius, C.: "On the Formation of Rock Salt Beds and Mother Liquor Salts," *Proc.,* Acad. Natural Sci. of Philadelphia (1888), v. 40, pp. 181-187.

O'Connor, J. P., Jr. and Hunt, V. G.: "Developments in East Texas in 1953," *Bull.,* AAPG (1954), v. 38, no. 6, pp. 1196-1207.

O'Donnell, Lawrence: "Jefferson Island Salt Dome, Iberia Parish, Louisiana," *Bull.,* AAPG (1935) v. 19, no. 11, pp. 1602-1644; *Gulf Coast Oil Fields*, AAPG (1936), pp. 983-1025.

Oil and Gas Journal: "Historic Wells in the American Fields," (1923), v. 22, no. 27, pp. 84, 86, 96.

Oil and Gas Journal: "Revival of Spindletop Recalls the Dream of Patillo Higgins," (1926), v. 25, no. 8, pp. 41, 107.

Oil and Gas Journal: "Spindletop Section," (1926), v. 25, no. 14, pp. 76A-76 P.

Oil and Gas Journal:, "Genetic Connection Between Salt Deposits and Petroleum," (1929), v. 28, no. 5, p. 159.

Oil and Gas Journal: "Odd Drilling in Bayous of Louisiana," (1930), v. 29, no. 14, pp. 42, 146.

Oil and Gas Journal: "City and Owners of Lots Solve Drilling Problems," (1935), v. 34, no. 21, p. 15.

Oil and Gas Journal: "Golden Meadow, LaFourche Parish, Louisiana," (1940), v. 38, no. 39, pp. 29-31.

Oil and Gas Journal: "Drilling Play Reflects Activity Near Gulf Coast Salt Domes," (1940), v. 38, no. 50, pp. 92, 95, 102.

Oil and Gas Journal: "Typical Oil Field Structure; Complexly Faulted Dome, Eola Field, Avoyelles Parish, Louisiana," (1942), v. 41, no. 2, pp. 50-51.

Oil and Gas Journal: "Typical Oil Field Structures; Salt Dome, Esperson and Barbers Hill, Coastal Texas," (1942), v. 41, no. 13, pp. 42-43.

Oil and Gas Journal: "Miniature Models Aid Mapping of Salt Dome Areas," (1946), v. 45, no. 27, p. 85.

Oil and Gas Journal: "Journal Guide to Gulf Coast Map of Texas, Louisiana, Mississippi Oil Fields, Gas Fields, Salt Domes," (1947), v. 46, no. 4.

Oil and Gas Journal: "Golden Oil Jubilee," (1951), v. 50, no. 20, p. 173.

Oil and Gas Journal: "Dome Interest Revived," (1952), v. 50, no. 37, pp. 58-59.

Oil and Gas Journal: "Where are Those Gulf Coast Salt Domes?" (1952), v. 51, no. 14, pp. 130-134.

Oil and Gas Journal: "Field Operations in Louisiana's Marshes—Venice Field's Circular Waterway Outlines an Oil Rich Structure," (1955), v. 54, no. 10, pp. 122-123.

Oil and Gas Journal: "Revived Oil Field Moves in on Houston," (1957), v. 55, no. 2, p. 73.

Oil and Gas Journal: "New Era for Barbers Hill and L. P. G.," (1957), v. 55, no. 34, pp. 72-73.

Oil and Gas Journal: "Where the Structures are Off Louisiana and Texas," (1959), v. 57, no. 24, p. 107.

Oil Weekly: "Rabb Ridge Important Potentially, Made Interesting by High Valuation," (1932), v. 67, no. 13, pp. 10-12, 40-42.

Oil Weekly: "Maritime or Offshore Drilling in the Gulf Coast," (1933), v. 69, no. 1, pp. 65-68.

Oil Weekly: "Gulf Coast Oil Fields, Salt Domes and Prospects, Geological Data and Developments," (1942), v. 105, no. 2, pp. 59-130.

Olcott, Perry: "Structures Controlling Accumulation," *Guidebook,* AAPG-SEPM-SEG Jt. Ann. Mtg. (March, 1953), Houston, Texas, pp. 33-36.

Olivas Ramirez, M. and Viniegra Osorio, Francisco: "La Acumulacion de Hidrocarburos en el Cretacico en Relacion al Analisis Tectonico Comparativo de la Sierra Madre y la Cuenca de Veracruz," *Resumenes de los Trabajos Presentados,* II Convencion, Asoc. Mex. de Geol. Petrol., pp. 34-35.

O'Neill, B. J., Jr., Hoy, R. B. and Foose, R. M.: "Structure of Winnfield Salt Dome, Winn Parish, Louisiana," *Bull.,* AAPG (1962), v. 46, no. 8, pp. 1444-1459.

Orchard, P. J. and McBee, W. B.: "Develop-ments in Louisiana Gulf Coast in 1948," *Bull.,* AAPG (1949), v. 33, no. 6, pp. 979-989.

Owens, F. C. and Taegel, E. A.: "Developments in South Texas in 1942," *Bull.,* AAPG (1943), v. 27, no. 6, pp. 739-746.

Owens, L.: "Moot Points in Salt Dome Theory," *Jour. Inst. Pet.* (1931), v. 17, pp. 334-337.

Paine, William R.: "Geology of Acadia and Jefferson Davis Parishes," *Bull. 36,* La. Geol. Svy. (1962), Dept. of Conserv.

Parker, T. J.: "Model Structures of Salt Dome Tectronics," *PhD Dissertation,* Tex. U. (1952), Dept. of Geol.

Parker, T. J. and McDowell, A. N.: "Notes on the Construction of Geologic Scale Models," *Mines Mag.* (1950), v. 40, no. 10, pp. 75-79.

Parker, T. J. and McDowell, A. N.: "Scale Models as Guide to Interpretation of Salt Dome Faulting," *Bull.,* AAPG (1951), v. 35, no. 9, pp. 2076-2086.

Parker, T. J. and McDowell, A. N.: "Model Studies of Salt Dome Tectonics," *Bull.,* AAPG (1955), v. 39, no. 12, pp. 2384-2470; Review by W. T. Born, *Geophysics,* v. 21, no. 4, p. 1121.

Parker, W. G. and Hanna, M. A.: "Notes on an Occurrence of Galena at Pierce Junction Salt Dome, Harris County, Texas," *Bull.,* AAPG (1933), v. 17, no. 4, pp. 438-439.

Patnode, H. W. and Trask, P. D.: *Source Beds of Petroleum,* Rept. of investigation supported jointly by the API and the Geol. Svy. of the U. S. Dept. of Interior from 1931 to 1941, AAPG (1942), 561 pp.

Patrick, H. G.: "Case History of the Friendswood (Webster) Oil Field, Harris County, Texas," *Geophysical Case Histories,* SEG (1948), v. 1, pp. 74-84.

Patrick, Thomas B. and Fox, Bruce W.: "Developments in East Texas in 1959," *Bull.,* AAPG (1960), v. 44, no. 6, pp. 810-818.

Patrick, W. W.: "Salt Dome Statistics," *Guidebook,* AAPG-SEPM-SEG Jt. Ann. Mtg. (1953), Houston, Texas, pp. 13-20.

Patton, J. L. and Murchison, E. A., Jr.: "Developments in Louisiana Gulf Coast in 1950," *Bull.,* AAPG (1951), v. 35, no. 6, pp. 1338-1344.

Paxson, R. B. and Barton, D. C.: "The Spindletop Salt Dome and Oil Field, Jefferson County, Texas," *Bull.,* AAPG (1925), v. 9, no. 3, pp. 594-612; *Geology of Salt Dome Oil Fields,* AAPG (1926), pp. 478-496.

Payne, W. M. and Harris, R. M.: "Developments in Southeastern States in 1946 and 1947," *Bull.,* AAPG (1948), v. 32, no. 6, pp. 1065-1076.

Payne, W. M. and Harris, R. M.: "Developments in Southeastern States in 1948," *Bull.,* AAPG (1949), v. 33, no. 6, pp. 1002-1010.

Pennington, H.: "Hydraulics of Salt Dome Waters," *Oil Weekly* (1929), v. 52, no. 7, pp. 27-29.

Perez Larios, Jose: *"Explotacion Minera de Sal en Domos en el Estado de Louisiana, E.U.A.,* Archivo Consejo de Recursos Naturales no Renovables (1960).

Perkins, J. M. and Lonsdale, J. T.: *Mineral Resources of the Texas Coastal Plain,* Bur. Econ. Geol. (1955), Texas U., Min. Res. Circ. 38, 49 pp.

Peters, J. W.: "Reconnaissance of Salt Dome by Fan Shooting and a Comparison of Seismic Refraction Depth Formulae," *Compass* (1938), v. 18, no. 4, pp. 211-217.

Peters, J. W. and Dugan, Albert F.: "Gravity and Magnetic Investigations at the Grand Saline Salt Dome, Van Zandt County, Texas," *Geophysics* (1945), v. 10, no. 3, pp. 376-393; *Geophysical Case Histories,* SEG (1948), v. 1, pp. 105-120.

Peterson, William A.: "Are Gulf Coast Oil Hunters Resting on Their Laurels?" *Oil and Gas Jour.* (1961), v. 59, no. 31, pp. 254-256.

Petroleum Week: "Pauley's Offshore Field May Make Mexico an Oil Exporter," *Pet. Week* (Sept. 2, 1960), p. 33.

Pettijohn, F. J.: *Sedimentary Rocks,* Second Edition, Harper & Brothers (1957), New York, 484 pp.

Pflug, Hans D.: (Review of) "Palynologic Age of Diapiric and Bedded Salt in the Gulf Coastal Province, by Ulrich Jux," *Bull.,* AAPG (1963), v. 47, no. 1, pp. 180-181.

Pinkley, G. R.: "Numerous Types of Structures, Multiple Sands, and Deep Producing Possibilities Outstanding Features of South Texas Geology," *Oil Weekly* (1936), v. 83, no. 3, pp. 51-53, 56, 58, 60.

Pirtle, C. W. and Wendlandt, E. A.: "Developments in East Texas During 1938," *Bull.,* AAPG (1939), v. 23, no. 6, pp. 889-895.

Pitt, William D.: "Clear Lake Field, Harris County, Texas," *Typical Oil and Gas Fields of Southeast Texas,* Houston Geol. Soc. (1962), pp. 38-41.

Pittman, J. W. and Sheeler, J. E. R.: "Weeks Island," *The Petroleum Engineer* (March, 1952), pp. B-7–B-10.

Playfair, John: *Illustrations of the Huttonian Theory of the Earth,* Edinburgh (1802).

Plummer, F. B.: "Migration of Oil and Origin of Oil Pools," *Oil and Gas Jour.* (1944), v. 43, no. 24, pp. 139-140.

Plummer, F. B., Sellards, E. H. and Adkins, W. S.: "The Geology of Texas; Volume 1, Stratigraphy," *Bull. 3232,* Tex. U. (1933), Bur. Econ. Geol., 1007 pp.

Pollack, J. M.: "Sugarland Oil Field, Fort Bend County, Texas," *Guidebook,* AAPG-SEPM-SEG Jt. Ann. Mtg., Houston, Texas (March, 1953), pp. 153-156.

Porter, R. L. and Seren, G. W.: "Damon Mound Field, Brazoria County, Texas," *Guidebook,* AAPG-SEPM-SEG Jt. Ann. Mtg. (March, 1953), Houston, Texas, pp. 107-109.

Powell, L. C. and Culligan, L. B.: "Developments in Southeastern States in 1954," *Bull.,* AAPG (1955), v. 39, no. 6, pp. 1004-1014.

Powers, Sidney: "The Butler Salt Dome, Freestone County, Texas," *Am. Jour. Sci.* (1920), ser. 4, v. 49, pp. 127-142.

Powers, Sidney: "The Sabine Uplift, Louisiana," *Bull.,* AAPG (1920), v. 4, no. 2, pp. 117-136.

Powers, Sidney: "Interior Salt Domes of Texas," *Bull.,* AAPG (1926), v. 10, no. 1, pp. 1-60; *Geology of Salt Dome Oil Fields,* AAPG (1926), pp. 209-268.

Powers, Sidney and Hopkins, O. B.: "The Brooks, Steen and Grand Saline Salt Domes, Smith and Van Zandt Counties, Texas," *Bull. 736,* USGS (1922), pp. 179-239.

Pratt, W. E.: "A New Gulf Coast Dome, Fort Bend County, Texas," *Bull.,* AAPG (1922), v. 6, no. 3, pp. 252-254.

Pratt, W. E.: "Two New Salt Domes in Texas (Moss Bluff and Boggy Creek Domes)," *Bull.,* AAPG (1926), v. 10, no. 11, pp. 1171-1172.

Pratt, W. E.: "A Geologist Looks at the Gulf Coast," *Oil and Gas Jour.* (1926), v. 25, no. 30, pp. 91-92.

Pratt, W. E.: "Some Questions on the Cause of the Subsidence of the Surface in the Goose Creek Field, Texas," *Bull.,* AAPG (1927), v. 11, no. 8, pp. 887-889.

Prommel, H. W. C. and Crum, H. E.: "Salt Domes of Permian and Pennsylvanian Age in Southeastern Utah and Their Influence on Oil

Accumulation," *Bull.,* AAPG (1927), v. 11, no. 4, pp. 373-393.

Purzer, Joseph and Weeks, W. B: "Developments in Southern Arkansas and Northern Louisiana During 1939," *Bull.,* AAPG (1940), v. 24, no. 6, pp. 1092-1099. (abs.). v. 25, no. 6,

Purzer, Joseph and Weeks, W. B.: "Developments in Southern Arkansas and Northern Louisiana During 1940," *Bull.,* AAPG (1941), v. 25, no. 6, pp. 1024-1036; (abs.) v. 25, no. 6, p. 943.

Pyle, G. T. and Babisak, Julius: "Structure of the Woodlawn Field, Jefferson Davis Parish, Louisiana," *Trans.,* GCAGS (1951), v. 1, pp. 200-210.

Quarles, Miller, Jr.: "Salt Ridge Hypothesis on Origin of Texas Gulf Coast Type of Faulting," *Bull.,* AAPG (1953), v. 37, no. 3, pp. 489-508.

Raggio, David L., Sandberg, Adolph E., Martin, James L. and Hough, Leo W.: "Geology of Webster Parish," *Bull. 29,* La. Geol. Svy. (1954), Dept. of Conserv., 252 pp.

Rainwater, E. H. and Zingula, R. P. (ed.): "Sulphur Mine at Boling Dome," *Field Excursion No. 7,* Geology of the Gulf Coast and Central Texas and Guidebook of Excursions, Houston Geol. Soc. (1962), Houston, Texas, pp. 278-280.

Ramanes, James: "Salt Domes of Northern Germany," *Jour. Inst. Pet.* (1931), v. 17, pp. 252-259.

Ransone, K. and Rosaire, E. E.: "The Growth of Company Owned Operations in Gulf Coast Geophysical Prospecting Since July, 1930," *Geophysics* (1936), v. 1, no. 3, pp. 306-312.

Ransone, K. and Rosaire, E. E.: "The Amount and Distribution of Seismic and Gravity Exploration in the Gulf Coast Through 1936," *Geophysics* (1937), v. 2, no. 1, pp. 1-16.

Raymond, J. P., Jr. (ed.): *Salt Domes of South Louisiana, Vol. I,* first revision, New Orleans Geol. Soc. (1963), 133 pp.

Rayne, John R., Craft, B. C. and Hawkins, Murray F., Jr.: "The Reservoir Mechanism of Sulfur Recovery," *Trans.,* AIME (1956), v. 207. pp. 246-251; *Tech. Paper 4385,* AIME; *Jour. of Pet. Tech.* (1956), v. 8, no. 11, pp. 246-251.

Read, J. L., Jr.: "Developments in East Texas in 1951," *Bull.,* AAPG (1952), v. 36, no. 6, pp. 1188-1200.

Reed, L. C.: "The Welsh, Louisiana Oil Field," *Bull.,* AAPG (1925), v. 9, no. 3, pp. 464-478; *Geology of Salt Dome Oil Fields,* AAPG (1926), pp. 437-451.

Reed, R. D.: "Review of Steinsalz and Kalisalze,

Geology by Franz Lotze, 1938," *Bull.,* AAPG (1939), v. 23, no. 2, pp. 254-256.

Reedy, M. F., Jr.: "Stratigraphy of the Frio Formation, Orange and Jefferson Counties, Texas," *Bull.,* AAPG (1949), v. 33, no. 11, pp. 1830-1858; (abs.), no. 1, pp. 108-109; *Oil and Gas Jour.* (1949), v. 47, no. 32, p. 104.

Reichert, H. C.: "Tigre Lagoon—An Example of Structural Development in Relation to Salt Dome Growth," *Trans.,* GCAGS, (1955), v. 5, pp. 199-208.

Reidel, John C.: "L. P. G. Goes Underground for Summer." *Oil and Gas Jour.* (1952), v. 51, no. 12, p. 302.

Reinecke, L., Harris, G. D. and Maurey, F. J.: "Rock Salt, Its Origin, Geological Occurrence and Economic Importance in the State of Louisiana, Together With Brief Notes and References to All Known Salt Deposits and Industries of the World," *Bull.,* La. Geol. Svy. (1908), v. 7, 259 pp.

Renick, B. C.: "Recently Discovered Salt Domes in East Texas," *Bull.,* AAPG (1928), v. 12, no. 5, pp. 527-547.

Renick, B. C.: "The Jackson Group and the Catahoula and Oakville Formations in a Part of the Texas Gulf Coastal Plain," *Bull. 3619,* Tex. U. (1936), 104 pp.

Reynolds, J. Rex and Sholl, Vinton H.: "Developments in the Upper Gulf Coast of Texas in 1962," *Bull.,* AAPG (1963), v. 47, no. 6, pp. 1081-1087.

Rhodes, E. J.: "Geology of the Gulf Coast Salt Domes," *BS Thesis,* MIT (1931), Dept. of Geol. and Geophysics.

Rhodes, M. L. and Adams, J. E.: "Dolomitization by Seepage Refluxion," *Bull.,* AAPG (1960), v. 44, no. 12, pp. 1912-1920.

Rich, John L.: "Problems of the Origin, Migration and Accumulation of Oil," *Problems of Petroleum Geology,* AAPG (1934), pp. 337-345.

Richardson, H. T. and Ferrando, Al: "Barataria Field, Jefferson Parish, Louisiana," *Bull.,* AAPG (1941), v. 25, no. 2, pp. 322-323.

Richardson, P. H.: "Minden Salt Dome," *Guidebook,* 1960 Spring Field Trip, Shreveport Geol. Soc., pp. 17-26.

Richey, W. E., Love, Donald W. and Kirkland, R. A.: "Developments in East Texas in 1956," *Bull.,* AAPG (1957), v. 41, no. 6, pp. 1171-1180.

Riddell, John T.: "Esperson Dome Field, Liberty County, Texas," *Typical Oil and Gas Fields in Southeast Texas,* Houston Geol. Soc. (1962), pp. 47-52.

Ritz, C. H.: "Geomorphology of Gulf Coast Salt Structures and Its Economic Application," *Bull.*, AAPG (1936), v. 20, no. 11, pp. 1413-1438.

Ritz, C. H., Hickey, Maude and Barton, D. C.: "Gulf Coast Geosyncline," *Bull.*, AAPG (1933), v. 17, no. 12, pp. 1446-1458; *Gulf Coast Oil Fields* (1936), pp. 192-204; (abs.) *Pan Am. Geologist*, v. 59, p. 230.

Roach, C. B.: "Subsurface Study of Jennings Field, Acadia Parish, Louisiana," *Bull.*, AAPG (1943), v. 27, no. 8, pp. 1102-1122; (abs.) *Bull.*, AAPG (1941), v. 25, no. 5, p. 929; *Oil and Gas Jour.* (1941), v. 39, no. 47, p. 56.

Roach, C. B.: "Intrusive Shale Dome in South Thornwell Field, Jefferson Davis and Cameron Parishes, Louisiana," *Bull.*, AAPG (1962), v. 46, no. 12, pp. 2121-2132.

Robinson, V. D. and Hoffmeister, W. S.: "Developments in South Arkansas and North Louisiana in 1945," *Bull.*, AAPG (1946), v. 30, no. 6, pp. 1007-1009.

Rogers, A. F.: "Anhydrite and Associated Minerals from Salt Mines of Central Kansas," *Am. Jour. Sci.* (1910), ser. 4, v. 29, pp. 258-261.

Rogers, G. S.: "Intrusive Origin of Gulf Coast Salt Domes," *Econ. Geol.* (1918), v. 13, pp. 447-485; (discussion) v. 14, pp. 178-180.

Rogers, G. S.: "Origin of Salt Domes of the Gulf Coast," *Jour.*, Washington Acad. Sci. (1919), v. 9, no. 10, pp. 291-292.

Rogers, J. K., Spice, W. H., Jr. and Vesely, L. A.: "Developments in South Texas in 1951," *Bull.*, AAPG (1952), v. 36, no. 6, pp. 1177-1187.

Rogers, Walter F.: *Composition and Properties of Well Drilling Fluids*, Gulf Publishing Co. (1963), Houston, Texas, 818 pp.

*Rojas, Antonio Garcia: "Mexican Oil Fields," *Bull.*, AAPG (1949), v. 33, no. 8, pp. 1336-1350.

*Roldan, Pascual Gutierrez: "Petroleos Mexicanos," *World Pet.* (1963), v. 34, no. 6, pp. 507-512.

Rolshausen, F. W.: "Occurrence of Siderite in Cap Rock at Carlos Dome, Grimes County, Texas," *Bull.*, AAPG (1934), v. 18, no. 4, pp. 543-546; *Gulf Coast Oil Fields*, AAPG (1936), pp. 133-135.

Romberg, Frederick E.: "Key Variables of Gravity," *Geophysics* (1957), v. 23, no. 4, pp. 684-700.

Romeyn, H.: "Salt Mines of Avery's Island," *Mines and Min.* (1900), v. 20, pp. 348-349.

Rosaire, E. E.: "On the Strategy and Tactics of Exploration for Petroleum," *Jour. Soc. Pet. Geophys.* (1935), v. 6, no. 1, pp. 11-26; *Early Geophysical Papers*, SEG (1957), pp. 255-270.

Rosaire, E. E.: "Exploration on the Gulf Coast to 1936," (abs.) *World Pet.* (1936), v. 7, no. 8, p. 404.

Rosaire, E. E.: (Review) "The Interrelationship of Geology and Geophysics, by O. L. Brace," *Geophysics* (1937), v. 2, no. 1, pp. 63-67.

Rosaire, E. E.: "Shallow Stratigraphic Variations Over Gulf Coast Structures," *Geophysics* (1938), v. 3, no. 2, pp. 96-115; (discussion) pp. 115-112.

Rosaire, E. E.: "On the Strategy and Tactics of Exploration for Petroleum, II," *Geophysics* (1938), v. 3, no. 1, pp. 22-39.

Rosaire, E. E.: "On the Strategy and Tactics of Exploration for Petroleum, III," *Geophysics* (1939), v. 4, no. 3, pp. 155-166.

Rosaire, E. E.: "Symposium on Geochemical Exploration, Geochemical Prospecting for Petroleum," *Bull.*, AAPG (1940), v. 24, no. 8, pp. 1400-1443.

Rosaire, E. E. and Lester, O. C., Jr.: "Seismological Discovery and Partial Detail of Vermilion Bay Salt Dome, Louisiana," *Bull.*, AAPG (1932), v. 16, no. 12, pp. 1221-1229; *Geophysical Case Histories*, SEG (1948), v. 1, no. 1, pp. 135-143; *Trans.*, Soc. Pet. Geophy. (1933), v. 3, pp. 51-59; *Early Geophysical Papers*, SEG (1947), pp. 381-389.

Rosaire, E. E. and Ransone, K.: "The Growth of Company Owned Operations in the Gulf Coast Geophysical Prospecting since July 1930," *Geophysics* (1936), v. 1, no. 3, pp. 306-312.

Rosaire, E. E. and Ransone, K.: "The Amount and Distribution of Seismic and Gravity Exploration in the Gulf Coast Through 1936," *Geophysics* (1937), v. 2, no. 1, pp. 1-16.

Rosaire, E. E. and Stiles, M. E.: "Distribution of Salt Domes in Depth," (abs.) *Pan Am. Geologist* (1932), v. 57, no. 4, p. 316.

Rosaire, E. E. and Stiles, M. E.: "Exploration and Production in the Gulf Coast Through 1935," *Geophysics* (1936), v. 1, no. 1, pp. 141-148.

Rose, Walter: "New Interest Focuses on Lake Fausse Pointe Field," *Oil and Gas Jour.* (1952), v. 50, no. 47, pp. 80-81.

Rose, Walter: "Drilling and Producing Report,

---

* See footnote, page 388.

Venice Field, Plaquemines Parish, Louisiana," *Oil and Gas Jour.* (1952), v. 51, no. 11, pp. 62-64.

Rosenthal, Stanley H.: "Hankamer Field, Liberty County, Texas," *Typical Oil and Gas Fields of Southeast Texas,* Houston Geol. Soc. (1962), pp. 74-75.

Rotan, R. A., Jr., Stout, E. D. and Cockerham, K. L., Jr.: "Developments in Upper Gulf Coast of Texas in 1955," *Bull.,* AAPG (1956), v. 40, no. 6, pp. 1239-1252.

Roth, E. P., Jr. and Smith, Norman E.: "Developments in Louisiana Gulf Coast in 1962," *Bull.,* AAPG (1963), v. 47, no. 6, pp. 1088-1096.

Roth, E. P., Jr. and Vallas, H. A.: "Developments in Louisiana Gulf Coast in 1961," *Bull.,* AAPG (1962), v. 46, no. 6, pp. 929-937.

Ruhe, Robert W., Jr. and Harper, Douglas C.: "Maps Predict P r o b l e m Formations," *Oil and Gas Jour.* (April 29, 1963).

Russell, R. D.: (abs.) "Salt Domes of Bienville Parish, Louisiana," *Bull.,* AAPG (1942), v. 26, no. 5, p. 904.

Russell, R. J., McGuirt, J. H. and Howe, H. V.: "Physiography of Coastal Southwest Louisiana," *Bull 6,* La. Geol. Svy. (1935), pp. 1-68.

Russell, R. J., McGuirt, J. H., Craft, B. C., Stephenson, M. B. and Howe, H. V.: "Reports on the Geology of Cameron and Vermilion Parishes," *Bull.* 6, La. Geol. Svy. (1935), 242 pp.

Russell, William L.: *Structural Geology for Petroleum Geologists,* McGraw-Hill Book Co., Inc. (1955), New York, N. Y.

Ryan, J. P., Miller, W. C., Netzeband, F. F. and Early, T h o m a s R.: "Sulfur Resources and Production in Texas, Louisiana, Missouri, Oklahoma, Arkansas and Mississippi, and Markets for the Sulfur," *Inf. Circ. 8222* (1964), U. S. Dept. of the Interior, Bur. of Mines, (1964), 77 pp.

Sachs, K. N. and Squires, D. F.: "Corals and Larger Foraminifera at Anse la Butte Reef, Louisiana," *Bull.,* AAPG (1957), v. 41, no. 4, pp. 746-749.

Salas, Guillermo P.: *Geologia Economica del Azufre en el Istmo de Tehuantepec,* Trabajo inedito (1957), Mexico, D. F.

Sandberg, Adolph E., Martin, James L., Hough, Leo W. and Raggio, David L.: "Geology of Webster Parish," *Bull. 29,* La. Geol. Svy. (1954), Dept. of Conserv., 252 pp.

Sanders, C. W.: "Emba Salt Dome Region, U.S.S.R. and Some Comparisons with Other Salt Dome Regions," *Bull.,* AAPG (1939), v. 23, no. 4, pp. 492-516.

Sannemann, D.: *Zur Entwicklung von Salzstock-Familien* (1960). In preparation.

Sannemann, D.: "Salt Stock Families in Northwestern Germany," (abs.) *Bull.,* AAPG (1965), v. 49, no. 3, p. 357.

St. John, F. B., Jr. and Lusk, Tracy W.: "Developments in Southeastern States in 1959," *Bull.,* AAPG (1960), v. 44, no. 6, pp. 842-850.

Sansores, Enrique: "Estructuras Salinas del Sureste de Mexico," *V C o n v. An. de la AIPM,* en Abril de 1963 en Coatzacoalcos, pp. 7, 11.

Sansores, Enrique and Contreras, Hugo V.: "Geologia del Domo Salino de 'El Rosario' en el Estado de Tabasco y sus Posibilidades Petroliferas," *Bol. Asoc. Mex. Geol. Petrol.* (1953), v. 5, nos. 1-2, pp. 57-74.

Sansores, J. C.: "Analisis Paleomicroontologico de las Formaciones Encontradas en los Pozos del Campo de Moloacan y Correlaciones Estratigraficas Entre Dichos Pozos," *Tesis Prof.,* Universidad Nacional Autonoma de Mexico (1950).

Santillan, Manuel: "Synopsis of the Geology of Mexico," *Oil Weekly* (1936), v. 81, no. 2, pp. 34-37, 40-41.

Sawtelle, George: "The Batson Oil Field, Hardin County, Texas," *Bull.,* AAPG (1925), v. 9, no. 9, pp. 1277-1282; *Geology of Salt Dome Oil Fields,* AAPG (1926), pp. 524-529.

Sawtelle, George: "Salt Dome Statistics," *Bull.,* AAPG (1936), v. 20, no. 6, pp. 726-735; *Gulf Coast Oil Fields,* AAPG (1936), pp. 109-118.

Sawtelle, George and Barton, Donald C. (ed.): *Gulf Coast Oil Fields,* American Association of Petroleum Geologists (1936), Tulsa, Oklahoma, 1070 pp.

Saye, Frank, Hower, Wayne, Aulick, Burton and Hopkins, H. F.: "Improved Production by Chemical Treatment in Gulf Coast Areas," *Jour. of Pet. Tech.* (1952), v. 4, no. 9, pp. 13-16.

Sayre, A. N.: "Geology and Ground Water Resources of Duval County, Texas," *Paper 776,* USGS (1937), Water-Supply Dept., 116 pp.

Scharon, LeRoy: "Electrical Resistivity Surveys in Salt Mines," *Symposium on Salt,* Northern Ohio Geol. Soc., Inc. (1963), Cleveland, Ohio, pp. 379-389.

Schmidt, C.: "Geophysical Investigations Carried out in Salt Dome Areas of Texas and Louisiana," *Jour. Inst. Pet.* (1931), v. 17, pp. 381-383.

Schmidt, K. A.: "Long Lake Field, Anderson, Freestone and Leon Counties, Texas," *Pub 5116,* Tex. U. (1951), pp. 201-206.

Schneider, S. J.: "Bay Saint Elaine Oil Field, Southern Louisiana," *Bull.* AAPG (1959), v. 43, no. 10, pp. 2456-2469.

Schuchert, Charles: *Historical Geology of the Antillean-Caribbean Region or the Lands Bordering the Gulf of Mexico and the Caribbean Sea,* Wiley, (1935), New York, 811 pp; (abs.) *Bull.,* GSA (1929), v. 40, pp. 204-205, 337-359; *Science,* new ser., v. 69, pp. 139-145; (summary) *Pan Am. Geologist,* v. 51, no. 2, pp. 157-159.

Scott, K. R., Hayes, W. E. and Fietz, R. P.: "Geology of the Eagle Mills Formation," *Trans.,* GCAGS (1961), v. 11, pp. 1-14.

Scrafford, Bruce: "Developments in South Texas in 1944," *Bull.,* AAPG (1945), v. 29, no. 6, pp. 777-784.

Scrafford, Bruce: "Developments in South Texas in 1945," *Bull.,* AAPG (1946), v. 30, no. 6, pp. 972-979.

Scrafford, Bruce: "Developments in South Texas in 1946," *Bull.,* AAPG (1947), v. 31, no. 6, pp. 1052-1058.

Scrafford, Bruce: "Developments in South Texas in 1947," *Bull.,* AAPG (1948), v. 32, no. 6, pp. 997-1008.

Scrafford, Bruce: "Developments in South Texas in 1948," *Bull.,* AAPG (1949), v. 33, no. 6, pp. 945-955.

Scrafford, Bruce: "Developments in South Texas in 1949," *Bull.,* AAPG (1950), v. 34, no. 6, pp. 1158-1169.

Scrafford, Bruce and Jenswold, Nancy: "Developments in South Texas in 1950," *Bull.,* AAPG (1951), v. 35, no. 6, pp. 1300-1312.

Scruton, P. C.: "Deposition of Evaporites," *Bull.,* AAPG (1953), v. 37, no. 11, pp. 2498-2512.

Seale, Tom, Finley, J. C. and McGee, D. A.: "Oil in the Gulf of Mexico," (abs.) *Proc.,* Okla. Acad. Sci. (1950) v. 29, pp. 60-61.

Seglund, James A.: "Geologically Speaking, Here's the Picture in South Louisiana," *Oil and Gas Jour.* (1956), v. 54, no. 59, pp. 217-222.

Seismograph Service Corporation: "Gulf, Mexican, and Caribbean Oil Zones," *Oil and Gas Jour.* (1944), v. 43, no. 34, pp. 182-199.

Self, S. R., Warner, C. A., Allison, A. P.,

Beckelhymer, R. L., Benson, Don G., Hutchins, R. M., Jr., Lake, C. L., Lewis, Ray C. and O'Bannon, P. H.: "Geology of Katy Field, Waller, Harris and Fort Bend Counties, Texas," *Bull.,* AAGP (1946), v. 30, no. 2, pp. 157-180.

Sellards, E. H.: "Subsidence in Gulf Coastal Plain Salt Domes," *Bull. 3001,* Tex. U. (1930), Bur. Econ. Geol., pp. 9-36.

Sellards, E. H.: "Mineral Locality Map of Texas Showing Occurence of Useful Minerals, Rocks and Other Geologic Substances," *Proc. and Trans.,* Tex. Acad. Sci. (1944), v. 27, p. 138.

Sellards, E. H.: "Mineral Resources of Texas," *Tex Geol. Mag.* (1944), v. 8, no. 2, pp. 19-30.

Sellards, E. H., Adkins, W. S. and Plummer, F. B.: "The Geology of Texas; Volume I, Stratigraphy," *Bull. 3232,* Tex. U. (1933), Bur. Econ. Geol., 1007 pp.

Sellards, E. H. and Baker, C. L.: "The Geology of Texas; Volume 2, Structural and Economic Geology," *Bull. 3401,* Tex. U. (1934), Bur. Econ. Geol., 884 pp.

Sellards, E. H. and Evans, G. L.: "Index to Mineral Resources of Texas by Counties," *Min. Res. Circ. 29,* Tex. U. (1944), 21 pp.

Sellards, E. H. and Hendricks, L. C.: "Occurrence of Oil and Gas in Texas," *Pub. 4301,* Tex. U. (1946), pp. 179-190.

Sellards, E. H. and Hendricks, L. C.: *Structural Map of Texas,* Third Ed., Texas U. (1946), Bur. Econ. Geol.

Seren, G. W. and Porter, R. L.: "Damon Mound Field, Brazoria County, Texas," *Guidebook,* AAPG-SEPM-SEG Jt. Ann. Mtg. (1953), Houston, Texas, pp. 107-109.

Serna Vigueras, Reyes, Marquez Pineda, Aremos and Viveros Juarez, Manuel: "Depositos de Sal y Azufre en la Cuenca Salina del Istmo, Ver.," *Bol. 64* (1964), Consejo de Recursos Naturales no Renovables, 76 pp.

Sevier, Richard P. and Hundley, H. B.: "Developments in Arkansas and North Louisiana in 1961," *Bull.,* AAPG (1962), v. 46, no. 6, pp. 938-952.

Sevier, Richard P. and Jenkinson, Lewis F.: "Developments in Arkansas and North Louisiana in 1960," *Bull.,* AAPG (1961), v. 45, no. 6, pp. 889-902.

Shaffer, H. R. and Lowe, W. O.: "Developments in Arkansas and North Louisiana in 1953," *Bull.,* AAPG (1954), v. 38, no. 6, pp. 1233-1241.

Shaffer, H. R. and Womack, S. A., Jr.: "Developments in Arkansas and North Louisiana in 1952," *Bull.,* AAPG (1953), v. 37, no. 6, pp. 1449-1459.

Shaub, H. P. and Jackson, A.: "The Northwestern Oil Basin of Borneo," *Habitat of Oil,* AAPG (1958), pp. 1330-1336.

Shaw, E. W.: "Possibility of Using Gravity Anomalies in the Search for Salt Dome Oil and Gas Pools," *Science,* new ser. (1917), v. 46, pp. 553-556.

Shaw, E. W.: (abs.) "Stratigraphy of the Gulf Coastal Plain as Related to Salt Domes," *Jour.,* Washington Acad. Sci. (1919), v. 9, no. 10, pp. 289-291.

Shead, W. C. and Allen, Edwin R.: "Is a Salt Dome's North Flank Its Best Prospect?" *World Oil* (1956), v. 142, no. 5, pp. 158-160.

Shearer, H. K.: "Developments in South Arkansas and North Louisiana in 1937," *Bull.,* AAPG (1938), v. 22, no. 6, pp. 719-727.

Sheeler, J. E. R. and Pittman, J. W.: "Weeks Island," *The Petroleum Engineer* (March, 1952), pp. B-7–B-10.

Shelby, T. H. and Loetterle, G. J.: "Developments in East Texas During 1945," *Bull.,* AAPG (1946), v. 30, no. 6, pp. 980-990.

Shelby, T. H., Bell, J. S. and Wendlandt, E. A.: "Hawkins Field, Wood County, Texas," *Bull.,* AAPG (1946), v. 30, no. 6, pp. 1830-1856.

Sheldon, Ruth: "Poza Rica Field, Backbone of Oil Industry in Mexico," *Oil and Gas Jour.* (1939), v. 38, no. 2, pp. 26-29, 104.

Shepard, F. P.: "Salt Domes Related to Mississippi Submarine Trough," *Bull.,* GSA (1937) v. 48, pp. 1349-1361; (abs.) *Proc.* (1936), pp. 101-102; *Geophysics,* v. 2, no. 2, p. 169.

Shepard, G. F.: "Developments in Louisiana Gulf Coast in 1944," *Bull.,* AAPG (1945), v. 29, no. 6, pp. 792-802.

Shepard, G. F.: "Developments in Louisiana Gulf Coast in 1946," *Bull.,* AAPG (1947), v. 31, no. 6, pp. 1078-1083; (abs.) *Trans.,* AAPG-SEPM-SEG Jt. Ann. Mtg. (1947), Los Angeles, Calif., p. 138.

Sholl, Vinton H. and Critz, James S.: "Developments in Upper Gulf Coast of Texas in 1961," *Bull.,* AAPG (1962), v. 46, no. 6, pp. 921-928.

Sholl, Vinton H. and Reynolds, J. Rex: "Devel-opments in the Upper Gulf Coast of Texas in 1962," *Bull.,* AAPG (1963), v. 47, no. 6, pp. 1081-1087.

Shreveport Geological Society: *Reference Report in Certain Oil and Gas Fields of North Louisiana, South Arkansas, Mississippi and Alabama,* Vol. 1, Shreveport Geol. Soc. (1945).

Shreveport Geological Society: *Reference Report on Certain Oil and Gas Fields of North Louisiana, South Arkansas, Mississippi, and Alabama,* Vol. 1, Shreveport Geol. Soc. (1946), 328 pp.

Shreveport Geological Society: *Reference Report on Certain Oil and Gas Fields of North Louisiana, South Arkansas, Mississippi, and Alabama,* Vol. 2, Shreveport Geol. Soc. (1947), pp. 317-503.

Shreveport Geological Society: *Reference Report on Certain Oil and Gas Fields of North Louisiana, South Arkansas, Mississippi, and Alabama,* Vol. 3, Shreveport Geol. Soc. (1951), no. 1, 42 pp.

Shreveport Geological Society: *Reference Report on Certain Oil and Gas Fields of North Louisiana, South Arkansas, Mississippi, and Alabama,* Vol. 3, Shreveport Geol. Soc. (1953), no. 2, 108 pp.

Shrewsbury, R. D.: "A Theory on the Occurrence of Salt," *Oil Weekly* (1946), v. 122, no. 1, pp. 36-39.

Singleton, F. L.: "Potentialities of Dickinson Area May Rival Anahuac and Hastings Fields," *Oil and Gas Jour.* (1935), v. 34, no. 12, p. 23.

Singleton, F. L.: "City and Owners of Lots Solve Drilling Problems," *Oil and Gas Jour.* (1935), v. 34, no. 21, p. 15.

Singleton, F. L.: "Flank Production of New Iberia Climaxes 20 Years of Effort," *Oil and Gas Jour.* (1936), v. 35, no. 33, p. 316.

Singleton, F. L.: "See Greater Possibilities in Dickinson," *Oil and Gas Jour.* (1937), v. 35, no. 52, pp. 102, 118.

Singleton, F. L.: "Friendswood Field has Three Factors Attracting Notice," *Oil and Gas Jour.* (1937), v. 36, no. 13, p. 43.

Singleton, F. L.: "Maritime Development Certain to Assume More Importance," *Oil and Gas Jour.* (1941), v. 39, no. 49, pp. 96-97.

Skinner, Hubert C.: "A Comparison of the Mississippi Submarine Trench with the Iberian Trough," *Trans.,* GCAGS (1960), v. 10, pp. 1-6.

Skrivanos, N. C. and Norton, R. G.: "Liquefied Petroleum Gas Storage in Arcadia Salt Dome,"

Guidebook, 1960 Spring Field Trip, Shreveport Geol. Soc., pp. 48-56.

Smiley, T. F.: "Plastic Flow Theory in Explanation of Salt Domes on the Gulf Coast," *Oil and Gas Jour.* (1936), v. 34, no. 40, p. 48.

Smith, Cecil W.: "Gulf Coast Oil Fields, Geological Data, Development History," *World Oil* (1950), v. 130, no. 7, pp. 60-120.

Smith, Cecil W. and Logan, L. J.: "Continental Shelf Activity Intensified (Gulf Coast)," *World Oil* (1948), v. 123, no. 3, sec. 1, pp. 37-40.

Smith, Derrell A.: "Geology of South Pass Block 27 Field, Offshore, Plaquemines Parish, Louisiana," *Bull.,* AAPG (1960), v. 45, no. 1, pp. 51-71.

Smith, E. R. and Burtchaell, E. P.: "Pressure Control by Water Injection—A Resume of Case Histories," *Jour. of Pet. Tech.* (1952), v. 4, no. 7, pp. 15-18.

Smith, Fred L., Jr. and Goodwyn, J. T., Jr.: "Batson Field, Hardin County, Texas," *Typical Oil and Gas Fields of Southeast Texas,* Houston Geol. Soc. (1962), pp. 8-13.

Smith, G. J.: "Review of Developments in 1942, Gulf Coast of Upper Texas and Louisiana," *Bull.,* AAPG (1943), v. 27, no. 6, pp. 730-738.

Smith, Norman E. and Roth, E. P., Jr.: "Developments in Louisiana Gulf Coast in 1962," *Bull.,* AAPG (1963), v. 47, no. 6, pp. 1088-1096.

Sollars, P. F. and Walters, J. E.: "Geology of the Danbury Salt Dome," *Trans.,* GCAGS (1952), v. 2, p. 7.

South Louisiana Geological Society: "Regional Correlation Section, Five Island Trend (Jefferson Island to Belle Isle, Louisiana)," *No. 3, Tertiary,* (1954).

South Louisiana Oil Scouts Association and Texas Gulf Coast Oil Scouts Association: "Old Hackberry Salt Dome," *Bull. 1* (1930), pp. 121-123.

South Louisiana Oil Scouts Association and Texas Gulf Coast Oil Scouts Association: "Kelso Bayou or East Hackberry Dome," *Bull. 1* (1930), pp. 124-125.

South Texas Geological Society: "Mesozoic Stratigraphy and Structure, Saltillo-Galeana Areas, Coahuila and Nuevo Leon," *Guidebook,* 1959 Field Trip, pp. 11-13.

Sovinsky, V. N.: "New Look at Salt Dome Geology May Increase Gulf Coast Reserves," *World Oil,* Part I, (1958), v. 147, no. 5, pp. 180-181; Part II, no. 6, pp. 111-114.

Spaulding, W. M.: "Salt Domes; Their Nature, Origin, and Composition," *MS Thesis,* Mich. U. (1952), Dept. of Geol.

Speed, C. D., Jr.: "Application of Name 'Ferguson Crossing Dome', Brazos and Grimes Counties, Texas," *Bull.,* AAPG (1939), v. 23, no. 7, pp. 1092-1093.

Spice, W. H., Jr.: "Developments in South Texas in 1943," *Bull.,* AAPG (1944), v. 28, no. 6, pp. 858-863.

Spice, W. H., Jr., Vesely, L. A. and Rogers, J. K.: "Developments in South Texas in 1951," *Bull.* AAPG (1952), v. 36, no. 6, pp. 1177-1187.

Spillers, James P. (ed.): *Salt Domes of South Louisiana, Vol. II,* New Orleans Geol. Soc. (1962), 107 pp.

Spooner, W. C.: "Interior Salt Domes of Louisiana," *Bull.,* AAPG (1926), v. 10, no. 3, pp. 217-292; *Geology of Salt Dome Oil Fields,* AAPG (1926), pp. 269-344.

Spooner, W. C.: "Salt in Smackover Field, Union County, Arkansas," *Bull.,* AAPG (1932), v. 16, no. 6, pp. 601-608.

Spooner, W. C.: "Oil and Gas Geology of the Gulf Coastal Plain in Arkansas," *Bull. 2,* Ark. Geol. Svy. (1935), pp. 1-474.

Spooner, W. C.: "Development in Southern Arkansas and Northern Louisiana in 1938," *Bull.,* AAPG (1939), v. 23, no. 6, pp. 896-902; *Guidebook,* 14th Ann. Field Trip, Shreveport Geol. Soc., pp. 71-77.

Spooner, W. C., et al: *Structure of Typical American Oil Fields,* Vol. II, American Association of Petroleum Geologists (1929), Tulsa, Oklahoma, 780 pp.

Spooner, W. C., Hazzard, R. T. and Blanpied, B. W.: "Notes on Correlations of the Cretaceous of East Texas, South Arkansas, North Louisiana, Mississippi, and Alabama," *1945 Ref. Rept.,* Shreveport Geol. Soc. (1947), v. 2, pp. 472-481.

Spooner, W. C., Blanpied, B. W. and Hazzard, R. T.: "Notes on the Stratigraphy of Formations which Underlie the Smackover Limestone in South Arkansas, Northeast Texas, and North Louisiana," *1945 Ref. Rept.,* Shreveport Geol. Soc. (1947), v. 2, pp. 483-503.

Squires, D. F. and Sachs, K. N: "Corals and Larger Foraminifera at Anse la Butte Reef, Louisiana," *Bull.,* AAPG (1957), v. 41, no. 4, pp. 746-749.

Stahl, A. F. V.: (abs.) "Salt Structures in Their Relation to Petroleum Deposits," *Jour. Inst. Pet.* (1929), v. 15, pp. 315A-316A.

Stamey, R. A. and Judson, S. A.: "Overhanging Salt on Domes of Texas and Louisiana," *Bull., AAPG* (1933), v. 17, no. 12, pp. 1492-1520; *Gulf Coast Oil Fields* (1936), pp. 141-169; *Oil Weekly,* v. 71, no. 11, pp. 18-24; no. 12, pp. 18-22; no. 13, pp. 18, 20-24; *Oil and Gas Jour.* (1934), v. 32, no. 21, pp. 16, 30; no. 22, pp. 18, 22; no. 25, pp. 16, 18; no. 27, p. 18; (abs.) *Pan Am Geologist,* v. 59, no. 3, p. 230.

Stamey, R. A., Judson, S. A. and Murphy, P. C.: "Overhanging Cap Rock and Salt at Barbers Hill, Chambers County, Texas," *Bull., AAPG* (1932), v. 16, no. 5, pp. 469-482.

Stanley, Herbert M., Jr. and Eisenhardt, Wm. C.: "Developments in East Texas in 1960," *Bull., AAPG* (1961), v. 45, no. 6, pp. 861-867.

Stanley, L., Allen, W. E. and Caillouet, H. J.: "Gravity Investigations in the Hockley Salt Dome, Harris County, Texas," *Geophysics* (1936), v. 20, no. 4, pp. 829-840.

Steenland, Nelson C.: "Review of 'Spindletop' by James A. Clark and Michel T. Halbouty," *Geophysics* (1953), v. 18, no. 1, p. 236.

Steinmayer, R. A.: "Salt Dome Possibilities," *Bull. 22,* La. Geol. Svy. (1933), pp. 17-30.

Steinmayer, R. A.: "Salt Domes and Their Ceramic Deposits," *Bull.,* Am. Ceramic Soc. (1938), v. 17, no. 6, pp. 260-262.

Stenzel, H. B.: "The Geology of Leon County, Texas," *Bull. 3818,* Tex. U. (1938), 295 pp.

Stenzel, H. B.: "Faulting in Northwestern Houston County, Texas," *Min. Res. Circ. 23,* Tex. U. (1943), 9 pp; *Pub. 4301,* Tex. U. (1946), pp. 19-27.

Stenzel, H. B.: "Gypsum Mining Near Hockley, Harris County, Texas," *Min. Res. Circ. 35,* Tex. U. (1946), 21 pp.

Stenzel, H. B.: "Gypsum Resources and Mining on the Hockley Dome, Harris County, Texas," *Pub. 4301,* Tex. U. (1946), Bur. Econ. Geol; pp. 207-226.

Stephenson, L. W.: "Significance of Upper Cretaceous Fossils from Wells in Mississippi," *Bull., AAPG* (1945), v. 29, no. 7, pp. 1008-1018.

Stephenson, L. W., Cooke, C. W. and Gardner, J. A.: "The Atlantic and Gulf Coastal Plain," in Erich Krenkel (ed.), *Geologie der Erde, Nord Amerika,* Berlin, Gebruder Borntraeger (1939), v. 1, pp. 519-578.

Stephenson, M. B., Howe, H. V., Russell, R. J., McGuirt, J. H. and Craft, B. C.: "Reports on the Geology of C a m e r o n and Vermilion Parishes," *Bull. 6,* La. Geol. Svy. (1935), 242 pp.

Stephenson, M. B.: "Some Microfossils of the Potamides Matsoni Zone of Louisiana," *Bull. 6,* La. Geol. Svy. (1935), pp. 187-188.

Stern, A. R.: "New Accumulations Found Beneath North Flank Overhang Cote Blanche Island, St. Mary Parish, Louisiana," *Trans.,* GCAGS (1955), v. 5, pp. 173-179.

Stevens, G. D. and Goldston, W. L.: "Esperson Dome, Liberty County, Texas," *Bull.,* AAPG (1934), v. 18, no. 12, pp. 1632-1654; *Gulf Coast Oil Fields,* AAPG (1936), pp. 857-879.

Stiles, M. E. and Rosaire, E. E.: (abs.) "Distribution of Salt Domes in Depth," *Pan Am. Geologist* (1932), v. 57, no. 4, p. 316.

Stiles, M. E. and Rosaire, E. E.: "Exploration and Production in the Gulf Coast Through 1935," *Geophysics* (1936), v. 1, no. 1, pp. 141-148.

Stiles, S. and Hager, D. S.: "The Blue Ridge Salt Dome, Fort Bend County, Texas," *Bull.,* AAPG (1925), v. 9, no. 2, pp. 304-316; *Geology of Salt Dome Oil Fields* (1926), pp. 600-612.

Stille, H.: "Das Aufsteigen der Salzgebirges," *Zeitschr. f. Prakt. Geologie,* 19 (1911), p. 91.

Stille, H.: "Injektivfaltung und damit Zusammenhangende Erscheinungen," *Geol. Rundschau,* 8 (1917), p. 89.

Stille, H.: "The Upthrust of the Salt Masses of Germany," *Bull.,* AAPG (1925), v. 9, no. 3, pp. 417-441; *Geology of Salt Dome Oil Fields,* AAPG (1926), pp. 142-146.

Stipe, J. C. (ed.): *Salt Domes of South Louisiana, Vol. I,* New Orleans Geol. Soc. (1960), 145 pp.

Stipe, J. C. and Limes, L. L.: "Occurrence of Miocene Oil in South Louisiana," *Trans.,* GCAGS (1959), v. 9, pp. 77-90.

Stipe, J. C. and Limes, L. L.: "Offshore Louisiana: One of the Largest Undrilled Reserves in the World," *Oil and Gas Jour.* (1959), v. 57, no. 48, pp. 126-130.

Storm, L. W.: "Notes on the Boggy Creek Salt Dome, Located in Anderson and Cherokee Counties, Texas," *Magazine,* Colorado School of Mines (1929), v. 19, no. 7, pp. 20-22.

Stout, E. D., Cockerham, K. L., Jr. and Rotan,

R. A., Jr.: "Developments in Upper Gulf Coast of Texas in 1955," *Bull.*, AAPG (1956), v. 40, no. 6, pp. 1239-1252.

Stroud, B. K.: "Use of Barytes as a Mud-Laden Fluid," *Oil World* (June 5, 1925), p. 29.

Struxness, E. G.: "Storage of Radioactive Waste in Mine Cavities," (abs.) *Symposium on Salt* (1963), Northern Ohio Geol. Soc., Inc., p. 412.

Stuart, Murray: "A Contribution to Salt Dome Geochemistry," *Jour. Inst. Pet.* (1931), v. 17, pp. 338-345.

Sullins, R. S. and Cannan, G. E.: "Problems Encountered in Drilling Pressure Formations," *Drilling and Production Practice 1946*, API (1947), N. Y., pp. 29-33; *Drilling* (June 1946), pp. 48-50; (abs.) *Oil Weekly* (May 20, 1946), p. 31.

Suman, J. R.: "The Saratoga Oil Field, Hardin County, Texas," Bull., AAPG (1925), v. 9, no. 2, pp. 263-285; *Geology of Salt Dome Oil Fields,* AAPG (1926), pp. 501-523.

Sundberg, K.: "Salt Dome Studies by Geoelectrical Methods," *Jour. Inst. Pet.* (1931), v. 17, pp. 376-380.

Sundt, Olaf F.: "Recent Developments in Gravity Prospecting on Gulf Coast," *Bull.*, AAPG (1935), v. 19, no. 1, pp. 19-24; *Trans.*, SEG, v. 5, pp. 19-24; *Early Geophysical Papers,* SEG (1957), pp. 679-684.

Suter, H. H.: "Relations Between Kinds of Well Data and Apparent Faulting," *Bull.*, AAPG (1946), v. 30, no. 11, pp. 1910-1917.

Swan, B. G.: "Local Areal Distribution of Velocities in the Texas Gulf Coast," *Geophysics* (1942), v. 7, no. 4, pp. 367-392.

Swartz, Charles A.: "Seismograph Evidence on the Depth of the Salt in Southern Mississippi," *Geophysics* (1943), v. 8, no. 1, pp. 1-2.

Swartz, Charles A. and Lindsey, R. W.: "Reflected Refractions," *Geophysics* (1942), v. 7, no. 1, pp. 78-91.

Szabo, A., Tudge, A., Macnamara, J. and Thode, H. G.: "The Distribution of S34 in Nature and the Sulphur Cycle," *Science* (1950), v. 111, pp. 464-465.

Taegel, E. A. and Owens, F. C.: "Developments in S o u t h T e x a s in 1942," *Bull.* (1943), v. 27, no. 6, pp. 739-746.

Tague, Glenn C. and Burgess, Curtis W., Jr.: "Developments in Upper Gulf Coast of Texas in 1960," *Bull.*, AAPG (1961), v. 45, no. 6, pp. 868-878.

Tansil, John T. and Moore, Leslie M., Jr.: "Automatic Custody-Transfer System at Lake Pelto, Louisiana," *Jour. of Pet. Tech.* (1960), v. 12, no. 10, pp. 15-19.

Tatum, E. P., Jr.: "Upper Cretaceous Chalk in Cap Rock on McFaddin Beach Salt Dome, Jefferson County, Texas," *Bull.*, AAPG (1939), v. 23, no. 3, pp. 339-342.

Taylor, R. E.: "Water-Insoluble Residues in Rock Salt of Louisiana Salt Plugs," *Bull.*, AAPG (1937), v. 21, no. 10, pp. 1268-1310; corrections, v. 21, pp. 1494, 1496; (abs.) *World Pet.*, v. 9, no. 1, pp. 60-61.

Taylor, R. E.: "Origin of the Cap Rock of Louisiana Salt Domes," *Bull.* 11, La. Geol. Svy. (1938), Dept. of Conserv., 191 pp; *PhD Dissertation,* LSU, Dept. of Geol.; review by R. E. Jannsen, *Jour. Geol.* (1939), v. 47, p. 222.

Taylor, R. E.: (abs.) "Salt Dome Terminology," *Oil and Gas Jour.* (1938), v. 36, no. 44, p. 58.

Taylor, R. E.: "The Mineralogy of the Salt and Cap Rock of Gulf Coast Salt Domes," (abs.) *Trans.*, GCAGS (1953), v. 3, pp. 147-148.

Taylor, R. E.: "Field Trip to South Louisiana Salt Domes," *Guides to Southeastern Geology,* GSA and Assoc. Soc. (1955), pp. 538-548.

Taylor, R. E. and Hurlbut, C. S., Jr.: "Hilgardite, a New Mineral Species from Choctaw Salt Dome, Louisiana," *Am. Mineralogist* (1937), v. 22, no. 10, pp. 1052-1057.

Taylor, R. E. and Hurlbut, C. S. Jr.: "Notes on Minerals Assocated with Hilgardite," *Am. Mineralogist* (1938), v. 23, no. 12, pt. 1, pp. 898-902.

Tschopp, H. J.: "The Isthmian Saline Basin," *Geol. Rept. V-305* (Nov., 1931), Inedito.

Teas, L. P.: "Hockley Salt Shaft, Harris County, Texas," *Bull.*, AAPG (1931), v. 15, no. 4, pp. 465-469; *Gulf Coast Oil Fields,* AAPG (1936), pp. 136-140.

Teas, L. P.: "Cameron Meadows and Iowa, Two New Coastal Louisiana Fields," *Bull.*, AAPG (1932), v. 16, no. 3, pp. 255-256.

Teas, L. P.: "Natural Gas of Gulf Coast Salt Dome Area," *Geology of Natural Gas,* AAPG (1935), pp. 683-740.

Teas, L. P., et al: *Structure of Typical American Oil Fields,* Vol. 1, American Association of Petroleum Geologists (1929), Tulsa, Oklahoma, 510 pp.

Teas, L. P. and Miller, Charis R.: "Raccoon

Bend Oil Field, Austin County, Texas," *Bull.,* AAPG (1933), v. 17, no. 12, pp. 1459-1491; *Gulf Coast Oil Fields,* AAPG (1936), pp. 676-708.

Texas Gulf Coast Oil Scouts Association and South Louisiana Oil Scouts Association: "Old Hackberry Salt Dome," *Bull. 1,* (1930), pp. 121-123.

Texas Gulf Coast Oil Scouts Association and South Louisiana Oil Scouts Association: "Kelso Bayou or East Hackberry Dome," *Bull. 1* (1930), pp. 124-125.

Thacker, R. B.: "Height of Petroliferous Salt Dome Increasing," *Pet. Age* (1924), v. 11, p. 530.

Thacker, R. B.: "Gulf Coast Saline Domes," *Pet. Age* (1924), v. 13, no. 7, p. 20.

Thacker, R. B.: "Do All Gulf Salt Domes Have Vents?" *Eng. and Mining Jour.* (1926), v. 121, no. 17, pp. 684-686.

Thalmann, H. E.: (abs.) "Miocene Agueguexquite Formation in the Isthmus of Tehuantepec," *Region Proc.,* GSA (1935), p. 116.

Thode, H. G., Szabo, A., Tudge, A. and Macnamara, J.: "The Distribution of S34 in Nature and the Sulphur Cycle," *Science* (1950), v. 111, pp. 464-465.

Thomas, E. P.: "Mississippi Structures and Their Relation to Oil Accumulation," *Bull.,* AAPG (1950), v. 34, no. 7, pp. 1502-1516.

Thomas, G. T. and Hines, E. R., Jr.: "Developments in Southeastern States in 1957," *Bull.,* AAPG (1958), v. 42, no. 6, pp. 1327-1338.

Thomas, G. W. and Vernon, Roger, C.: "Developments in East Texas in 1961," *Bull.,* AAPG (1962), v. 46, no. 6, pp. 914-920.

Thomas, Kirby: "Saline Domes and Other Salt Deposits," *Min. Sci. Press.* (1918), v. 117, p. 226.

Thomas, Kirby: "The Coast Domes in Relation to Sulphur Supply," *Eng. and Mining Jour.* (1918), v. 106, no. 1, p. 7.

Thomassy, R.: *Geologie Pratique de la Louisiana,* Paris, (1960).

Thompson, S. A. and Eichelberger, O. H.: "Vinton Salt Dome, Louisiana," *Bull.,* AAPG (1928), v. 12, no. 4, pp. 385-394.

Thompson, W. C.: "The Midway Limestone of Northeast Texas," *Bull.,* AAPG (1922), v. 6, no. 4, pp. 323-332.

Thompson, W. C.: "Geologic Sections in Texas and Adjoining States," *Bull.,* AAPG (1937), v. 21, no. 8, pp. 1083-1087.

Thompson, W. C., Culbertson, J. A. and Eby,

J. B.: "Guide for Field Trips," *Guidebook,* AAPG, 26th Ann. Mtg. (1941), Houston, Texas, 28 pp.

Thompson, W. C. and Day, W. L.: "Geophysics and Geology of the Discovery and Development of Esperson Dome, Texas," *Geophysical Case Histories,* SEG (1948), v. 1, pp. 48-65.

Timm, B. C. and Maricelli, J. J.: "Formation Waters in Southwest Louisiana," *Bull.,* AAPG (1953), v. 37, no. 2, pp. 394-409.

Todd, John D.: "Complex Structure of Wilcox Trend Being Unraveled," *Oil Weekly* (1940), v. 99, no. 3, pp. 52-57; (abs.) *World Pet.* v. 12, no. 4, p. 104.

Todd, John D.: "Mississippi (Oil Fields) Where Persistence Pays," *Oil Weekly* (1945), v. 118, no. 7, pp. 49-52.

Todd, John D.: "What's Wrong with the Eastern Gulf Coast?" *Oil Weekly* (1946), v. 123, no. 3, pp. 89-91.

Toledo, Alfonso Carnejo: "Southern Mexico Still Offers Good Prospects to Pemex Wildcatters," *Petroleo Interamericano* (1964), v. 22, no. 2, pp. 46-48.

Tomlinson, C. W.: "Relation of Oil and Gas Accumulation to Geologic Structure in the Mid-Continent Region," *Problems of Petroleum Geology,* AAPG (1934), p. 579.

Torrey, P. D. and Fralich, C. E.: "An Experimental Study of the Origin of Salt Domes," *Jour. Geol.* (1926), v. 34, no. 3, pp. 224-234; (abs.) *Oil and Gas Jour.* v. 23, no. 45, p. 133.

Trask, P. D. and Patnode, H. W.: *Source Beds of Petroleum,* Rept. of investigation supported jointly by the API and the Geol. Svy. of the U. S. Dept. of Interior from 1931 to 1941, AAPG (1942), 561 pp.

Trowbridge, R. M. and Burnett, T. J.: "Developments in East Texas in 1942," *Bull.,* AAPG (1943), v. 27, no. 6, pp. 782-789.

Trowbridge, R. M. and Denton, R. F.: "Developments in East Texas During 1940," *Bull.,* AAPG (1941), v. 25, no. 6, pp. 1081-1089.

Trowbridge, R. M. and Denton, R. F.: "Developments in East Texas in 1942," *Bull.,* AAPG (1943), v. 27, no. 6, pp. 782-789.

Trumpy, D.: "Regional Tectonics and Oil Prospect of Eastern Mexico," *Geological Report No. 247* (1932), Archivo de Petroleos Mexicanos.

Trusheim, F.: "Uber Halokinese und ihre Bedeutung fur die Strukturelle Entwicklung Norddeutschlands," *Zeits. Deutsch. Geol. Ges.* (1957), v. 98, pp. 7-29.

Trusheim, F.: "On the Mechanism of Salt Migration in Northern Germany," *Bull.,* AAPG (1960), v. 44., no. 9, pp. 1519-1540.

Tschirley, N. K., Gray, Dr. George R. and Allen, G. G.: "Gulf Coast Drilling Mud Practices Demand Attention to Special Problems," *World Oil* (1956), v. 142, no. 7, pp. 155-160.

Tudge, A., Macnamara, J., Thode, H. G. and Szabo, A.: "The Distribution of S34 in Nature and the Sulphur Cycle," *Science* (1950), v. 111, pp. 464-465.

Udden, J. A.: (discussion) "The Theory of Volcanic Origin of Salt Domes," *Bull. 139,* AIME (1918), p. 1147; *Trans.,* AIME (1918), v. 61, pp. 456-477.

Udden, J. A.: "Oil Bearing Formations in Texas," *Bull.,* AAPG (1919), v. 3, no. 1, pp. 82-98.

Udden, J. A.: "Laminated Anhydrite in Texas," *Bull.,* AAPG (1924), v. 35, no. 2, pp. 347-354.

Usiglio, J.: "Analyse de l'Eau de la Mediterranee sur la Cote de France," *Ann. Chim. et Phys.* (1849), ser. 3, v. 27, pp. 92-172.

Utterback, Donald D.: "Bayou Choctaw Salt Dome Producing 3000 Barrels Daily After 22 Years," *Oil and Gas Jour.* (1953), v. 52, no. 7, pp. 277-281.

Vallas, H. A. and Roth, E. P., Jr.: "Developments in Louisiana Gulf Coast in 1961," *Bull.,* AAPG (1962), v. 46, no. 6, pp. 929-937.

Vallas, H. A. and Vidrine, Louis O.: "Developments in Louisiana Gulf Coast in 1960," *Bull.,* AAPG (1961), v. 45, no. 6, pp. 879-888.

Van Fossan, N. E.: "Where U. S. Salt Deposits Are Located," *Oil and Gas Jour.* (1955), v. 54, no. 19, p. 145.

Van London, Wilma: "Third Try—Success," *Oil and Gas Jour.* (1953), v. 51, no. 37, p. 63.

Van Orstrand, C. E.: "Temperature Gradients," *Problems of Petroleum Geology,* AAPG (1934), pp. 989-1021.

Van Rensselaer, Jeremiah: *An Essay on Salt, Containing Notices of Its Origin, Formation, Geological Position, and Principal Localities, Embracing a Particular Description of the American Salines,* (1823), New York, 80 pp.

Van Tuyl, F. M.: "Contribution to Salt Dome Problem," *Bull.,* AAPG (1930), v. 14, no. 8, pp. 1041-1047; (abs.) *Pan Am. Geologist,* v. 53, no. 3, p. 221.

Varvaro, Gasper G.: "Geology of Evangeline and

St. Landry Parishes," *Bull. 31,* La. Geol. Svy. (1957), Dept. of Conserv., 295 pp.

Vaughan, F. E.: "The Five Islands, Louisiana," *Bull.,* AAPG (1925), v. 9, no. 4, pp. 756-797; *Geology of Salt Dome Oil Fields,* AAPG (1926), pp. 356-397.

Veatch, A. C.: "The Salines of North Louisiana," *Rept. of 1902,* Geol. Svy. of La. (1902), pp. 47-100.

Veatch, A. C.: "The Shreveport Area, The Five Islands," *Geology and Agriculture of Louisiana* (1899), La. State Expt. Sta., pt. 5, pp. 149-262.

Veatch, A. C. and Harris, G. D.: "A Preliminary Report on the Geological Survey of Louisiana," *Rept. of 1899,* Geol. Svy. of La. (1899), pp. 9-138

Vernon, R. C. and Thomas, G. W.: "Developments in East Texas in 1961," *Bull.,* AAPG (1962), v. 46, no. 6, pp. 914-920.

Vernon, R. O. and Erwin, Walter: "Developments in Southeastern States in 1955," *Bull.,* AAPG (1956), v. 40, no. 6, pp. 1272-1282.

Ver Wiebe, W. A.: "Salt Domes of the Isthmus of Tehauntepec," *Pan Am. Geologist* (1926), v. 45, no. 5, pp. 349-358.

Ver Wiebe, W. A.: *Oil Fields in North America,* Edwards Brothers, Inc. (1949), Ann Arbor, Mich., 251 pp.

Vesely, L. A., Rogers, J. K. and Spice, W. H., Jr.: "Developments in South Texas in 1951," *Bull.,* AAPG (1952), v. 36, no. 6, pp. 1177-1187.

Vetter, John M.: "Gulf Coast Development Trend is Away from Salt Domes," *Oil Weekly* (1940), v. 99, no. 3, pp. 47-49.

Vidrine, Louis O.: "Regional Study of Jefferson, Plaquemines and St. Charles Parishes, Louisiana," *Trans.,* GCAGS (1958), v. 8, pp. 105-115.

Vidrine, Louis O. and Vallas, H. A.: "Developents in Louisiana Gulf Coast in 1960," *Bull.,* AAPG (1961), v. 45, no. 6, pp. 879-888.

Viniegra Osorio, Francisco, and Olivas Ramirez, M.: "La Acumulacion de Hidrocarburos en el Cretacico en Relacion al Analisis Tectonico Comparativo de la Sierra Madre y la Cuenca de Veracruz," *Resumenes de los Trabajos Presentados,* II Convencion, Asoc. Mex. de Geol. Petrol., pp. 34-35.

Vittrup, L. J.: "Drilling for Steeply Dipping Oil Producing Sands Saratoga Salt Dome, Hardin County, Texas," *Bull.,* AAPG (1947), v. 31, no. 11, pp. 2041-2044.

Viveros Juarez, Manuel: "Estudio Sobre los Yacimientos de Azufre en la Cuenca Salina del Istmo de Tehuantepec," *Tesis Profesional* (1958).

Viveros Juarez, Manuel, Serna Vigueras, Reyes and Marquez Pineda, Aremos: "Depositos de Sal y Azufre en la Cuenca Salina del Istmo, Ver.," *Bol. 64* (1964), Consejo de Recursos Naturales no Renovables, 76 pp.

Voitesti, I. P.: "Geology of the Salt Domes in the Carpathian Region of Rumania," *Bull.*, AAPG (1925), v. 9, no. 8, pp. 1165-1206.

Wade, G.: "Review of the Heaving Shale Problem in the Gulf Coast Region," *RI 3618*, U. S. Bur. of Mines (1942), 64 pp.

Wahl, C. C.: "Developments in Upper Gulf Coast of Texas in 1954," *Bull.*, AAPG (1955), v. 39, no. 6, pp. 976-987.

Walden, Wm. and Jacoby, C. H.: "Exploration by Horizontal Drilling at Avery Island, Louisiana, *Symposium on Salt,* Northern Ohio Geol. Soc., Inc. (1963), Cleveland, Ohio, pp. 367-378.

Waldron, Robert P.: "A Seasonal Ecological Study of Foraminifera From Timbalier Bay, Louisiana," *Trans.,* GCAGS (1962), v. 12, p. 302.

Wall, J. R. and Murray, G. E.: "Preliminary Report on Intrusive Gypsum Sierra del Fraile, State of Nuevo Leon, Mexico," *Guidebook,* 1959 Field Trip, South Texas Geol. Soc., pp. D1-D7; Spanish Trans. by P. E. Narvarte, pp. D8-D12.

Wallace, W. E., Jr.: "A Study of Deep Seated Domes of South Louisiana," *PhD Dissertation* (1943), LSU, Dept. of Geol.

Wallace, W. E., Jr.: "Structure of South Louisiana Deep Seated Domes," *Bull.,* AAPG (1944), v. 28, no. 9, pp. 1249-1312.

Wallace, W. E., Jr.: "Deep Seated Domes of South Louisiana, A Regional Interpretation," *AAPG Reg. Mtg.* (1949), Biloxi, Miss.

Wallace, W. E., Jr.: "South Louisiana Fault Trends," *Trans.,* GCAGS (1952), v. 2, pp. 63-67.

Wallace, W. E., Jr. (ed.): "Fault and Salt Map of South Louisiana (1966 Edition)," *Trans.,* GCAGS (1966), v. 16.

Wallace, W. E., Jr. and DeHart, B. H.: "Calcasieu Lake Salt Dome, Cameron Parish, Louisiana," *Trans.,* GCAGS (1953), v. 3, pp. 71-81.

Walters, J. E. and Sollars, P. F.: "Geology of the Danbury Salt Dome," *Trans.,* GCAGS (1952), v. 2, p. 7.

Ward, Thomas: "The Salt Deposits of the United States of America and Canada," *Trans.,*

Manchester Geol. Soc. (1890), v. 20, pp. 471-498.

Warner, C. A.: "History of Gulf Coast 40 Years of Brilliant Achievement," *Oil and Gas Jour.* (1941), v. 39, no. 49, pp. 64-65, 129-130, 133, 135, 138, 140, 164, 166.

Warner, C. A., Allison, A. P., Beckelhymer, R. L., Benson, Don G., Hutchins, R. M., Jr., Lake, C. L., Lewis, Ray C., O'Bannon, P. H. and Self, S. R. "Geology of Katy Field, Waller, Harris and Fort Bend Counties, Texas," *Bull.,* AAPG (1946), v. 30, no. 2, pp. 157-180.

Warren, A. D.: "The Anahuac and Frio Sediments in Louisiana," *Trans.,* GCAGS (1957), v. 7, pp. 221-238.

Washburne, C. W.: "Salt Domes, Meteor Craters, and Crypto-Volcanic Structures," *Bull.,* AAPG (1937), v. 21, no. 5, pp. 629-630.

Wasson, Theron: "Lost Lake Salt Dome, Texas," *Bull.,* AAPG (1927), v. 11, no. 6, p. 633.

Wasson, Theron: "Creole Field, Gulf of Mexico, Coast of Louisiana," *Structure Of Typical American Oil Fields,* AAPG (1948), pp. 281-298.

Waters, J. A., Ferguson, W. B. and Heath, F. E.: "Clay Creek Salt Dome, Washington County, Texas," *Bull.,* AAPG (1931), v. 15, no. 1, pp. 43-60; (abs.) *Pan Am. Geologist* (1930), v. 53, no. 3, p. 226.

Waters, K. M. and Beu, R. D.: "Developments in Louisiana Gulf Coast in 1956," *Bull.,* AAPG (1957), v. 41, no. 6, pp. 1190-1200.

Waters, K. M. and Duncan, R. L.: "Developments in Louisiana Gulf Coast in 1955," *Bull.,* AAPG (1956), v. 40, no. 6, pp. 1253-1262.

Watson, J. G. and Kerlin, M. L.: "Developments in Louisiana Gulf Coast in 1952," *Bull.,* AAPG (1953), v. 37, no. 6, pp. 1443-1448.

Weatherby, B. B.: "The History and Development of Seismic Prospecting," *Geophysical Case Histories,* SEG (1948), v. 1, pp, 7-20; *Geophysics,* (1940), v. 5, no. 3, pp. 215-230.

Weaver, C. E., Flawn, P. T., Goldstein, A., Jr. and King, P. B.: "The Ouachita System," *Pub. 6120,* Tex. U. (1961), 399 pp.

Weaver, Paul: (abs.) "The Salt Dome and Its Peculiarities as a Geologic Structure and as a Cause of Localizing Oil Deposits," *Oil* (1941), v. 1, no. 10, p. 24.

Weaver, Paul: "The Geologic History of the Formation of Salt Deposits," *Tulsa Geol. Soc. Digest* (1946), v. 14, p. 51.

Weaver, Paul: "Modern Views as to Salt Dome Mechanics," *Unpublished Paper,* AAPG Reg. Mtg. (1948), Houston, Texas.

Weaver, Paul: "Application of Geophysical Technique to Finding More Flank Production of Piercement Type salt Domes," *Oil and Gas Jour.* (1952), v. 51, no. 7, pp. 90-94.

Weeks, W. B. and Purzer, Joeseph: "Developments in Southern Arkansas and Northern Louisiana During 1939," *Bull.,* AAPG (1940), v. 24, no. 6, pp. 1092-1099.

Weeks, W. B. and Purzer, Joseph: "Developments in Southern Arkansas and Northern Louisiana During 1940," *Bull.,* AAPG (1941), v. 25, no. 6, pp. 1024-1036; (abs.) v. 25, no. 6, p. 943.

Weingartner, R. A.: "Geophysical Case History of the Hastings Oil Field, Brazoria and Galveston Counties," *Geophysical Case Histories,* SEG (1956), v. 2, pp. 156-165.

Weinzierl, L. L. L. and Applin, E. R.: "The Claiborne Formation on the Coastal Domes," *Jour. Paleontology* (1929), v. 3, pp. 384-410.

Weirich, T. E.: "South Tyler Field, Smith County, Texas," *Bull.,* AAPG (1944), v. 28, no. 11, pp. 1646-1647.

Wendlandt, E. A. and Herold, C. L.: "Resume of Developments in East Texas During 1937," *Bull.,* AAPG (1938), v. 22, no. 6, pp. 728-735.

Wendlandt, E. A. and Knebel, G. M.: "Lower Claiborne of East Texas, with Special Reference to Mount Sylvan Dome and Salt Movements," *Bull.,* AAPG (1929), v. 13, no. 10, pp. 1347-1375.

Wendlandt, E. A. and Knebel, G. M.: "Mount Sylvan Dome, Smith County, Texas," *Gulf Coast Oil Fields,* AAPG (1936), pp. 1041-1049.

Wendlandt, E. A. and McLellan, H. J.: "Developments in East Texas During 1939," *Bull.,* AAPG (1940), v. 24, no. 6, pp. 1062-1068.

Wendlandt, E. A., Murchison, E. A. and McLellan, H. J.: "Boggy Creek Salt Dome, Anderson and Cherokee Counties, Texas," *Bull.,* AAPG (1932), v. 16, no. 6, pp. 584-600; (abs.) *Pan Am. Geologist,* v. 57, no. 4, p. 308.

Wendlandt, E. A. and Pirtle, C. W.: "Developments in East Texas During 1938," *Bull.,* AAPG (1939), v. 23, no. 6, pp. 889-895.

Wendlandt, E. A., Shelby, T. H., Jr. and Bell, J. S.: "Hawkins Field, Wood County, Texas," *Bull.,* AAPG (1946), v. 30, no. 6, pp. 1830-1856.

Wenger, R., Belmonte, Y. and Hirtz, P.: "The Salt Basins of the Gabon and the Congo (Brazzaville): A Tentative Paleogeographic Interpretation," *Salt Basins Around Africa,* The Institute of Petroleum (1965), London, pp. 55-78.

Weston, H. C. and Hollingsworth, W. E.: "Chacahoula Dome, LaFourche and Terrebonne Parishes, Louisiana," *Geophysical Case Histories,* SEG (1956), v. 2, pp. 113-129.

Wharton, J. B., Jr.: "Jefferson Island Salt Dome, Iberia and Vermilion Parishes, Louisiana," *Bull.,* AAPG (1953), v. 37, no. 2, pp. 433-443; (abs.) *Trans.,* GCAGS (Nov., 1952), p. 1.

Wharton, J. B., Jr. and Bates, F. W.: "Anse La Butte Dome, St. Martin Parish, Louisiana," *Bull.,* AAPG (1943), v. 27, no. 8, pp. 1123-1156.

Wharton, J. B., Jr. and Bates, F. W.: "Developments in Louisiana Gulf Coast in 1945," *Bull.,* AAPG (1946), v. 30, no. 6, pp. 999-1006.

White, W. S., Jr. and Durham, C. O., Jr.: "A Guided Geological Tour Through North and Central Louisiana," *Guidebook,* 1960 Spring Field Trip, Shreveport Geol. Soc., pp. 83-147.

Whitcombe, Bruce: "Report on the Mineral Resources of Anderson County, Texas," *Min. Res. Circ. 22,* Tex. U. (1939), 5 pp.

Wickizer, C. L.: "High Pressure Gas Lift System Restores Deep Wells to Production in Weeks Island Field," *Oil and Gas Jour.* (1963), v. 61, no. 37, pp. 106-115.

Wilcox, R. C.: "Map of Gulf Coast Oil Fields, Showing Domes and Hypothetical Fault Lines," *Oil Trade Jour.* (1921), v. 12 ,p. 17.

Wilhelm, O. G.: "Classification of Petroleum Reservoirs," *Bull.,* AAPG (1945), v. 29, no. 11, pp. 1537-1580.

Wilhelm, O. G.: "Piercement Trap Reservoirs," *Oil and Gas Jour.* (1946), v. 44, no. 51., p. 147.

Williams, J. R.: "Developments in Arkansas and North Louisiana in 1946," *Bull.,* AAPG AAPG (1947), v. 31, no. 6, pp. 1084-1105.

Williams, J. R.: "Developments in Arkansas and North Louisiana in 1947," *Bull.,* AAPG (1948), v. 32, no. 6, pp. 1040-1064.

Williams, J. R.: "Developments in Arkansas and North Louisiana in 1948," *Bull.,* AAPG (1949), v. 33, no. 6, pp. 990-1001.

Williams, J. S. and Imlay, R. W.: "Late Paleozoic Age of Morehouse Formation of Northeastern Louisiana," *Bull.,* AAPG (1942), v. 26, no. 10, pp. 1672-1673.

Williams, K. O.: "Clam Lake Field, Jefferson County, Texas," *Typical Oil and Gas Fields of Southeast Texas,* Houston Geol. Soc. (1962), pp. 34-37.

Williams, Neil: "Starks Dome is Making Oil History," *Oil and Gas Jour.* (1927), v. 26, no. 19, pp. 184-185.

Williams, Neil: "Sorrento Dome Notable Achievement," *Oil and Gas Jour.* (1928), v. 26, no. 43, pp. 33, 86.

Williams, Neil: "Fourth Test Opened Sorrento Dome," *Oil and Gas Jour.* (1928), v. 26, no. 44, pp. 34, 92.

Williams, Neil: "Bouillon Dome, Another Coastal Pool," *Oil and Gas Jour.* (1928), v. 26, no. 44, pp. 51, 122-123, 138.

Williams, Neil: "Three New Salt Domes Reported, All in Harris County, Texas," *Oil and Gas Jour.* (1928), v. 27, no. 14, p. 32.

Williams, Neil: "Geophysics Big Factor on Gulf Coast," *Oil and Gas Jour.* (1928), v. 27, no. 25, pp. 35, 88, 91.

Williams, Neil: "Big Potential Reserve on Gulf Coast," *Oil and Gas Jour.* (1930), v. 28, no. 49, pp. 42-43, 118.

Williams, Neil: "Repressuring Successful at Sugarland," *Oil and Gas Jour.* (1930), v. 29, no. 12, pp. 31, 112, 114.

Williams, Neil: "Repressuring Test at Saratoga Dome," *Oil and Gas Jour.* (1930), v. 29, no. 15, pp. 39, 146-147.

Williams, Neil: "New Light Thrown on Coastal Domes," *Oil and Gas Jour.* (1930, v. 29, no. 22, pp. 30-31, 107.

Williams, Neil: "Union Sulphur Drills 9,250 Feet in Salt Dome Test in Louisiana," *Oil and Gas Jour.* (1931), v. 29, no. 52, p. 143.

Williams, Neil: "Eight New Pools on Gulf Coast in 1931," *Oil and Gas Jour.* (1932), v. 30, no. 37, pp. 70-76.

Williams, Neil: "Second Compressor Unit for Repressuring at Saratoga," *Oil and Gas Jour.* (1932), v. 30, no. 38, p. 67.

Williams, Neil: "New Practices in Going Through Cavities in Salt Domes Reduce Coastal Drilling Costs," *Oil and Gas Jour.* (1932), v. 31, no. 5, pp. 49-50.

Williams, Neil: "Rapid Succession of Gas Bowouts and Craters Following Increase in Coastal Wildcatting," *Oil and Gas Jour.* (1933), v. 32, no. 7, pp. 8, 36.

Williams, Neil: "Sixty-three Discoveries of Pools on Gulf Coast are Credited to the Use of Geophysics," *Oil and Gas Jour.* (1933), v. 32, no. 20, pp. 10-11, 34.

Williams, Neil: "Intensive Play in Progress on Old Hull Dome," *Oil and Gas Jour.* (1933), v. 32, no. 25, pp. 21-22.

Williams, Neil: "Iowa Field Becomes Largest in Louisiana," *Oil and Gas Jour.* (1933), v. 32, no. 26, pp. 13-14.

Williams, Neil: "Sweet Lake Field in Coastal Louisiana is Good Example of Maritime Drilling Operations," *Oil and Gas Jour.* (1934), v. 32, no. 48, pp. 15-16.

Williams, Neil: "Remarkable Development at Leesville is Making Field One of Most Active on Gulf Coast," *Oil and Gas Jour.* (1934), v. 32, no. 50, pp. 13, 36.

Williams, Neil: "Gun Perforation of Wells Successful at Bosco; New Procedure in Testing Sands Described," *Oil and Gas Jour.* (1934), v. 33, no. 3, p. 8.

Williams, Neil: "Advance in Production Practice Used at Bosco with Double Set of Drawworks and Engines," *Oil and Gas Jour.* (1934), v. 33, no. 6, p. 16.

Williams, Neil: "Deeper Drilling West Columbia Field Revives Brazoria County," *Oil and Gas Jour.* (1934), v. 33, no. 20, pp. 11, 44.

Williams, Neil: "Heaving Shale Hazard in Big Hill, Texas Field Overcome in Deep Test," *Oil and Gas Jour.* (1935), v. 33, no. 41, pp. 26, 61.

Williams, Neil: "Extensions at Manvel, Northern Brazoria County, May Lead to Larger Field Than First Expected," *Oil and Gas Jour.* (1935), v. 33, no. 41, pp. 77-79.

Williams, Neil: "Exploration for Oil out in the Gulf is Within Engineering Possibilities," *Oil and Gas Jour.* (1935), v. 34, no. 8, pp. 42, 45.

Williams, Neil: "Completion of St. Martinville Producer Confirms Long Cherished Dreams," *Oil and Gas Jour.* (1935), v. 34, no. 27, p. 13.

Williams, Neil: "Laying Oil Line from Lafitte Field is More Than Ordinary Undertaking," *Oil and Gas Jour.* (1936) v. 34, no. 37, p. 39.

Williams, Neil: "Potentialities on the Gulf Coast Spurring Search for Reserves," *Oil and Gas Jour.* (1936), v. 34, no. 48, pp. 80-82, 87.

Williams, Neil: "Hazardous Fishing Job is Tackled by Gulf Engineers in the Orchard

Field," *Oil and Gas Jour.* (1936), v. 34, no. 51, pp. 46, 48.

Williams, Neil: "Lafitte, Coastal Louisiana, Regarded as World's Deepest Commercial Field," *Oil and Gas Jour.* (1936), v. 35, no. 7, pp. 71-72.

Williams, Neil: "Spindletop Wells Worked Over by Stanolind to Control Water," *Oil and Gas Jour.* (1936), v. 35, no. 26, pp. 89, 91.

Williams, Neil: "Comb Coastal Louisiana for Overlooked Reserves in Salt Domes and Old Fields," *Oil and Gas Jour.* (1936), v. 35, no. 27, pp. 11-12.

Williams, Neil: "Search for Oil in Southern Mississippi Encouraging," *Oil and Gas Jour.* (1938), v. 37, no. 5, pp. 20-22, 36.

Williams, Neil: "Wildcat Developments on Coastal Salt Domes," *Oil and Gas Jour.* (1938), v. 37, no. 12, pp. 33-34.

Williams, Neil: "Shallow Sands Pay in Chareton," *Oil and Gas Jour.* (1938), v. 37, no. 17, pp. 26-27.

Williams, Neil: "Fire After Blowout at Hester Dome Wreaks Destruction," *Oil and Gas Jour.* (1939), v. 37, no. 43, p. 28.

Williams, Neil: "Drilling Activity Assuming Boom Proportions in Golden Meadows," *Oil and Gas Jour.* (1939), v. 38, no. 18, pp. 24-25, 34.

Williams, Neil: "Redrilling and Workover Program in Humble Field," *Oil and Gas Jour.* (1940), v. 39, no. 5, pp. 61, 64.

Williams, Neil: "Operating Efficiency Increased at Manvel by Standardization," *Oil and Gas Jour.* (1940), v. 39, no. 9, pp. 57, 64.

Williams, Neil: "Finding of Deeper Pay Revives Iowa Field in South Louisiana," *Oil and Gas Jour.* (1940), v. 39, no. 27, pp. 82, 85.

Williams, Neil: "Anse La Butte Salt Dome Shows Brisk Development," *Oil and Gas Jour.* (1941), v. 39, no. 37, pp. 14-15, 30.

Williams, Neil: "Spindletop Offers Opportunity for Prolonged Productive Life," *Oil and Gas Jour.* (1941), v. 40, no. 22, pp. 16-17.

Williams, Neil: "Directional Drilling as Development Aid in Coastal Louisiana Salt Dome Field," *Oil and Gas Jour.* (1944), v. 43, no. 31, pp. 66-68.

Williams, Neil: "Geological Eccentricities in Mississippi Pose Completion and Production Problems in Oil and Gas Fields," *Oil and Gas Jour.* (1945), v. 43, no. 42, pp. 124-129, 148.

Williams, Neil: "Weeks Island Salt Dome Operation, Louisiana," *Oil and Gas Jour.* (1948), v. 47, no. 18, pp. 58-60, 89.

Williams, Neil: "Houston's Pierce Junction Lives Again," *Oil and Gas Jour.* (1956), v. 54, no. 63, pp. 166-169.

Willis, B.: "Artesian Salt Formations," *Bull.*, AAPG (1948), v. 32, no. 7, pp. 1227-1264.

Willson, K. M. and Ley, H. A.: "Gas Fields in Northeast Texas Embayment," *Geology of Natural Gas*, AAPG (1935), pp. 651-682.

Wilson, J. M.: "Cedar Point Field, Chambers County, Texas," *Bull.*, AAPG (1938), v. 22, no. 11, pp. 1601-1602.

Wilson, R. M.: "Developments in South Arkansas and North Louisiana in 1944," *Bull.*, AAPG (1945), v. 29, no. 6, pp. 803-814.

Wise, W. H. and Morrow, E. H.: "Developments in Arkansas and North Louisiana in 1956," *Bull.*, AAPG (1957), v. 41, no. 6, pp. 1201-1209.

Wise, W. H. and Mount, Tom M.: "Developments in Arkansas and North Louisiana in 1955," *Bull.*, AAPG (1956), v. 40, no. 6, pp. 1263-1271.

Wojciechowski, W. A.: "Gulf Coast Salt Domes; Their Distribution, Description, and Origin," *MS Thesis*, Mich. U. (1952), Dept. of Geol.

Wolf, A. G.: "Gulf Coast Salt Domes," *Magazine*, Colorado School of Mines (1920), v. 10, no. 9, pp. 171-177.

Wolf, A. G.: "Relation of Topography to the Oil Fields of the Texas Gulf Coastal Region," *Eng. Mechanics Jour.* (1921), v. 111, pp. 474-475.

Wolf, A. G.: "The Origin of Salt Domes," *Eng. and Mining Jour.* (1923), v. 115, no. 9, pp. 412-414.

Wolf, A. G.: "Big Hill Salt Dome, Matagorda County, Texas," *Bull.*, AAPG (1925), v. 9, no. 4, pp. 711-737; *Geology of Salt Dome Oil Fields*, AAPG (1926), pp. 691-717.

Wolf, A. G.: "Hauerite in a Salt Dome Cap Rock," *Bull.*, AAPG (1926), v. 10, no. 5, pp. 531-532.

Wolf, A. G.: "The Boling Dome, Texas," *Guidebook 6* Excursion A-6, International Geol. Cong., 16th Session (1933), Washington, D. C., pp. 86-90.

Wolf, A. G.: "Salt Dome Sulphur Mining," *Guidebook*, AAPG-SEPM-SEG Jt. Ann. Mtg. (1953), Houston, Texas, pp. 39-40.

Wolf, A. G. and Hanna, M. A.: "Texas and Louisiana Salt Dome Cap Rock Minerals," *Bull.*,

AAPG (1934), v. 18, no. 2, pp. 212-225; *Gulf Coast Oil Fields,* AAPG (1936), pp. 119-132.

Wolf, A. G. and Hanna, M. A.: "Argonite in Texas and Louisiana Salt Dome Cap Rocks," *Bull.,* AAPG (1938), v. 22, no. 2, pp. 217-220.

Wolf, A. G. and Hanna, M. A.: "Gold, Silver, and Other Elements in Salt Dome Cap Rocks," *Bull.,* AAPG (1941),v. 25, no. 4, pp. 750-752.

Wolf, Alexander: "Refraction Surveying of Salt Domes," *World Oil* (1947), v. 127, no. 7, pp. 120-125.

Womack, S. A., Jr. and Hundley, H. B.: "Developments in Arkansas and North Louisiana in 1951," *Bull.,* AAPG (1952), v. 36, no. 6, pp. 1220-1227.

Womack, S. A., Jr. and Shaffer, H. R.: "Developments in Arkansas and North Louisiana in 1952," *Bull.,* AAPG (1953), v. 37, no. 6, pp. 1149-1459.

Woodard, A. E., Cantrell, R. B. and Montgomery, J. C.: "Heterostegina Reef on Nash and Other Piercement Salt Domes in Northwestern Brazoria County, Texas," *Trans.,* GCAGS (1959), v. 9, pp. 59-62.

Woodhams, R. L. and Ewing, J. M.: "Developments in East Texas in 1962," *Bull.,* AAPG (1963), v. 47, no. 6, pp. 1073-1080.

Woodruff, E. G.: "Discussion on Coastal Salt Dome by W. Kennedy," *Bull. 1,* Southwest Assoc. Pet. Geol. (1917), p. 79.

Woodruff, E. G.: "Oil Fields of the Gulf Coast Area Found in Sediments of Late Geological Age," *Oil and Gas Jour.* (1935), v. 33, no. 64, pp. 38-39, 149.

Woods, R. D.: "Jackson in Bayou des Glaises Salt Dome, Iberville Parish, Louisiana," *Bull.,* AAPG (1955), v. 39, no. 8, pp. 1650-1652.

Woollet, L. A.: "Developments in Upper Gulf Coast of Texas in 1953," *Bull.,* AAPG (1954), v. 38, no. 6, pp. 1208-1220.

Woolley, W. C., Gray, Helen, and Musgrove, A. W.: "Outlining of Salt Masses by Refraction Methods," *Geophysics* (1960), v. 25, no. 1, pp. 141-167.

Wooton, P.: "Louisiana Salt Mines, Their Operation and Output," *Min. World* (1912), v. 36, pp. 401-402.

World Oil: "Spindletop Given High Place in History of Industry," (1951), v. 132, no. 1, pp. 225-227.

World Oil: "Spindletop's Production Peaks: 1902 and 1927," (1951), v. 132, no. 1, p. 232.

World Oil: "Captain Lucas—Titan of Spindletop," (1951), v. 132, no. 1, p. 254.

World Oil: "The Giants Came Home," (1951), v. 132, no. 2, pp. 41-42.

World Oil: "Engineering and Geological Data on Mexico," (1952), v. 135, no. 2, p. 122.

World Oil: "Oil Found Under Huge Salt Dome Overhang," (1955), v. 140, no. 6, p. 97.

World Oil: "How Deep is Miocene Production in Southern Louisiana," (1956), v. 142, no. 7, pp. 216-218.

Wrather, W. E.: "Vinton, Louisiana Oil Field, The," *Bull.,* AAPG (1921), v. 5, no. 2, pp. 339-480.

Wrather, W. E. and Lahee, F. H. (ed.): *Problems of Petroleum Geology,* American Association of Petroleum Geologists (1934), Tulsa, Oklahoma, 1073 pp.

Wyatt, Francis: "Salt," *Eng. and Mining Jour.* (1887), v. 44, pp. 411, 432-433, 448-449.

Yzaguierre, Lauro A. and Gutierrez, Gil Roberto: "A Look at the Isthmus of Tehuantepec," *Oil and Gas Jour.* (1960), v. 58, no. 7, pp. 159-163.

Yzaguierre, Lauro A. and Gutierres, Gil Roberto: "Tehuantepec Oil Domes May Mark Potential Oil Territory for Mexico," *Oil and Gas Jour.* (1960) v. 58, no. 8, pp. 150-161.

Yust, M. R. and Brixey, A. D., Jr.: "Developments in Upper Gulf Coast of Texas in 1958," *Bull.,* AAPG (1959), v. 43, no. 6, pp. 1304-1311.

Zingula, R. P. and Rainwater, E. H. (ed.): "Sulphur Mine at Boling Dome," *Field Excursion No. 7,* Geology of the Gulf Coast and Central Texas and Guidebook of Excursions, Houston Geol. Soc. (1962), Houston, Texas, pp. 278-280.

Bibliography Arranged According to Subject Matter

1. "Acadia and Jefferson Davis Parishes, Geology of": Paine, William R., *Bull. 36,* La. Geol. Svy. (1962), Dept. of Conserv.

2. "Accumulation, Stratigraphic Versus Structural": Levorsen, A. I., *Bull.,* AAPG (1936), v. 20, no. 5, pp. 521-530.

3. "Accumulation, Structures Controlling": Olcott, Perry, *Guidebook,* AAPG-SEPM-SEG Jt. Ann. Mtg. (March, 1953), Houston, Texas, pp. 33-36.

4. "Aerial Photomosaic of Barbers Hill Area, Chambers County, Texas, Reading the": Barton, D. C., *Gulf Coast Oil Fields,* AAPG (1936), pp. 15-22.

5. "Aerial Photos of Multiple Surface Faults May Locate Deep Seated Salt Domes": Desjardins, Louis, *Oil and Gas Jour.* (1952), v. 51, no. 13, pp. 82-84.

6. "Alabama's Geology—and Summary of State's Oil and Gas Development": Jones, Walter B., *Oil and Gas Jour.* (1952), v. 51, no. 6 pp. 328-340.

6a. "Alabama and Offshore Tidelands, Salt Domes in Texas, Louisiana, Mississippi: A Survey": Hawkins, Murphy E. and Jirik, C. J., *Inf. Circ.* U. S. Dept. of the Interior, Bur. of Mines (in press, 1966).

6b. "Algerian Sahara, The Triassic Salt in the": Demaison, G. J., *Salt Basins Around Africa,* The Institute of Petroleum (1965), London, pp. 91-100.

7. "Anahuac and Frio Formations of Texas and Louisiana, Summary of Oil Occurrence in": Burke, R. A., *Bull.,* AAPG (1958), v. 42, no. 12, pp. 2935-2950.

8. "Anahuac and Frio Sediments in Louisiana": Warren, A. D., *Trans.,* GCAGS (1957), v. 7, pp. 221-238.

9. "Anahuac (Oil Field), Texas, Geology and Economic Significance of": Halbouty, Michel T. and Eby, J. B., *World Pet.* (1937), v. 8, no. 4, pp. 46-55.

10. "Anderson County, Texas, Report on the Mineral Resources of": Whitcombe, Bruce, *Min. Res. Circ. 22,* Tex. U. (1939), 5 pp.

11. "Anhydrite and Associated Minerals from Salt Mines of Central Kansas": Rogers, A. F., *Am. Jour. Sci.* (1910), ser. 4, v. 29, pp. 258-261.

12. "Anhydrite Cap Rock of American Salt Domes, Origin of the": Goldman, M. I., *Prof. Paper 175,* USGS (1933), pp. 83-114; Review of by Marcus A. Hanna, *Econ. Geol.* (1936), v. 31, no. 6, pp. 642-644).

13. "Anhydrite Cap Rock, Origin of": Goldman, M. I., *Econ. Geol.* (1936), v. 31, no. 8, p. 881.

14. "Anhydrite, Laminated, in Texas": Udden, J. A., *Bull.,* AAPG (1924), v. 35, no. 2, pp. 347-354.

15. "Anomalias Gravimetricas en la Cuenca Salina del Istmo, Planicie Costera de Tabasco, Campeche and Peninsula de Yucatan": Cornejo, Toledo Alfonso and Hernandez, Osuna Alfonso, *Bol.,* Asoc. Mex. Geol. Petrol. (1950), v. 2, no. 7, pp. 453-460.

16. "Anse la Butte Dome, St. Martin Parish, Louisiana": Bates, F. W. and Wharton, J. B., Jr., *Bull.,* AAPG (1943), v. 27, no. 8, pp. 1123-1156.

17. "Anse la Butte, Lafayette and St. Martin Parishes, Louisiana—A Study in Gulf Coast Tertiary Reefs, The Heterostegina Zone at": Forman, McLain J., *Trans.,* GCAGS (1955), v. 5, pp. 65-72.

18. "Anse la Butte Reef, Louisiana, Corals and Larger Foraminifera at": Squires, D. F. and Sachs, K. N., *Bull.,* AAPG (1957), v. 41, no. 4, pp. 746-749.

19. "Anse la Butte Salt Dome Shows Brisk Development": Williams, Neil, *Oil and Gas Jour.,* (1941), v. 39, no. 37, pp. 14-15, 30.

20. *Antillean-Caribbean Region, or the Lands Bordering the Gulf of Mexico and the Caribbean Sea, Historical Geology of the*: Schuchert, Charles, Wiley (1935), New York, 811 pp.; (abs.) *Bull.,* GSA (1929), v. 40, pp. 204-205, 337-359; *Science,*

new ser., v. 69, pp. 139-145; (summary) *Pan Am. Geologist,* v. 51, no. 2, pp. 157-159.

21. "Aragonite in Texas and Louisiana Salt Dome Cap Rocks": Hanna, M. A. and Wolf, A. G., *Bull.,* AAPG (1938), v. 22, no. 2, pp. 217-220.

22. "Arcadia Salt Dome, Liquefied Petroleum Gas Storage in": Skrivanos, N. C. and Norton, R. G., *Guidebook,* 1960 Spring Field Trip, Shreveport Geol. Soc., pp. 48-56.

23. "Ark-La-Tex Area, Regional Geology and Geophysics of the": Bryan, C. L., *Geophysics* (1951), v. 16, no. 3, pp. 401-415.

24. "Arkansas, South, and Louisiana, North, Tabulation of Wells Which have Encountered Salt or Cap Rock in": Lambert, Ernest H., Jr., *Guidebook,* 1960 Spring Field Trip, Shreveport Geol. Soc., pp. 61-69.

24a. "Arkansas, South, Northeast Texas and North Louisiana, Notes on the Stratigraphy of Formations Which Underlie the Smackover Limestone in": Hazzard, R. T., Spooner, W. C. and Blanpied, B. W., *Ref. Rept.* (1945), v. 2, Shreveport Geol. Soc. (1947), pp. 483-503.

25. "Arkansas, Southern, Jurassic and Lower Cretaceous Formations of, and Their Oil and Gas Possibilities": Imlay, R. W., *Inf. Circ. 12,* Ark. Geol. Svy. (1940), 64 pp.

26. "Artesian Salt Formation": Willis, B., *Bull.,* AAPG (1948), v. 32, no. 7, pp. 1227-1264.

27. "Ascension and Iberville Parishes, Louisiana, Salt Domes of": Howe, H. V. and McGuirt, J. H., *Bull. 13,* La. Geol. Svy. (1938), pp. 87-187.

28. "Atlantic and Gulf Coastal Plain, in Erich Krenkel (ed.)": Stephenson, Lloyd W., Cooke, C. W. and Gardner, J. A., *Geologie der Erde, Nord Amerika,* Berlin, Gebruder Borntraeger (1939), v. 1, pp. 519-578.

28a. "Aufsteigen der Salzgebirges, Das": Stille, H., *Zeitschr. f. Prakt. Geologie,* 19 (1911), p. 91.

28b. "Avery Island, Louisiana, Exploration by Horizontal Drilling at": Walden, Wm., and Jacoby, C. H., *Symposium on Salt,* Northern Ohio Geol. Soc., Inc. (1963), Cleveland, Ohio, pp. 367-378.

29. "Avery Island Salt Mine and the Joseph Jefferson Salt Deposit": Lucas, A. F., *Eng. and Mining Jour.* (1896), v. 62, pp. 463-464.

30. "Avery Island Salt Dome, Iberia Parish, Louisiana, Geology of": Bates, F. W., Copeland, R. R., Jr. and Dixon, K. P., *Bull.,* AAPG (1959), v. 43, no. 5, pp. 944-957.

31. "Avery's Island, Sandstone Inclusion in Salt

in Mine on": Heald, K. C., *Bull.,* AAPG (1924), v. 8, no. 5, pp. 674-676.

32. "Avery's Island, Salt Mines of": Romeyn, H., *Mines and Min.* (1900), v. 20, pp. 438-439.

33. "Avoyelles and Rapides Parishes, Louisiana, Geology of": Fisk, Harold N., *Bull. 18,* La. Geol. Svy. (1940), 240 pp.

33a. "Azufre en el Casquete de los Domos Salinos, Origen del, de la Cuenca Salina del Istmo de Tehuantepec": Hungsberg, Ulrich, *Bol. 51* (1960), Consejo de Recursos Naturales no Renovables, 96 pp.

33b. *Azufre en el Istmo de Tehuantepec, Geologia Economica del*: Salas, Guillermo P., Trabajo inedito (1957), Mexico, D. F.

33c. "Azufre en la Cuenca Salina del Istmo de Tehuantepec, El": Bustillos, S. Gonzalo, *Tesis Profesional* (1959).

33d. "Azufre en la Cuena Salina del Istmo de Tehuantepec, Estudio Sobre los Yacimientos de": Viveros Juarez, Manuel, *Tesis Profesional* (1958).

33e. "Azufre en la Cuenca Salina del Istmo, Ver., Depositos de Sal y": Marquez Pineda, Aremos, Viveros Juarez, Manuel and Serna Vigueras, Reyes, *Bol. 64* (1964), Consejo de Recursos Naturales no Renovables, 76 pp.

33f. *Azufre, Yacimientos de, Sintesis de la Morfologia de las Masas de Sal del Istmo de Tehuantepec en Relacion con los:* Gibson, B. Juan, Inedito, Archivo Consejo de Recursos Naturales no Renovables (1957).

34. "Barataria Field, Jefferson Parish, Louisiana": Ferrando, Al and Richardson, H. T., *Bull.,* AAPG (1941), v. 25, no. 2, pp. 322-323.

34a. "Barber's Hill Area, Chambers County, Texas, Reading the Aerial Photomosaic of": Barton, D. C., *Gulf Coast Oil Fields,* AAPG (1936), pp. 15-22.

35. "Barbers Hill, Chambers County, Texas, Deep Sand Development at": Murphy, P. C. and Judson, S. A., *Bull.,* AAPG (1930), v. 14, no. 6, pp. 719-741; (abs.) *Pan Am. Geologist,* v. 53, no. 3, p. 221.

36. "Barbers Hill, Chambers County, Texas, Overhanging Cap Rock and Salt at": Judson, Sidney A., Murphy, P. C. and Stamey, R. A., *Bull.,* AAPG (1932), v. 16, no. 5, pp. 469-482.

37. "Barbers Hill, Chambers County, Texas; A Study in Quantitative Calculations from Torsion-Balance Data, Prediction of Overhang at": Barton, D. C., *Bull.,* AAPG (1935), v 19, no. 1, pp. 25-36; *Trans.,* Soc. Pet. Geophy. (1935), v. 5, pp. 25-36; *Early Geophysical Papers,* SEG (1947), pp. 685-696.

38. "Barbers Hill Dome (Texas), Geology and Economic Significance of", Halbouty, Michel T., *World Pet.* (1939), v. 10, no. 1, pp. 40-55.

39. "Barbers Hill and Esperson, Coastal Texas, Typical Oil Field Structures—Salt Dome": *Oil and Gas Jour.*, (1942), v. 41, no. 13, pp. 42-43.

40. "Barbers Hill Field, Chambers County, Texas, The": Bevier, G. M., *Bull.*, AAPG (1925), v. 9, no. 6, pp. 958-973; *Geology of Salt Dome Oil Fields*, AAPG (1936), pp. 530-545.

41. "Barbers Hill and L. P. G., New Era for": *Oil and Gas Jour.* (1957), v. 55, no. 34, pp. 72-73.

42. "Barite Pisolites from the Batson and Saratoga Oil Fields, Further Notes on the": Barton, D. C. and Mason, S. L., *Bull.*, AAPG (1925), v. 9, no. 9, pp. 1294-1295.

42a. "Barytes as a Mud-Laden Fluid, Use of": Stroud, B. K., *Oil World* (June 5, 1925), p. 29.

43. "Batson Field, Hardin County, Texas": Smith, Fred L., Jr. and Goodwyn, J. T., Jr., *Typical Oil and Gas Fields of Southeast Texas*, Houston Geol. Soc. (1962), pp. 8-13.

44. "Batson Oil Field, Hardin County, Texas": Sawtelle, George, *Bull.*, AAPG (1925), v. 9, no. 9, pp 1277-1282; *Geology of Salt Dome Oil Fields*, AAPG (1926), pp. 524-529.

42. "Batson and Saratoga Oil Fields, Further Notes on Barite Pisolites from the": Barton, D. C. and Mason, S. L., *Bull.*, AAPG (1925), v. 9, no. 9, pp. 1294-1295.

45. "Bay Marchand, Practical Offshore Production Practices at": Kastrop, J. E., *World Oil* (1951), v. 132, no. 7, pp. 167-172, 174.

46. "Bay St. Elaine Oil Field, Southern Louisiana": Schneider, S. J., *Bull.*, AAPG (1959), v. 43, no. 10, pp. 2456-2469.

47. "Bayou Blue Salt Dome, Iberville Parish, Louisiana, Peripheral Faulting at": Mais, W. R., *Bull.*, AAPG (1957), v. 41, no. 9, pp. 1915-1951.

48. "Bayou Bouillon Salt Dome, St. Martin Parish, Louisiana": Donoghue, D., *Bull.*, AAPG (1925), v. 9, no. 9, pp. 1283-1289; *Geology of Salt Dome Oil Fields*, AAPG (1926), pp. 345-351.

49. "Bayou Choctaw Salt Dome Producing 3,000 Barrels Daily, After 22 Years": Utterback, Donald D., *Oil and Gas Jour.* (1953), v. 52, no. 7, pp. 277-281.

50. "Bayou Couba Dome, The Geophysical Discovery and Development of the": Melchoir, L. F., *Geophysics* (1953), v. 18, no. 2, pp. 371-382; *Geo-physical Case Histories, SEG* (1956), v. 2, pp. 130-141.

51. "Bayou des Glaise Salt Dome, Iberville Parish, Louisiana, Jackson in": Woods, R. D., *Bull.*, AAPG (1955), v. 39, no. 8, pp. 1650-1652.

52. "Beinville Parish, Louisiana, Salt Domes of (abs.)": Russell, R. D., *Bull.*, AAPG (1942), v. 26, no. 5, p. 904.

53. "Belle Isle, Louisiana, A Review of the Exploration at": Lucas, A. F., *Bull.*, *129*, AIME (1917), pp. 1435-1447; *Trans.*, AIME, v. 57, pp. 1034-1049.

54. "Belle Isle Salt Dome, St. Mary Parish, Louisiana": Barton, D. C., *Bull.*, AAPG (1935), v. 19, no. 5, pp. 644-650; *Gulf Coast Oil Fields*, AAPG (1936), pp. 1033-1039; *Trans.*, SEG, v. 1, p. 29.

55. "Belle Isle Torsion Balance Survey, St. Mary Parish, Louisiana": Barton, D. C., *Bull.*, AAPG (1931), v. 15, no. 11, pp. 1335-1350; *Trans.*, Soc. Pet. Geophys. (1931), v. 1, pp. 29-44; *Early Geophysical Papers*, SEG (1947), pp. 53-68.

56. "Big Creek Can Increase Production When Oil is Wanted": Davis, Wallace, *Oil Weekly* (1927), v. 45, no. 8, p. 39.

57. "Big Hill Salt Dome, Jefferson County, Texas": Henley, A. S., *Bull.*, AAPG (1925), v. 9, no. 3, pp. 590-593; *Geology of Salt Dome Oil Fields*, AAPG (1926), pp. 497-500.

58. "Big Hill Salt Dome, Matagorda County, Texas": Wolf, A. G., *Bull.*, AAPG (1925), v. 9, no. 4, pp. 711-737; *Geology of Salt Dome Oil Fields*, AAPG (1926), pp. 691-717.

59. "Big Hill, Texas, Field Overcome in Deep Test, Heaving Shale Hazard in": Williams, Neil, *Oil and Gas Jour.* (1935), v. 33, no. 41, pp. 26, 61.

60. "Block 126 Field, Eugene Island, Gulf of Mexico, Radiocarbon Age Determination of Recent-Pleistocene Contact in": Bray, E. E. and Nelson, H. F., *Bull.*, AAPG (1956), v. 40, no. 1, pp. 173-177.

61. "Blue Ridge Field, Fort Bend County, Texas": Hinson, Hillord, *Guidebook*, AAPG-SEPM-SEG Jt. Ann. Mtg. (March, 1953), Houston, Texas, pp. 82-85.

62. "Blue Ridge Field Stages Comeback": Kornfeld, Joseph A., *Oil and Gas Jour.* (1950), v. 49, no. 34, pp. 52-55.

63. "Blue Ridge Salt Dome, Fort Bend County, Texas": Hager, D. S. and Stiles, S., *Bull.*, AAPG (1925), v. 9, no. 2, pp. 304-316; *Geology of Salt Dome Oil Fields*, AAPG (1926), pp. 600-612.

64. "Boggy Creek Field, Anderson and Cherokee

Counties, Texas": Eaton, R. W., *Pub. 5116,* Tex. U. (1951), pp. 29-34.

65. "(Boggy Creek and Moss Bluff Domes), Two New Salt Domes in Texas": Pratt, W. E., *Bull.,* AAPG (1926), v. 10, no. 11, pp. 1171-1172.

66. "Boggy Creek Salt Dome, Anderson and Cherokee Counties, Texas": McLellan, H. J., Wendlandt, E. A. and Murchison, E. A., *Bull.,* AAPG (1932), v. 16, no. 6, pp. 584-600; (abs.) *Pan Am. Geologist,* v. 57, no. 4, p. 308.

67. "Boggy Creek Salt Dome Located in Anderson and Cherokee Counties, Texas, Notes on the": Storm, L. W., *Magazine,* Colorado School of Mines (1929), v. 19, no. 7, pp. 20-22.

68. "Boling Dome, Sulphur Mine at": Rainwater, E. H. and Zingula, R. P. (ed.), *Field Excursion no. 7,* Geology of the Gulf Coast and Central Texas and Guidebook of Excursions, Houston Geol. Soc. (1962), Houston, Texas, pp. 278-280.

69. "Boling Dome, Texas": Wolf, A. G., *Guidebook 6,* Excursion A-6, International Geol. Cong. 16th Session (1933), Washington, D. C., pp. 86-90.

70. "Boling Field, Fort Bend and Wharton Counties, Texas": Cantrell, R. B., *Guidebook,* AAPG-SEPM-SEG Jt. Ann. Mtg. (1953), Houston, Texas, pp. 87-96.

71. "Boling Salt Dome, Wharton County, Texas, New Exploration Possibilities on Piercement Type Salt Domes Established by Thrust Fault at": Halbouty, Michel T. and Hardin, George C., Jr., *Bull.,* AAPG (1954), v. 38, no. 8, pp. 1725-1740.

71a. "Borneo, The Northwestern Oil Basin of": Shaub, H. P. and Jackson, A.: *Habitat of Oil,* AAPG (1958), pp. 1330-1336.

72. "Bosco, Advance in Production Practice Used at, With Double Set of Drawworks and Engines": Williams, Neil, *Oil and Gas Jour.* (1934), v. 33, no. 6, p. 16.

73. "Bosco Detailed Subsurface Geological Data are Benefiting Field Operations": Leyendecker, Charles, *Oil Weekly* (1935), v. 76, no. 11, pp. 66-67.

74. "Bosco, Gun Perforation of Wells Successful at; New Procedure in Testing Sands Described": Williams, Neil, *Oil and Gas Jour.* (1934), v. 33, no. 3, p. 8.

74a. "Bosquejo Estratigrafico de la Cuenca Salina del Istmo de Tehuantepec": Castillo Tejero, Carlos, *Bol.,* Asoc. Mex. Geol. Petrol. (1955), v. 7, nos. 5-6, p. 173.

75. "Boullion Dome Another Coastal Pool":

Williams, Neil, *Oil and Gas Jour.* (1928), v. 26, no. 44, pp. 51, 122-123, 138.

76. "Brenham Field, Washington and Austin Counties, Texas": Burford, S. O., *Typical Oil and Gas Fields of Southeast Texas,* Houston Geol. Soc. (1962), pp. 28-29.

77. "Brenham Salt Dome, Washington and Austin Counties, Texas": Hopkins, O. B., *Bull. 661,* USGS (1917), pp. 271-280.

78. "Brenham Salt Dome, Washington and Austin Counties, Texas, Structural Features of": Burford, S. O., *Bull.,* AAPG (1935), v. 19, no. 9, pp. 1330-1338; *Gulf Coast Oil Fields,* AAPG (1936), pp. 780-788; *Bull.,* Houston Geol. Soc., pp. 28-29.

78a. "Brine Field at Mont Belvieu, Texas, Diamond Alkali": Moore, M. L., *Symposium on Salt,* Northern Ohio Geol. Soc., Inc. (1963), Cleveland, Ohio, pp. 539-545.

79. "Brines, Oil Field, Subsurface Disposal of, in Southern Louisiana": Fuellhart, Donald E., *Oil and Gas Jour.* (1938), v. 36, no. 34, pp. 46, 48-50.

80. "Brooks, Steen and Grand Saline Salt Domes, Smith and Van Zandt Counties, Texas": Powers, Sidney and Hopkins, O. B., *Bull. 736,* USGS (1922), pp. 179-239.

81. "Brookshire (San Felipe) Field, Waller County, Texas": Davies, W. J., *Guidebook,* AAPG, SEPM, SEG, Jt. Ann. Mtg. (March, 1953), Houston, Texas, pp. 97-99.

82. "Bryan Heights Salt Dome, Brazoria County, Texas": Kennedy, William, *Bull.,* AAPG (1925), v. 9, no. 3, pp. 613-625; *Geology of Salt Dome Oil Fields,* AAPG (1926), pp. 678-690.

83. *Bulletins and Annual Reports, Jackson, Mississippi, Oil and Gas*: Mississippi State Oil and Gas Board.

84. "Butler Salt Dome, Freestone County, Texas": Powers, Sidney, *Am. Jour. Sci.* (1920), ser. 4, v. 49, pp. 127-142.

85. "Caillou Island, Louisiana, Clays of Deep Shale Zone": Kerr, P. F. and Barrington, Jonathan, *Bull.,* AAPG (1961), v. 45, no. 10, pp. 1697-1712.

86. "Calcasieu Lake Finally Pays Off After 31 Years of Probing": Gardner, Frank J., *Oil and Gas Jour.* (1958), v. 56, no. 30, p. 263.

87. "Calcasieu Lake Salt Dome, Cameron Parish, Louisiana": Wallace, W. E., Jr. and DeHart, B. H., *Trans.,* GCAGS (1953), v. 3, pp. 71-81.

87a. "Calcium Sufate, The Reduction of, by

Carbon Monoxide and the Oxidation of Calcium Sulfide": Hofman, H. O. and Mostowitsch, W., *Trans.,* AIME (1910), v. 41, pp. 763-783.

88. Caldwell and Winn Parishes, Louisiana, Geology of": Huner, John Jr., *Bull. 15,* La. Geol. Svy. (1939), 356 pp.

89. "Cameron Meadows Dome, Cameron Parish, Louisiana, History of the Geophysical Exploration of the": McGuckin, Glenn M., *Geophysics* (1945), v. 10, no. 1, pp. 1-16; *Geophysical Case Histories,* SEG (1948), v. 1, pp. 161-174; *Oil Weekly,* v. 118, no. 12, pp. 46-52; (abs.) *Dallas Digest* (1948), p. 98.

90. "Cameron Meadows and Iowa, Two New Coastal Louisiana Fields": Teas, L. P., *Bull.,* AAPG (1932), v. 16, no. 3, pp. 255-256.

90a. "Cameron and Vermillion Parishes, A Partial List of Maps Dealing with": McGuirt, J. H., *Bull. 6,* La. Geol. Svy. (1935), pp. 197-203.

91. "Cameron and Vermillion Parishes, Reports on the Geology of": Howe, H. V., Russell, R. J., McGuirt, J. H., Craft, B. C. and Stephenson, M. B., *Bull. 6,* La. Geol. Svy. (1935), 242 pp. Includes: "Physiography of Coastal Southwest Louisiana": Howe, H. V., Russell, R. J. and McGuirt, J. H., pp. 1-68; "Salt Domes of Cameron and Vermilion Parishes": Howe, H. V. and McGuirt, J. H., pp. 73-166; "Salt Dome Prospects": McGuirt, J. H., pp. 167-179; "Mineral Development": Craft, B. C., pp. 181-186; "Some Microfossils of the Potamides Matsoni Zone of Louisiana": Stephenson, M. B., pp. 187-188; "A Partial List of Maps Dealing with Cameron and Vermillion Parishes": McGuirt, J. H., pp. 197-203.

92. "Cameron and Vermillion Parishes, Salt Domes of": Howe, H. V. and McGuirt, J. H., *Bull. 6,* La. Geol. Svy. (1935), pp. 73-166.

93. "Canada and United States of America, Salt Deposits of the": Ward, Thomas, *Trans.,* Manchester Geol. Soc. (1890), v. 20, pp. 471-498.

94. "Cap Rock, Bearing of, on Subsidence on Chestnut Dome, Natchitoches Parish, Louisiana and Clay Creek Salt Dome, Washington County, Texas": Goldman, M. I., *Bull.,* AAPG (1931), v. 15, no. 9, pp. 1105-1113.

95. "Cap Rock of the Gulf Coast Salt Domes, Origin of the": DeGolyer, E. L., (discussion), *Econ. Geol.* (1918), v. 13, pp. 616-620.

96. "Cap Rock of Louisiana Salt Domes, Origin of the": Taylor, R. E., *Bull. 11,* La. Geol. Svy. (1938), Dept. of Conserv., 191 pp; *PhD Dissertation,* LSU, Dept. of Geol.; Review of by R. E. Janssen, *Jour. Geol.* (1939), v. 47, p. 222.

97. "Cap Rock Petrography": Brown, L. S., *Bull.,* AAPG (1931), v. 15, no. 5, pp. 509-529.

98. "Cap Rock of Salt Domes, The origin of the": Hackford, J. E., *Oil Eng. and Finance* (1924), v. 5, no. 101, p. 512.

99. "Cap Rock, Winnfield Salt Dome, Louisiana, Metallic Minerals in"; Barnes, V. E., *Am. Mineralogist* (1933), v. 18, pp. 335-340.

21. "Cap Rocks, Aragonite in Texas and Louisiana Salt Dome": Hanna, Marcus A. and Wolf, A. G., *Bull.,* AAPG (1938), v. 22, no. 2, pp. 217-220.

100. "Caplen Field, Galveston County, Texas": Musolff, Neale C., *Typical Oil and Gas Fields of Southeast Texas,* Houston Geol. Soc. (1962), pp. 30-33.

101. "Captain Lucas—Titan of Spindletop": *World Oil* (1951), v. 132, no. 1, p. 254.

102. "Carlos Dome, Grimes County, Texas, Occurrence of Siderite in Cap Rock at": Rolshausen, F. W., *Bull.,* AAPG (1934), v. 18, no. 4, pp. 543-546; *Gulf Coast Oil Fields,* AAPG (1936), pp. 133-135.

103. "Carpathian Region of Rumania, Geology of the Salt Domes in the": Voitesti, I. P., *Bull.,* AAPG (1925), v. 9, no. 8, pp. 1165-1206.

104. "Caribbean Oil Zones, Gulf, Mexican, and": Seismograph Service Corporation, *Oil and Gas Jour.* (1944), v. 43, no. 34, pp. 182-199.

105. "Cavities in Salt Domes Reduce Coastal Drilling Costs, New Practices in Going Through": Williams, Neil, *Oil and Gas Jour.* (1932), v. 31, no. 5, pp. 49-50.

106. "Cavities in Salt, Effect of Pressure and Temperature on": Brown, K. E. and Jessen, F. W., *Trans.,* AIME (1959), v. 216, pp. 341-345; *Jour. of Pet. Tech.* (1959), v. 11, no. 12.

107. "Cedar Point Field, Chambers County, Texas": Wilson, J. M., *Bull.,* AAPG (1938), v. 22, no. 11, pp. 1601-1602.

108. "Chacahoula Dome, LaFourche and Terrebonne Parishes, Louisiana, Geophysical History": Hollingsworth, W. E. and Weston, H. C., *Geophysical Case Histories,* SEG (1956), v. 2, pp. 113-129.

109. "Chacahoula Field, Prolific Sands Found in the": Moresi, C. K., *Oil* (1941), v. 1, pp. 16-18.

110. "Chapeno Salt Dome, Tamaulipas, Mexico": Belt, B. C., *Bull.,* AAPG (1925), v. 9, no. 1,

pp. 134-135; *Geology of Salt Dome Oil Fields,* AAPG (1926), pp. 772-773.

111. "Charenton, Shallow Sands Pay in": Williams, Neil, *Oil and Gas Jour.* (1938), v. 37, no. 17, pp. 26-27.

112. "Chestnut Dome, Natchitoches Parish, Louisiana": Lahee, F. H., *Bull.,* AAPG (1931), v. 15, no. 3, pp. 277-278.

94. "Chestnut Dome, Natchitoches Parish, Louisiana and Clay Creek Salt Dome, Washington County, Texas, Bearing of Cap Rock on Subsidence on": Goldman, M. I., *Bull.,* AAPG (1931), v. 15, no. 9, pp. 1105-1113.

113. "Chiapas y Tabasco, Resena Acerca de la Geologia de": Bose, E., *Bol.,* Ints. Geol. Mexico, num. 20, 116 pp., 9 lams.

113a. "Chinameca, Ver., Estudio Geologico del Domo Salino de": Marquez Pineda, Aremos, *Tesis Profesional* (1962).

114. "Choctaw Salt Dome, Louisiana, Hilgardite, a New Mineral Species from": Hurlbut, C. S., Jr. and Taylor, R. E., *Am. Mineralogist* (1937), v. 22, no. 10, pp. 1052-1057.

115. *Chronological History of the Petroleum and Natural Gas Industries*: Clark, James A., Clark Book Co. (1963), Houston, Texas, 317 pp.

116. "Ciudad Victoria Area, Tamaulipas, Mexico, Jurassic Formations of the": Mixon, R. B., *MS Thesis,* LSU (1958), Dept of Geol.

117. "Claiborne Formation on the Coastal Domes": Weinzierl, L. L. L. and Applin, E. R., *Jour. Paleontology* (1929), v. 3, pp. 384-410.

118. "Clam Lake Field, Jefferson County, Texas": Williams, K. O., *Typical Oil and Gas Fields of Southeast Texas,* Houston Geol. Soc. (1962), pp. 34-37.

119. "Clam Lake Field, Jefferson County, Texas, A Study of Intersecting Faults and Their Effects on Accumulation in the": Hillyer, L. D., *Trans.,* GCAGS, 1st Ann. Mtg. (Nov., 1951), New Orleans, La.

120. Clay Creek Salt Dome, Washington County, Texas": Ferguson, W. B. and Minton, J. W., *Bull.,* AAPG (1936), v. 20, no. 1, pp. 68-90; *Gulf Coast Oil Fields,* AAPG (1936), pp. 757-779; (abs.) *World Pet.,* v. 7, no. 3, p. 150.

121. "Clay Creek Salt Dome, Washington County, Texas": Heath, F. E., Waters, J. A. and Ferguson, W. B., *Bull.,* AAPG (1931), v. 15, no. 1, pp. 43-60; (abs.) *Pan Am. Geologist,* v. 53, no. 3, p. 226.

122. "Clay Creek Dome, Washington County, Texas": Lahee, F. H., *Bull.,* AAPG (1931), v. 15, no. 3, pp. 279-283.

94. "Clay Creek Salt Dome, Washington County, Texas and Chestnut Dome, Natchitoches Parish Louisiana, Bearing of Cap Rock on Subsidence on": Goldman, M. I., *Bull.,* AAPG (1931), v. 15, no. 9, pp. 1105-1113.

123. "Clay Creek Salt Dome, Washington County, Texas, The Origin of the Structual Depression over Gulf Coast Salt Domes, with Particular Reference to": McDowell, A. N., *MS Thesis,* Tex. A&M U. (1951), Dept. of Geol.

124. "Clear Lake Field, Harris County, Texas": Pitt, William D., *Typical Oil and Gas Fields of Southeast Texas,* Houston Geol. Soc. (1962), pp. 38-41.

125. "Coastal Fields, Salt and Sulphur Valuable Deposits in": McGreal, P. L., *Oil and Gas Jour.* (1927), v. 25, no. 35, p. 107.

125a. "Coastal (Mesozoic and Tertiary) Basins, The Influence of Basement Structures on the Evolution of the": Kennedy, W. Q., *Salt Basins Around Africa,* The Institute of Petroleum (1965), London, pp. 7-16.

126. "Coastal Plain of Texas and Louisiana, Secondary Salt Dome Materials of": Hanna, Marcus A., *Bull.,* AAPG (1930), v. 14, no. 11, 1469-1475.

127. "Coastal Salt Domes": Kennedy, William, *Bull.,* AAPG (1917), v. 1, no. 1, pp, 34-59; Discussion by E. G. Woodruff, *Bull.,* AAPG (1917), v. 1, no. 1, p. 79.

128. "Coastal Southeast Texas and South Louisiana, Post-Fleming Surface Formations of": Doering, John, *Bull.,* AAPG (1935), v. 19, no. 5, pp. 651-688; *Gulf Coast Oil Fields,* AAPG (1936), pp. 432-469.

128a. "Colorado-Utah Salt Domes": *Bull.* AAPG (1927), v. 11, no. 2, pp. 111-133.

129. "Concord Salt Dome, Anderson County, Texas": Alexander, C. I., *Bull.,* AAPG (1944), v. 28, no. 10, pp. 1537-1538.

129a. "Congo (Brazzaville), Salt Basins of the Gabon and the: A Tentative Palaeogeographic Interpretation": Belmonte, Y., Hirtz, P. and Wenger, R. *Salt Basins Around Africa,* The Institute of Petroleum (1965), London, pp. 55-78.

130. "Continental Margin at Texas-Louisiana Gulf Coast": Barton, D. C. and Hickey, Maude, *Trans.,* Am. Geophys. Union, 14th Ann. Mtg. (1933), pp. 16-20.

131. Continental Shelf Activity Intensified (Gulf Coast)": Logan, L. J. and Smith, Cecil, *World Oil* (1948), v. 123, no. 3, pp. 37-40.

132. "Continental Shelf of the Gulf of Mexico, Geology and Petroleum Development of the": Atwater, Gordon, *Preprint,* Fifth World Pet. Cong.; *Trans.,* GCAGS (1959), v. 9, pp. 131-145.

133. "Continental Shelf Off Louisiana, Geology of: Its Influence on Offshore Foundation Design": Fisk, Harold N. and McClelland, Bramlette, *Bull.,* GSA (1959), v. 70, pp. 1369-1394.

18. "Corals and Larger Foraminifera at Anse la Butte Reef, Louisiana": Squires, D. F. and Sachs, K. N., *Bull.* AAPG (1957), v. 41, no. 4, pp. 746-749.

134. "Cores from a Deep Well at Rodessa, Caddo Parish, Louisiana": Israelsky, M. C., *Bull.,* AAPG (1938), v. 22, no. 6, pp. 764-770.

135. "Correlation by Resistivity Values of Electrical Logs, New Method of": Claudet, A. P., *Bull.,* AAPG (1949), v. 34, no. 10, pp. 2027-2060.

136. "Cote Blanche Island, St. Mary Parish, Louisiana, New Accumulations Found Beneath North Flank Overhang": Stern, A. R., *Trans.,* GCAGS (1955), v. 5, pp. 173-179.

137. "Cote Blanche Salt Dome, St Mary Parish, Louisiana, Late Recent History of": Barton, D. C., *Bull.,* AAPG (1936), v. 20, no. 2, pp. 179-185; *Gulf Coast Oil Fields,* AAPG (1936), pp. 1026-1032; (abs.) *World Pet.,* v. 7, p. 278.

138. "Creole Field, Gulf of Mexico, Coast of Louisiana": Wasson, Theron, *Structure of Typical American Oil Fields,* AAPG (1948), pp. 281-298.

139. "Cretaceous of East Texas, South Arkansas, North Louisiana, Mississippi and Alabama, Notes on Correlations of the": Hazzard, R. T., Blanpied, B. W. and Spooner, W. C., *1945 Ref. Rept.,* Shreveport Geol. Soc. (1947), v. 2, pp. 472-481.

140. "Cretaceous Formation, First Authentic, Found on Gulf Coast Salt Domes of Texas": Morrison, T. E., *Bull.,* AAPG (1929), v. 13, no. 8, pp. 1065-1069.

141. "Cretaceous Ostracoda of Protho and Rayburn's Salt Domes, Bienville Parish, Louisiana": Butler, E. Ann and Jones, Douglas E., *Bull. 32,* La. Geol. Svy. (1957), Dept. of Conserv., 65 pp.

142. "Cretaceous, Upper, Fossils from Wells in Mississippi, Significance of": Stephenson, L. W., *Bull.,* AAPG (1945), v. 29, no. 7, pp. 1008-1018.

143. "Cross Sections Through South Louisiana": *New Orleans Geol. Soc.* (1954).

144. "Crowville Dome, Franklin Parish, Louisiana": Bryan, C. L. and Hamilton, W. F., *Bull.,* AAPG (1947), v. 31, no. 11, pp. 2049-2050.

145. "Crude Oil, Evolution of Gulf Coast": Barton, D. C., *Bull.,* AAPG (1937), v. 21, no. 7, pp. 914-946.

146. "Crude Oil, Natural History of the Gulf Coast": Barton, D. C., *Problems of Petroleum Geology,* AAPG (1934), pp. 109-156.

147. "Cuenca Salina del Istmo, El Metodo Sismologico de Refraccion en la", Basurto Garcia, Jesus and Islas Leal, Juventino, *Bol.* Assoc. Mex. Geol. Petrol. (1950), v. 2, no. 7, pp. 461-472.

15. "Cuenca Salina del Istmo, Planicie Costera de Tabasco, Campeche y Peninsula de Yucatan, Las Anomalias Gravimetricas en la", Cornejo Toledo, Alfonso and Hernandez Osuna, Alfonso, *Bol.,* Asoc. Mex. Geol. Petrol. (1950), v. 2, no. 7, pp. 453-460.

148. "Cuenca Salina del Istmo de Tehuantepec, Condiciones Estatigraficos de las Formaciones Miocenicas de la": Calderon Garcia, Alejandro, *Bol.,* Asoc. Mex. Geol. Petrol. (1951), v. 3, nos. 3, 7-8, pp. 229-259.

149. "Cuenca Salina Istmo de Tehuantepec, Sintesis Geologico de la", Alvarez, Manuel Jr., *Bol.,* Asoc. Mex. Geol. Petrol. (1950), v. 2, no. 7, pp. 445-452.

150. "Damon Mound, Brazoria County, Texas, Limestone on": (summary), Hurlbut, E. M., Jr., *Min. Res. Circ. 31,* Tex. U. (1944), 3 pp.

151. "Damon Mound Field, Brazoria County, Texas": Porter, R. L. and Seren, G. W., *Guidebook,* AAPG-SEPM-SEG Jt. Ann. Mtg. (1953), Houston, Texas, pp. 107-109.

152. "Damon Mound Oil Field, Texas": Bevier, G. M., *Bull.,* AAPG (1925), v. 9, no. 3, pp. 505-535; *Geology of Salt Dome Oil Fields,* AAPG (1926), pp. 613-643.

153. "Damon Mound Salt Dome, Brazoria County, Texas, Limestone in the Heterostegina Zone (Oligocene-Miocene) on": Ballard, Eva O., *Trans,* GCAGS (1961), v. 11, pp. 213-223.

154. "Damon and Nash Mounds, Brazoria and Fort Bend Counties, Texas, Gravity Anomalies of": Barton, D. C., *Tech Pub. 1760,* AIME (1944); *Jour. Pet. Tech.* (1944), v. 7, no. 6, pp. 2-9; *Geophysical Case Histories,* SEG (1948), v. 1, pp. 35-42.

155. "Danbury Salt Dome, Geology of the": Sollars, P. F. and Walters, J. E., *Trans.,* GCAGS (1952), v. 2, p. 7.

156. "Darrow Dome, Ascension Parish, Louisiana, Geophysical History of": Eby, J. B. and Hark-

ins, T. I., Tech. Pub. 1495, AIME (1942); *Trans.,* AIME, v. 151, pp. 253-260; *Geophysical Case Histories,* SEG (1948), v. 1, pp. 144-152.

157. "Darrow Salt Dome, Ascension Parrish, Louisiana": Cook, C. E., *Bull.,* AAPG (1938), v. 22, no. 10, pp. 1412-1422; (abs.) *Oil and Gas Jour.* (1938), v. 36, no. 44, pp. 51, 53; *World Pet.* (1938), v. 9, no. 13, pp. 54.

158. "Deep Hunting Gounds": Cram, Ira H., *Bull.,* AAPG (1963), v. 47, no. 12, pp. 2009-2014.

158a. "Delaware Basin, West Texas and Southeastern New Mexico, Upper Permian Ochoa Series of": Adams, J. E., *Bull.,* AAPG (1944), v. 28, no. 11, pp. 1598-1625.

158b. "Deposition of Evaporites": Scruton, P. C., *Bull.,* AAPG (1953), v. 37, no. 11, pp. 2498-2512.

159. "Deutschlands Kalisalzlanger": Lang, Otto, *Chemische Industrie* (1900), H. Gaertner, H. Heyfelder, Berlin, v. 23, pp. 153, 159, 169-174, 193-197.

160. "Development, Domestic, in 1946, Highlights of": Heald, K. C. *Bull.,* AAPG (1947), v. 31, no. 7, pp. 1125-1134.

161. "Development, Gulf Coast, Highlights of": Critz, James S., *Oil Weekly* (1946), v. 123, no. 3, 81-86, 88.

161a. *Development, International Oil and Gas:* International Oil Scouts Association and Society of Petroleum Engineers of AIME, Year Book (1960-1961), Vols. 30-31, Austin, Texas.

161b. *Development, International Oil and Gas:* International Oil Scouts Association, Yearbook (1962-1965), Vols. 32-35, Austin, Texas.

162. "Development, Maritime, Certain to Assume More Importance": Singleton, F. L., *Oil and Gas Jour.* (1941), v. 39, no. 49, pp. 96-97.

162a. "Development, Mineral," Craft, B. C., *Bull. 6,* La. Geol. Svy. (1935), pp. 181-186.

163. "Development, Oil and Gas, of South Texas During 1937": Halbouty, Michel T., *Trans.,* AIME Petroleum Development and Technology (1938), v. 127, pp. 552-579.

164. "Development, Oil and Gas, of South Texas 1938": Halbouty, Michel T., *Trans.,* AIME Petroleum Development and Technology (1939), v. 132, pp. 453-493

165. "Development, Oil and Gas, of South Texas During 1939": Halbouty, Michel T., *Trans.,* AIME Petroleum Development and Technology (1940), v. 136, pp. 458-498.

166, 'Development, Oil and Gas, of South Texas During 1940": Halbouty, Michel T., *Trans.,* AIME Petroleum Development and Technology (1941), v. 142, pp. 476-504.

167. "Development, Oil and Gas, of South Texas During 1941": Halbouty, Michel T. and Halbouty, James J., *Trans.,* AIME Petroleum Development and Technology (1942), v. 146, pp. 475-508.

168. "Development, Oil and Sulphur, in the Texas and Louisiana Gulf Coast Salt Dome Region": Anonymous, *Bull. 1,* Texas Gulf Coast Oil Scouts Assoc. and South Louisiana Oil Scouts Assoc. (1930), 128 pp.

169. "Development Trend, Gulf Coast, is away from Salt Domes": Vetter, John M., *Oil Weekly* (1940), v. 99, no. 3, pp. 47-49.

170. "Development Trends in Salt Dome Exploration (U. S. Gulf Coast)": Hagen, Cecil and Cantrell, R. B., *Oil Weekly* (1946), v. 123, no. 3, pp. 87-88.

170a. *Development in United States and Canada, Oil and Gas Fields:* National Oil Scouts and Landmen's Association, Year Book (1931-1959), Vols. 1-29, Austin, Texas.

171. "Developments in Arkansas and North Louisiana in 1946": Williams, J. R., *Bull.,* AAPG (1947), v. 31, no. 6, pp. 1084-1105.

172. "Developments in Arkansas and North Louisiana in 1947": Williams, J. R., *Bull.,* AAPG (1948), v. 32, no. 6, pp. 1040-1064.

173. "Developments in Arkansas and North Louisiana in 1948": Williams, J. R., *Bull.,* AAPG (1949), v. 33, no. 6, pp. 990-1001.

174. "Developments in Arkansas and North Louisiana in 1949": Corbin, M. W., *Bull,* AAPG (1950), v. 34, no. 6, pp. 1199-1211.

175. "Developments in Arkansas and North Louisiana in 1950": Collier, L. D., *Bull.,* AAPG (1951), v. 35, no. 6, pp. 1345-1351

176. "Developments in Arkansas and North Louisiana in 1951": Womack, S. A., Jr. and Hundley, H. B., *Bull.,* AAPG (1952), v. 36, no. 6, pp. 1220-1227.

177. "Developments in Arkansas and North Louisiana in 1952": Womack, S. A., Jr. and Shaffer, H. R., *Bull.,* AAPG (1953), v. 37, no. 6, pp. 1449-1459.

178. "Developments in Arkansas and North Louisiana in 1953": Shaffer, H. R. and Lowe, W. O., *Bull.,* AAPG (1954), v. 38, no. 6, pp. 1233-1241.

179. "Developments in Arkansas and North Louisiana in 1955": Mount, Tom M. and Wise, W. H., *Bull.,* AAPG (1956), v. 40, no. 6, pp. 1263-1271.

180. "Developments in Arkansas and North Louisiana in 1956": Wise, W. H. and Morrow, E. H., *Bull.*, AAPG (1957), v. 41, no. 6, pp. 1201-1209.

181. "Developments in Arkansas and North Louisiana in 1957": Morrow, Ernest H. and Champion, W. L., *Bull.*, AAPG (1958), v. 42, no. 6, pp. 1319-1326.

182. "Developments in Arkansas and North Louisiana in 1958": Champion, W. L. and Blanton, S. A., *Bull.*, AAPG (1959), v. 43, no. 6, pp. 1322-1330.

183. "Developments in Arkansas and North Louisiana in 1959": Blanton, Sankey L. and Duschatko, R. W., *Bull.*, AAPG (1960), v. 44, no. 6, pp. 834-841.

184. "Developments in Arkansas and North Louisiana in 1960": Jenkinson, Lewis F. and Sevier, Richard P., *Bull.*, AAPG (1961), v. 45, no. 6, pp. 889-902.

185. "Developments in Arkansas and North Louisiana in 1961": Sevier, Richard P. and Hundley, H. B., *Bull.* AAPG (1962), v. 46, no. 6, pp. 938-952.

186. "Developments in East Texas During 1937, Resume of": Wendlandt, E. A. and Herold, C. L., *Bull.*, AAPG (1938), v. 22, no. 6, pp. 728-735.

187. "Developments in East Texas During 1938" Wendlandt, E. A. and Pirtle, C. W., *Bull.*, AAPG (1939), v. 23, no. 6, pp. 889-895.

188. "Developments in East Texas During 1939": McLellan, H. J. and Wendlandt, E. A., *Bull.*, AAPG (1940), v. 24, no. 6, pp. 1062-1068.

189. "Developments in East Texas During 1940": Denton, R. F. and Trowbridge, R. M., *Bull.*, AAPG (1941), v. 25, no. 6, pp. 1081-1089.

190. "Developments in East Texas During 1941" Denton, F. R., *Bull.*, AAPG (1942), v. 26, no. 6, pp. 1050-1057; (abs.) v. 26, no. 6, p. 905.

191. "Developments in East Texas in 1942": Trowbridge, R. M. and Burnet, T. J., *Bull.*, AAPG (1943), v. 27, no. 6, pp. 782-789.

192. "Developments in East Texas in 1943": Alexander, C. I. and Burnett, T. J., Jr., *Bull.*, AAPG (1944), v. 28, no. 6, pp. 841-852.

193. "Developments in East Texas in 1944": East Texas Geological Society, *Bull.*, AAPG (1945) v. 29, no. 6, pp. 766-776.

193a. "Developments in East Texas During 1945": Loetterle, G. J. and Shelby, T. H., Jr., *Bull.*, AAPG (1946), v. 30, no. 6, pp. 980-990.

194. "Developments in East Texas During 1946" Cash, T. C. and Loetterle, G. J., *Bull.*, AAPG (1947), v. 31, no. 6, pp. 1059-1070.

195. "Developments in East Texas in 1947": Lester, H. H., *Bull.*, AAPG (1948), v. 32, no. 6, pp. 1009-1023.

196. "Developments in East Texas in 1948": Clark, G. C., *Bull.*, AAPG (1949), v. 33, no. 6, pp. 956-965.

197. "Developments in East Texas in 1949": Gibson, D. T., *Bull.*, AAPG (1950), v. 34, no. 6, pp. 1170-1178.

198. "Developments in East Texas in 1950": Hayes, Mack, Jr., *Bull.*, AAPG (1951), v. 35, no. 6, pp. 1313-1321.

199. "Developments in East Texas in 1951": Read, J. L., Jr., *Bull.*, AAPG (1952), v. 36, no. 6, pp. 1188-1200.

200. "Developments in East Texas in 1952": Eaton, R. W., *Bull.*, AAPG (1953), v. 37, no. 6, pp. 1416-1430.

201. "Developments in East Texas in 1953": Hunt, V. G. and O'Connor, J. P., Jr., *Bull.*, AAPG (1954), v. 38, no. 6, pp. 1196-1207.

202. "Developments in East Texas in 1954": Kitchens, Joe C., *Bull.*, AAPG (1955), v. 39, no. 6, pp. 967-975.

203. "Developments in East Texas in 1956": Love, Donald W., Kirkland, R. A. and Richey, W. E., *Bull.*, AAPG (1957), v. 41, no. 6, pp. 1171-1180.

204. "Developments in East Texas in 1957": Mabra, D. A. and Gardner, G. D., *Bull.*, AAPG (1958), v. 42, no. 6, pp. 1289-1298.

205. "Developments in East Texas in 1958": Koonce, G. K. and Battan, F. P., *Bull.*, AAPG (1959), v. 43, no. 6, pp. 1293-1303.

206. "Developments in East Texas in 1959": Fox, Bruce W. and Patrick, Thomas B., *Bull.*, AAPG (1960), v. 44, no. 6, pp. 810-818.

207. "Developments in East Texas in 1960": Stanley, Herbert M., Jr. and Eisenhardt, Wm. C., *Bull.*, AAPG (1961), v. 45, no. 6, pp. 861-867.

208. "Developments in East Texas in 1961": Thomas, G. W. and Vernon, Roger C., *Bull.*, AAPG (1962), v. 46, no. 6, pp. 914-920.

209. "Developments in East Texas in 1962": Ewing, J. M. and Woodhams, R. L., *Bull.*, AAPG (1963), v. 47, no. 6, pp. 1073-1080.

210. "Developments, Gulf Coast of Southeast Texas and Louisiana, in 1938, Review of": Brace, O. L., *Bull.*, AAPG (1939), v. 23, no. 6, pp. 871-888.

211. "Developments, Gulf Coast of Upper Texas

and Louisiana, in 1941, Review of": Brace, O. L., *Bull.,* AAPG (1940), v. 24, no. 6, pp. 1079-1091.

212. "Developments, Gulf Coast of Upper Texas and Louisiana, in 1940, Review of": Brace, O. L., *Bull.,* AAPG (1941), v. 25, no. 6, pp. 1004-1015.

213. "Developments, Gulf Coast of Upper Texas and Louisiana, in 1941, Review of": Brace, O. L., *Bull.,* AAPG (1942), v. 26, no. 6, pp. 983-990; (abs.) v. 26, no. 6, pp. 905-906.

214. "Developments, Gulf Coast of Upper Texas and Louisiana, in 1942, Review of": Smith, G. J., *Bull.,* AAPG (1943), v. 27, no. 6, pp. 730-738.

215. "Developments in Gulf Coast of Upper Texas and Louisiana in 1943": Leavenworth, P. B., *Bull.,* AAPG (1944), v. 28, no. 6, pp. 853-857.

216. "Developments, Gulf Coastal, in 1936": Brace, O. L., *Bull.,* AAPG (1937), v. 21, no. 8, pp. 1050-1062.

217. "Developments, Gulf Coastal, in 1937": Brace, O. L., *Bull.,* AAPG (1938), v. 22, no. 6, pp. 736-749; (abs.) *Oil and Gas Jour.* (1938), v. 36, no. 44, p. 56.

218. "Developments in Louisiana Gulf Coast in 1944": Shepard, G. F., *Bull.,* AAPG (1945), v. 29, no. 6, pp. 792-802.

219. "Developments in Louisiana Gulf Coast in 1945": Bates, F. W. and Wharton, J. B., Jr., *Bull.,* AAPG (1946), v. 30, no. 6, pp. 999-1006.

220. "Developments in Louisiana Gulf Coast in 1946": Shepard, G. F., *Bull.,* AAPG (1947), v. 31, no. 6, pp. 1078-1083; (abs.) *Trans.,* AAPG-SEPM-SEG Jt. Ann. Mtg. (1947), Los Angeles, California, p. 138.

221. "Developments in Louisiana Gulf Coast in 1947": Neill, W. B., *Bull.,* AAPG (1948), v. 32 ,no. 6, pp. 1032-1039.

222. "Developments in Louisiana Gulf Coast in 1948": McBee, W. B. and Orchard, P. J., *Bull.,* AAPG (1949), v. 33, no. 6, pp. 979-989.

223. "Developments in Louisiana Gulf Coast in 1949": May, G. N., *Bull.,* AAPG (1950), v. 34, no. 6, pp. 1191-1198.

224. "Developments in Louisiana Gulf Coast in 1950": Murchison, E. A., Jr. and Patton, J. L., *Bull.,* AAPG (1951), v. 35, no. 6, pp. 1338-1344.

225. "Developments in Louisiana Gulf Coast in 1950": Iles, G. G., *Bull.,* AAPG (1952), v. 36, no. 6, pp. 1211-1219.

226. "Developments in Louisiana Gulf Coast in 1952": Watson, J. G. and Kerlin, M. L., *Bull.,* AAPG (1953), v. 37, no. 6, pp. 1443-1448.

227. "Developments in Louisiana Gulf Coast in 1953": Crain, H. F., *Bull.,* AAPG (1954), v. 38, no. 6, pp. 1221-1232.

228. "Developments in Louisiana Gulf Coast in 1954": Meier, D. R. and Kerlin, M. L., *Bull.,* AAPG (1955), v. 39, no. 6, pp. 988-994.

229. "Developments in Louisiana Gulf Coast in 1955": Waters, K. M. and Duncan, R. L., *Bull.,* AAPG (1956), v. 40, no. 6, pp. 1253-1262.

230. "Developments in Louisiana Gulf Coast in 1956": Waters, K. M. and Beu, R. D., *Bull.,* AAPG (1957), v. 41, no. 6, pp. 1190-1200.

231. "Developments in Louisiana Gulf Coast in 1957": Limes, Leonard L., *Bull.,* AAPG (1958), v. 42, no. 6, pp. 1308-1318.

232. "Developments in Louisiana Gulf Coast in 1958": Hyer, D. E. and Latshaw, W., *Bull.,* AAPG (1959), v. 43, no. 6, pp. 1312-1321.

233. "Developments in Louisiana Gulf Coast in 1959": Love, Donald W. and Duncan, Donald R., *Bull.,* AAPG (1960), v. 44, no. 6, pp. 827-833.

234. "Developments in Louisiana Gulf Coast in 1960": Vidrine, Louis O. and Vallas, H. A., *Bull.,* AAPG (1961), v. 45, no. 6, pp. 879-888.

235. "Developments in Louisiana Gulf Coast in 1961": Vallas, H. A. and Roth, E. P., Jr., *Bull.,* AAPG (1962), v. 46, no. 6, pp. 929-937.

236. "Developments in Louisiana Gulf Coast in 1962": Roth, E. P., Jr., and Smith, Norman E., *Bull.,* AAPG (1963), v. 47, no. 6, pp. 1088-1096.

237. "Developments in Mississippi in 1940": Hughes, U. B., *Bull.,* AAPG (1941), v. 25, no. 6, pp. 1015-1023.

238. "Developments in Northern Louisiana and South Artkansas in 1941": Blanpied, B. W. and Hazzard, R. T., *Bull.,* AAPG (1942), v. 26, no. 6, pp. 1250-1276.

239. "Developments in South Arkansas and North Louisiana in 1937": Shearer, H. K., *Bull.,* AAPG (1938), v. 22, no. 6, pp. 719-727.

240. "Developments in South Arkansas and North Louisiana in 1944": Wilson, R. M., *Bull.,* AAPG (1945), v. 29, no. 6, pp. 803-814.

241. "Developments in South Arkansas and North Louisiana in 1945": Hoffmeister, W. S. and Robinson, V. D., *Bull.,* AAPG (1946), v. 30, no. 6, pp. 1007-1009.

242. "Developments in the South Mid-Continent, Recent": MacNaughton, Lewis W., *Bull.,* AAPG (1940), v. 24, no. 6, pp. 1025-1032.

243. "Developments in South Texas 1938-1939,

Petroleum": Kidd, Gentry, *Bull.,* AAPG (1939), v. 23, no. 6, pp. 860-870.

244. "Developments in South Texas, 1939, and Status of Oil Reserves": Herring, L. B., *Bull.,* AAPG (1940), v. 24, no. 6, pp. 1068-1078.

245. Developments in South Texas During 1940": Herring, L. B., *Bull.,* AAPG (1941), v. 25, no. 6, pp. 1037-1043; (abs.), v. 25, no. 6, pp. 931-932.

246. "Developments in South Texas During 1941": Herring, L. B., *Bull.,* AAPG (1942), v. 26, no. 6, pp. 1000-1006.

247. "Developments in South Texas in 1942": Owens, F. C. and Taegel, E. A., *Bull.,* AAPG (1943), v. 27, no. 6, pp. 739-746.

248. "Developments in South Texas in 1943": Spice, W. H., Jr., *Bull.,* AAPG (1944), v. 28, no. 6, pp. 858-863.

249. "Developments in South Texas in 1944": Scrafford, Bruce, *Bull.,* AAPG (1945), v. 29, no. 6, pp. 777-784.

250. "Developments in South Texas in 1945": Scrafford, Bruce, *Bull.,* AAPG (1946), v. 30, no. 6, pp. 972-979.

251. "Developments in South Texas in 1946": Scrafford, Bruce, *Bull.,* AAPG (1947), v. 31, no. 6, pp. 1052-1058.

252. "Developments in South Texas in 1947": Scrafford, Bruce, *Bull.,* AAPG (1948), v. 32, no .6, pp. 997-1008.

253. "Developments in South Texas in 1948": Scrafford, Bruce, *Bull.,* AAPG (1949), v. 33, no. 6, pp. 945-955.

254. "Developments in South Texas in 1949": Scrafford, Bruce, *Bull.,* AAPG (1950), v. 34, no. 6, pp. 1158-1169.

255. "Developments in South Texas in 1950": Scrafford, Bruce and Jenswold, Nancy, *Bull.,* AAPG (1951), v. 35, no. 6, pp. 1300-1312.

256. "Developments in South Texas in 1951": Rogers, J. K., Spice, W. H., Jr. and Vesely, L. A., *Bull.,* AAPG (1952), v. 36, no. 6, pp. 1177-1187.

257. "Developments in South Texas in 1952": Miller, C. C., Bianchi, J. C., Jr. and Briggs, K. S., *Bull.,* AAPG (1953), v. 37, no. 6, pp. 1405-1415.

258. "Developments in South Texas in 1953": Bianchi, J. C., Jr., Janosky, R. A. and Grayson, R. W., *Bull.,* AAPG (1954), v. 38, no. 6, pp. 1184-1195.

259. "Developments in South Texas in 1957": Hendy, W. J., Dobbins, W. D. and Morren, J. H., *Bull.,* AAPG (1958), v. 42, no. 6, pp. 1279-1288.

260. "Developments in Southeastern States in 1944": Alexander, C. W., Morgan, C. L. and Norman, M. E., *Bull.,* AAPG (1945), v. 29, no. 6, pp. 815-835.

261. "Developments in Southeastern States in 1945": Alexander, C. W., *Bull.,* AAPG (1946), v. 30, no. 6, pp. 1020-1050; (abs.) *Trans.,* AAPG-SEPM-SEG Jt. Ann. Mtg. (1946), Los Angeles, Calif., pp. 37-38.

262. "Developments in Southeastern States in 1946 and 1947": Harris, R. M. and Payne, W. M., *Bull.,* AAPG (1948), v. 32, no. 6, pp. 1065-1076.

263. "Developments in Southeastern States in 1948": Harris, R. M. and Payne, W. M., *Bull.,* AAPG (1949), v. 33, no. 6, pp. 1002-1010.

264. "Developments in Southeastern States in 1949": Holden, F. T., *Bull.,* AAPG (1950), v. 34, no. 6, pp. 1212-1223.

265. "Developments in Southeastern States in 1950": Holden, F. T., *Bull.,* AAPG (1951), v. 35, no. 6, pp. 1352-1365.

266. "Developments in Southeastern States in 1951": Finfrock, L. J., *Bull.,* AAPG (1952), v. 36, no. 6, pp. 1228-1237.

267. "Developments in Southeastern States in 1952": Finfrock, L. J. and Morton, R. B., *Bull.,* AAPG (1953), v. 37, no. 6, pp. 1460-1474.

268. "Developments in Southeastern States in 1953": Allen, W. H., *Bull.,* AAPG (1954), v. 38, no. 6, pp. 1242-1251.

269. "Developments in Southeastern States in 1954": Powell, L. C. and Culligan, L. B., *Bull.,* AAPG (1955), v. 39, no. 6, pp. 1004-1014.

270. "Developments in Southeastern States in 1955": Vernon, R. O. and Erwin, Walter, *Bull.,* AAPG (1956), v. 40, no. 6, pp. 1272-1282.

271. "Developments in Southeastern States in 1957": Hines, E. R., Jr. and Thomas, G. T., *Bull.,* AAPG (1958), v. 42, no. 6, pp. 1327-1338.

272. "Developments in Southeastern States in 1959": St. John, F. B., Jr. and Lusk, Tracy W., *Bull.,* AAPG (1960), v. 44, no. 6, pp. 842-850.

273. "Developments in Southeastern States in 1960": Harrell, David C. and Lynch, William D., *Bull.,* AAPG (1961), v. 45, no. 6, pp. 903-909.

274. "Developments in Southeastern States in 1961": Adams, Emmett R. and Davis, David C., *Bull.,* AAPG (1962), v. 46, no. 6, pp. 953-958.

275. "Developments in Southeastern States in 1962": Davis, David C. and Kargos, Harold E., *Bull.,* AAPG (1963), v. 47, no. 6, pp. 1109-1115.

276. "Developments in Southeastern United States in 1941": Hughes, U. B., *Bull.,* AAPG (1942), v. 26, no. 6, pp. 991-999.

277. "Developments in Southeastern United States in 1943": Hughes, U. B., *Bull.,* AAPG (1944), v. 28, no. 6, pp. 801-805.

278. "Developments in Southern Arkansas and Northern Louisiana in 1938": Spooner, W. C., *Bull.,* AAPG (1939), v. 23, no. 6, pp. 896-902; *Guidebook,* 14th Ann. Field Trip, Shreveport Geol. Soc., pp. 71-77.

279. "Developments in Southern Arkansas and Northern Louisiana During 1939": Weeks, W. B. and Purzer, Joseph., *Bull.,* AAPG (1940), v. 24, no. 6, pp. 1092-1099.

280. "Developments in Southern Arkansas and Northern Louisiana During 1940": Weeks, W. B. and Purzer, Joseph, *Bull.,* AAPG (1941), v. 25, no. 6, pp. 1024-1036; (abs.) v. 25, no. 6, p. 943.

282. "Developments in Upper Gulf Coast of Texas in 1944": Noble, H. A., *Bull.,* AAPG (1945), v. 29, no. 6, pp. 785-791.

283. "Developments in Upper Gulf Coast of Texas in 1945": Davis, D. M. and Beilharz, C. F., *Bull.,* AAPG (1946), v. 30, no. 6, pp. 991-998.

284. "Developments in the Upper Gulf Coast of Texas in 1946": Allison, A. P. and Claypool, C. B., *Bull.,* AAPG (1947), v. 31, no. 6, pp. 1071-1077.

285. "Developments in Upper Gulf Coast of Texas in 1947": Clark, P. H., *Bull.,* AAPG (1948), v. 32, no. 6, pp. 1024-1031.

286. "Developments in Upper Gulf Coast of Texas in 1948": Mettner, F. E., *Bull.,* AAPG (1949), v. 33, no. 6, pp. 966-978.

287. "Developments in Upper Gulf Coast of Texas in 1949": Ballard, J. L., *Bull.,* AAPG (1950), v. 34, no. 6, pp. 1179-1190.

288. "Developments in Upper Gulf Coast District of Texas in 1950": Allen, H. H., *Bull.,* AAPG (1951), v. 35, no. 6, pp. 1322-1337.

289. "Developments in Upper Gulf Coast District of Texas in 1951": McMahan, W. W., Jr., *Bull.,* AAPG (1952), v. 36, no. 6, pp. 1201-1210.

290. "Developments in Upper Gulf Coast of Texas in 1952": Cooke, W. F., Jr., *Bull.,* AAPG (1953), v. 37, no. 6, pp. 1431-1442.

291. "Developments in Upper Gulf Coast of Texas in 1953": Woollet, L. A., *Bull.,* AAPG (1954), v. 38, no. 6, pp. 1208-1220.

292. "Developments in Upper Gulf Coast of Texas in 1954": Wahl, C. C., *Bull.,* AAPG (1955), v. 39, no. 6, pp. 976-987.

293. "Developments in Upper Gulf Coast of Texas in 1955": Cockerham, K. L., Jr., Rotan, R. A., Jr. and Stout, E. D., *Bull.,* AAPG (1956), v. 40, no. 6, pp. 1239-1252.

294. "Developments in Upper Gulf Coast in 1956": Cockerham, K. L., Jr., *Bull.,* AAPG (1957), v. 41, no. 6, pp. 1181-1189.

295. "Developments in Upper Gulf Coast of Texas in 1957": Cockerham, K. L., Jr., *Bull.,* AAPG (1958), v. 42, no. 6, pp. 1299-1307.

296. "Developments in Upper Gulf Coast of Texas in 1958": Brixey, A. D., Jr. and Yust, M. R., *Bull.,* AAPG (1959), v. 43, no. 6, pp. 1304-1311.

297. "Developments in Upper Gulf Coast of Texas in 1960": Tague, Glenn C. and Burgess, Curtis W., Jr., *Bull.,* AAPG (1961), v. 45, no. 6, pp. 868-878.

298. "Developments in Upper Gulf Coast of Texas in 1961": Critz, James S. and Sholl, Vinton H., *Bull.,* AAPG (1962), v. 46, no. 6, pp. 921-928.

299. "Developments in the Upper Gulf Coast of Texas in 1962": Sholl, Vinton H. and Reynolds, J. Rex, *Bull.,* AAPG (1963), v. 47, no. 6, pp. 1081-1087.

300. "Developments, Wildcat, on Coastal Salt Domes": Williams, Neil, *Oil and Gas Jour.* (1938), v. 37, no. 12, pp. 33-34.

78a. "Diamond Alkali Brine Field at Mont Belvieu, Texas": Moore, M. L., *Symposium on Salt,* Northern Ohio Geol. Soc., Inc. (1963), Cleveland, Ohio, pp. 539-545.

301. "Dickinson Area, Potentialities of, May Rival Anahuac and Hastings Fields": Singleton, F. L., *Oil and Gas Jour.* (1935), v. 34, no. 12, p. 23.

302. "Dickinson, Gillock and South Gillock Fields, Galveston County, Texas": Gahagan, Donald I., *Guidebook,* AAPG-SEPM-SEG Jt. Ann. Mtg. (1953), Houston, Texas, pp. 110-113.

303. "Dickinson, See Greater Possibilities in": Singleton, F. L., *Oil and Gas Jour.* (1937), v. 35, no. 52, pp. 102, 118.

304. "Directional Drilling as Development Aid in Coastal Louisiana Salt Dome Field": Williams, Neil, *Oil and Gas Jour.* (1944), v. 43, no. 31, pp. 66-68.

305. "Directional Drilling from Man Made Islands": Nicholson, Gordon B., *Oil Weekly* (1946), v. 121, no. 9, pp. 18-19, 21.

306. "Directional Drilling for Salt Dome Oil Production": Joynt, K. R. and Massad, A. H., *World Oil* (1956), v. 142, no. 7, pp. 192, 194, 199, 202.

307. "Discoveries": Deussen, Alexander, *Geophysics* (1938), v. 3, no. 3, pp. 177-197.

308. "Discoveries, New Coast, Throw Additional Light on Salt Dome Area as Future Reserve": Mills, Brad, *Oil Weekly* (1935), v. 78, no. 10, pp. 19-20, 22-23.

309. "Discoveries and Developments in Northeastern Texas in 1928, Resume of": Judson, Sidney A., *Bull.*, AAPG (1929), v. 13, no. 6, pp. 611-613.

310. "Discoveries, Salt Dome, in North Louisiana in 1942": Blanpied, B. W. and Hazzard, R. T., *Bull.*, AAPG (1944), v. 28, no. 4, pp. 561-562.

311. "Discovery of Much Oil From Known Domes, Predict": Hagen, Cecil, *Oil and Gas Jour.* (1941), v. 39, no. 49, pp. 82-86, 97-98.

311a "Dolomitization by Seepage Refluxion": Adams, J. E. and Rhodes, M. L., *Bull.*, AAPG (1960), v. 44, no. 12, pp. 1912-1920.

312. "Dome, Complexly Faulted, Eola Field, Avoyelles Parish, Louisiana, Typical Oil Field Structure": *Oil and Gas Jour.* (1942), v. 41, no. 2, pp. 50-51.

313. "Dome, Highly Complex, Yields Many Secrets": Atwater, Gordon I., *Oil and Gas Jour.* (1959), v. 57, no. 31, pp. 250-252.

314. "Dome Interest Revived": *Oil and Gas Jour.* (1952), v. 50, no. 37, pp. 58-59.

314a. "Dome Mining: Floor vs. Roof Extraction": Nicola, Nicolas J., *Symposium on Salt*, Northern Ohio Geol. Soc., Inc. (1963), Cleveland, Ohio, pp. 390-398.

315. "Dome, New Gulf Coast, Fort Bend County, Texas": Pratt, W. E., *Bull.*, AAPG (1922), v. 6, no. 3, pp. 252-254.

316. "Dome, New Life for an Old": Baird, James A., *Oil and Gas Jour.* (1962), v. 60, no. 40, pp. 113-114.

317. "Dome Production, Gulf Coast, Rhythm May Determine": Bradley, D., *Oil Trade Jour.* (1921), v. 12, p. 32.

318. "Dome, Sixth 'Dry', Yields Oil in East Texas": Gardner, Frank J., *Oil and Gas Jour.* (1960), v. 58, no. 7, p. 157.

319. "Dome Theories Applied to Gulf Coast Geology": Harris, G. D., *Science* (1912), new ser., v. 36, pp. 173-174.

320. "Dome Theory of the Coastal Plain": Lucas, A. F., *Science* (1912), new ser., v. 35, pp. 961-964.

117. "Domes, Coastal, Claiborne Formation on the": Weinzierl, L. L. L. and Applin, E. R., *Jour. of Paleontology* (1929), v. 3, pp. 384-410.

321. "Domes, Coastal, New Light Thrown on": Williams, Neil, *Oil and Gas Jour.* (1930), v. 29, no. 22, pp. 30-31, 107.

322. "Domes, Deep Seated, of South Louisiana, A Regional Interpretation": Wallace, W. E. Jr., *AAPG Reg. Mtg.* (1949), Biloxi, Miss.

323. "Domes, Deep Seated, of South Louisiana, A Study of": Wallace, W. E., Jr., *PhD Dissertation* (1943), LSU, Dept. of Geol.

324. "Domes, Structure of South Louisiana Deep Seated": Wallace, W. E., Jr., *Bull.*, AAPG (1944), v. 28, no. 9, pp. 1249-1312.

325. "Domes, 'Dry', Drillers Eye Texas": Enright, Robert J., *Oil and Gas Jour.* (1963), v. 61, no. 52, pp. 210-214.

326. "Domes, The Gulf Coast, in Relation to Sulphur Supply": Thomas, Kirby, *Eng. and Mining Jour* (1918), v. 106, no. 1, p. 7.

311. "Domes, Known, Predict Discovery of Much Oil From": Hagen, Cecil, *Oil and Gas Jour.* (1941), v. 39, no. 49, pp. 82-86, 97-98.

327. "Domes, Southern Louisiana, Reviewed": Ames, E. R., *Oil and Gas Jour.* (1930), v. 28, no. 45, pp. 42, 159-160.

328. "Domes, Structure Elements of": Balk, Robert, *Bull.*, AAPG (1936), v. 20, no. 1, pp. 51-67; (abs.), v. 19, no. 1, p. 136; *World Pet.*, v. 7, no. 3, p. 150.

329. "Domes of Texas and Louisiana, Overhanging Salt on": Judson, Sidney A. and Stamey, R. A., *Bull.*, AAPG (1933), v. 17, no. 12, pp. 1492-1520; *Gulf Coast Oil Fields* (1936), pp. 141-169; *Oil Weekly* (1934), v. 71, no. 11, pp. 18-24; no. 12 pp. 18-22; no. 13, pp. 18, 20-24; *Oil and Gas Jour.* (1934), v. 32, no. 21, pp. 16, 30; no. 22, pp. 18, 22; no. 25, pp. 16, 18; no. 27, p. 18; (abs.) *Pan Am. Geologist*, v. 59, no. 3, p. 230.

330. "Domes, Texas, Origin of the": Dumble E. T., *Bull.*, AIM E (1918), v. 142, pp. 1629-1636.

331. "Domo Salino de 'El Rosario' en el Estado de Tabasco y sus Posibilidades Petroliferas": Contreras, Hugo V. and Sansores, Enrique, *Bol.*, Asoc. Mex. Geol. Petrol. (1953), v. 5, nos. 1-2, pp. 57-74.

331a. *Domos en el Estado de Louisiana, E.U.A. Explotacion Minera de Sal en:* Perez Larios, Jose,

Archivo Consejo de Recursos Naturales no Renovables Inedite (1960).

33a. "Domos Salinos de la Cuenca Salina del Istmo de Tehuantepec, Origen del Azufre en el Casquete de los": Hungsberg, Ulrich, *Bol. 51* (1960), Consejo de Recursos Naturales no Renovables, 96 pp.

332. "Domos Salinos del Istmo de Tehuantepec, Morfologia y Origen de los": Contreras, Hugo and Castillon, B. M., *Bol.*, Asoc. Mex. Geol. Petrol. (1960), v. 12, nos. 7-8, pp. 221-242.

332a. "Drilling Abnormal Pressure Formations, Problems Encountered in": Cannan, G. E. and Sullins, R. S., *Drilling and Production Practice 1946*, API (1947), N. Y., pp. 29-33; *Drilling* (June, 1946), pp. 48-50; (abs.) *Oil Weekly* (May 20, 1946), p. 31.

333. "Drilling Boom, Seven Discoveries in Gulf of Mexico": McCaslin, Leigh S., Jr., *Oil and Gas Jour.* (1948), v. 47, no. 22, pp. 64-67.

333a. *Drilling Fluids, Composition and Properties of Oil Well*: Rogers, Walter F., Gulf Publishing Co. (1963), Houston, Texas, 818 pp.

334. "Drilling, Maritime or Offshore, in the Gulf Coast": *Oil Weekly* (1933), v. 69, no. 1, pp. 65-68.

335. "Drilling Mud Practices, Gulf Coast, Demand Attention to Special Problems": Gray, Dr. George R., Allen, G. C. and Tschirley, N. K., *World Oil* (1956), v. 142, no. 7, pp. 155-160.

336. "Drilling, Odd, in Bayous of Louisiana": *Oil and Gas Jour.* (1930), v. 29, no. 14, pp. 42, 146.

337. "Drilling Play Reflects Activity Near Gulf Coast Salt Domes": *Oil and Gas Jour.* (1940), v. 38, no. 50, pp. 92, 95, 102.

337a. "Drilling Pressure Formations, Problems Encountered in": Sullins, R. S. and Cannan, G. E., *Drilling and Production Practice 1946*, API (1947), N. Y., pp. 29-33; *Drilling* (June 1946), pp. 48-50; (abs.), *Oil Weekly* (May 20, 1946), p. 31.

338. "Drilling Problems, City and Owners of Lots Solve": *Oil and Gas Jour.* (1935), v. 34, no. 21, p. 15.

339. "Drilling, Wildcat, in 1941, with Some Comments on Discovery Rate": Lahee, F. H., *Bull.*, AAPG (1942), v. 26, no. 6, pp. 969-982; (abs.) no. 5, p. 904; *Yearbook*, National Oil Scouts and Landman's Assoc. (1942), pp. 22-28.

340. "Duval County, Texas, Geology and Ground Water Resources of": Sayre, A. N., *Paper 776*, USGS (1937), Water Supply Dept., 116 pp.

340a. "Eagle Mills Formation, Geology of the": Scott, K. R., Hayes, W. E. and Fietz, R. P., *Trans.*, GCAGS (1961), v. 11, pp. 1-14.

341. "Earth Cycling Operation (Louisiana Gas Field)": Anonymous, *Oil and Gas Jour.* (1945), v. 43, no. 45, pp. 65-88.

342. "East Hackberry Field, Louisiana, Salt Water Injection for Pressure Maintenance in": Euwer, M. L., *Oil and Gas Jour.* (1945), v. 44, no. 21, pp. 100-102, 131.

343. "East Hackberry or Kelso Bayou Dome": Texas Gulf Coast Oil Scouts Association and South Louisiana Oil Scouts Association. *Bull. 1* (1930), pp. 124-125.

344. "East Hackberry, Pressure Maintenance of": Euwer, M. L., *Oil Weekly* (1945), v. 119, no. 6, pp. 46, 49-51.

345. "East Hackberry Salt Dome, Cameron Parish, Louisiana": Bauernschmidt, A. J., Jr., *Bull.*, AAPG (1931), v. 15, no. 3, pp. 247-256.

346. "Economic Importance of Salt Domes": Barton, D. C., *Bull. 2801*, Tex. U. (1928), pp. 7-53.

347. "Edgerly Oil Field, Louisiana": Minor, H. E., *Bull.*, AAPG (1925), v. 9, no. 3, pp. 497-504; *Geology of Salt Dome Oil Fields*, AAPG (1926), pp. 470-477.

347a. *Economic Mineral Deposits:* Bateman, Alan M., 2nd Edition, Wiley and Sons (1950), New York, N. Y.

347b. *Ekzeme und Tektonik:* Lachmann, R., Zentralbl. f. Min. usw. (1917), 414 pp.

347c. "Electrical Resistivity Surveys in Salt Mines": Scharon, LeRoy, *Symposium on Salt*, Northern Ohio Geol. Soc., Inc. (1963), Cleveland, Ohio, pp. 379-389.

347d. *El Moralar, Geological Report No. 191 on the Salt Dome of:* Nolthenius, Tutein A. B., Archive Petroleos Mexicanos (1922).

331. " 'El Rosario', Domo Salino de, en el Estado de Tabasco y sus Posibilidades Petroliferas", Contreras, Hugo and Sansores, Enrique, *Bol.* Asoc. Mex. Geol. Petrol (1953), v. 5, nos. 1-2, pp. 57-74,

348. "Emba Salt Dome Region, U.S.S.R. and Some Comparisons with Other Salt Dome Regions"; Sanders, C. W., *Bull.*, AAPG (1939), v. 23, no. 4, pp. 492-516.

349. "Engineering and Geological Data on Mexico": *World Oil* (1952), v. 135, no. 2, p. 122.

312 "Eola Field, Avoyelles Parish, Louisiana, Typical Oil Field Structure; Complexly Faulted Dome": *Oil and Gas Jour.* (1942), v. 41, no. 2, pp. 50-51.

350. "Eotvos Torsion Balance Method of Mapping Geologic Structure"; Barton, D. C., *Tech. Pub. 50*, AIME (1928), 51 pp.; *Trans.*, v. 81, pp. 416-479; (abs.) *Mining and Metallurgy*, v. 9, no. 254, p. 83.

350a. "Erscheinungen, Injektivfaltung and damit Zusammenhangende": Stille, H., *Geol. Rundschau*, 8 (1917), p. 89.

39. "Esperson and Barbers Hill, Coastal Texas, Typical Oil Field Structures; Salt Dome": *Oil and Gas. Jour.* (1942), v. 41, no. 13, pp. 42-43.

351. "Esperson Dome Field, Liberty County, Texas": Riddell, John T., *Typical Oil and Gas Fields of Southeast Texas*, Houston Geol. Soc. (1962), pp. 47-52.

352. "Esperson Dome, Liberty County, Texas": Goldston, W. L. and Stevens, G. D., *Bull.*, AAPG (1934), v. 18, no. 12, pp. 1632-1654; *Gulf Coast Oil Fields*, AAPG (1936), pp. 857-879.

353. "Esperson Dome Field, Liberty and Harris Counties, Texas": Garwick, R. W., Krisle, Jack E. and Ellison, R. F., *Guidebook*, AAPG-SEPM-SEG Jt. Ann. Mtg. (1953), Houston, Texas, pp. 115-116.

354. "Esperson Dome, Texas, Geophysics and Geology of the Discovery and Development of": Thompson, Wallace C. and Day, W. L., *Geophysical Case Histories*, SEG (1948), v. 1, pp. 48-65.

355. "Esperson Salt Dome, Liberty County, Texas, Torsion-Balance Survey of": Barton, D. C., *Bull.*, AAPG (1930), v. 14, no. 9, pp. 1129-1143.

356. "Esperson, Torsion Balance Survey at": Barton, D. C., *Oil and Gas Jour.* (1930), v. 28, no. 46, pp. 38, 141.

357. "Evangeline and St. Landry Parishes, Geology of": Varvaro, Gasper G., *Bull., 31*, La. Geol. Svy. (1957), Dept. of Conserv., 295 pp.

357a. "Evaporite Basin in Southern Tanzania": Kent, P. E., *Salt Basins Around Africa*, The Institute of Petroleum (1965), London, pp. 41-54.

158b. "Evaporites, Deposition of": Scruton, P. C., *Bull.*, AAPG (1953), v. 37, no. 11, pp. 2498-2512.

358. "Exploration on the Gulf Coast to 1936": Rosaire, E. E., (abs.) *World Pet.* (1936), v. 7, no. 8, p. 404.

359. "Exploration for Oil Out in the Gulf is Within Engineering Possibilities": Williams, Neil, *Oil and Gas Jour.* (1935), v. 34, no. 8, pp. 42, 45.

360. "Exploration for Petroleum, On the Strategy and Tactics of": Rosaire, E. E., *Jour. of Soc. of Pet. Geophys.* (1935), v. 6, no. 1, pp. 11-26; *Early Geophysical Papers*, SEG (1957), pp. 255-270.

361. "Exploration for Petroleum, II, On the Strategy and Tactics of": Rosaire, E. E., *Geophysics* (1938), v. 3, no. 1, pp. 22-39.

362. "Exploration for Petroleum, III, On the Strategy and Tactics of": Rosaire, E. E., *Geophysics* (1939), v. 4, no. 3, pp. 155-166.

363. "Exploration and Production in the Gulf Coast Through 1935": Rosaire, E. E. and Stiles, M. E., *Geophysics* (1936), v. 1, no. 1, pp. 141-148.

364. "Exploration Techniques, Present and Future on Salt Domes of the Gulf Region of the United States, A Geological Appraisal of": Halbouty, Michel T. and Hardin, George C., Jr., *Paper 5*, Fifth World Pet. Cong. (1959), sec. 1, pp. 1-13; *Oil* (1959), v. 19, no. 8, pp. 33-42.

365. "Exploration Techniques on Salt Domes of the Gulf Region of the United States": Halbouty, Michel T. and Hardin, George C., Jr., *Oil and Gas Jour.* (1959), v. 57, no. 24, pp. 134-137.

366. "Fannett Field, Jefferson County, Texas, Distribution of Heterostegina Lime": Hough, W. H., (abs.) *Oil and Gas Jour.* (1948), v. 47, no. 30, p. 93.

366a. "Fault and Salt Map of South Louisiana (1966 Edition)": Wallace, W. E., Jr. (ed.), *Trans.*, GCAGS (1966), v. 16.

367. "Fault Trends, South Louisiana": Wallace, W. E., Jr., *Trans.*, GCAGS (1952), v. 2, pp. 63-67.

368. "Faulted Structures Play Big Roles in Gulf Coastal Production": Kornfeld, J. A., *Oil Weekly* (1938), v. 90, no. 13, pp. 17-18.

369. "Faulting in Northwestern Houston County, Texas": Stenzel, H. B., *Min. Res. Circ. 23*, Tex. U. (1943), 9 pp; *Pub. 4301*, Tex. U. (1946), pp. 19-27.

370. "Faulting Patterns Aids Piercement Salt Dome Development, Better Concept of": Kornfeld, M. M., *Oil Weekly* (1941), v. 100, no. 10, pp. 19-20.

371. "Faulting, Salt Ridge Hypothesis on Origin of Texas Gulf Coast Type of": Quarles, Miller, Jr., *Bull.*, AAPG (1953), v. 37, no. 3, pp. 489-508.

372. "Faults, Contemporaneous Normal, of Gulf Coast and Their Relation to Flexures": Hardin, Frank R. and Hardin, George C. Jr., *Bull.*, AAPG (1961), v. 45, no. 2, pp. 238-248.

373. "Faults, Growth, of South Louisiana": Ocamb, Rayburn D., *Trans.*, GCAGS (1961), v. 11, pp. 139-175.

119. "Faults, A Study of Intersecting, and Their Effects on Accumulation in the Clam Lake Field, Jefferson County, Texas": Hillyer, L. D., *Trans.*,

GCAGS, 1st Ann. Mtg. (Nov., 1951), New Orleans, La.

374. " 'Ferguson Crossing Dome,' Brazoria and Grimes Counties, Texas Application of Name": Speed, C. D., Jr., *Bull.,* AAPG (1939), v. 23, no. 7, pp. 1092-1093.

374a. "Ferry Lake Anhydrite, The Genesis and Petrography of the; and A Correlation and Regional Stratigraphic Analysis of the Formation of the Trinity Group of the Companchean Cretaceous of the Gulf Coastal Plain": Forgotson, J. M., Jr., *Trans.,* GCAGS (1956), v. 6, pp. 91-105.

375. *Field Trips, Guidebook for:* Culbertson, J. A., Eby, J. B. and Thompson, W. C., AAPG, 26th Ann. Mtg. (1941), Houston, Texas, 28 pp.

376. "Fields in the Gulf Coast Belt of Texas and Louisiana Have High Per-Acre Recovery": Leyendecker, Charles, *Oil Weekly* (1936), v. 82, no. 10, pp. 14-15.

377. "Fields, Old, Never Die in South Louisiana": Morrisey, Norman S., *Oil and Gas Jour.* (1956), v. 54, no. 59, pp. 213-214.

378. "Five Island Trend (Jefferson Island to Belle Isle, Louisiana), Regional Correlation Section": *No. 3 Tertiary,* South La. Geol. Soc. (1954).

379. "Five Islands, Iberia and St. Mary Parishes, Louisiana, The Geology of the": Atwater, Gordon, *Trans.,* GCAGS, 1st Ann. Mtg. (Nov. 1951), New Orleans, La., p. 212.

380. "Five Islands, Louisiana": Vaughan, F. E., *Bull.,* AAPG (1925), v. 9, no. 4, pp. 756-797; *Geology of Salt Dome Oil Fields,* AAPG (1926), pp. 356-397.

381. "Five Islands, The Shreveport Area": Veatch, A. C., *Geology and Agriculture of Louisiana* (1899), La. State Expt. Sta., pt. 5, pp. 149-262.

382. "Fluid Mechanics of Salt Domes": Nettleton, L. L., *Bull.,* AAPG (1934), v. 18, no. 9, pp. 1175-1204; *Gulf Coast Oil Fields,* AAPG (1936), pp. 79-108.

383. "Foraminifera from Timbalier Bay, Louisiana, A Seasonal Ecological Study of" (abs.): Waldron, Robert P., *Trans.,* GCAGS (1962), v. 12, p. 302.

384. "Formation and Geology of the Salt Deposits": Jones, F. O., *Sci. Am.* (1902), v. 87, p. 59.

385. "Formation of Salt Domes, Mechanics of, With Special Reference to Gulf Coast Salt Domes of Texas and Louisiana": Barton, D. C., *Bull.,* AAPG (1933), v. 17, no. 9, pp. 1025-1083; *Gulf Coast Oil Fields,* AAPG (1936), pp. 20-78.

385a. "France, Analyse de l'Eau de la Mediterranee sur la Cote de": Usiglio, J., *Ann. Chim. et Phys.* (1849), ser. 3, 27, pp. 92-172.

385b. "Frage der Aufpressungsvorgilange und der Alters der Nordwestdeutschen Salzvorkommen, Zur": Harbort, E., *Kali* (1913), Heft 5, p. 112.

386. "Friendswood Field Has Three Factors Attracting Notice": Singleton, F. L., *Oil and Gas Jour.* (1937), v. 36, no. 13, p. 43.

387. "Friendswood Field, Harris County, Texas": Bell, Olin G., *Bull.,* AAPG (1938), v. 22, no. 11, pp. 1602-1603.

388. "Friendswood (Webster) Oil Field, Harris County, Texas, Case History of the": Patrick, H. G., *Geophysical Case Histories,* SEG (1948), v. 1, pp. 74-84.

7. "Frio and Anahuac Formations of Texas and Louisiana, Summary of Oil Occurrence in": Burke, R. A., *Bull.,* AAPG (1958), v. 42, no. 12, pp. 2935-2950.

8. "Frio and Anahuac Sediments in Louisiana": Warren, A. D., *Trans.,* GCAGS (1957), v. 7, pp. 221-238.

389. "Frio Discovery in Old Salt Dome Field is Major Strike": Carroll, Don L., *Oil Weekly* (1943), v. 112, no. 1, pp. 12-13.

390. "Frio Formation, Stratigraphy of the, Jefferson and Orange Counties, Texas": Reedy, M. F., Jr., *Bull.,* AAPG (1949), v. 33, no. 11, pp. 1830-1858; (abs.) *Bull.,* AAPG (1949), v. 33, no. 1, pp. 108-109; *Oil and Gas Jour.* (1949), v. 47, no. 32, p. 104.

129a. "Gabon and the Congo (Brazzaville), Salt Basins of the: A Tentative Palaeogeographic Interpretation": Belmonte, Y., Hirtz, P. and Wenger, R., *Salt Basins Around Africa,* The Institute of Petroleum (1965), London, pp. 55-78.

391. "Galena, Notes on an Occurrence of, at Pierce Junction Salt Dome, Harris County, Texas": Hanna, Marcus A. and Parker, W. G., *Bull.,* AAPG (1933), v. 17, no. 4, pp. 438-439.

392. "Galena and Spalerite in the Fayette at Orchard Salt Dome, Fort Bend County, Texas": Hanna, Marcus A., *Bull.,* AAPG (1929), v. 13, no. 4, pp. 384-385.

393. "Gas Blowouts and Craters, Rapid Sucession of, Following Increase in Coastal Wildcatting": Williams, Neil, *Oil and Gas Jour.* (1933), v. 32, no. 7, pp. 8, 36.

341. "Gas Field, Louisiana, Earth Cycling Op-

eration": Anonymous, *Oil and Gas Jour.* (1945), v. 43, no. 45, pp. 65-88.

394. "Gas Fields in Northeast Texas Embayment": Ley, H. A. and Willson, K. M., *Geology of Natural Gas,* AAPG (1935), pp. 651-682.

395. "Gas Well, Wild, Rice Land and Heavy Rains Test Man's Ingenunity in a Struggle for Control": Bignell, L. G. E., *Oil and Gas Jour.* (1933), v. 32, no. 13, p. 12.

395a. "Genesis of Some Sulphur Deposits of the U.S.S.R.": Murzaiev, P. M., *Econ. Geol.* (1937), v. 32, pp. 69-109.

396. "Geochemicial Exploration, Symposium on, Geochemical Prospecting for Petroleum": Rosaire, E. E., *Bull.,* AAPG (1940), v. 24, no. 8, pp. 1400-1433.

397. "Geochemical Prospecting": Horvitz, Leo, *Geophysics* (1939), v. 4, no. 3, pp. 210-228.

398. "Geochemical Prospecting for Petroleum, Recent Developments in": Horvitz, Leo, *Geophysics* (1945), v. 10, no. 4, pp. 487-493.

399. "Geochemistry, Salt Dome, A Contribution to": Stuart, Murray, *Jour. Inst. Pet.* (1931), v. 17, pp. 338-345.

113. "Geologia de Chiapas y Tabasco, Resena Acerca de la": Bose, E., *Bol.,* Ints. Geol. Mexico, num. 20, 116 pp, 9 lams.

400. "Geo-electrical Methods, Salt Dome Studies by": Sundberg, K., *Jour Inst Pet.* (1931), v. 17, pp. 376-380.

33b. *Geologia Economica del Azufre en el Istmo de Tehuantepec:* Salas, Guillermo P., Trabajo inedito (1957), Mexico, D.F.

400a. "Geologia Petrolera de Mexico": Guzman, Eduardo J., Juarez, C. Rodolfo and Lopez Ramos, Ernesto, *Bol.,* Asoc. Mex. Geol. Petrol. (1955), v. 7, pp. 137-171.

400b. "Geologic Aspects of Origin of Petroleum": Hedberg, Hollis D., *Bull.,* AAPG (1964), v. 48, no. 11, pp. 1775-1803.

401. "Geologic History of the Formation of Salt Deposits" (abs.): Weaver, Paul, *Tulsa Geol. Soc. Digest* (1946), v. 14, p. 51.

350. "Geologic Structure, Eotvos Torsion Balance Method of Mapping": Barton, D. C., *Tech. Pub.* 50, AIME (1928), 51 pp; *Trans.,* v. 81, pp. 416-479; (abs.) *Min. and Metallurgy,* v. 9, no. 254, p. 83.

402. "Geologic Structure, Quantitative Calculations of, from Gravimetric Data": Barton, D. C., *Geophysical Case Histories,* SEG (1948), v. 1, pp.

251-280; *Tech. Pub.* 1760, AIME; *Pet. Tech.* (1944), v. 7, no. 6, pp. 22-49.

403. "Geologic Structure, Regional and Local Magnetic Vector Study of, in Principal Oil States": Jenny, W. P., *Early Geophysical Papers,* SEG (1948), v. 1, pp. 335-363; *Trans.,* SEG (1932), v. 3, pp. 7-33.

404. "Geologic Structure, Role of, in the Accumulation of Petroleum": Clapp, F. G., *Structure of Typical American Oil Fields,* AAPG (1929), v. 2, pp. 667-716.

405. "Geologic Structures, Theory of Scale Models as Applied to the Study of": Hubbert, M. K., *PhD Dissertation,* Chicago U. (1937), Dept. of Geol.; *Bull.,* GSA (1937), v. 48, pp. 1459-1519.

406. "Geological Appraisal of Wildcat Prospects, Economic Factors in the": Hardin, George C., Jr., *Trans.,* GCAGS (1958), v. 8, pp. 14-19; *World Oil,* Part I (1959), v. 148, no. 4, pp. 119-120; Part II (1959), v. 148, no. 5, pp. 138-141.

407. "Geological Aspects of Abnormal Reservoir Pressures in Gulf Coast Louisiana": Dickinson, George, *Bull.,* AAPG (1953), v. 37, no. 2, pp. 410-432; *Proc.,* Third World Pet. Cong. (1951), The Hague, Holland.

408. "Geological Concepts and Economic Significance of Salt Domes in the Gulf Region, A Review of": Halbouty, Michel T., *Bull.,* Houston Geol. Soc. (Oct 1959), v. 2, no. 2.

409. "Geological Data, Development History, Gulf Coast Oil Fields": Critz, James S., *Oil Weekly* (1946), v. 123, no. 3, pp. 110-159.

410. "Geological Data, Development History, Gulf Coast Oil Fields": Smith, Cecil W., *World Oil* (1950), v. 130, no. 7, pp. 60-120.

411. "Geological Data and Development History, Gulf Coast Oil Fields, Salt Domes and Prospects": Leyendecker, C., *Oil Weekly* (1936), v. 81, no. 1, pp. 85-164.

412. "Geological Data and Developments, Gulf Coast Oil Fields, Salt Domes and Prospects": *Oil Weekly* (1942), v. 105, no. 2, pp. 59-130.

413. "Geological Eccentricities in Mississippi Pose Completion and Production Problems in Oil and Gas Fields": Williams, Neil, *Oil and Gas Jour.* (1945), v. 43, no. 42, pp. 124-129, 148.

414. "Geological and Engineering Thinking in the Gulf Coast of Texas and Louisiana—Past, Present and Future": Halbouty, Michel T., *Jour. Pet. Tech.* (May 1957), v. 9, no. 5, pp. 19-20; *Texas Oil Jour.,* pp. 18-19, 26; *The Independent Petro-*

leum Association of America Monthly, pp. 30-32, 39.

415. "Geological History of Gulf of Mexico, On the": Hilgard, E. W., *Am. Jour. Sci.* (1871), ser. 3, v. 2, pp. 391-404; *Proc.,* Am. Assoc. Adv. Sci., v. 20, pp. 222-336; *Sup. Ann. Rept.,* LSU (1872), pp. 207-222; *Am. Naturalist,* v. 5, pp. 514-518.

416. "Geological Occurrence of Rock Salt in Louisiana and East Texas": Harris, G. D., *Econ. Geol.* (1909), v. 4, pp. 12-34.

417. "Geological Prospects for Discoveries Brighter Than Ever": Halbouty, Michel T., (Editorial) *World Oil,* Gulf Coast Issue (1958), v. 146, no. 7, pp. 102-103, 127-128.

418. "Geological Reconnaissance of Louisiana, Preliminary Report of": Hilgard, E. W., *DeBow's New Orleans Monthly Rev.* (1869), v. 37-38, pp. 754-769.

419. "Geological Structures": Bignell, L. G. E., *Oil and Gas Jour.* (1938), v. 37, no. 20, pp. 60, 62.

419a. "Geological Survey of Louisiana, A Preliminary Report on the": Harris, G. D. and Veatch, A. C., *Rept. for 1899,* Geol. Svy. of La. (1899), pp. 9-138.

420. *Geological Survey of Texas, First Annual Report of the:* Dumble, E. T. (1889), 410 pp.

421. "Geological Tour, Guided, Through North and Central Louisiana": Durham, C. O., Jr. and White, W. S., Jr., *Guidebook,* 1960 Spring Field Trip, Shreveport Geol. Soc., pp. 83-147.

422. "Geologically Speaking, Here's the Picture in South Louisiana": Seglund, James A., *Oil and Gas Jour.* (1956), v. 54, no. 59, pp. 217-222.

149. "Geologico de la Cuenca Salina del Istmo de Tehuantepec, Sintesis": Alvarez, Manuel, Jr., *Bol.,* Asoc. Mex. Geol. Petrol. (1950), v. 2, no. 7, pp. 445-452.

113a. "Geologico, Estudio, del Domo Salino de, Chinameca, Ver.": Marquez Pineda, Aremos, *Tesis Profesional* (1962).

423. "Geologico del Istmo de Tehuantepec, Bosquejo": Garcia, Tijeriana N., *Bol.,* Asoc. Mex. Geol. Petrol. (1950), v. 2, no. 7, pp. 435-444.

423a. "Geologie der Nordhannoverschen Salzhorste, Zur": Harbort, E., *Monatsber. d. Deutsch. Geol. Ges.,* 62 (1910), p. 326.

423b. *Geologie Pratique de la Louisiana:* Thomassy, R., Paris (1860).

424. "Geologia Petrolera de Mexico, Notas Sobre la": Benavides, G. Luis, Simposium, *Sobre Yacimientos de Petroleo y Gas,* Tomo III, Amer-

ica del Norte, 20, Congreso Geologico Internacional Mexico, 1956.

1. "Geology of Acadia and Jefferson Davis Parishes": Paine, William R., *Bull. 36,* La. Geol. Svy. (1962), Dept. of Conserv.

425. "Geology Applied to Petroleum": Illing, V. C., *Proc.,* Geologists Assoc. (1942), v. 53, pts. 3 and 4, pp. 156-187.

426. "Geology Applied to Petroleum: Part I, Petroleum in the Sedimentary Cycle" Illing, V. C., *Oil Weekly* (1946), v. 122, no. 7, pp. 34-35, 42; "Parts II and III, Types of Regional Structure": no. 13, pp. 30-33, v. 123, no. 1, pp. 27-29; "Part IV, Oil Recovery and Exploration": no. 2, pp. 39-42, 44; "Part V, Influence of Oil on Geology"; no. 3, pp. 174, 176.

427. *Geology of the Atlantic and Gulf Coastal Province of North America:* Murray, G. E., Harper & Brothers (1961), New York, 692 pp.

30. "Geology of Avery Island Salt Dome, Iberia Parish, Louisiana": Bates, F. W., Copeland R. R., Jr. and Dixon, K. P., *Bull.,* AAPG (1959), v. 43, no. 5, pp. 944-957.

33. "Geology of Avoyelles and Rapides Parishes, Louisiana": Fisk, H. N., *Bull. 18,* La. Geol. Svy. (1940), 240 pp.

88. "Geology of Caldwell and Winn Parishes, Louisiana": Huner, John, Jr., *Bull. 15,* La. Geol. Svy. (1939), 356 pp.

91. "Geology of Cameron and Vermilion Parishes, Reports on the": Howe, H. V., Russell, R. J., McGuirt, J. H., Craft, B. C. and Stephenson, M. B., *Bull. 6,* La. Geol. Svy. (1935), 242 pp. Includes: "Physiography of Coastal Southwest Louisiana": Howe, H. V., Russell, R. J. and McGuirt, J. H., pp. 1-68; "Salt Domes of Cameron and Vermilion Parishes": Howe, H. V. and McGuirt, J. H., pp. 73-166; "Salt Dome Prospects": McGuirt, J. H., pp. 167-179; "Mineral Development": Craft, B. C., pp. 181-186; "Some Microfossils of the Potamides Matsoni Zone of Louisiana": Stephenson, M. B., pp. 187-188; "A Partial List of Maps Dealing with Cameron and Vermilion Parishes": McGuirt, J. H., pp. 197-203.

133. "Geology of Continental Shelf Off Louisiana: Its Influence on Offshore Foundation Design": Fisk, Harold N. and McClelland, Bramlette, *Bull.,* GSA (1959), v. 70, pp. 1369-1394.

155. "Geology of the Danbury Salt Dome": Sollars, P. F. and Walters, J. E., *Trans.,* GCAGS (1952), v. 2, p. 7.

428. "Geology of the Delta, and the Mudlumps

of the Passes of the Mississippi, On the": Hilgard, E. W., *Am. Jour. Sci.* (1871), ser. 3, v. 1, pp. 238-246, 356-368, 425-434.

340a. "Geology of the Eagle Mills Formation": Scott, K. R., Hayes, W. E. and Fietz, R. P., *Trans.,* GCAGS (1961), v. 11, pp. 1-14.

429. "Geology of East Texas": Dumble, E. T., *Bull.* 1869, Tex. U. (1918), 388 pp.

9. "Geology and Economic Significance of Anahuac (Oil Field), Texas": Halbouty, Michel T. and Eby, J. B., *World Pet.* (1937), v. 8, no. 4, pp. 46-55.

38. "Geology and Economic Significance of Barbers Hill Dome (Texas)": Halbouty, Michel T., *World Pet.* (1939), v. 10, no. 1, pp. 40-55.

430. "Geology and Economic Significance of Hastings Field, Brazoria County, Texas": Halbouty, Michel T., *World Pet.* (Sept., 1937), pp. 36-51.

357. "Geology of Evangeline and St. Landry Parishes": Varvaro, Gasper G., *Bull. 31,* La. Geol. Svy. (1957), Dept. of Conserv., 295 pp.

379. "Geology of the Five Islands, Iberia and St. Mary Parishes, Louisiana": Atwater, Gordon, *Trans.,* GCAGS, 1st Ann. Mtg. (Nov., 1951), New Orleans, La.

384. "Geology and Formation of the Salt Deposits": Jones, F. O., *Sci. Am.* (1902), v. 87, p. 59.

430a. "Geology and Geophysics of the Gulf of Mexico": Lyons, P. L., *Trans., GCAGS* (1957), v. 7, pp. 1-10; (abs.) *Bull.,* AAPG (1965), v. 49, no. 3, p. 348.

431. "Geology and Geophysics, Interrelationship of": Brace, O. L., *Bull.,* AAPG (1937), v. 21, no. 2, pp. 197-211; Review of by E. E. Rosaire, *Geophysics* (1937), v. 2, no. 1, pp. 63-67.

23. "Geology and Geophysics, Regional, of the Ark-La-Tex Area": Bryan, C. L., *Geophysics* (1951), v. 16, no. 3, pp. 401-415.

432. "Geology and Geophysics Showing Cap Rock and Salt Overhang of High Island Dome, Galveston County, Texas": Halbouty, Michel T., *Bull.,* AAPG (1936), v. 20, no. 5, pp. 560-611; correction, p. 818; *Gulf Coast Oil Fields* AAPG (1936), pp. 909-960; (abs.) *World Pet.,* v. 7, no. 8, p. 404.

433. "Geology and Geophysics of Southeast Flank Jennings Dome, Acadia Parish, Louisiana, With Special Reference to Overhang": Halbouty, Michel T., *Bull.,* AAPG (1935), v. 19, no. 9, pp. 1308-1329; *Gulf Coast Oil Fields,* AAPG (1936), pp. 961-982.

340. "Geology and Ground Water Resources of

Duval County, Texas": Sayre, A. N., *Paper 776,* USGS (1937), Water Supply Dept., 116 pp.

434. "Geology of the Gulf Coast Salt Domes": Hanna, Marcus A., *Problems of Petroleum Geology,* AAPG (1934), pp. 629-678.

435. "Geology of the Gulf Coast Salt Domes": Rhodes, E. J., *BS Thesis,* MIT (1931), Dept. of Geol. and Geophysics.

436. "Geology of Gulf Coastal Area and Continental Shelf": Carsey, J. B., *Bull.,* AAPG (1950), v. 34, no. 3, pp. 361-385.

437. "Geology of Gulf Coastal Area and the Continental Shelf, Basic": Carsey, J. B., *Oil and Gas Jour.* (1948), v. 47 no. 8, pp. 246-251; 266-267; (abs.) no. 25, p. 129; *Bull.,* AAPG (1948), v. 32, no. 12, p. 2315.

438. "Geology of the Heidelberg Oil Field, Mississippi": McCullough, R. A., *Oil* (1944), v. 4, no. 8, pp. 8-9.

20. *Geology, Historical, of the Antillean-Caribbean Region or the Lands Bordering the Gulf of Mexico and the Caribbean Sea*: Schuchert, Charles, Wiley (1935), New York, 811 pp.; (abs.) *Bull.,* GSA (1929), v. 40, pp. 204-205, 337-359; *Science* new ser., v. 69, pp. 139-145; (summary) *Pan Am. Geologist,* v. 51, no. 2, pp. 157-159.

439. "Geology, Historical, and Stratigraphy of Gulf Coastal Plain in Vicinity of Harris County, Texas": Meyer, W. G., *Bull.,* AAPG (1939), v. 23, no. 2, pp. 145-211; *PhD Dissertation,* Cincinnati U. (1941), Dept. of Geol. and Geography; (abs.) *World Pet.,* v. 10, no. 6, p. 109.

440. "Geology of Iberia Parish, Louisiana": Howe, H. V. and Moresi, C. K., *Bull. 1,* La. Geol. Svy. (1931), 187 pp.

440a. "Geology of Katy Field, Waller, Harris and Fort Bend Counties, Texas": Allison, A. P., Beckelhymer, R. L., Benson, Don G., Hutchins, R. M., Jr., Lake, C. L., Lewis, Ray C., O'Bannon, P. H., Self, S. R. and Warner, C. A., *Bull.,* AAPG (1946), v. 30, no. 2, pp. 157-180.

441. "Geology of Lafayette and St. Martin Parishes, Louisiana": Howe, H. V. and Moresi, C. K., *Bull. 3,* La. Geol. Svy. (1933), 328 pp.

442. "Geology of Leon County, Texas": Stenzel, H. B., *Bull. 3818,* Tex. U. (1938), 295 pp.

443. "Geology of Lower Louisiana and the Rock Salt Deposit of Petite Anse": Hilgard, E. W., *Am. Jour. Sci.* (1869), ser. 2, v. 47, pp. 77-88.

444. "Geology of Lower Louisiana and Salt Deposit on Petite Anse Island": Hilgard, E. W., *Art. 3,*

Smithsonian Contr. Knowledge (1872), no. 248, 34 pp.

445. "Geology of Mexico, Northeast, Notes on": Humphrey, W. E., Corpus Christi Geol. Soc. (1956), 41 pp; *Guidebook,* Laredo to Monterrey Field Trip (Supp.), Corpus Christi Geol. Soc. (1956), pp. 9-11; *Guidebook,* Corpus Christi Geol. Soc., 11th Ann. Field Trip (1961), pp. 6-8.

446. "Geology of Mexico, Synopsis of the": Santillan, Manuel, *Oil Weekly* (1936), v. 81, no. 2, pp. 34-37, 40-41.

447. "Geology of Mississippi, General": McGlothlin, Tom, *Bull., * AAPG (1944), v. 28, no. 1, pp. 29-62.

447a. *Geology of Natural Gas*: Ley, Henry A. (ed.), American Association of Petroleum Geologists (1935), Tulsa, Oklahoma, 1227 pp.

448. "Geology, Oil and Gas, of the Gulf Coastal Plain in Arkansas": Spooner, W. C., *Bull. 2,* Ark. Geol. Svy. (1935), pp. 1-474.

449. *Geology, Petroleum:* Landes, Kenneth K., John Wiley & Sons (1951), New York, 660 pp.

132. "Geology and Petroleum Development of the Continental Shelf of the Gulf of Mexico": Atwater, Gordon, *Preprint,* Fifth World Pet. Cong.; *Trans.,* GCAGS (1959), v. 9, pp. 131-145.

450. "Geology, Petroleum, of the Gulf Coast (United States)": Halbouty, Michel T. and Hardin, George C., Jr., *Oil and Gas Jour.* (1947), v. 46, no. 4, pp. 136-141, 194-196.

33. "Geology of Rapides and Avoyelles Parishes, Louisiana": Fisk, Harold N., *Bull. 18,* La. Geol. Svy. (1940), 240 pp.

441. "Geology of St. Martin and Lafayette Parishes, Louisiana": Howe, H. V. and Moresi, C. K., *Bull. 3,* La. Geol. Svy. (1933), 328 pp.

451. *Geology of Salt Dome Oil Fields*: Moore, R. C. (ed.), American Association of Petroleum Geologists (1926), 797 pp.

452. "Geology and Stratigraphy of the Port Barre Salt Dome": Crain, H. F., *Thesis,* Kan. U. (1947), Dept. of Geol.

453. *Geology, Structural:* Second Edition, Billings, M. P., Prentice-Hall (1954), New York, 514 pp.

454. *Geology, Structural, of North America*: Eardley, A. J., Harper (1951), New York, 624 pp.

454a. "Geology of the Winnfield Sheet, Notes on the": Harris, G. D., *Rept. of 1907,* Geol. Svy. of La. (1907), *Bull. 5.*

455. "Geology, Subsurface, of Northeast Texas, Resume of, with Emphasis on Salt Structures":

Eaton, R. W., *Trans.,* GCAGS (1956), v. 6, pp. 79-84.

456. "Geology of the Sulphur and Sulphur Oil Deposits of the Coastal Plain": Lucas, A. F., *Indus. and Chem. Eng. Jour.* (1912), v. 4, pp. 140-143.

457. "Geology of Texas, Thirty-five Years of Progress in the Knowledge of the": Deussen, Alexander, *Bull. 3501,* Tex. U. (1935), pp. 37-57.

458. "Geology of Texas: Volume 1, Stratigraphy": Sellards, E. H., Adkins, W. S. and Plummer, F. B., *Bull. 3232,* Tex. U. (1933), Bur. Econ. Geol., 1007 pp.

459. "Geology of Texas, Volume 2, Structural and Economic Geology": Baker, C. L. and Sellards, E. H., *Bull. 3401,* Tex. U. (1934), Bur. Econ. Geol., 884 pp.

460. "Geology and Types of Hydrocarbon Accumulation of South Liberty Salt Dome, Liberty County, Texas": Halbouty, Michel T. and Hardin, George C., Jr., *Bull.,* AAPG (1951), v. 35, no. 9, pp. 1939-1977.

461. "Geology of Webster Parish": Martin, James L., Hough, Leo W., Raggio, David L. and Sandberg, Adolph E., *Bull. 29,* La. Geol. Svy. (1954), Dept. of Conserv., 252 pp.

88. "Geology of Winn and Caldwell Parishes, Louisiana": Huner, John, Jr., *Bull. 15,* La. Geol. Svy. (1939), 356 pp.

461b. *Geology, Structural, for Petroleum Geologists:* Russel, William L., McGraw-Hill Book Co., Inc. (1955), New York, N. Y.

462. "Geomorphology of Gulf Coast Salt Structures and its Economic Application": Ritz, C. H., *Bull.,* AAPG (1936), v. 20, no. 11, pp. 1413-1438.

463. "Geophysical Activity in Louisiana and Texas, Current"; Barton, D. C., *Trans.,* Amer. Geophys. Union, 17th Ann. Mtg. (1936), pt. 1, pp. 76-77; *Earthquake Notes,* no. 8, p. 76.

464. "Geophysical Aspects, Part IV of Sedimentary Volumes in Gulf Coastal Plain of the United States and Mexico": Nettleton, L. L., *Bull.,* GSA (1952), v. 63, pp. 1221-1228.

465. *Geophysical Case Histories:* Nettleton, L. L. (ed.), SEG (1948), v. 1, 671 pp.

466. "Geophysical Case History of the Hastings Oil Field, Brazoria and Galveston Countries,Texas": Weingartner, R. A., *Geophysical Case Histories,* SEG (1956), v. 2, pp. 156-165.

50. "Geophysical Discovery and Development of the Bayou Couba Dome": Melchior, L. F., *Geo-*

physics (1953), v. 18, no. 2, p. 371-382; *Geophysical Case Histories*, SEG (1936), v. 2, pp. 130-141.

89. "Geophysical Exploration of the Cameron Meadows Dome, Cameron Parish Louisiana, History of the": McGuckin, Glenn M., *Geophysics* (1945), v. 10, no. 1, pp. 1-16; *Geophysical Case Histories*, SEG (1948), v. 1, pp. 161-174; *Oil Weekly*, v. 118, no. 12, pp. 46-52; (abs.) *Dallas Digest* (1948), p. 98.

467. "Geophysical Exploration by Telluric Currents, with Special Reference to a Survey of the Haynesville Salt Dome, Wood County, Texas": Boissonas, Eric and Leonardon, E. G., *Geophyscis* (1948), v. 13, no. 3, pp. 387-403.

467a. "Geophysical and Geological Investigations in the Gulf of Mexico": Ewing, M, et al, *Geophysics* (1955), v. 20, pp. 1-18.

108. "Geophysical History, Chacahoula Dome, LaFourche and Terrebonne Parishes, Louisiana": Hollingsworth, W. E. and Weston, H. C., *Geophysical Case Histories*, SEG (1956), v. 2, pp. 113-129.

156. "Geophysical History of Darrow Dome, Ascension Parish, Louisiana": Eby, J. B. and Harkins, T. I., *Tech. Pub. 1495*, AIME (1942); *Trans.*, AIME, v. 151, pp. 253-260; *Geophysical Case Histories*, SEG (1948), v. 1, pp. 144-152.

468. "Geophysical History of Grand Isle, Block 18, Oil Field, Gulf of Mexico, Louisiana": Markley, Leo A., *Geophysical Case Histories*, SEG (1956), v. 2, pp. 103-112.

469. "Geophysical History of the Iowa Field, Calcasieu and Jefferson Davis Parishes, La.": Eby, J. B., *Geophysics* (1943), v. 8, no. 4, pp. 348-355; *Geophysical Case Histories*, SEG (1948), v. 1, pp 153-160.

470. "Geophysical History of South Houston Salt Dome and Oil Field, Harris County, Texas": Eby, J. B., *Bull.*, AAPG (1945), v. 29, no. 2, pp. 210-214; *Geophysical Case Histories*, SEG (1948), v. 1, pp. 43-47.

471. "Geophysical History of Typical Mississippi Piercement Salt Domes": Nettleton, L. L., *Geophysics* (1947), v. 12, no. 1, pp. 30-42; *Geophysical Case Histories*, SEG (1948), v. 1, pp. 239-250; (abs.) *Geophysics* (1947), v. 11, no. 3, p. 418; *Oil and Gas Jour.*, v. 44, no. 48, p. 98.

472. "Geophysical Investigations Carried Out in Salt Dome Areas of Texas and Louisiana": Schmidt, C., *Jour. Inst. Pet.* (1931), v. 17, pp. 381-383.

473. "Geophysical Prospecting in Gulf Coast District Had to Overcome Many Difficulties":

Jenny, W. P., *Oil and Gas Jour.* (1932), v. 31, no. 8, pp. 14, 16.

474. "Geophysical Prospecting for Petroleum on Gulf Coast": Barton, D. C., *Oil and Gas Jour.* (1930), v. 28, no. 50, pp. 70, 142-143.

475. "Geophysical Prospecting Since July 1930, Growth of Company Owned Operations in Gulf Coast": Rosaire, E. E. and Ransone, K., *Geophysics* (1936), v. 1, no. 3, pp. 306-312.

476. "Geophysical Technique, Application of, to Finding More Flank Production on Piercement Type Salt Domes": Weaver, Paul, *Oil and Gas Jour.* (1952), v. 51, no. 7, pp. 90-94.

477. "Geophysics, Applied, in the Petroleum Industry, Notes on the Early History of": DeGolyer, E., *Geophysics* (1935), v. 6, no. 1, pp. 1-10; *Early Geophysical Papers*, SEG (1957), pp. 245-255.

478. "Geophysics Big Factor on Gulf Coast": Williams, Neil, *Oil and Gas Jour.* (1928), v. 27, no. 25, pp. 35, 88, 91.

479. "Geophysics, Fifteen Years of: A Chapter in the Exploration of the United States and Canada, 1924-1939": Macelwane, James B., *Geophysics* (1940), v. 5, no. 3, pp. 250-258.

480. "Geophysics—Full Partner": Davis, Morgan J., *Geophysics* (1956), v. 22, no. 2, pp. 225-232.

354. "Geophysics and Geology of the Discovery and Development of Esperson Dome, Texas": Thompson, W. C. and Day, W. L., *Geophysical Case Histories*, SEG (1948), v. 1, pp. 48-65.

481. "Geophysics to Geology, The Relationship of": Kannenstine, F. M., *Geophysics* (1939), v. 4, no. 3, pp. 149-154.

482. "Geophysics to Salt Dome Structure, Relation of": Eby J. B. and Clark, R. P., *Bull.*, AAPG (1935), v. 19, no. 3, pp. 356-377; *Gulf Coast Oil Fields*, AAPG (1936), pp. 170-191.

483. "Geophysics to Salt Dome Structure, Relation of, (with discussion by J. B. Eby and R. B. Clark)": Barret, Wm. M., *Bull.*, AAPG (1935), v. 19, no. 7, pp. 1069-1073.

484. "Geophysics, Sixty-three Discoveries of Pools on Gulf Coast are Credited to the Use of": Williams, Neil, *Oil and Gas Jour.* (1933), v. 32, no. 20, pp. 10-11, 34.

485. "Germany, Northern, on the Mechanism of Salt Migration in": Trusheim, F., *Bull.*, AAPG (1960), v. 44, no. 9, pp. 1519-1540.

486. "Germany, Northern, Salt Domes of": Ramanes, James, *Jour. Inst. Pet.* (1931), v. 17, pp. 252-259.

486a. "Germany, Northwestern, Salt Stock Families in" (abs.): Sannemann, D., *Bull.*, AAPG (1965), v. 49, no. 3, p. 357.

487. "Germany, Salt Masses of, The Upthrust of the": Stille, H., *Bull.*, AAPG (1925), v. 9, no. 3, pp. 417-441; *Geology of Salt Dome Oil Fields*, AAPG (1926), pp. 152-146.

488. "Giants Came Home": *World Oil* (1951), v. 132, no. 2, pp. 41-42.

302. "Gillock, South Gillock and Dickinson Fields, Galveston County, Texas": Gahagan, Donald I., *Guidebook*, AAPG-SEPM-SEG Jt. Ann. Mtg. (March, 1953), Houston, Texas, pp. 110-113.

489. "Gold, Silver, and Other Elements in Salt Dome Cap Rocks": Hanna, Marcus A. and Wolf, A. G., *Bull.*, AAPG (1941), v. 25, no. 4, pp. 750-752.

490. "Golden Meadow, LaFourche Parish, Louisiana": *Oil and Gas Jour.* (1940), v. 38, no. 39, pp. 29-31.

491. "Golden Meadows, Drilling Activity Assuming Boom Proportions in": Williams, Neil, *Oil and Gas Jour.* (1939), v. 38, no. 18, pp. 24-25, 34.

492. "Golden Oil Jubilee": *Oil and Gas Jour.* (1951), v. 50, no. 20, p. 173.

493. "Goose Creek Field, Texas, Some Questions on the Cause of the Subsidence of the Surface in the": Pratt, W. E., *Bull.*, AAPG (1927), v. 11, no. 8, pp. 887-889.

494. "Goose Creek Oil Field, Harris County, Texas": Minor, H. E., *Geology of Salt Dome Oil Fields*, AAPG (1926), pp. 546-557.

495. "Grabens in Gulf Coast Anticlines and Their Relation to Other Faulted Troughs": Meyer, W. G., *Bull.*, AAPG (1943), v. 28, no. 4, pp. 541-553.

496. "Grand Cote Island, A Piece of Difficult Shaft Sinking in Developing the Salt Mines of": Hazelhurst, J. N., *Eng. News* (Nov. 7, 1901).

497. "Grand Ecaille Sulphur Deposit, Development of the": Lundy, W. T., *Tech. Pub. 553*, AIME (1925), pp. 3-18.

468. "Grand Isle, Block 18, Oil Field, Gulf of Mexico, Louisiana, Geophysical History of": Markley, Leo A., *Geophysical Case Histories*, SEG (1956), v. 2, pp. 103-112.

80. "Grand Saline, Brooks and Steen Salt Domes, Van Zandt and Smith Counties, Texas": Powers, Sidney and Hopkins, O. B., *Bull. 736*, USGS (1922), pp. 179-239.

498. "Grand Saline and Palestine Salt Domes":

Muehlberger, Wm. R., Clabaugh, Patricia S. and Hightower, Maxwell L., *Field Excursion No. 6, Geology of the Gulf Coast and Central Texas and Guidebook of Excursions*, Houston Geol. Soc. (1962), Houston, Texas, pp. 266-277.

499. "Grand Saline Salt Dome, Van Zandt County, Texas, Gravity and Magnetic Investigations at the": Peters, J. W. and Dugan, A. F., *Geophysics* (1945), v. 10, no. 3 pp. 376-393; *Geophysical Case Histories*, SEG (1948), v. 1, pp. 105-120.

500. "Grand Saline Salt Dome, Van Zandt County, Texas, Internal Structure of the": Muehlberger, Wm. R., *RI 38*, Tex. U. (1959), Bur. Econ. Geol., 24 pp.

501. "Grand Saline Salt Dome, Van Zandt County, Texas, Structure of": Balk, Robert, *Bull.*, AAPG (1949), v. 33, no. 11, pp. 1791-1829.

502. "Grand Saline, Texas, Note on the Radio Transmission Demonstration at": Barret, Wm. M., *Geophysics* (1952), v. 17, no. 3, pp. 544-549.

503. "Grandison Complex, LaFourche and Jefferson Parishes, Louisiana": Oakes, R. L., *Trans.*, GCAGS (1959), v. 9, pp. 111-120.

402. "Gravimetric Data, Quantitative Calculations of Geologic Structure from": Barton, D. C., *Geophysical Case Histories*, SEG (1948), v. 1, pp. 251-280; *Tech. Pub. 1760*, AIME; *Pet. Tech.* (1944), v. 7, no. 6, pp. 22-49.

154. "Gravity Anomalies of Nash and Damon Mounds, Brazoria and Fort Bend Counties, Texas": Barton, D. C., *Tech. Pub. 1760*, AIME (1944); *Pet. Tech.*, (1944), v. 7, no. 6, pp. 2-9; *Geophysical Case Histories*, SEG (1948), v. 1, pp. 35-42.

504. "Gravity Anomalies, Possibility of Using, in the Search for Salt Dome Oil and Gas Pools": Shaw, E. W., *Science* (1917), new ser., v. 46, pp. 553-556.

505. "Gravity Detailing, Submarine, San Luis Pass Dome, Brazoria County, Texas": Nettleton, L. L., *Geophysics* (1957), v. 22, no. 2, pp. 348-358.

506. "Gravity Expression of the Hatchetigbee Anticline": McCollum, E. V., *Geophysics* (1943), v. 8, no. 1, pp. 46-50.

507. "Gravity Investigations in the Hockley Salt Dome, Harris County, Texas": Allen, W. E., Caillouet, H. J. and Stanley, L., *Geophysics* (1936), v. 20, no. 4, pp. 829-840.

508. "Gravity, Key Variables of": Romberg, Frederick E., *Geophysics* (1957), v. 23, no. 4, pp. 684-700.

509. "Gravity Method of Prospecting for Oil, A Brief History of the": Eckhardt, E. A., *Geophys-*

ics (1940), v. 5, no. 3, pp. 231-242; *Geophysical Case Histories,* SEG (1948), v. 1, pp. 21-32.

510. "Gravity Minimum at Tepetate on Very Deep Salt Dome, Acadia Parish, Louisiana": Barton, D. C., *Geophysical Case Histories,* SEG (1948), v. 1, pp. 175-183; *Tech. Pub.* 1760, AIME; *Pet. Tech.* (1944), v. 7, no. 6, pp. 15-22.

511. "Gravity Prospecting on Gulf Coast, Recent Developments in": Sundt, Olaf F., *Bull., AAPG* (1935), v. 19, no. 1, pp. 19-24; *Trans.,* SEG, v. 5, pp. 19-24; *Early Geophysical Papers,* SEG (1957), pp. 679-684.

512. "Gravity Survey Over a Gulf Coast Continental Shelf Mound": Nettleton, L. L., *Geophysics* (1957), v. 22, no. 3, pp. 630-642; (abs.) *Trans.,* GCAGS (1957), v. 7, p. 301.

495. "Gulf Coast Anticlines, Grabens in, and Their Relation to Other Faulted Troughs": Meyer, W. G., *Bull., AAPG* (1943), v. 28, no. 4, pp. 541-553.

513. "Gulf Coast Area, Changing Conception of Structural Features in the": Clark, R. P., *Oil and Gas Jour.* (1937), v. 35, no. 48, pp. 87-88; (abs.) *World Pet.,* v. 8, p. 106.

514. "Gulf Coast Areas, Improved Production by Chemical Treatment in": Aulick, Burton, Hopkins, H. F., Saye, Frank and Hower, Wayne, *Jour. of Pet. Tech.* (1952), v. 4, no. 9, pp. 13-16.

515. "Gulf Coast, Big Potential Reserve on": Williams, Neil, *Oil and Gas Jour.* (1930), v. 28, no. 49, pp. 42-43, 118.

512. "Gulf Coast Continental Shelf Mound, Gravity Survey Over a": Nettleton, L. L., *Geophysics* (1957), v. 22, no. 3, pp. 630-642; (abs.) *Trans.,* GCAGS (1957), v. 7, p. 301.

473. "Gulf Coast District, Geophysical Prospecting in, Had to Overcome Many Difficulties": Jenny, W. P., *Oil and Gas Jour.* (1932), v. 31, no. 8, pp. 14, 16.

515a. "Gulf Coast Domes, Structure of Salt in": Kupfer, Donald H., *Symposium on Salt,* Northern Ohio Geol. Soc., Inc. (1963), Cleveland, Ohio, pp. 104-123.

516. "Gulf Coast, Eastern, Habitat of Oil in": Braunstein, Jules, *Habitat of Oil,* AAPG (1958), pp. 511-522.

517. "Gulf Coast, Eastern, What's Wrong with the": Todd, John D., *Oil Weekly* (1946), v. 123, no. 3, pp. 89-91.

518. "Gulf Coast, A Geologist Looks at the": Pratt, Wallace E., *Oil and Gas Jour.* (1926), v. 25, no. 30, pp. 91-92.

319. "Gulf Coast Geology, Dome Theories Applied to": Harris, G. D., *Science* (1912), new ser., v. 36, pp. 173-174.

474. "Gulf Coast, Geophysical Prospecting for Petroleum on": Barton, D. C., *Oil and Gas Jour.* (1930), v. 28, no. 50, pp. 70, 142-143.

475. "Gulf Coast Geophysical Prospecting Since July 1930, Growth of Company Owned Operations in": Rosaire, E. E. and Ransone, K., *Geophysics* (1936), v. 1, no. 3, pp. 306-312.

478. "Gulf Coast, Geophysics Big Factor on": Williams, Neil, *Oil and Gas Jour.* (1928), v. 27, no. 25, pp. 35, 88, 91.

519. "Gulf Coast Geosyncline": Barton, D. C., Ritz, C. H. and Hickey, Maude, *Bull., AAPG* (1933), v. 17, no. 12, pp. 1446-1458; *Gulf Coast Oil Fields,* AAPG (1936), pp. 192-204; (abs.)*Pam Am. Geologist,* v. 59, p. 230.

520. "Gulf Coast, History of, 40 Years of Brilliant Achievement": Warner, C. A., *Oil and Gas Jour.* (1941), v. 39, no. 49, pp. 64-65, 129-130, 133, 135, 138, 140, 164, 166.

520a. *Gulf Coast Oil Fields*: Barton, D. C. and Sawtelle, George (ed.), American Association of Petroleum Geologists (1936), Tulsa, Oklahoma, 1070, pp.

409. "Gulf Coast Oil Fields, Geological Data, Development History": Critz, James S., *Oil Weekly* (1946), v. 123, no. 3, pp. 110-159.

410. "Gulf Coast Oil Fields, Geological Data, Development History": Smith, Cecil W., *World Oil* (1950), v. 130, no. 7, pp. 60-120.

521. "Gulf Coast Oil Fields, An Introduction to": *Houston Geol. Soc.* (1941), Houston, Texas, 22 unnumbered pages.

522. "Gulf Coast Oil Fields, Map of, Showing Domes and Hypothetical Fault Lines": Wilcox, R. C., *Oil Trade Jour.* (1921), v. 12, p. 17.

523. "Gulf Coast Oil Fields, Salt Domes, and Prospects": Logan, Jack, *Oil Weekly* (1934), v. 74 no. 5, pp. 67-138.

524. "Gulf Coast Oil Fields, Salt Domes and Prospects": Leyendecker, C., *Oil Weekly* (1938), v. 90, no. 7, pp. 143-228.

411. "Gulf Coast Oil Fields, Salt Domes and Prospects—Geological Data and Development History": Leyendecker, C., *Oil Weekly* (1936), pp. 85-164.

412. "Gulf Coast Oil Fields, Salt Domes and Prospects, Geological Data, and Developments": *Oil Weekly* (1942), v. 105, no. 2, pp. 59-130.

525. "Gulf Coast Oil, Fifty-six Years of": Kast-

rop, J. E., *World Oil* (1950), v. 130, no. 7, 58-59.

526. "Gulf Coast Oil Hunters, Are They Resting on Their Laurels?": Petersen, William A., *Oil and Gas Jour.* (1961), v. 59, no. 31, pp. 254-256.

527. "Gulf Coast, Oil Reserves of the": Deussen, Alexander, *Oil Weekly* (1933), v. 69, no. 1, pp. 16-18.

528. "Gulf Coast, Potentialities on the, Spurring Search for Reserves": Williams, Neil, *Oil and Gas Jour.* (1936), v. 34, no. 48, pp. 80-82, 87.

529. *Gulf Coast Producing Horizons, Petrographic and Physical Characteristics of Sands from Seven:* Halbouty, Michel T., Gulf Publishing Co. (1937), Houston, Texas, 106 pp.

408. "Gulf Coast Region, A Review of Geological Concepts and Economic Significance of Salt Domes in the": Halbouty, Michel T., *Bull.*, Houston Geol. Soc. (1959), v. 2, no. 2.

530. "Gulf Coast Region, Salt Domes of the": Hanna, Marcus A., *Oil* (1944), v. 4, no. 4, pp. 29-30.

531. "Gulf Coast Reserves, New Look at Salt Dome Geology May Increase": Sovinsky, V. N., *World Oil,* Part I (1958), v. 147, no. 5, pp. 180-181; Part II (1958), v. 147, no. 6, pp. 111-114.

532. "Gulf Coast, Result of Operations on": Judson, Sidney A., *Oil and Gas Jour.* (1927), v. 25, no. 40, pp. 97, 151-152, 155.

533. "Gulf Coast Saline Domes": Thacker, R. B., *Pet. Age* (1924), v. 13, no. 7, p. 20.

534. "Gulf Coast Salt Dome Area, Petroleum Industry of the": Bradley, Virginia, *Econ. Geol.* (1939), v. 15, no. 4, pp. 395-407.

535. "Gulf Coast Salt-Dome Formation, History of Concepts of": Nettleton, L. L., *Bull., AAPG* (1955), v. 39, no. 12, pp. 2373-2383.

536. "Gulf Coast, Salt Dome Interest Centers on": Eby, J. B., *World Oil* (1956), v. 143, no. 5, pp. 143-150; *Proc.,* International Geol. Cong., (1956).

537. "Gulf Coast Salt Domes": Hill, R. T., *Econ. Geol.* (1919), v. 14, no. 8, pp. 643-644.

538. "Gulf Coast Salt Domes": Wolf, A. G., *Magazine,* Colorado School of Mines (1920), v. 10, no. 9, pp. 171-177.

434. "Gulf Coast Salt Domes, Geology of the": Hanna, Marcus A., *Problems of Petroleum Geology,* AAPG (1934), pp. 629-678.

435. "Gulf Coast Salt Domes, Geology of the": Rhodes, E. J., *BS Thesis,* MIT (1931), Dept. of Geol. and Geophysics.

539. "Gulf Coast, Origin of Salt Domes of the": Rogers, G. S., *Jour.,* Washington Acad. Sci. (1919), v. 9, no. 10, pp. 291-292.

540. "Gulf Coast Salt Domes, Salt Volume of": Hammer, Sigmund, *Trans.,* AAPG-SEPM-SEG Jt. Ann. Mtg. (1953), Houston, Texas, p. 9 unpublished ms (Courtesy Sigmund Hammer and Gulf Research and Development Company).

541. "Gulf Coast, Salt Domes Still Reign in": Ingalls, Phillip C., *Oil and Gas Jour.* (1953), v. 52, no. 7, p. 357.

542. "Gulf Coast Salt Domes, Their Distribution, Description and Origin": Wojciechowski, W. A., *MS Thesis,* Mich. U. (1952), Dept. of Geol.

543. "Gulf Coast, Salt Domes of the, and Their Relation to Petroleum": Hare, J. E., *MS Thesis,* Yale U. (1922), Dept. of Geol.

544. "Gulf Coast Salt Domes, Where are Those?": *Oil and Gas Jour.* (1952), v. 51, no. 14, pp. 130-134.

545. "Gulf Coast Salt Plug in Late Oligocene, Evidence of Erosion of Salt Stock in": Hanna, Marcus A., *Bull.,* AAPG (1939), v. 23, no. 4, pp. 604-607; corrections, p. 1576; v. 27, no. 1, pp. 85-86.

462. "Gulf Coast Salt Structures, Geomorphology of, and Its Economic Application": Ritz, C. H., *Bull.,* AAPG (1936), v. 20, no. 11, pp. 1413-1438.

546. "Gulf Coast, Stratigraphic Traps on, Probably Undiscovered": Halbouty, Michel T., *World Pet.* (1938), v. 9, no. 6, pp. 27-39.

547. "Gulf Coast Structures, Shallow Stratigraphic Variations Over": Rosaire, E. E., *Geophysics* (1938), v. 3, no. 2, pp. 96-115; (discussion) pp. 115-121.

548. "Gulf Coast Tectonics": Bornhauser, Max, *Bull.,* AAPG (1958) v. 42, no. 2, pp. 339-370.

549. "Gulf Coast of Texas and Louisiana, Occurrence of Sulphur Waters in the, and Their Significance in Locating New Domes": Henninger, W. F., *Bull.,* AAPG (1925), v. 9, no. 1, pp. 35-37; *Geology of Salt Dome Oil Fields,* AAPG (1926), pp. 774-776.

414. "Gulf Coast of Texas and Louisiana—Past, Present and Future, Geological and Engineering Thinking in the": Halbouty, Michel T., *Jour. of Pet. Tech.* (May, 1957), pp. 19-20; *Texas Oil Jour.,* pp. 18-19, 26; *The Independent Petroleum Association of America Monthly,* pp. 30-32, 39.

550. "Gulf Coast Through 1936, The Amount and Distribution of Seismic and Gravity Exploration in the": Rosaire, E. E. and Ransone, K., *Geophysics* (1937), v. 2, no. 1, pp. 1-16.

450. "Gulf Coast (United States), Petroleum Geology of the": Halbouty, Michel T. and Hardin, George C., Jr., *Oil and Gas Jour.* (1947), v. 46, no. 4, pp. 136-141, 194-196.

437. "Gulf Coastal Area and the Continental Shelf, Basic Geology of": Carsey, J. B., *Oil and Gas Jour.* (1948), v. 47, no. 8, pp. 246-251, 266-267; (abs.) no. 25, p. 129; *Bull.,* AAPG (1948), v. 32, no. 12, p. 2315.

436. "Gulf Coastal Area and Continental Shelf, Geology of": Carsey, J. B., *Bull.,* AAPG (1950), v. 34, no. 3, pp. 361-385.

448. "Gulf Coastal Plain in Arkansas, Oil and Gas Geology of the": Spooner, W. C., *Bull.* 2, Ark. Geol. Svy. (1935), pp. 1-474.

551. "Gulf Coastal Plain, Genesis of Salt Domes of": Halbouty, Michel T. and Hardin, George C., Jr., *Bull.,* AAPG (1956), v. 40, no. 4, pp. 737-746.

552. "Gulf Coastal Plain, Oil Field Waters of the": Minor, H. E., *Problems of Petroleum Geology,* AAPG (1934), pp. 891-905.

553. "Gulf Coastal Plain of the United States, Origin of the Salt Domes of the": DeGolyer, E. L., *Jour. Inst. Pet.* (1931), v. 17, pp. 331-333.

554. "Gulf Coastal Province, Palynologic Age of Diapiric and Bedded Salt in the": Jux, Ulrich, *Bull.* 38, La. Geol. Svy. (1961), Dept. of Conserv., 46 pp.; Review of by Hans D. Pflug, *Bull.,* AAPG (1963), v. 47, no. 1, pp. 180-181.

555. "Gulf Lures Mexicans": Franco, Alvaro, *Oil and Gas Jour.* (1964), v. 62, no. 38, p. 102.

104. "Gulf, Mexican, and Caribbean Oil Zones": Seismograph Service Corporation, *Oil and Gas Jour.* (1944), v. 43, no. 34, pp. 182-199.

555a. "Gulf of Mexico Basin, Salt Structures of —A Review": Murray, G. E., *Bull.,* AAPG (1966), v. 50, no. 3, pp. 439-478.

556. "Gulf of Mexico Discovery, Spectacular": Barnes, Kenneth B. and McCaslin, Leigh S., Jr., *Oil and Gas Jour.* (1948), v. 46, no. 46, pp. 96-99, 113-114.

415. "Gulf of Mexico, On the Geological History of": Hilgard, E. W., *Am. Jour. Sci.* (1871), ser. 3, v. 2, pp. 391-404; *Proc.,* Am. Assoc. Adv. Sci., v. 20, pp. 222-336; *Supt. Ann. Rept.,* LSU (1872), pp. 207-222; *Am. Naturalist,* v. 5, pp. 514-518.

430a. "Gulf of Mexico, Geology and Geophysics of the": Lyons, P. L., *Trans.,* GCAGS (1957), v. 7, pp. 1-10; (abs.) *Bull.,* AAPG (1965), v. 49, no. 3, p. 348.

467a. "Gulf of Mexico, Geophysical and Geolog-

ical Investigations in the": Ewing, M., et al, *Geophysics* (1955), v. 20, pp. 1-18.

557. "Gulf of Mexico, Oil in the" (abs.): McGee, D. A., Seale, Tom and Finley, J. C., *Proc.,* Okla. Acad. Sci. (1950), v. 29, pp. 60-61.

558. "Gulf of Mexico, Possibility of Oil Structures Out in the": Kern, Charles E., *Oil and Gas Jour.* (1927), v. 25, no. 42, pp. 80, 225-226 .

559. "Gulf of Mexico, Sediments from": Levorsen, A. I., *Bull.,* AAPG (1939), v. 23, no. 7, p. 1123.

560. "Gulf Region, Eastern, Oil Search in": Kornfeld, J. A., *Mines Mag.* (1944), v. 34, no. 9, pp. 476-484.

561. "Gulf Region of North America, Including United States, Mexico, and Cuba, Jurassic Formations of": Imlay, R. W., *Bull.,* AAPG (1943), v. 27 no. 11, pp. 1407-1533.

562. "Gulf Salt Domes, Do all have vents?": Thacker, R. B., *Eng. and Mining Jour.* (1926); v. 121, no. 17, pp. 684-686.

563. "Gypsum-Anhydrite Cap Rock, Sulphur Salt Dome, Louisiana, Deformation, Metamorphism, and Mineralization in": Goldman, M. I., *Memoir* 50, GSA (1952), 169 pp.

564. "Gypsum-Anhydrite Salt Dome Cap Rock, Features of" (abs.): Goldman, M. I., *Bull.,* GSA (1929), v. 40, pp. 99-100.

565. "Gypsum in Gulf Coast Salt Domes, Occurrence of": Barton, D. C., *Econ. Geol.* (1922), v. 17, no. 2, pp. 141-143.

566. "Gypsum, Intrusive, Sierra del Fraile, State of Nuevo Leon, Mexico, Preliminary Report on": Murray, G. E. and Wall, J. R., *Guidebook,* 1959 Field Trip, South Texas Geol. Soc., pp. D1-D7; Spanish Trans. by P. E. Narvarte, pp. D8-D12.

567. "Gypsum Mining Near Hockley, Harris County, Texas": Stenzel, H. B., *Min. Res. Circ.* 35, Tex. U. (1946), 21 pp.

568. "Gypsum Resources and Mining on the Hockley Dome, Harris County, Texas": Stenzel, H. B., *Pub. 4301,* Tex. U. (1946), *Bur. Econ. Geol.,* pp. 207-226.

569. "Gypsum and Salt Deposits, Origin of Thick": Branson, E. B., *Bull.,* GSA (1915), v. 26, no. 6, pp. 231-242; (abs.) pp. 103-104.

570. "Hackberry Foraminiferal Zonation of Starks Field, Calcasieu Parish, Louisiana": Kornfeld, M. M., *Bull.,* AAPG (1939) v. 23, no. 12, pp. 1835-1836.

571. "Hackberry Salt Dome, Old": Texas Gulf Coast Oil Scouts Association and South Louisiana

Oil Scouts Association, *Bull. 1* (1930), pp. 121-123.

571a. "Halokinese, Einige Physikalische Uberle-gungen zum Problem der": Durschner, H., *Zeits Deutsch. Geol. Ges.* (1957), v. 109, pp. 152-158.

572. "Hankamer Field, Liberty County, Texas": Rosenthal, Stanley H., *Typical Oil and Gas Fields of Southeast Texas,* Houston Geol. Soc. (1962), pp. 74-75.

573. "Hardin Dome, Liberty County, Texas": Brace, O. L., *Bull.,* AAPG (1936), v. 20, no. 8, pp. 1122-1123.

439. "Harris County, Texas, Stratigraphy and Historical Geology of Gulf Coastal Plain in Vicinity of": Meyer, W. G., *Bull.,* AAPG (1939), v. 23, no. 2, pp. 145-211; *PhD Dissertation,* Cincinnati U. (1941), Dept. of Geol. and Geography; (abs.) *World Pet.,* v. 10, no. 6, p. 109.

574. "Harris County, Texas, Three New Salt Domes Reported All in": Williams, Neil, *Oil and Gas Jour.* (1928), v. 27, no. 14, p. 32.

575. "Harris and Waller Counties, Texas, Stratigraphy of": Beckelhymer, R. L., *Bull.,* AAPG (1946), v. 30, no. 1, pp. 52-62.

430. "Hastings Field, Brazoria County, Texas, Geology and Economic Significance of": Halbouty, Michel T., *World Pet.* (Sept., 1937), pp. 36-51.

466. "Hastings Oil Field, Brazoria and Galveston Counties, Texas, Geophysical Case History of the": Weingartner, R. A., *Geophysical Case Histories,* SEG (1956), v. 2, pp. 156-165.

506. "Hatchetigbee Anticline, Gravity Expression of the": McCollum, E. V., *Geophysics* (1943), v. 8, no. 1, pp. 46-50.

576. "Hauerite in a Salt Dome Cap Rock": Wolf, A. G., *Bull.,* AAPG (1926), v. 10, no. 5, pp. 531-532.

577. "Hawkins Field—Valuable Addition to Nation's Reserves": Halbouty, Michel T., *World Pet.* (Feb., 1941), pp. 24-26.

578. "Hawkins Field, Wood County, Texas": Wendlandt, E. A., Shelby, T. H., Jr. and Bell, J. S., *Bull.,* AAPG (1946), v. 30, no. 6, pp. 1830-1856.

467. "Haynesville Salt Dome, Wood County, Texas, Geophysical Exploration by Telluric Currents, with Special Reference to a Survey of the": Boissonas, Eric and Leonardon, E. G., *Geophysics* (1948), v. 13, no. 3, pp. 387-403.

59. "Heaving Shale Hazard in Big Hill, Texas, Field Overcome in Deep Test": Williams, Neil, *Oil and Gas Jour.* (1935), v. 33, no. 41, pp. 26, 61.

579. "Heaving Shale Problem in the Gulf Coast Region, Review of the": Wade, G., *RI 3618,* U. S. Bur. of Mines (1942), 64 pp.

580. "Heaving Shales, Characteristics, Methods of Combating and Economic Importance of": Halbouty, Michel T. and Kaldenbach, N. A., *Oil Weekly* (1938), v. 91, no. 7, pp. 17-26; no. 8, pp. 42-54.

581. "Heaving Shales, Mud Treatment for": Halbouty, Michel T., *World Pet.* (May 1936), pp. 268-273.

438. "Heidelberg Oil Field, Mississippi, Geology of the": McCullough, R. A., *Oil* (1944), v. 4, no. 8, pp. 8-9.

582. "Hester Dome, Fire After Blowout at, Wreaks Destruction": Williams, Neil, *Oil and Gas Jour.* (1939), v. 37, no. 43, p. 28.

366. "Heterostegina Lime, Fannett Field, Jefferson County, Texas, Distribution of" (abs.): Hough, W. H., *Oil and Gas Jour.* (1948), v. 47, no. 30, p. 93.

583. "Heterostegina Reef on Nash and Other Piercement Salt Domes in Northwestern Brazoria County, Texas": Cantrell, R. B., Montgomery, J. C. and Woodard, A. E., *Trans.,* GCAGS (1959), v. 9, pp. 59-62.

17. "Heterostegina Zone at Anse la Butte, Lafayette and St. Martin Parishes, Louisiana—A Study in Gulf Coast Tertiary Reefs": Forman, McLain J., *Trans.,* GCAGS (1955), v. 5, pp. 65-72.

584. "Hidrocarburos en el Cretacico en Relacion al Analisis Tectonico Comparativo de la Sierra Madre y la Cuenca de Veracruz, La Acumulacion de": Viniegra Osorio, Francisco and Olivas, Ramirez M., *Resumeres de los Trabajos Presentados,* II Convencion, Asoc. Mex. de Geol. Petrol., pp. 34-35.

585. "High Island Dome, Galveston County, Texas": Halbouty, Michel T., *Bull.,* AAPG (1932), v. 16, no. 7, pp. 701-702.

432. "High Island Dome, Galveston County, Texas, Geology and Geophysics Showing Cap Rock and Salt Overhang of": Halbouty, Michel T., *Bull.,* AAPG (1936), v. 20, no. 5, pp. 560-611; correction, p. 818; *Gulf Coast Oil Fields,* AAPG (1936), pp. 909-960; (abs.) *World Pet.,* v. 7, no. 8, p. 404.

586. "Hilgardite, Minerals Associated with, Notes on": Hurlbut, C. S., Jr. and Taylor, R. E., *Am. Mineralogist* (1938), v. 23, no. 12, pt. 1, pp. 898-902.

114. "Hilgardite, a New Mineral Species from Choctaw Salt Dome, Louisiana": Hurlbut, C. S., Jr.

and Taylor, R. E., *Am. Mineralogist* (1937), v. 22, no. 10, pp. 1052-1057.

568. "Hockley Dome, Harris County, Texas, Gypsum Resources and Mining on the": Stenzel, H. B., *Pub. 4301*, Tex. U. (1946), Bur. Econ. Geol., pp. 207-226.

587. "Hockley Field, Harris County, Texas": Canada, W. R., *Guidebook*, AAPG-SEPM-SEG Jt. Ann. Mtg. (1953), Houston, Texas, pp. 125-128; *Typical Oil and Gas Fields of Southeast Texas*, Houston Geol. Soc. (1962), pp. 76-79.

567. "Hockley, Harris County, Texas, Gypsum Mining Near": Stenzel, H. B., *Min. Res. Circ. 35*, Tex. U. (1946), 21 pp.

588. "Hockley Salt Dome": Chapman, L. C., *Bull.*, AAPG (1923), v. 7, no. 3, pp. 297-299.

589. "Hockley Salt Dome, Harris County, Texas": Deussen, Alexander and Lane, L. L., *Bull.* AAPG (1926), v. 9, no. 7, pp. 1031-1060; *Geology of Salt Dome Oil Fields*, AAPG (1926), pp. 570-599.

507. "Hockley Salt Dome, Harris County, Texas, Gravity Investigations in the": Allen, W. E., Caillouet, H. J. and Stanley, L., *Geophysics* (1936), v. 20, no. 4, pp. 829-840.

590. "Hockley Salt Shaft, Harris County, Texas": Teas, L. P., *Bull.*, AAPG (1931), v. 15, no. 4, pp. 465-469; *Gulf Coast Oil Fields*, AAPG (1936), pp. 136-140.

591. "Hoskins Mound Salt Dome, Brazoria County, Texas": Marx, A. H., *Bull.*, AAPG (1936), v. 20, no. 2, pp. 155-178; *Gulf Coast Oil Fields*, AAPG (1936), pp. 833-856.

592. "Hoskins Mound Salt Dome, Texas, Deep Correlation Reflections Near": Campbell, F. F., *Geophysics* (1941), v. 6, no. 3, pp. 259-263.

369. "Houston County, Texas, Faulting in Northwestern": Stenzel, H. B., *Min. Res. Circ. 23.* Tex. U. (1943), 9 pp.; *Pub. 4301*, Tex. U. (1946), pp. 19-27.

592a. "Huizachal Group (Mesozoic), State of Tamaulipas, Mexico, Age and Correlation of": Mixon, R. B., Murray, G. E. and Diaz, Teodoro, *Bull.*, AAPG (1959), v. 43, no. 4, pp. 757-771; (addendum), v. 43, p. 2499.

593. "Hull Dome, Intensive Play in Progress on": Williams, Neil, *Oil and Gas Jour.* (1933), v. 32, no. 25, pp. 21-22.

594. "Humble Field, Redrilling Workover Program in": Williams, Neil, *Oil and Gas Jour.* (1940), v. 39, no. 5, pp. 61, 64.

594a. *Huttonian Theory of the Earth, Illustrations of the:* Playfair, John, Edinburgh; 1802.

594b. "Hydrogen Sulphide in Persian Natural Gas, The Origin of, and a Method of Preparing Unsaturated Hydrocarbons": Cadman, W. H., *Jour. Inst. Pet.* (1925), v. 2, pp. 487-489.

440. "Iberia Parish, Geology of": Howe, H. V. and Moresi, C. K., *Bull. 1*, La. Geol. Svy. (1931), 187 pp.

595. "Iberian Structural Axis, Louisiana": Barton, D. C., *Jour. Geol.* (1932), v. 41, no. 3, pp. 225-242; (abs.) *Bull.*, GSA, v. 43, p. 248.

27. "Iberville and Ascension Parishes, Louisiana, Salt Domes of": Howe, H. V. and McGuirt, J. H., *Bull. 13*, La. Geol. Svy. (1938), pp. 87-187.

596. "If They Had No Fear, Why Should We?": Halbouty, Michel T., *Jour. of Pet. Tech.* (1962), v. 14, no. 8, pp. 821-824.

350a. "Injektivfaltung und damit Zusammenhangende Erscheinungen": Stille, H., *Geol. Rundschau,* 8 (1917), p. 89.

597. "Interior Salt Domes of East Texas" (abs.): Clark, G. C., *Bull.*, AAPG (1949), v. 33, no. 12, pp. 2067-2068; *Oil and Gas Jour.* (1949), v. 48, no. 25, p. 87.

598. "Interior Salt Domes of Louisiana": Spooner, W. C., *Bull.*, AAPG (1926), v. 10, no. 3, pp. 217-292; *Geology of Salt Dome Oil Fields,* AAPG (1926), pp. 269-344.

599. "Interior Salt Domes in Northeast Louisiana, Three New": Bornhauser, Max and Marshall, L. R., *Bull.*, AAPG (1940), v. 24, no. 3, pp. 483-486.

600. "Interior Salt Domes and Tertiary Stratigraphy of North Louisiana": Lambert, Ernest H., Jr., *Guidebook,* 1960 Spring Field Trip, Shreveport Geol. Soc., 147 pp.

601. "Interior Salt Domes of Texas": Powers, Sidney, *Bull.*, AAPG (1926), v. 10, no. 1, pp. 1-60; *Geology of Salt Dome Oil Fields*, AAPG (1926), pp. 209-268.

602. "Interior Salt Domes of Texas, Louisiana and Mississippi": Clark, G. C., *Guidebook,* 1960 Spring Field Trip, Shreveport Geol. Soc., pp. 3-16; (abs.) *Bull.*, AAPG (1959), v. 43, no. 7, pp. 1776-1777.

602a. "Intrusive Masses, Energy Source of" (abs.): Gussow, W. C., *Bull.*, AAPG (1965), v. 49, no. 3, p. 343.

602b. "Intrusive Shale Dome in South Thornwell Field, Jefferson Davis and Cameron Parishes,

Louisiana": Roach, C. B., *Bull.,* AAPG (1962), v. 46, no. 12, pp. 2121-2132.

90. "Iowa and Cameron Meadows, Two New Coastal Louisiana Fields": Teas, L. P., *Bull.,* AAPG (1932), v. 16, no. 3, pp. 255-256.

603. "Iowa Field Becomes Largest in Louisiaana": Williams, Neil, *Oil and Gas Jour.* (1933), v. 32, no. 26, pp. 13-14.

469. "Iowa Field, Calcasieu and Jefferson Davis Parishes, La., Geophysical History of the": Eby, J. B., *Geophysics* (1943), v. 8, no. 4, pp. 348-355; *Geophysical Case Histories,* SEG (1948), v. 1, pp. 153-160.

604. "Iowa Field, High Gravity Oil, Great Depth, Typical of New Era Along Coast": Logan, Jack, *Oil Weekly* (1933), v. 71, no. 13, pp. 12-13, 16.

605. "Iowa Field in South Louisiana, Finding of Deeper Pay Revives": Williams, Neil, *Oil and Gas Jour.* (1940), v. 39, no. 27, pp. 82, 85.

606. "Isostatic Adjustments on a Minor Scale, in Their Relation to Oil Domes": Albertson, M., *Trans.,* AIME (1931), v. 65, pp. 418-420; (abs.) *Mining and Metallurgy,* no. 170, pp. 38-39.

606a. "Isthmian Saline Basin": Tschopp, H. J., *Geol. Rept. V-305* (Nov. 1931), Inedito.

74a. "Istmo de Tehuantepec, Bosquejo Estratigrafico de la Cuenca Salina del": Castillo Tejero, Carlos, *Bol.,* Asoc. Mex. Geol. Petrol. (1955), v. 7, nos. 5-6, p. 173.

423. "Istmo de Tehuantepec, Bosquejo Geologico del": Garcia, Tijeriana N., *Bol.* Asoc. Mex. Geol. Petrol. (1950), v. 2, no. 7, pp. 435-444.

148. "Istmo de Tehuantepec, Cuenca Salina del, Condiciones Estatigraficos de las Formaciones Miocenicas de la": Calderon Garcia, Alejandro, *Bol.,* Asoc. Mex. Geol. Petrol. (1951), v. 3, nos. 3, 7-8, pp. 229-259.

33c. "Istmo de Tehuantepec, El Azufre en la Cuenca Salina del": Bustillos, S. Gonzalo, *Tesis Profesional* (1959).

33f. *Istmo de Tehuantepec en Relacion con los Yacimientos de Azufre, Sintesis de las Morfologia de las Masas de Sal del:* Gibson, B. Juan, Inedito, Archivo Consejo de Recursos Naturales Renovables (1957).

33d. "Istmo de Tehuantepec, Estudio Sobre los Yacimientos de Azufre en la Cuenca Salina del": Viveros Juarez, Manuel, *Tesis Profesional* (1958).

33b. *Istmo de Tehuantepec, Geologia Economica del Azufre en el:* Salas, Guillermo P., Trabajo inedito (1957), Mexico, D. F.

33a. "Istmo de Tehuantepec, Origen del Azufre en el Casquete de los Domos Salinos de la Cuenca Salina del": Hungsberg, Ulrich, *Bol. 51* (1960), Consejo de Recursos Naturales no Renovables, 96 pp.

33e. "Istmo, Ver., Depositos de Sal y Azufre en la Cuenca Salina del": Marquez Pineda, Aremos, Viveros Juarez, Manuel and Serna Vigueras, Reyes, *Bol. 64* (1964), Consejo de Recursos Naturales no Renovables, 76 pp.

607. "Isthmus of Tehuantepec, A Look at the": Gutierrez, Gil and Yzaguierre, Lauro A., *Oil and Gas Jour.* (1960), v. 58, no. 7, pp. 159-163.

607a. "Isthmus of Tehuantepec, Miocene Agueguexquite Formation in the" (abs.): Thalmann, H. E., *Region Proc.,* GSA (1935), p. 116.

608. "Isthmus of Tehuantepec, Salt Deposits of the": Castillon, B. M., *Symposium on Salt,* Northern Ohio Geol. Soc., Inc. (1963), Cleveland, Ohio, pp. 263-280.

609. "Isthmus of Tehuantepec, Salt Domes of the": Ver Wiebe, W. A., *Pan-Am. Geologist* (1926), v. 45, no. 5, pp. 349-358.

610. "Jackson Fault, Alabama, Possible Salt Deposits in the Vicinity of the": Barksdale, Jelks, *Circ. 10,* Ala. Geol. Svy. (1929), 22 pp.

611. "Jackson Group of Formations in Texas With Notes on Frio and Vicksburg": Ellisor, A. C., *Bull.,* AAPG (1933), v. 17, no. 11, pp. 1293-1350; *Gulf Coast Oil Fields,* AAPG (1936), pp. 470-527.

612. "Jackson Group and the Catahoula and Oakville Formations in a Part of the Texas Gulf Coastal Plain": Renick, B. C., *Bull* 3619, Tex. U. (1936), 104 pp.

1. "Jefferson Davis and Acadia Parishes, Geology of": Paine, Williams R., *Bull. 36,* La. Geol. Svy. (1962), Dept. of Conserv.

613. "Jefferson Island Salt Dome, Iberia and Vermilion Parishes, Louisiana, Salt Structure of": Balk, Robert, *Bull.,* AAPG (1953), v. 37, no. 11 pp. 2455-2474.

614. "Jefferson Island Salt Dome, Iberia Parish, Louisiana": O'Donnell, Lawrence, *Bull.,* AAPG (1935), v. 19, no. 11, pp. 1602-1644; *Gulf Coast Oil Fields,* AAPG (1936), pp. 983-1025.

615. "Jefferson Island Salt Dome, Iberia and Vermilion Parishes, Louisiana": Wharton, J. B., Jr., *Bull.,* AAPG (1953), v. 37, no. 2, pp. 433-443; (abs.) *Trans.,* GCAGS (Nov. 1952), p. 1.

503. "Jefferson and LaFourche Parishes, Louisiana, Grandison Complex": Oakes, R. L., *Trans.,* GCAGS (1959), v. 9, pp. 111-120.

390. "Jefferson and Orange Counties, Texas, Stratigraphy of the Frio Formation": Reedy, M. F., Jr., *Bull.*, AAPG (1949), v. 33, no. 11, pp. 1830-1858; (abs.) *Bull.*, AAPG (1949), v. 33, no. 1, pp. 108-109; *Oil and Gas Jour.*, v. 47, no. 32, p.104.

616. "Jefferson, Plaquemines and St. Charles Parishes, Louisiana, Regional Study of": Vidrine, Louis O., *Trans.*, GCAGS (1958), v. 8, pp. 105-115.

433. "Jennings Dome, Acadia Parish, Louisiana, Geology and Geophysics of Southeast Flank of, with Special Reference to Overhang": Halbouty, Michel T., *Bull.*, AAPG (1935), v. 19, no. 9, pp. 1308-1329; *Gulf Coast Oil Fields*, AAPG (1936), pp. 961-982.

617. "Jennings Field, Acadia Parish, Louisiana, Subsurface Study of": Roach, C. B., *Bull.*, AAPG (1943), v. 27, no. 8, pp. 1102-1122; (abs.) *Bull.*, AAPG (1941), v. 25, no. 5, p. 929; *Oil and Gas Jour.* (1941), v. 39, no. 47, p. 56.

618. "Jennings Oil Field, Acadia Parish, Louisiana": Barton, D. C. and Goodrich, R. H., *Bull.*, AAPG (1926), v. 10, no. 1, pp. 72-92; *Geology of Salt Dome Oil Fields*, AAPG (1926), pp. 398-418.

29. "Joseph Jefferson Salt Deposit and the Avery Island Salt Mine, Louisiana": Lucas, A. F., *Eng. and Mining Jour.*, (1896), v. 62, pp. 463-464.

116. "Jurassic Formations of the Ciudad Victoria Area, Tamaulipas, Mexico": Mixon, R. B., *MS Thesis*, LSU (1958), Dept. of Geol.

619. "Jurassic Formations in Eastern Mexico, Stratigraphic Relations of Certain": Imlay, R. W., Cepeda, E., Alvarez, M. and Diaz, T. *Bull.*, AAPG (1948), v. 32, no. 9, pp. 1750-1761.

561. "Jurassic Formations of Gulf Region of North America, Including United States, Mexico, and Cuba": Imlay, R. W., *Bull.*, AAPG (1943), v. 27, no. 11, pp. 1407-1533.

25. "Jurassic and Lower Cretaceous Formations of Southern Arkansas and Their Oil and Gas Possibilities": Imlay, R. W., *Inf. Circ. 12,* Ark. Geol. Svy. (1940), 64 pp.

620. "Jurassic, Upper, Formations of the Southern States" (abs.): Imlay, R. W., *Bull., GSA* (1942), v. 53, pp. 1803-1804.

621. "Kalisalze and Steinsalz, Review of, Geology by Franz Lotze, 1938": Reed, R. D., *Bull.,* AAPG (1939), v. 23, no. 2, pp. 254-256.

159. "Kalisalzlanger, Deutschlands": Lang, Otto, *Chemische Industrie* (1900), H. Gaertner, H. Heyfelder, Berlin, v. 23, pp. 153, 159, 169-174, 193-197.

11. "Kansas, Central, Anhydrite and Associated Minerals from Salt Mines of": Rogers, A. F., *Am.*

Jour. Sci. (1910), ser. 4, v. 29, pp. 258-261.

440a. "Katy Field, Waller, Harris and Fort Bend Counties, Texas, Geology of": Allison, A. P., Beckelhymer, R. L., Benson, Don G., Hutchins, R. M., Jr., Lake, C. L., Lewis, Ray C., O'Bannon, P. H., Self, S. R. and Warner, C. A., *Bull.*, AAPG (1946), v. 30, no. 2, pp. 157-180.

343. "Kelso Bayou or East Hackberry Dome": Texas Gulf Coast Oil Scouts Association and South Louisiana Oil Scouts Association, *Bull. 1* (1930), pp. 124-125.

441. "Lafayette and St. Martin Parishes, Louisiana, Geology of": Howe, H. V. and Moresi, C. K., *Bull. 3,* La. Geol. Svy. (1933), 328 pp.

622. "Lafitte, Coastal Louisiana, Regarded as World's Deepest Commercial Field": Williams, Neil, *Oil and Gas Jour.* (1936), v. 35, no. 7, pp. 71-72.

623. "Lafitte Field, Laying Oil Line From, Is More than Ordinary Undertaking": Williams, Neil, *Oil and Gas Jour.* (1936), v. 34, no. 37, p. 39.

624. "Lafitte—World's Deepest Major Field": Halbouty, Michel T., *World Pet.* (May, 1938), pp. 44-48.

503. "LaFourche and Jefferson Parishes, Louisiana, Grandison Complex": Oakes, R. L., *Trans.*, GCAGS (1959), v. 9, pp. 111-120.

625. "Lake Fausse Pointe Field, New Interest Focuses on": Rose, Walter, *Oil and Gas Jour.* (1952), v. 50, no. 47, pp. 80-81.

626. "Lake Pelto, Louisiana, Automatic Custody-Transfer System at": Tansil, John T. and Moore, Leslie M., Jr., *Jour. of Pet. Tech.* (1960), v. 12, no. 10, pp. 15-19.

627. "Leesville, Remarkable Development at, Is Making Field One of Most Active on Gulf Coast": Williams, Neil, *Oil and Gas Jour.* (1934), v. 32, no. 50, pp. 13, 36.

442. "Leon County, Texas, The Geology of": Stenzel, H. B., *Bull. 3818,* Tex. U. (1938), 295 pp.

627a. *Levantamiento Sismologico de Refraccion en el Area de Chinameca, Ver.*: Del Castillo, G. L. and Beutelspacher, S. R., Inedito, Archivo Consejo Recursos Naturales no Renovables (1961).

628. "Limestone Cap Rock of Salt Domes, A Theory for the Formation of": McLeod, Richard R., *Trans.*, GCAGS (1960), v. 10, pp. 151-153.

150. "Limestone on Damon Mound, Brazoria County, Texas, (Summary)": Hurlbut, E. M., Jr., *Min. Res. Circ. 31,* Tex. U. (1944), 3 pp.

153. "Limestone in the Heterostegina Zone (Oligocene-Miocene) on Damon Mound Salt Dome, Brazoria County, Texas": Ballard, Eva O., *Trans.*, GCAGS (1961), v. 11, pp. 213-223.

22. "Liquefied Petroleum Gas Storage in Arcadia Salt Dome": Skrivanos, N. C. and Norton, R. G., *Guidebook,* 1960 Spring Field Trip, Shreveport Geol. Soc., pp. 48-56.

629. "Long Lake Field, Anderson, Freestone and Leon Counties, Texas": Schmidt, K. A., *Pub. 5116,* Tex. U. (1951), pp. 201-206.

630. "Lost Lake Salt Dome, Texas": Wasson, Theron, *Bull.,* AAPG (1927), v. 11, no. 6, p. 633.

631. "Louann Salt and Its Relationship to Gulf Coast Salt Domes": Andrews, Donald I., *Trans.,* GCAGS (1960), v. 10, pp. 215-240.

631a. "Louisiana, Coastal Southwest, Pysiography of": Howe, H. V., Russell, R. J. and McGuirt, J. H., *Bull. 6,* La. Geol. Svy. (1935), pp. 1-68.

631b. "Louisiana, East, and the Bluff, Prairie, Hill Lands of S. W. Louisiana, Louisiana State Experimental Station, A Preliminary Report Upon the Florida Parishes of": Clendenin, W. W., *Geology and Agriculture* (1896), v. 3, pp. 236-240.

331a. *Louisiana, Estado de, E. U. A., Explotacion Minera de Sal en Domos en el:* Perez Larios, Jose, Archivo Consejo de Recursos Naturales no Renovables (1960).

8. "Louisiana, Frio and Anahuac Sediments in": Warren, A. D., *Trans.,* GCAGS (1957), v. 7, pp. 221-238.

418. "Louisiana, Geological Reconnaissance of, Preliminary Report of": Hilgard, E. W., *DeBow's New Orleans Monthly Rev.* (1869), v. 37-38, pp. 754-769.

423b. *Louisiana, Geologie Pratique de la:* Thomassy, R., Paris (1860).

632. "Louisiana Gulf Coast and Texas, Salt Domes of": Clapp, F. G., *Jour. Inst. Pet.* (1931), v. 17, pp. 281-299.

598. "Louisiana, Interior Salt Domes of": Spooner, W. C., *Bull.,* AAPG (1926), v. 10, no. 3, pp. 217-292; *Geology of Salt Dome Oil Fields,* AAPG (1926), pp. 269-344.

6a. "Louisiana, Mississippi, Alabama and Offshore Tidelands, Salt Domes in Texas: A Survey": Hawkins, Murphy E. and Jirik, C. J., *Inf. Circ.,* U. S. Dept. of the Interior, Bur. of Mines (in press, 1966).

24. "Louisiana, North, and Arkansas, South, Tabulation of Wells Which Have Encountered Salt or Cap Rock in": Lambert, Ernest H., Jr., *Guidebook,* 1960 Spring Field Trip, Shreveport Geol. Soc., pp. 61-69.

421. "Louisiana, North and Central, A Guided Geological Tour Through": Durham, C. O., Jr. and White, W. S., Jr., *Guidebook,* 1960 Spring Field Trip, Shreveport Geol. Soc., pp. 83-147.

600. "Louisiana, North, Interior Salt Domes and Tertiary Stratigraphy of": Lambert, Ernest H., Jr., *Guidebook,* 1960 Spring Field Trip, Shreveport Geol. Soc., 147 pp.

633. "Louisiana, North, in 1942, Interesting Wildcat Wells Drilled in": Blanpied, B. W. and Hazzard, R. T., *Bull.,* AAPG (1944), v. 28, no. 4, pp. 554-561.

24a. "Louisiana, North, Northeast Texas, and South Arkansas, Notes on the Stratigraphy of Formations Which Underlie the Smackover Limestone in": Hazzard, R. T., Spooner, W. C. and Blanpied, B. W., *Ref. Rept.* (1945), v. 2, Shreveport Geol. Soc. (1947), pp. 483-503.

633a. "Louisiana, North, The Salines of": Veatch, A. C., *Rept. of 1902,* Geol. Svy. of La. (1902), pp. 47-100.

634. "Louisiana, North, Salt Domes, Tabulation of": Blanpied, B. W., *Guidebook,* 1960 Spring Field Trip, Shreveport Geol. Soc., pp. 57-60.

635. "Louisiana, North, Surface Structure Evidence is Small": Easton, H. D., Jr., *Oil Weekly* (1935), v. 77, no. 2, pp. 35-38.

599. "Louisiana, Northeast, Three New Interior Salt Domes in": Bornhauser, Max and Marshall, L. R., *Bull.,* AAPG (1940), v. 24, no. 3, pp. 483-486.

636. "Louisiana, Northeastern, Late Paleozoic Age of Morehouse Formation of": Imlay, R. W. and Williams, J. S., *Bull.,* AAPG (1942), v. 26, no. 10, pp. 1672-1673.

637. "Louisiana, Offshore, One of the Largest Undrilled Reserves in the World": Limes, Leonard L. and Stipe, Jack C., *Oil and Gas Jour.* (1959), v. 57, no. 48, pp. 126-130.

638. Louisiana Oil Fields, Future": Howe, H. V., *Oil* (1944), v. 4, pp. 22-24.

638a. "Louisiana, Physiography of Coastal Southwest": McGuirt, J. H., Howe, H. V. and Russell, R. J., *Bull. 6,* La. Geol. Svy. (1935), pp. 1-68.

419a. "Louisiana, A Preliminary Report on the Geological Survey of": Harris, G. D. and Veatch, A. C., *Rept. for 1899,* Geol. Svy. of La. (1899), pp. 9-138.

638b. "Louisiana, Report of Topographical Survey of": Lockett, S. H., *Rept. of Supt. for 1870,* LSU (1871), pp. 16-26.

639. "Louisiana, Resume of Salt and Sulphur in": Murray, G. E., *Proc.,* Southeastern Mineral Symposium (1950), *Spec. Pub. 1,* Ky. Geol. Svy. (1953), pp. 48-68.

640. "Louisiana, Review of Tertiary Stratigraphy of": Howe, H. V., *Bull.,* AAPG (1933), v. 17, no. 6, pp. 613-655; *Gulf Coast Oil Fields,* AAPG (1936), pp. 383-424.

641. "Louisiana, Rock Salt in": Lucas, A. F., *Trans.,* AIME (1900), v. 29, pp. 462-474; (abs.) *Eng. and Mining Jour.,* v. 68, pp. 577-578.

642. "Louisiana, Salt in, With Special Reference to Its Geologic Occurrence": Harris, G. D., *Bull.,* La. Geol Svy. (1908), v. 7, pp. 5-59.

643. "Louisiana Salt Mines, Their Operation and Output": Wooten, P., *Min. World* (1912), v. 36, pp. 401-402.

643a. "Louisiana, Some Microfossils of the Potamides Matsoni Zone of": Stephenson, M. B., *Bull. 6,* La. Geol. Svy. (1935), pp. 187-188.

366a. "Louisiana, South, Fault and Salt Map of (1966 Edition)": Wallace, W. E., Jr. (ed.), *Trans.,* GCAGS (1966), v. 16.

422. "Louisiana, South, Geologically Speaking, Here's the Picture in": Seglund, James A., *Oil and Gas Jour.* (1956), v. 54, no. 59, pp. 217-222.

644. "Louisiana, South, Occurrence of Miocene Oil in": Limes, Leonard L. and Stipe, Jack C., *Trans.,* GCAGS (1959), v. 9, pp. 77-90.

645. *Louisiana, South, Salt Domes of, Vol. I* Stipe, Jack C. (ed), New Orleans Geol. Soc. (1960), 145 pp.; *Vol. II:* Spillers, James P. (ed.), New Orleans Geol. Soc. (1962), 107 pp.; *Vol. I (first revision):* Raymond, J. P., Jr. (ed.), New Orleans Geol. Soc. (1963), 133 pp.

646. "Louisiana, South, Salt Domes, Field Trip to": Taylor, R. E., *Guides to Southeastern Geology,* GSA and Assoc. Soc. (1955), pp. 538-548.

647. "Louisiana, Southern, 1940 Reference Report": *Lockwood's, C. D. Oil Report,* Houston, Texas (Oct., 1940), 343 pp.

648. "Louisiana, Southern, Inspissation of Post-Oligocene Sediments in": Crouch, Robert W., *Bull.,* GSA (1959), v. 70, pp. 1283-1292.

649. "Louisiana, Southern, Miocene Production in, How Deep is": *World Oil* (1956), v. 142, no. 7, pp. 216-218.

650. "Louisiana, Southern, Salt Domes, Nature of Growth of, and Its Effect on Petroleum Accumulation": Atwater, Gordon and Forman, McLain J., *Bull.,* AAPG (1959), v. 43, no. 11, pp. 2592-2622; (abs.) *Trans.,* GCAGS (1958), v. 8, pp. 20-21.

651. "Louisiana, Southern, Salt Domes, Present Activities Among" (abs.): Ames, E. R., *Pan Am. Geologist,* v. 53, no. 3, pp. 220-221.

652. "Louisiana, Southwest, Formation Waters in": Timm, B. C. and Maricelli, J. J., *Bull.,* AAPG (1953), v. 37, no. 2, pp. 394-409.

631a. "Louisiana, S. W., Louisiana State Experimental Station, A Preliminary Report Upon the Florida Parishes of East Louisiana and the Bluff, Prairie, Hill Lands of": Clendenin, W. W., *Geology and Agriculture* (1896), v. 3, pp. 236-240.

653. "Louisiana, Southwest and Texas, Southeast, Torsion Balance Surveys in": Barton, D. C., *Trans.,* Am. Geophys. Union, 13th Ann. Mtg. (1932), pp. 40-42.

653a. *"Louisiana State Geological Survey, First Annual Report of the; Annual Report of Board of Supervisors of the Louisiana State Seminary of Learning and Military Academy for the Year Ending Dec. 31, 1869,* New Orleans (1870), pp. 77-109.

463. "Louisiana and Texas, Current Geophysical Activity in": Barton, D. C., *Trans.,* Amer. Geophys. Union (1936), 17th Ann. Mtg., pt. 1, pp. 76-77; *Earthquake Notes,* no. 8, p. 76.

472. "Louisiana and Texas, Geophysical Investigations Carried Out in Salt Dome Areas of": Schmidt, C., *Jour. Inst. Pet.* (1931), v. 17, pp. 381-383.

602. "Louisiana, Texas and Mississippi, Interior Salt Domes of": Clark, G. C., *Guidebook,* 1960 Spring Field Trip, Shreveport Geol. Soc., pp. 3-16; (abs.) *Bull.,* AAPG (1959), v. 43, no. 7, pp. 1776-1777.

654. "Louisiana and Texas, Oil Producing Horizons of Gulf Coast in": Deussen, Alexander, *Bull.,* AAPG (1934), v. 18, no. 4, pp. 500-518; *Gulf Coast Oil Fields,* AAPG (1936), pp. 1-19.

655. "Louisiana and Texas Salt Dome Cap Rock Minerals": Hanna, Marcus A. and Wolf, A. G., *Bull.,* AAPG (1934), v. 18, no. 2, pp. 212-225; *Gulf Coast Oil Fields,* AAPG (1936), pp. 119-132.

656. "Louisiana and Texas, Salt Domes of": Deussen, Alexander, *Oil Weekly* (1922), v. 24, no. 4, pp. 11, 16, 18.

657. "Louisiana and Texas, Salt Domes of":

Harris, G. D., *Science* (1908), new ser., v. 27, pp. 347-348.

658. "Louisiana and Texas, Where the Srtuctures Are Off": *Oil and Gas Jour.* (1959), v. 57, no. 24, p. 107.

659. "Louisiana's Sulphur Mines": Moresi, C. K., *Review,* La. Conserv. (1934), v. 4, no. 1, pp. 44-48.

660. "Lower Claiborne of East Texas, With Special Reference to Mount Sylvan Dome and Salt Movements": Wendlandt, E. A. and Knebel, G. M., *Bull.,* AAPG (1929), v. 13, no. 10, pp. 1347-1375.

25. "Lower Cretaceous and Jurassic Formations of Southern Arkansas and Their Oil and Gas Possibilities": Imlay, R., *Inf. Circ. 12,* Ark Geol. Svy. (1940), 64 pp.

41. "L. P. G. and Barbers Hill, New Era for": *Oil and Gas Jour.* (1957), v. 55, no. 34, pp. 72-73.

660a. "L. P. G. Goes Underground for Summer": Reidel, John C., *Oil and Gas Jour.* (1952), v. 51, no. 12, p. 302.

661. "Macuspana, Region de, Tabasco, Yacimientos Petroliferos en la": Gutierrez, Gil R., *Bol.,* Asoc. Mex. Geol. Petrol. (1950), v. 2, no. 8, pp. 499-510.

403. "Magnetic Vector Study of Regional and Local Geologic Structure in Principal Oil States": Jenny, W. P., *Early Geophysical Papers,* SEG (1957), pp. 335-363; *Trans.,* SEG (1932), v. 3, pp. 7-33.

662. "Manvel Field, Brazoria County, Texas": Davis, R. A., *Guidebook,* AAPG-SEPM-SEG Jt. Ann. Mtg. (March, 1953), Houston, Texas, pp. 136-137.

663. "Manvel, Northern Brazoria County, Extensions at, May Lead to Larger Field Than First Expected": Williams, Neil, *Oil and Gas Jour.* (1935), v. 33, no. 41, pp. 77-79.

664. "Manvel, Operating Efficiency Increased at, by Standardizations": Williams, Neil, *Oil and Gas Jour.* (1940), v. 39, no. 9, pp. 57, 64.

665. "Many Salt Dome, Sabine Parish, Louisiana": Howe, H. V., *Bull.,* AAPG (1925), v. 9, no. 1, pp. 170-171.

522. "Map of Gulf Coast Oil Fields Showing Domes and Hypothetical Fault Lines": Wilcox, R. C., *Oil Trade Jour.* (1921), v. 12, p. 17.

666. "Map of Gulf Coast of Texas, Louisiana, Mississippi, Oil Fields, Gas Fields, Salt Domes, Journal Guide to": *Oil and Gas Jour.* (1947), v. 46, no. 4.

667. "Map of Louisiana, Oil and Gas": *Louisiana Geological Survey* (1959), Dept. of Conserv.

668. "Map of Texas, Mineral Locality, Showing Occurrence of Useful Minerals, Rocks and Other Geologic Substances": Sellards, E. H., *Proc. and Trans.,* Tex. Acad. Sci. (1944), v. 27, p. 138.

669. *Map of Texas, Structural,* Third Ed.: Sellards, E. H. and Hendricks, L. C., Bur. Econ. Geol. (1946), Tex. U.

90a. "Maps Dealing with Cameron and Vermilion Parishes, A Partial List of," McGuirt, J. H., *Bull. 6,* La. Geol. Svy. (1935), pp. 197-203.

669a. "Maps Predict Problem Formations": Harper, Douglas C. and Ruhe, Robert W., Jr., *Oil and Gas Jour.* (April 29, 1963).

670. "Maritime Drilling Operations, Sweet Lake Field in Coastal Louisiana is Good Example of": Williams, Neil, *Oil and Gas Jour.* (1934), v. 32, no. 48, pp. 15-16.

671. "McFaddin Beach Salt Dome, Jefferson County, Texas, Upper Cretaceous Chalk in Cap Rock on": Tatum, E. P., Jr., *Bull.,* AAPG (1939), v. 23, no. 3, pp. 339-342.

671a. "Mediterranean Basin, The": Gill, W. D., *Salt Basins Around Africa,* The Institute of Petroleum (1965), London, pp. 101-111.

672. "Megashearing, Crustal, Are Salt Domes Genetically Related to Zones of": Keith, B. A., *Oil Weekly* (1942), v. 108, no. 3, p. 24.

672a. "Mesozoica, Secuencia, Anticlinal de las Grutas de Garcia en la Sierra del Fraile, a 30 Kilometros al NW de la Ciudad de Monterrey": Humphrey, W. E. and Diaz Gonzalez, T. E., *Congreso Geologico Internacional* (1958), pp. 26-31.

672b. "Mesozoica, Secuencia, en la Arroyo de San Rogue, Cerro de la Silla, Nuevo Leon, Aproximadamente a 15 Kilometros al SE de la Ciudad de Monterrey, Nuevo Leon": Humphrey, W. E. and Diaz Gonzalez, T. E., *Congreso Geologico Internacional* (1958), pp. 18-23.

672c. "Mesozoica, Secuencia, Portal de la Muralla, Sierra de la Gavia, Coahuila": Humphrey, W. E. and Diaz Gonzalez, T. E., *Congreso Geologico Internacional* (1958), pp. 41-45.

104. "Mexican, Gulf and Carribbean Oil Zones": Seismograph Service Corporation, *Oil and Gas Jour.* (1944), v. 43, no. 34, pp. 182-199.

673. "Mexican Oil Fields": Garcia Rojas, Antonio, *Bull.,* AAPG (1949), v. 33, no. 8, pp. 1336-1350.

592a. "Mexico, Age and Correlation of Huizachal

Group (Mesozoic), State of Tamaulipas": Mixon, R. B., Murray, G. E. and Diaz, Teodoro, *Bull., AAPG* (1959), v. 43, no. 4, pp. 757-771; (addendum), v. 43, p. 2499.

673a. "Mexico, Eastern, Regional Tectonics and Oil Prospects of": Trumpy, D., *Geological Report No. 247* (1932), Archivo de Petroleos Mexicanos.

619. "Mexico, Eastern, Stratigraphic Relations of Certain Jurassic Formations in": Imlay, R. W., Cepeda, E., Alvarez, M. and Diaz, T.: *Bull., AAPG* (1948), v. 32, no. 9, pp. 1750-1761.

349. "Mexico, Engineering and Geological Data on": *World Oil* (1952), v. 135, no. 2, p. 122.

673b. *Mexico, entre Torreon y Monterrey, Tectonica de la Sierra Madre Oriental de:* Czerna, Zoltan de, 20th Congreso Geologico Internacional (1956).

671. "Mexico, Estructuras Salinas del Sureste de Mexico": Sansores, Enrique, *V Conv. An. de la AIPM,* en Abril de 1963 en Coatzacoalcos, pp. 7, 11.

400a. "Mexico, Geologia Petrolera de": Guzman, Eduardo J., Juarez, C. Rodolfo and Lopez Ramos, Ernesto, *Bol., Asoc. Mex. Geol. Petrol.* (1955), v. 7, pp. 137-171.

445. "Mexico, Northeast, Notes on Geology of": Humphrey, W. E., Corpus Christi Geol. Soc. (1956), 41 pp; *Guidebook,* Laredo to Monterrey Field Trip (Supp.), Corpus Christi Geol. Soc. (1956), pp. 9-11; *Guidebook,* Corpus Christi Geol. Soc., 11th Ann. Field Trip (1961), pp. 6-8.

675. "Mexico, Northeast, Tectonic Framework of": Humphrey, W. E., *Trans.,* GCAGS (1956), v. 6, pp. 25-35.

424. "Mexico, Notas Sobre la, Geologia Petrolera de": Benavides, G. Luis, Simposium, *Sobre Yacimientos de Petroleo y Gas,* Tomo III, America del Norte, 20 Congreso Geologico Internacional Mexico, 1956.

676. "Mexico an Oil Exporter, Pauley's Offshore Field May Make": *Pet. Week* (Sept. 2, 1960), p. 33.

677. "Mexico, Pozo Rica Field, Backbone of Oil Industry in": Sheldon, Ruth, *Oil and Gas Jour.* (1939), v. 38, no. 2, pp. 26-29, 104.

677a. "Mexico, Southeast, Notes on the Stratigraphy of": Nuttall, W. L. F., *Geol. Rept.* 192, (March, 1929), (inedito).

678. "Mexico, Southern, Still Offers Good Prospects to Pemex Wildcatters": Toledo, Alfonso Cornejo, *Petroleo Interamericano* (1964), v. 22, no. 2, pp. 46-48.

446. "Mexico, Synopsis of the Geology of": Santillan, Manuel, *Oil Weekly* (1936), v. 81, no. 2, pp. 34-37, 40-41.

679. "Mexico, Tectonics of": Alvarez, Manuel, Jr., *Bull.,* AAPG (1949), v. 33, no. 8, pp. 1319-1335; *Bol.,* Soc. Geol. Mex. (1949), Tomo 14.

680. "Mexico, Tehuantepec Oil Domes May Mark Potential Oil Territory for": Gutierrez, Gil and Yzaguirre, Lauro A., *Oil and Gas Jour.* (1960), v. 58, no. 8, pp. 150-161.

681. "Mexico's No. 2 Field, Santa Ana": Lawrence, Carl, *Oil and Gas Jour.* (1961), v. 59, no. 35, pp. 80-82.

682. "Micromagnetic and Reflection Data, Structural Correlation of": Jenny, W. P., *Oil Weekly* (1946), v. 124, no. 3, pp. 32-33.

683. "Midway Limestone of Northeast Texas": Thompson, W. C., *Bull.,* AAPG (1922), v. 6, no. 4, pp. 323-332.

684. "Midway or Scanlon Dome, Lamar County, Mississippi": Munroe, D. J., *Bull.,* AAPG (1938), v. 22, no. 7, pp. 816-822; (abs.) *Oil and Gas Jour.,* v. 36, no. 44, pp. 58, 62; *World Pet.,* v. 9, no. 10, p. 70.

685. "Migration and Accumulation of Oil and Gas, Present Interpretations of the Structural Theory for": McCoy, Alex, W. and Keyte, W. Ross, *Problems of Petroleum Geology,* AAPG (1934), p. 276.

686. "Migration of Oil, Lateral and Vertical, A Study of the Evidences for": Lahee, Frederick H., *Problems of Petroleum Geology,* AAPG (1934), pp. 399-427.

687. "Migration of Oil and Origin of Oil Pools": Plummer, F. B., *Oil and Gas Jour.* (1944), v. 43, no. 24, pp. 139-140.

688. "Minden Dome (Paleontologic Interpretations), Correlation Problem": Anderson, E. G. *Guidebook,* 1960 Spring Field Trip, Shreveport Geol. Soc., pp. 27-28.

689. "Minden Salt Dome": Richardson, P. H., *Guidebook,* 1960 Spring Field Trip, Shreveport Geol. Soc., pp. 17-26.

689a. "Mine Cavities, Storage of Radioactive Waste in" (abs.): Struxness, E. G., *Symposium on Salt,* Northern Ohio Geol. Soc., Inc. (1963), p. 412.

347a. *Mineral Deposits, Economic:* Bateman, Alan M., 2nd Edition, Wiley and Sons (1950), New York, N. Y.

162a. "Mineral Development,": Craft, B. C., *Bull.* 6, La. Geol. Svy. (1935), pp. 181-186.

668. "Mineral Locality Map of Texas Showing Occurrence of Useful Minerals, Rocks and Other Geologic Substances": Sellards, E. H., *Proc. and Trans.,* Tex. Acad. Sci. (1944), v. 27, p. 138.

10. "Mineral Resources of Anderson County, Texas, Report on the": Whitcombe, Bruce, *Min. Res. Circ. 22,* Tex. U. (1939), 5 pp.

689b. "Mineral Resources of the Texas Coastal Plain": Perkins, J. M. and Lonsdale, J. T., *Bur. Econ. Geol.* (1955), Tex. U., Min. Res. Circ. 38, 49 pp.

690. "Mineralogy of the Salt and Cap Rock of Gulf Coast Salt Domes" (abs.): Taylor, R. E., *Trans.,* GCAGS (1953), v. 3, pp. 147-148.

607a. "Miocene Agueguexquite Formation in the Isthmus of Tehuantepec" (abs.): Thalmann, H. E., *Region Proc.,* GSA (1935), p. 116.

691. "Miocene Gas Strike Spurs Rio Grande Embayment Work": Kornfeld, J. A., *Oil and Gas Jour.* (1953), v. 52, no. 7, pp. 358, 360.

644. "Miocene Oil in South Louisiana, Occurrence of": Limes, Leonard L. and Stipe, J. C., *Trans.,* GCAGS (1959), v. 9, pp. 77-90.

649. "Miocene Production in Southern Louisiana, How Deep Is": *World Oil* (1956), v. 142, no. 7, pp. 216-218.

6a. "Mississippi, Alabama and Offshore Tidelands, Salt Domes in Texas, Louisiana: A Survey": Hawkins, Murphy E. and Jirik, C. J., *Inf. Circ.,* U. S. Dept. of the Interior, Bur. of Mines (in press, 1966).

692. "Mississippi Becomes a Major Oil Center": Ives, G. O., *Oil Weekly* (1945), v. 118, no. 4, pp. 33-42.

447. "Mississippi, General Geology of": McGlothlin, Tom, *Bull.,* AAPG (1944) v. 28, no. 1, pp. 29-62.

693. "Mississippi Offers Domal Prospects": Gardner, Frank J., *Oil and Gas Jour.* (1962), v. 60, no. 29, p. 131.

694. "Mississippi Oil Field and Salt Dome Names": Mississippi Geological Society, *Bull.,* AAPG (1944), v. 28, no. 7, pp. 1046-1049.

695. "Mississippi (Oil Fields), Where Persistence Pays": Todd, John D., *Oil Weekly* (1945), v. 118, no. 7, pp. 49-52.

696. "Mississippi Oil Resources": Morse, W. C., *Quarterly Bull.,* Interstate Oil Compact (1944), v. 3, no. 4, pp. 11-16; *Mississippi Oil Rev.,* pp. 3-7; *World Pet.,* v. 16, no. 2, pp. 53-54.

471. "Mississippi Piercement Salt Domes, Geo-physical History of Typical": Nettleton, L. L., *Geophysics* (1947), v. 12, no. 1, pp. 30-42; *Geophysical Case Histories,* SEG (1948), v. 1, pp. 239-250; (abs.) *Geophysics* (1947), v. 11, no. 3, p. 418; *Oil and Gas Jour.,* v. 44, no. 48, p. 98.

697. "Mississippi Salt Basin, Faulting Associated With Deep Seated Salt Domes in the Northeast Portion of the": Hughes, Dudley J., *Trans.,* GCAGS (1960), v. 10, pp. 154-173.

698. "Mississippi, Southern, Search for Oil Encouraging in": Williams, Neil, *Oil and Gas Jour.* (1938), v. 37, no. 5, pp. 20-22, 36.

699. "Mississippi, Southern, Seismograph Evidence on the Depth of the Salt in": Swartz, Charles A., *Geophysics* (1943), v. 8, no. 1, pp. 1-2.

700. "Mississippi Structures and Their Relation to Oil Accumulation": Thomas, E. P., *Bull.,* AAPG (1950), v. 34, no. 7, pp. 1502-1516.

701. "Mississippi Submarine Trench, A Comparison of the, with the Iberian Trough": Skinner, Hubert C., *Trans.,* GCAGS (1960), v. 10, pp. 1-6.

702. "Mississippi Submarine Trough, Salt Domes Related to": Shepard, F. P., *Bull.,* GSA (1937), v. 48, pp. 1349-1361; (abs.) *Proc.* (1936), pp. 101-102; *Geophysics,* v. 2, no. 2, p. 169.

602. "Mississippi, Texas and Louisiana, Interior Salt Domes of": Clark, G. C., *Guidebook,* 1960 Spring Field Trip, Shreveport Geol. Soc., pp. 3-16; (abs.) *Bull.,* AAPG (1959), v. 43, no. 7, pp. 1776-1777.

703. "Model, Fluid Salt Dome, Some Quantitative Experiments on, and Their Geological Implications": Dobrin, M. B., *Trans.,* Am. Geophys. Union, 22nd Ann. Mtg. (1941), pt. 2, pp. 528-542.

704. Model Structures of Salt Dome Tectonics": Parker, T. J., *PhD Dissertation,* Tex. U. (1952), Dept. of Geol.

705. "Model Studies of Salt Dome Tectonics": McDowell, A. N. and Parker, T. J., *Bull.,* AAPG (1955), v. 39, no. 12, pp. 2384-2470; Review by W. T. Born, *Geophysicis* (1955), v. 21, no. 4, p. 1121.

706. "Models, Geologic, from Powdered Material": Nettleton, L. L. and Elkins, T. A., *Trans.,* Am. Geophys. Union (1947), v. 28, no. 3, pp. 451-466.

707. "Models, Miniature, Aid Mapping of Salt Dome Areas": *Oil and Gas Jour.* (1946), v. 45, no. 27, p. 85.

708. "Models, Scale, as Guide to Interpretation of Salt Dome Faulting": Parker, T. J. and McDowell, A. N., *Bull.,* AAPG (1951), v. 35, no. 9, pp. 2076-2086.

709. "Moloacan, Campo de, Analisis Paleomicroontologicio de las Formaciones Encontradas en los Pozos del, y Correlaciones Enstratigraficas Entre Dichos Pozos": Sansores, J. C., *Tesis Prof.,* Universidad Nacional Autonoma de Mexico, 1950.

710. "Moloacan-Ixhuatlan, Alto Salino de, Posibilidades del": Contreras, Hugo, *Bol.,* Asoc. Mex. Geol. Petrol. (1950), v. 2, no. 7, pp. 473-485.

78a. "Mont Belvieu, Texas, Diamond Alkali Brine Field at": Moore, M. L., *Symposium on Salt,* Northern Ohio Geol. Soc., Inc. (1963), Cleveland, Ohio, pp. 539-545.

710a. "Mont Belvieu, Texas Terminal, Design Development of Underground Storage Caverns at Texas Eastern's": Cozad, D. J., *Symposium on Salt,* Northern Ohio Geol. Soc., Inc. (1963), Cleveland, Ohio, pp. 634-661.

636. "Morehouse Formation of Northeastern Louisiana, Late Paleozoic Age of": Imlay, R. W. and Williams, J. S., *Bull.,* AAPG (1942), v. 26, no. 10, pp. 1672-1673.

332. "Morfologia y Origen de los Domos Salinos del Istmo de Tehuantepec": Contreras, Hugo and Castillon, B. M., *Bol.,* Asoc. Mex. Geol. Petrol. (1960), v. 12, nos. 7 and 8, pp. 221-242.

65. "(Moss Bluff and Boggy Creek Domes), Two New Salt Domes in Texas": Pratt, W. E., *Bull.,* AAPG (1926), v. 10, no. 11, pp. 1171-1172.

711. "Moss Bluff Dome, Texas, Seismograph Evidence on Depth of Salt Column": Hoylman, H. Wayne, *Geophysics* (1946), v. 11, no. 2, pp. 128-134.

712. "Moss Bluff Revived": Kornfeld, Joseph A., *Oil and Gas Jour.* (1950), v. 49, no. 30, pp. 45-46.

713. "Moss Bluff Salt Dome Discovery" (Discussion): Barton, D. C., *Bull.,* AAPG (1927), v. 11, no. 3, p. 308.

714. "Mounds of the Southern Oil Fields": Hager, Lee, *Eng. and Mining Jour.* (1904), v. 78, pp. 137-139, 180-183.

715. "Mount Sylvan Dome, Smith County, Texas": Wendlandt, E. A. and Knebel, G. M., *Gulf Coast Oil Fields,* AAPG (1936), pp. 1041-1049.

42a. "Mud-Laden Fluid, Use of Barytes as a": Stroud, B. K., *Oil World* (June 5, 1925), p. 29.

154. "Nash and Damon Mounds, Brazoria and Fort Bend Counties, Texas, Gravity Anomalies of": Barton, D. C., *Tech. Pub.* 1760, AIME (1944); *Jour. of Pet. Tech.* (1944), v. 7, no. 6, pp. 2-9; *Geophysical Case Histories,* SEG (1948), v. 1, pp. 35-42.

583. "Nash and Other Piercement Salt Domes in Northwestern Brazoria County, Texas, Heterostegina Reef on": Cantrell, R. B., Montgomery, J. C. and Woodard, A. E., *Trans.,* GCAGS (1959), v. 9, pp. 59-62.

716. "Nash Salt Dome, Fort Bend and Brazoria Counties, Texas": Halbouty, Michel T. and Hardin, George C., Jr., *Typical Oil and Gas Fields of Southeast Texas,* Houston Geol. Soc. (1962), pp. 134-137.

429a. *Natural Gas, Geology of:* Ley, H. A. (ed.), American Association of Petroleum Geologists (1935), Tulsa, Oklahoma, 1227 pp.

717. "Natural Gas of Gulf Coast Salt Dome Area": Teas, L. P., *Geology of Natural Gas,* AAPG (1935), pp. 683-740.

717a. "Natural Gas and Petroleum, The Volcanic Origin of": Coste, Eugene, *Canadian Min. Inst. Jour.* (1903), v. 6, pp. 73-123.

718. "New Iberia, Flank Production of, Climaxes 20 Years of Effort" Singleton, F. L., *Oil and Gas Jour.* (1936), v. 35, no. 33, p. 316.

158a. "New Mexico, Southeastern Delaware Basin and West Texas, Upper Permian Ochoa Series of": Adams, J. E., *Bull.,* AAPG (1944), v. 28, no. 11, pp. 1598-1625.

719. "New Tools, New Completion Methods Salvage an Old Oil Field": Bleakley, W. B., *Oil and Gas Jour.* (1962), v. 60, no. 24, pp. 140-141.

720. "Newman Salt Dome, Warren County, Mississippi": Neely, Joseph, *Bull.,* AAPG (1941), v. 25, no. 3, p. 424.

720a. "Nolan Edward Field, Wood County, Texas": Moore, Hastings, *Pub.* 5116, Tex. U. (1951), pp. 266-268.

720b. "Norddeutschlands, Uber Halokinese und ihre Bedeutung fur die Strukturelle Entwicklung": Trusheim, F., *Zeits. Deutsch. Geol. Ges.* (1957), vol. 98, pp. 7-29.

427. *North America, Geology of the Atlantic and Gulf Coastal Province of:* Murray, G. E., Harper & Bros. (1961), New York, 692 pp.

721. "North America, Notes on the Salt Domes of" (abs.): DeGolyer, E. L., *Bull.,* GSA (1923), v. 34, p. 66.

722. *North America, Oil Fields in:* Ver Wiebe, W. A., Edwards Brothers, Inc. (1949), Ann Arbor, Mich., 251 pp.

454. *North America, Structural Geology of:* Eardley, A. J., Harper (1951), New York, 624 pp.

723. "North American Salt Domes, Origin of":

DeGolyer, E. L., *Bull.*, AAPG (1925), v. 9, no. 5, pp. 831-874; *Geology of Salt Dome Oil Fields*, AAPG (1926), pp. 1-44.

724. "Objective, A Neglected": Bernatchez, Gerry, *World Oil* (1957), v. 144, no. 7, pp. 179-181.

724a. "Offshore Directional Drilling Practices Today and Tomorrow": Cook, W. H., *Preprint*, presented Chicago Chapter of AIME (Nov., 1957), Chicago, Illinois; Presented Ann. Meeting AIME (Feb., 1957), New Orleans, La.

45. "Offshore Production Practices at Bay Marchand, Practical": Kastrop, J. E., *World Oil* (1951), v. 132, no. 7, pp. 167-172, 174.

6a. "Offshore Tidelands, Salt Domes in Texas, Louisiana, Mississippi, Alabama and: A Survey": Hawkins, Murphy E. and Jirik, C. J., *Inf. Circ.*, U. S. Dept. of the Interior, Bur. of Mines (in press, 1966).

725. "Oil Accumulation Around Some Texas Gulf Piercement-Type Salt Domes, Factors Affecting Quantity of": Halbouty, Michel T. and Hardin, George C., Jr., *Bull.*, AAPG (1955), v. 39, no. 5, pp. 697-711.

726. "Oil Concentration about Salt Domes": Harris, G. D., *Science* (1912), new ser., v. 35, pp. 546-547.

606. "Oil Domes, Isostatic Adjustments on a Minor Scale in Their Relation to": Albertson, M., *Trans.*, AIME (1931), v. 65, pp. 418-420; (abs.) *Mining and Metallurgy*, no. 170, pp. 38-39.

727. "Oil Field, Revived, Moves in on Houston": *Oil and Gas Jour.* (1957), v. 55, no. 2, p. 73.

694. "Oil Field and Salt Dome Names, Mississippi": Mississippi Geological Society, *Bull.*, AAPG (1944), v. 28, no. 7, pp. 1046-1049.

638. "Oil Fields, Future Louisiana": Howe, H. V., *Oil* (1944), v. 4, pp. 22-24.

520a. *Oil Fields, Gulf Coast*: Barton, D. C. and Sawtelle, George (ed.), American Association of Petroleum Geologists (1936), Tulsa, Oklahoma, 1070 pp.

728. "Oil Fields of Gulf Coast Area Found in Sediments of Late Geological Age": Woodruff, E. G., *Oil and Gas Jour.* (1935), v. 33, no. 64, pp. 38-39, 149.

673. "Oil Fields, Mexican": Garcia Rojas, Antionio, *Bull.*, AAPG (1949), v. 33, no. 8, pp. 1336-1350.

722. *Oil Fields in North America*: Ver Wiebe,

W. A., Edwards Brothers, Inc., (1949), Ann Arbor, Mich., 251 pp.

728a. *Oil Fields, Structure of Typical American*, Vol. I: Teas, L. P., et al, American Association of Petroleum Geologists (1929), Tulsa, Oklahoma, 510 pp.

728b. *Oil Fields, Structure of Typical American*, Vol II: Spooner, W. C., et al, American Association of Petroleum Geologists (1929), Tulsa, Oklahoma, 780 pp.

728c. *Oil Fields, Structure of Typical American*, Vol. III: Howell, J. V. (ed.), American Association of Petroleum Geologists (1948), Tulsa, Oklahoma, 516 pp.

729. "Oil Fields of the Texas Gulf Coastal Region, Relation of Topography to the": Wolf, A. G., *Eng. Mechanics Jour.* (1921), v. 111, pp. 474-475.

730. "Oil Found Under Huge Salt Dome Overhang": *World Oil* (1955), v. 140, no. 6, p. 97.

731. "Oil and Gas Accumulation to Geologic Structure in the Mid-Continent Region, Relation of": Tomlinson, C. W., *Problems of Petroleum Geology*, AAPG (1934), p. 579.

83. "Oil and Gas Bulletins and Annual Reports, Jackson, Mississippi": *Mississippi State Oil and Gas Board*.

161a. *Oil and Gas Development, International*: International Oil Scouts Association and Society of Petroleum Engineers of AIME, Year Book (1960-1961), Vols. 30-31, Austin, Texas.

161b. *Oil and Gas Development, International*: International Oil Scouts Association, Yearbook (1962-1965), Vols. 32-35, Austin, Texas.

170a. *Oil and Gas Field Development in United States and Canada:* National Oil Scouts and Landmen's Association, Year Book (1931-1959), Vols. 1-29, Austin, Texas.

732. *Oil and Gas Fields of North Louisiana, South Arkansas, Mississippi and Alabama, Reference Report in Certain*: Vol. 1, Shreveport Geol. Soc. (1945).

733. *Oil and Gas Fields of North Louisiana, South Arkansas, Mississippi, and Alabama, Reference Report on*: Vol. 1, Shreveport Geol. Soc. (1946), 328 pp.

734. *Oil and Gas Fields of North Louisiana, South Arkansas, Mississippi, and Alabama*: Vol. 2, Shreveport Geol. Soc. (1947), pp. 317-503.

735. *Oil and Gas Fields of North Louisiana,*

South Arkansas, Mississippi, and Alabama: Vol. 3, Shreveport Geol. Soc. (1951), no. 1, 42 pp.

736. *Oil and Gas Fields of North Louisiana, South Arkansas, Mississippi, and Alabama*: Vol. 3, Shreveport Geol. Soc. (1953), no. 2, 108 pp.

737. *Oil and Gas Fields of Southeast Texas, Typical*: Dunham, R. L. (ed.), Houston Geol. Soc. (1962), 243 pp.

737a. "Oil and Gas Fields of the Upper Cretaceous and Tertiary Formations of the West Coast": Adams, G. I., *Bull.,* USGS (1901), pp. 37-62.

667. "Oil and Gas Map of Louisiana": *Louisiana Geological Survey* (1959), Dept. of Conserv.

738. "Oil and Gas in Northeast Texas, Occurrence of": Herald, F. A. (ed.) *Pub. 5116,* Tex. U. (1951), 449 pp.

739. "Oil and Gas Pools, Relation of, to Unconformities in the Mid-Continent Region": Levorsen, A. I., *Problems of Petroleum Geology,* AAPG (1934), 780 pp.

740. "Oil and Gas Seeps in World Oil Exploration, Significance of"; Link, Walter K., *Bull.,* AAPG (1952), v. 36, no. 8, pp. 1505-1590.

741. "Oil and Gas in Texas, Occurrence of": Sellards, E. H. and Hendricks, L. C., *Pub. 4301,* Tex. U. (1946), pp. 179-190.

557. "Oil in the Gulf of Mexico" (abs.): McGee, D. A., Seale, Tom and Finley, J. C., *Proc.,* Okla. Acad. Sci. (1950), v. 29, pp. 60-61.

516. "Oil, Habitat of, in Eastern Gulf Coast": Braunstein, Jules, *Habitat of Oil,* AAPG (1958), pp. 511-522.

686. "Oil, Migration of, A Study of the Evidences for Lateral and Vertical": Lahee, F. H., *Problems of Petroleum Geology,* AAPG (1934), pp. 399-427.

7. "Oil Occurrence in Frio and Anahuac Formations of Texas and Louisiana, Summary of": Burke, R. A., *Bull.,* AAPG (1958), v. 42, no. 12, pp. 2935-2950.

742. "Oil, Origin and Accumulation of": Clark, Frank R., *Problems of Petroleum Geology,* AAPG (1934), pp. 309-335.

743. "Oil, Problems of the Origin, Migration and Accumulation of": Rich, John L., *Problems of Petroleum Geology,* AAPG (1934), pp. 337-345.

654. "Oil Producing Horizons of Gulf Coast in Texas and Louisiana": Deussen, Alexander, *Bull.,* AAPG (1934), v. 18, no. 4, pp. 500-518; *Gulf Coast Oil Fields,* AAPG (1936), pp. 1-19.

306. "Oil Production, Salt Dome, Directional Drilling for": Joynt, K. R. and Massad, A. H., *World Oil* (1956), v. 142, no. 7, pp. 192, 194, 199, 202.

673a. "Oil Prospects and Regional Tectonics of Eastern Mexico": Trumpy, D., *Geological Report No. 247* (1932), Archivo de Petroleos Mexicanos.

527. "Oil Reserves of the Gulf Coast": Deussen, Alexander, *Oil Weekly* (1933), v. 69, no. 1, pp. 16-18.

696. "Oil Resources, Mississippi": Morse, W. C., *Quarterly Bull.,* Interstate Oil Compact (1944), v. 3, no. 4, pp. 11-16; *Mississippi Oil Rev.,* pp. 3-7; *World Pet.,* v. 16, no. 2, pp. 53-54.

744. "Oil, Salt Domes; Favorite Home for": Hanna, Marcus A., *Oil and Gas Jour.* (1959), v. 57, no. 6, pp. 138-142.

560. "Oil Search in Eastern Gulf Region": Kornfeld, J. A., *Mines Mag.* (1944), v. 34, no. 9, pp. 476-484.

754. "Oil, 64 Chances to Find New Gulf Coast": Halbouty, Michel T. and Hardin, George C., Jr., *Oil and Gas Jour.* (1955), v. 54, no. 23, pp. 321-324.

558. "Oil Structures, Possibility of, Out in the Gulf of Mexico": Kern, Charles E., *Oil and Gas Jour.* (1927), v. 25, no. 42, pp. 80, 225-226.

746. "Oil and Sulphur Development in the Texas and Louisiana Gulf Coast Salt Dome Region": Anonymous, *Bull. 1,* Tex. Gulf Coast Oil Scouts Assoc. and South La. Oil Scouts Assoc. (1930), 128 pp.

333a. *Oil Well Drilling Fluids, Composition and Properties of:* Rogers, Walter F., Gulf Publishing Co. (1963), Houston, Texas, 818 pp.

747. "Oil Well Drilling and Production, Temperature as Affecting": Halbouty, Michel T., *Symposium on Temperatures,* Am. Inst. of Physics (1940), New York, pp. 1039-1057.

748. "Oil Well Drilling, Temperature Effects on, Part I": Halbouty, Michel T., *Oil Weekly* (1939), v. 96, no. 2; "Temperature Affecting Crude Oil Producing, Part II": (1939), v. 96, no. 3, pp. 15-19.

104. "Oil Zones, Gulf Mexican, and Carribbean": Seismograph Service Corporation, *Oil and Gas Jour.* (1944), v. 43, no. 34, pp. 182-199.

749. "Oolitic and Pisolitic Barite from the Saratoga Oil Field, Texas": Moore, E. S., *Bull.,* GSA (1914), v. 25, pp. 77-79.

532. "Operations on Gulf Coast, Result of":

Judson, Sidney A., *Oil and Gas Jour.* (1927), v. 25, no. 40, pp. 97, 151-152, 155.

750. "Orange Field, Orange County, Texas, New Development in": Beckelhymer, R. L., *Bull.*, AAPG (1939), v. 23, no. 4, pp. 602-603.

390. "Orange and Jefferson Counties, Texas, Stratigraphy of the Frio Formation": Reedy, M. F., Jr., *Bull.*, AAPG (1949), v. 33, no. 11, pp. 1830-1858; (abs.) *Bull.*, AAPG (1949), v. 33, no. 11, pp. 108-109; *Oil and Gas Jour.* v. 47, no. 32, p. 104.

751. "Orange, Texas Oil Field": Deussen, Alexander and Andrau, E. W. K., *Bull.*, AAPG (1936), v. 20, no. 5, pp. 531-559; *Problems of Petroleum Geology*, AAPG (1934) pp. 880-908.

752. "Orchard Field, Hazardous Fishing Job is Tackled by Gulf Engineers in": Williams, Neil, *Oil and Gas Jour.* (1936), v. 34, no. 51, pp. 46, 48.

392. "Orchard Salt Dome, Fort Bend County, Texas, Galena and Spalerite in the Fayette at": Hanna, Marcus A., *Bull.*, AAPG (1929), v. 13, no. 4, pp. 384-385.

752a. "Origin and Accumulation of Oil, Historical Review of Theories Advanced by American Geologists to Acccount for the": Campbell, M. R., *Econ. Geol.* (1911), v. 6, pp. 363-395.

753. "Origin of Gulf Coast Salt Dome Sulphur Deposits": Feely, H. W. and Kulp, J. L., *Bull.*, AAPG (1957), v. 41, no. 8, pp. 1802-1853.

594b. "Origin of Hydrogen Sulphide in Persian Natural Gas and a Method of Preparing Unsaturated Hydrocarbons, The": Cadman, W. H., *Jour. Inst. Pet.* (1925), v. 2, pp. 487-489.

754. "Origin, Intrusive, of Gulf Coast Salt Domes": Rogers, G. S., *Econ. Geol.* (1918), v. 13, pp. 447-485; (discussion), v. 14, pp. 178-180.

755. "Origin, Intrusive, of the Gulf Coast Salt Domes, Its Bearing on the Accumulation of Oil": Jones, W. A., *Econ. Geol.* (1918), v. 13, no. 8, pp. 621-622.

717a. "Origin of Natural Gas and Petroleum, The Volcanic": Coste, Eugene, *Canadian Min. Inst. Jour.* (1903), v. 6, pp. 73-123.

723. "Origin of North American Salt Domes": DeGolyer, E. L., *Bull.*, AAPG (1925), v. 9, no. 5, pp. 831-874; *Geology of Salt Dome Oil Fields*, AAPG (1926), pp. 1-44.

400a. "Origin of Petroleum, Geologic Aspects of": Hedberg, Hollis D., *Bull.*, AAPG (1964), v. 48, no. 11, pp. 1775-1803.

756. "Origin of Salt Domes, The Theory of Volcanic": DeGolyer, E. L., *Bull. 137*, AIME (1918), pp. 987-1000; Discussion by J. A. Udden, *Bull. 139*, AIME (1918), p. 1147; *Trans.*, AIME (1918), v. 61, pp. 456-477.

757. "Origin, Secondary Intrusive, of Gulf Coastal Plain Salt Domes": Matteson, W. G., and Coste, E., *Trans.*, AIME (1921), v. 65, pp. 295-334; pre-prints, nos. 1048, 1073, 1088; (abs.) *Mining and Metallurgy*, no. 170, p. 37.

569. "Origin of Thick Gypsum and Salt Deposits": Branson, E. B., *Bull.*, GSA (1915), v. 26, no. 6, pp. 231-242; (abs.) pp. 103-104.

757a. "Ouachita System": Flawn, P. T., Goldstein, A., Jr., King, P. B. and Weaver, C. E., *Pub. 6120*, Tex. U. (1961), 399 pp.

37. "Overhang at Barbers Hill, Chambers County, Texas: Prediction of a Study in Quantitative Calculations from Torsion Balance Data": Barton, D. C., *Bull.*, AAPG (1935), v. 19, no. 1, pp. 25-36; *Trans.*, v. 5, Soc. Pet. Geophy. (1935), pp. 25-36; *Early Geophysical Papers*, SEG (1947), pp. 685-696.

36. "Overhanging Cap Rock and Salt at Barbers Hill, Chambers County, Texas": Judson, Sidney A., Murphy, P. C. and Stamey, R. A., *Bull.*, AAPG (1932), v. 16, no. 5, pp. 469-482.

758. "Overhanging Cap Rock and Salt, Special Methods Required to Drill Through": Judson, Sidney A. and Battle, J. C., *Oil Weekly* (1933), v. 69, no. 1, pp. 59-60, 62.

329. "Overhanging Salt on Domes of Texas and Louisiana": Judson, Sidney A. and Stamey, R. A., *Bull.*, AAPG (1933), v. 17, no. 12, pp. 1492-1520; *Gulf Coast Oil Fields* (1936), pp. 141-169; *Oil Weekly*, v. 71, no. 11, pp. 18-24; no. 12, pp. 18-22; no. 13, pp. 18, 20-24; *Oil and Gas Jour.*, v. 32, no. 21, pp. 16, 30; no. 22, pp. 18, 22; no. 25, pp. 16, 18; no. 27, p. 18; (abs.) *Pan Am Geologist*, v. 59, no. 3, p. 230.

759. "Palangana Salt Dome, Duval County, Texas": Barton, D. C., *Econ. Geol.* (1920), v. 6, pp. 497-510.

709. "Paleomicroontologico, Analisis, de las Formaciones Encontradas en los pozos del Campo de Moloacan, y Correlaciones Estratigraficas Entre Dichos Pozos"; Sansores, J. C., *Tesis Prof.*, Universidad Nacional Autonoma de Mexico, 1950.

498. "Palestine and Grand Saline Salt Domes": Muehlberger, Wm., Clabaugh, Patricia S. and Hightower, Maxwell L., *Field Excursion No. 6, Geology of the Gulf Coast and Central Texas and Guidebook of Excursions*, Houston Geol. Soc. (1962), Houston, Texas, pp. 266-277.

760. "Palestine Salt Dome, Anderson County, Texas": Hopkins, O. B., *Bull. 661,* USGS (1917), pp. 253-270; (abs.) *Jour., Washington Acad. Sci.,* v. 8, p. 173.

554. "Palynologic Age of Diapiric and Bedded Salt in the Gulf Coastal Province": Jux, Ulrich, *Bull. 38,* La. Geol. Svy. (1961), Dept. of Conserv., 46 pp.; Review of by Hans D. Pflug, *Bull.,* AAPG (1963), v. 47, no. 1, pp. 180-181.

761. "Paragenesis and Petrography of Gulf Coast Salt Dome, Cap Rock Minerals": Brown, L. S., *Bull.,* GSA (1931), v. 42, pp. 228-229; (abs.) *Pan Am. Geologist,* v. 55, p. 314.

762. "Patillo Higgins, Revival of Spindletop Recalls the Dream of": *Oil and Gas Jour.* (1926), v. 25, no. 8, pp. 41, 107.

762a "Permian Castile Sea, Sedimentation in": King, R. H., *Bull.,* AAPG (1947), v. 31, no. 3, pp. 470-477.

762b. "Persia, South, Salt Diapirism in": O'Brien, C. A. E., *Geologie en Mijnbouw Nieuwe Serie,* 19e Jaargang (1957), pp. 357-376.

763. "Persia, Salt Domes in": Harrison, J. V., *Jour. Inst. Pet.* (1931), v. 17, pp. 300-320.

594b. "Persian Natural Gas, The Origin of Hydrogen Sulphide in, and a Method of Preparing Unsaturated Hydrocarbons": Cadman, W. H., *Jour. Inst. Pet.* (1925), v. 2, pp. 487-489.

764. "Pescadito—It's Texas' Deepest Salt Dome": Gardner, Frank J., *Oil and Gas Jour.* (1957), v. 55, no. 26, p. 189.

765 "Petite Anse, Louisiana, Notes on the Great Salt Deposits of": Bolton, H. C., *Trans.,* New York Acad. Sci. (1888), v. 7, pp. 122-127; *Sci. Am. Sup.,* v. 26, pp. 10,475-10,476.

766. "Petite Anse, Louisiana Rock Salt Company, on the Rock Salt Deposit of": Buck, C. E. and Goessmann, C. A., *Rept.,* Amer. Bur. of Mines (1867), 35 pp.

767. "Petite Anse, Remarks on the Age of the Rock Salt Deposits of": Hilgard, E. W., *Am. Naturalist* (1871), v. 5, p. 523.

529. *Petrographic and Physical Characteristics of Sands from Seven Gulf Coast Producing Horizons:* Halbouty, Michel T., Gulf Publishing Company (1937), 106 pp.

768. "Petrographic Study of Salt Dome Cap Rock": Barton, D. C., *Bull.,* AAPG (1930), v. 14, no. 12, pp. 1573-1574.

97. "Petrography, Cap Rock": Brown, L. S., *Bull.,* AAPG (1931), v. 15, no. 5, pp. 509-529.

761. "Petrography and Paragenesis of Gulf Coast Salt Dome, Cap Rock Minerals": Brown, L. S., *Bull.,* GSA (1931), v. 42, pp. 228-229; (abs.) *Pan Am. Geologist,* v. 55, p. 314.

769. "Petrography of Salt Dome Cap Rock": Goldman, M. I., *Bull.,* AAPG (1925), v. 9, no. 1, pp. 42-78; *Geology of Salt Dome Oil Fields,* AAPG (1926), pp. 50-86.

770. "Petroleos Mexicanos": Gutierrez Roldan, Pascual, *World Pet.* (1963), v. 34, no. 6, pp. 507-512.

404. "Petroleum, Accumulation of, Role of Geologic Structure in the": Clapp, F. G., *Structure of Typical American Oil Fields,* AAPG (1929), v. 2, pp. 667-716.

771. "Petroleum Deposits, Salt Structures in Their Relation to" (abs.): Stahl, A. F. V., *Jour. Inst. Pet.* (1929), v. 15, pp. 315A-316A.

772. "Petroleum, Effect of Salt Domes on the Accumulation of": Barton, D. C., *Bull.,* AAPG (1931), v. 15, no. 1, pp. 61-66.

454a. *Petroleum Geologists, Structural Geology for:* Russell, William L., McGraw-Hill Book Co., Inc. (1955), New York, N. Y.

449. *Petroleum Geology:* Landes, Kenneth K., John Wiley and Sons (1951), New York, 660 pp.

772a. *Petroleum Geology, Problems of:* Wrather, W. E. and Lahee, F. H. (ed.), American Association of Petroleum Geologists (1934), Tulsa, Okla., 1073 pp.

772b. *Petroleum, Source Beds of:* Rept. of investigation supported jointly by the API and the Geol. Svy. of the U. S. Dept. of Interior from 1931 to 1941, Trask, P. D. and Patnode, H. W., AAPG (1942), 561 pp.

534. "Petroleum Industry of the Gulf Coast Salt Dome Area": Bradley, Virginia, *Econ. Geol.* (1939), v. 15, no. 4, pp. 395-407.

115. *Petroleum and Natural Gas Industries, Chronological History of the:* Clark, James A., Clark Book Co. (1963), Houston, Texas, 317 pp.

773. "Petroleum Reservoirs, Classification of": Wilhelm, O. G., *Bull.,* AAPG (1945), v. 29, no. 11, pp. 1537-1580.

774. "Petroleum and Salt Deposits, Genetic Connection Between": *Oil and Gas Jour.* (1929), v. 28, no. 5, p. 159.

661. "Petroliferos, Yacimientos, en la Region de Macuspano, Tabasco": Gutierrez, Gil R., *Bol., Asoc. Mex. Geol. Petrol.* (1950), v. 2, no. 8, pp. 499-510.

775. "Photogeology in Gulf Coast Exploration": DeBlieux, Charles, *Bull., AAPG* (1949), v. 33, no. 7, pp. 1251-1259.

776. "Photogeology in Louisiana Coastal Marsh and Swamp": DeBlieux, Charles, *Trans.,* GCAGS (1962), v. 12, pp. 231-241.

777. "Phys-Chem. Beding-Ungen Beider Bildungen der Salzlager und Ihre Anwendung auf Geologische Probleme, Die": Lachmann, R. and Arrhenius, Sv., *Geol. Rundshau,* v. 3, no. 139.

778. "Physical Properties, Variation in" (Foreword): Barton, D. C., *Problems of Petroleum Geology,* AAPG (1934), pp. 97-99.

779. "Physik der Salzlagerstatten, Zur": Arrhenius, Sv., *Meddelanden fran K. Vetenskabsakodemiens Nobelinstitut,* v. 2, no. 20.

631a. "Physiography of Coastal Southwest Louisiana": McGuirt, J. H., Howe, H. V., and Russell, R. J., *Bull. 6,* La. Geol. Svy. (1935), pp. 1-68.

780. "Pierce Junction Field, Harris County, Texas": Glass, Charles N., *Guidebook,* AAPG-SEPM-SEG Jt. Ann. Mtg. (March, 1953), Houston, Texas, pp. 147-150.

781. "Pierce Junction is Hottest Spot on Texas Gulf Coast": Hoppins, Charles, *World Oil* (1956), v. 142, no. 7, pp. 205-214.

782. "Pierce Junction Lives Again": Williams, Neil, *Oil and Gas Jour.* (1956), v. 54, no. 63, pp. 166-169.

783. "Pierce Junction Salt Dome, Harris County, Texas": Bowman, W. F., *Oil Weekly* (1927), v. 46, no. 11, pp. 95-98.

391. "Pierce Junction Salt Dome, Harris County, Texas, Notes on an Occurrence of Galena at": Hanna, Marcus A. and Parker, W. G., *Bull., AAPG* (1933), v. 17, no. 4, pp. 438-439.

784. "Piercement Trap Reservoirs": Wilhelm, O. G., *Oil and Gas Jour.* (1946), v. 44, no. 51, p. 147.

785. "Pine Prairie Dome": Barton, D. C., *Bull.,* AAPG (1925), v. 9, no. 4, pp. 738-755; *Geology of Salt Dome Oil Fields,* AAPG (1926), pp. 419-436.

786. "Pine Prairie Dome, Louisiana, Gravity Determination of Cap Rock": Nettleton, L. L., *Geophysical Case Histories,* SEG (1956), v. 2, pp. 149-155.

787. "Planulina-Abbeville Trend, South Louisana, Sedimentation and Structure of the": Goheen, H. C., *Trans.,* GCAGS (1959), v. 9, pp. 91-103.

788. "Plaquemines and St. Barnard Parishes, Salt Domes of": Howe, H. V. and McGuirt, J. H., *Bull. 8,* La. Geol. Svy. (1936), pp. 200-278.

616. "Plaquemines and St. Charles Parishes, Louisiana, Regional Study of Jefferson Dome": Vidrine, Louis O., *Trans.,* GCAGS (1958), v. 8, pp. 105-115.

789. "Plastic Flow Theory in Explanation of Salt Domes on the Gulf Coast": Smiley, T. F., *Oil and Gas Jour.* (1936), v. 34, no. 40, p. 48.

790. "Pools, Eight New, on Gulf Coast in 1931": Williams, Neil, *Oil and Gas Jour.* (1932), v. 30, no. 37, pp. 70-76.

791. "Port Acres and Port Arthur Fields, Jefferson County, Texas": Halbouty, Michel T. and Barber, Thomas D., *Trans.,* GCAGS (1961), v. 11, pp. 225-234.

452. "Port Barre Salt Dome, Stratigraphy and the Geology of the": Crain, H. F., *Thesis,* Kan. U. (1947), Dept. of Geol.

710. "Posibilidades del Salino Alto, de Moloacon-Ixhuatlan": Contreras, Hugo, *Bol.,* Asoc. Mex. Geol. Petrol. (1950), v. 2, no. 7, pp. 473-485.

648. "Post-Oligocene Sediments in Southern Louisiana, Inspissation of": Crouch, Robert W., *Bull.,* GSA (1959) v. 70, pp. 1283-1292.

643a. "Potamides Matsoni Zone of Louisiana, Some Microfossils of the": Stephenson, M. B., *Bull. 6,* La. Geol. Svy. (1935), pp. 187-188.

792. "Potash Salts and Fossil Algae in Texas Salt Dome, Discovery of": DeGolyer, E. L., *Bull.,* AAPG (1925), v. 9, no. 2, pp. 348-349; *Geology of Salt Dome Oil Fields,* AAPG (1926), pp. 781-782.

677. "Pozo Rica Field, Backbone of Oil Industry in Mexico": Sheldon, Ruth, *Oil and Gas Jour.* (1939), v. 38, no. 2, pp. 26-29, 104.

793. "Pressure Control by Water Injection—A Resume of Case Histories": Burtchaell, E. P. and Smith, E. R., *Jour. of Pet. Tech.* (1952), v. 4, no. 7, pp. 15-18.

344. "Pressure Maintenance of East Hackberry": Euwer, M. L., *Oil Weekly* (1945), v. 119, no. 6, pp. 46, 49-51.

794. "Pre-Trinity Deposits in South Texas, Problem of": Getzendaner, F. M., *Bull.,* AAPG (1943), v. 27, no. 9, pp. 1228-1244; (abs.) v. 26 no. 5, pp. 904-905.

669a. "Problem Formations, Maps Predict":

Harper, Douglas C. and Ruhe, Robert W., Jr., *Oil and Gas Jour.* (April 29, 1963).

772a. *Problems of Petroleum Geology:* Wrather, W. E. and Lahee, F. H. (ed.), American Association of Petroleum Geologists (1934), Tulsa, Oklahoma, 1073 pp.

363. "Production and Exploration in Gulf Coast Through 1935": Rosaire, E. E. and Stiles, M. E., *Geophysics* (1936), v. 1, no. 1, pp. 141-148.

368. "Production, Gulf Coastal, Faulted Structures Play Big Roles in": Kornfeld, J. A., *Oil Weekly* (1938), v. 90, no. 13, pp. 17-18.

514. "Production, Improved, by Chemical Treatment in Gulf Coast Areas": Aulick, Burton, Hopkins, H. F., Saye, Frank and Hower, Wayne, *Jour. of Pet. Tech.* (1952), v. 4, no. 9, pp. 13-16.

795. "Production, Outer Rings of, Should Surround Salt Domes", Carroll, Don L., *Oil Weekly* (1943), v. 111, no. 9, p. 14.

72. "Production Practice, Advance in, Used at Bosco, With Double Set of Drawworks and Engines": Williams, Neil, *Oil and Gas Jour.* (1934), v. 33, no. 6, p. 16.

141. "Protho and Rayburn's Salt Domes, Bienville Parish, Louisiana, Cretaceous Ostracoda of": Butler, E. Ann and Jones, Douglas E., *Bull. 32,* La. Geol. Svy. (1957), Dept. of Conserv., 65 pp.

796. "Protho Salt Dome, Bienville Parish, Louisiana": Hull, J. P. D., *Bull.* AAPG (1925), v. 9, no. 5, pp. 904-906.

797. "Rabb Ridge Important Potentially, Made Interesting by High Valuation": *Oil Weekly* (1932), v. 67, no. 13, pp. 10-12, 40-42.

798. "Rabon Grande, El Campo Petrolero de, Sureste dei Estado de Veracruz, Mexico", Gatling, Leroy, *Bol.,* Asoc. Mex. Geol. Petrol. (1954), v. 6, nos. 3-4, pp. 139-151.

799. "Racoon Bend Oil Field, Austin County, Texas": Teas, L. P. and Miller, Charis R., *Bull.,* AAPG (1933), v. 17, no. 12, pp. 1459-1491; *Gulf Coast Oil Fields,* AAPG (1936), pp. 676-708.

800. "Racoon Bend Salt Dome, Austin County, Texas": McLellan, H. J., *Bull.,* AAPG (1946), v. 30, no. 8, pp. 1306-1307.

60. "Radiocarbon Age Determination of Recent -Pleistocene Contact in Block 126 Field, Eugene Island, Gulf of Mexico": Bray, E. E. and Nelson, H. F., *Bull.,* AAPG (1956), v. 40, no. 1, pp. 173-177.

502. "Radio-Transmission Demonstration at Grand Saline, Texas, Note on the": Barret, Wm. M., *Geophysics* (1952), v. 17, no. 3, pp. 544-549.

33. "Rapides and Avoyelles Parishes, Louisiana, Geology of": Fisk, Harold N., *Bull. 18,* La. Geol. Svy. (1940), 240 pp.

141. "Rayburn's and Protho Salt Domes, Bienville Parishes, Louisiana, Cretaceous Ostracoda of": Butler, E. Ann and Jones, Douglas E., *Bull. 32,* La. Geol. Svy. (1957), Dept. of Conserv., 65 pp.

647. "Reference Report Southern Louisiana 1940": *Lockwoods, C. D. Oil Report* (Oct., 1940), Houston, Texas, 343 pp.

801. "Reference Report Texas Upper Gulf Coast 1939": *Lockwood's, C. D. Oil Report* (Mar., 1939), Houston, Texas.

802. "Refraction Methods, Outlining of Salt Masses by": Musgrove, A. W., Woolley, W. C. and Gray, Helen, *Geophysics* (1960), v. 25, no. 1, pp. 141-167.

803. "Refraction Surveying of Salt Domes": Wolf, Alexander, *World Oil* (1947), v. 127, no. 7, pp. 120-125.

804. "Refractions, Reflected": Swartz, Charles A. and Lindsey, R. W., *Geophysics* (1942), v. 7, no. 1, pp. 78-91.

661. "Region de Macuspana, Tabasco, Yacimientos Petroliferos en la": Gutierrez, Gil R., *Bol.,* Asoc. Mex. Geol. Petrol. (1950), v. 2, no. 8, pp. 499-510.

616. "Regional Study of Jefferson, Plaquemines and St. Charles Parishes, Louisiana": Vidrine, Louis O., *Trans.,* GCAGS (1958), v. 8, pp. 105-115.

515. "Reserve, Big Potential, on Gulf Coast": Williams, Neil, *Oil and Gas Jour.* (1930), v. 28, no. 49, pp. 42-43, 118.

637. "Reserves, One of the Largest Undrilled, in the World, Offshore Louisiana": Limes, Leonard L. and Stipe, Jack C., *Oil and Gas Jour.* (1959), v. 57, no. 48, pp. 126-130.

528. "Reserves, Potentialities on the Gulf Coast Spurring Search for": Williams, Neil, *Oil and Gas Jour.* (1936), v. 34, no. 48, pp. 80-82, 87.

805. "Reservoir Mechanism of Sulfur Recovery": Rayne, John R., Craft, B. C., and Hawkins, Murray F., Jr., *Trans.,* AIME (1956), v. 207, pp. 246-251; *Tech Paper 4385,* AIME; *Jour. of Pet. Tech.* (1956), v. 8, no. 11, pp. 246-251.

407. "Reservoir Pressures in Gulf Coast Louisiana, Geological Aspects of, Abnormal": Dickinson, George, *Bull.,* AAPG (1953), v. 37, no. 2, pp. 410-432; *Proc.,* Third World Pet. Cong. Sectional (1951), The Hague, Holland.

784. "Reservoirs, Piercement Trap": Wilhelm,

O. G., *Oil and Gas Jour.* (1946), v. 44, no. 51, p. 147.

806. "Resources of Texas, Mineral": Sellards, E. H., *Tex Geol. Mag.* (1944), v. 8, no. 2, pp. 19-30.

807. "Resources of Texas by Counties, Index to Mineral": Sellards, E. H. and Evans, G. L., *Min. Res. Circ. 29,* Tex. U. (1944), 21 pp.

807a. "Rock Salt": Harris, G. D., *Rept. of 1907,* Geol. Svy. of La. (1908), Bull 7.

808. "Rock Salt Beds and Mother Liquor Salts, On the Formation of": Ochsenius, C., *Proc.,* Acad. Natural Sci. of Philadelphia (1888), v. 40, pp. 181-187.

766. "Rock Salt Deposit of Petite Anse, Louisiana Rock Salt Company": Buck, C. E. and Goessmann, C. A., *Rept.,* Amer. Bur. of Mines (1867), 35 pp.

767. "Rock Salt Deposits of Petite Anse, Remarks on the Age of the": Hilgard, E. W., *Am. Naturalist* (1871), v. 5, p. 523.

641. "Rock Salt in Louisiana": Lucas, A. F., *Trans.,* AIME (1900), v. 29, pp. 462-474; (abs.) *Eng. and Mining Jour.,* v. 68, pp. 577-579.

416. "Rock Salt in Louisiana and East Texas, The Geological Occurrence of": Harris, G. D., *Econ. Geol.* (1909), v. 4, pp. 12-34.

809. "Rock Salt of Louisiana Salt Plugs, Water-Insoluble Residues in": Taylor, R. E., *Bull.,* AAPG (1937), v. 21, no. 10, pp. 1268-1310; *(corrections)* v. 21, pp. 1494, 1496; (abs.) *World Pet.,* v. 9, no. 1, pp. 60-61.

810. "Rock Salt, its Origin, Geological Occurrence and Economic Importance in the State of Louisiana, Together with Brief Notes and References to all Known Salt Deposits and Industries of the World": Harris, G. D., Maurey, F. J. and Reinecke, L., *Bull.,* La. Geol. Svy. (1908), v. 7, 259 pp.

134. "Rodessa, Caddo Parish, Louisiana, Cores from a Deep Well at": Israelsky, M. C., *Bull.,* AAPG (1938), v. 22, no. 6, pp. 764-770.

811. "Rotary System of Drilling Pioneered at Spindletop": Kastrop, J. E., *World Oil* (1951), v. 132, no. 1, pp. 233-234, 238, 240, 244, 246, 248, 252.

811a. "Rumanischen Olgebiete, Der Bau der": Krejci, Karl, *Geol. Rundschau,* Band 16 (1926), Heft 1, S. 1-16; Heft 2, S. 99-127.

811b. "S34 in Nature and the Sulphur Cycle, The Distribution of": Szabo, A., Tudge, A., Macnamara, J. and Thode, H. G., *Science* (1950), v. 111, pp. 464-465.

812. "Sabine Uplift, Louisiana": Powers, Sidney, *Bull.,* AAPG (1920), v. 4, no. 2, pp. 117-136.

788. "St. Bernard and Plaquemines Parishes, Salt Domes of": Howe, H. V. and McGuirt, J. H., *Bull. 8,* La. Geol. Svy. (1936), pp. 200-278.

616. "St Charles, Jefferson and Plaquemines Parishes, Louisiana, Regional Study of": Vidrine, Louis O., *Trans.,* GCAGS (1958), v. 8, pp. 105-115.

357. "St. Landry and Evangeline Parishes, Geology of": Varvaro, Gasper G., *Bull 31,* La. Geol. Svy. (1957), Dept of Conserv., 295 pp.

441. "St. Martin and Lafayette Parishes, Louisiana, Geology of": Howe, H. V. and Moresi, C. K., *Bull. 3,* La. Geol. Svy. (1933), 328 pp.

813. "St. Martinville Producer, Completion of, Confirms Long Cherished Dreams": Williams, Neil, *Oil and Gas Jour.* (1935), v. 34, no. 27, p. 13.

33e. "Sal y Azufre en la Cuenca Salina del Istmo, Ver., Depositos de": Marquez, Pineda Aremos, Viveros, Juarez Manuel and Serna, Vigueras Reyes, *Bol. 64* (1964), Consejo de Recursos Naturales no Renovables, 76 pp.

331a. *Sal en Domos en el Estado de Louisiana, E.U.A. Explotacion Minera de:* Perez Larios, Jose, Archivo Consejo de Recursos Naturales no Renovables (1960).

33f. *Sal, las Masas de, Sintesis de la Morfologia de, del Istmo de Tehuantepec en Relacion con los Yacimientos de Azufre:* Gibson, B. Juan, Inedito, Archivo Conseo jde Recursos Naturales no Renovables (1957).

674. "Salinas, Estructuras, del Sureste de Mexico": Sansores, Enrique, *V Conv. An. de la AIPM,* en Abril de 1963 en Coatzacoalcos, pp. 7, 11.

533. "Saline Domes, Gulf Coast": Thacker, R. B., *Pet Age* (1924), v. 13, no. 7, p. 20.

814. "Saline Domes and Other Salt Deposits": Thomas, Kirby, *Min. Sci. Press* (1918), v. 117, p. 226.

815. "Saline Domes of the Texas-Louisiana Coastal Plain, Minerals of the": Hawkins, A. C., *Am. Mineralogist* (1918), v. 3, pp. 189-192.

816. "Salines, East Texas and Louisiana, The Origin of the": Norton, E. G., *Bull.,* AIME (1915), no. 97, pp. 93-102; no. 101, pp. 1120-1122; *Trans.,* AIME, v. 51, pp. 502-513.

633a. "Salines of North Louisiana": Veatch, A. C., *Rept. of 1902,* Geol. Svy. of La., pp. 47-100.

817. "Salt": Wyatt, Francis, *Eng. and Mining Jour.* (1887), v. 44, pp. 411, 432-433, 448-449.

818. "Salt Barrier Falls, Another": Gardner,

Frank J., *Oil and Gas Jour.* (1957), v. 55, no. 22, p. 167.

818a. "Salt Basin, The Senegal": Aymé, J. M., *Salt Basins Around Africa,* The Institute of Petroleum (1965), London, pp. 83-90.

129a. "Salt Basins of the Gabon and the Congo (Brazzaville): A Tentative Palaeogeographic Interpretation": Belmonte, Y., Hirtz, P. and Wenger, R., *Salt Basins Around Africa,* The Institute of Petroleum (1965), London, pp. 55-78.

690. "Salt and Cap Rock of Gulf Coast Salt Domes, The Mineralogy of the" (abs.): Taylor, R. E., *Trans., GCAGS* (1953), v. 3, pp. 147-148.

819. "Salt Concretions, Immense": Harris, G. D., *Pop. Sci. Monthly* (1913), v. 82, pp. 187-191.

820. "Salt Core Structures and Their Importance in Petroleum Geology": Bediz, P. I., *Mines Mag.* (1942), v. 32, no. 5, pp. 215-217, 255, 265; no. 6, pp. 287-289.

821. "Salt Deposits, The Form of": Hahn, F. F., *Econ. Geol.* (1912), v. 7, pp. 120-135.

384. "Salt Deposits, Formation and Geology of the": Jones, F. O., *Sci. Am.* (1902), v. 87, p. 59.

401. "Salt Deposits, Geologic History of the Formation of" (abs.): Weaver, Paul, *Tulsa Geol. Soc. Digest* (1946), v. 14, p. 51.

608. "Salt Deposits of the Isthmus of Tehuantepec": Castillon, B. M., *Symposium on Salt,* Northern Ohio Geol. Soc., Inc. (1963), Cleveland, Ohio., pp. 263-280.

765. "Salt Deposits of Petite Anse, Louisiana, Notes on the Great": Bolton, H. C., *Trans.,* New York Acad. Sci. (1888), v. 7, pp. 122-127; *Sci. Am. Supp.,* v. 26, pp. 10,475-10,476.

822. "Salt Deposits, Age of Gulf Border": Brown, L. S., *Bull.,* AAPG (1934), v. 18, no. 10, pp. 1227-1296.

774. "Salt Deposits and Petroleum, Genetic Connection Between": *Oil and Gas Jour.* (1929), v. 28, no. 5, p. 159.

610. "Salt Deposits, Possible, in the Vicinity of the Jackson Fault, Alabama": Barksdale, Jelks, *Circ. 10,* Ala. Geol. Svy. (1929), 22 pp.

814. "Salt Deposits, Saline Domes and Other": Thomas, Kirby, *Min. Sci. Press* (1918), v. 117, p. 226.

93. "Salt Deposits of the United States of America and Canada": Ward, Thomas, *Trans.,* Manchester Geol. Soc. (1890), v. 20, pp. 471-498.

823. "Salt Deposits, U. S., Where Located": Van Fossan, N. E., *Oil and Gas Jour.* (1955), v. 54, no. 19, p. 145.

824. "Salt, Depth of the, in Southeast Texas, Seismograph Evidence on the": Hoylman, H. Wayne, *Geophysics* (1945), v. 10, no. 3, p. 450.

554. "Salt, Diapiric and Bedded, Palynologic Age of, in the Gulf Coastal Province": Jux, Ulrich, *Bull. 38,* La. Geol. Svy. (1961), Dept. of Conserv., 46 pp; Review of by Hans D. Pflug, *Bull.,* AAPG (1963), v. 47, no. 1, pp. 180-181.

762a. "Salt Diapirism in South Persia": O'Brien, C. A. E., *Geologie en Mijnbouw Niewve Serie,* 19e Jaargang (1957), pp. 357-376.

825. "Salt Diffusion in Woodbine Sand Waters, East Texas": Horton, C. W., *Bull.,* AAPG (1944), v. 28, no. 11, pp. 1635-1641.

308. "Salt Dome Area as Future Reserve, New Coast Discoveries Throw Additional Light on": Mills, Brad, *Oil Weekly* (1935), v. 78, no. 10, pp. 19-20, 22-23.

717. "Salt Dome Area, Gulf Coast, Natural Gas Of": Teas, L. P., *Geology of Natural Gas,* AAPG (1935), pp. 683-740.

707. "Salt Dome Areas, Miniature Models Aid Mapping of": *Oil and Gas Jour.* (1946), v. 45, no. 27, p. 85.

826. "Salt Dome Boundary, Seismograph Determination of, Using Well Dectector Deep on Dome Flank": Gardner, L. W., *Geophysics* (1949), v. 14, no. 1, pp. 29-38; (abs.) *Oil and Gas Jour.* (1948), v. 46, no. 52, p. 115.

827. "Salt Dome Breccia": Kerr, Paul F. and Kopp, O. C., *Bull.,* AAPG (1958) v. 42, no. 3, pp. 548-560.

564. "Salt Dome Cap Rock, Features of Gypsum-Anhydrite" (abs.): Goldman, M. I., *Bull.,* GSA (1929), v. 40, pp. 99-100.

576. "Salt Dome Cap Rock, Hauerite in a": Wolf, A. G., *Bull.,* AAPG (1926), v. 10, no. 5, pp. 531-532.

761. "Salt Dome, Cap Rock Minerals, Petrography and Paragenesis of Gulf Coast": Brown, L. S., *Bull. GSA* (1931), v. 42, pp. 228-229; (abs.) *Pan Am. Geologist,* v. 55, p. 314.

655. "Salt Dome Cap Rock Minerals, Texas and Louisiana": Hanna, Marcus A. and Wolf, A. G., *Bull.,* AAPG (1934), v. 18, no. 2, pp. 212-225; *Gulf Coast Oil Fields,* AAPG (1936), pp. 119-132.

828. "Salt Dome Cap Rock, Origin, Nature, and Character of": Knaffle, L. L., *MS Thesis,* Mich. U. (1950), Dept. of Geol.

768. "Salt Dome Cap Rock, Petrographic Study

of": Barton, D. C., *Bull.*, AAPG (1930), v. 14, no. 12, pp. 1573-1574.

489. "Salt Dome Cap Rocks, Gold, Silver, and Other Elements in": Hanna, Marcus A. and Wolf, A. G., *Bull.*, AAPG (1941), v. 25, no. 4, pp. 750-752.

127. "Salt Dome, Coastal": Kennedy, William, *Bull. 1,* SW Assoc. Pet. Geol. (1917), pp. 39-59; Discussion by E. G. Woodruff, *Bull. 1,* SW Assoc. Pet. Geol. (1917), p. 79.

829. "Salt Dome, Coastal Louisiana, Fourth Well Drilled on, Finds Oil": Bignell, L. G. E., *Oil and Gas Jour.* (1937), v. 35, no. 38, pp. 17-18.

830. "Salt Dome Configuration" (abs.): Hanna, Marcus A., Bull., AAPG (1948), v. 33, no. 1, p. 109; *Oil and Gas Jour.* (1949), v. 47, no. 32, p. 104.

310. "Salt Dome Discoveries in North Louisiana in 1942": Blanpied, B. W. and Hazzard. R. T., *Bull.*, AAPG (1944), v. 28, no. 4, pp. 561-562.

347d. *Salt Dome of El Moralar, Geological Report No. 191 on the:* Nolthenius, Tutein, A. B., Archive Petroleos Mexicanos (1922).

39. "Salt Dome, Esperson and Barbers Hill, Texas, Typical Oil Field Structures": *Oil and Gas Jour.* (1942), v. 41, no. 13, pp. 42-43.

831. "Salt Dome Exploration Picks Up in East Texas": Hoot, Carl, *Oil and Gas Jour.* (1958), v. 56, no. 10, pp. 248-250.

170. "Salt Dome Exploration (U. S. Gulf Coast), Development Trends in": Hagen, Cecil and Cantrell, R. B., *Oil Weekly* (1946), v. 123, no. 3, pp. 87-88.

708. "Salt Dome Faulting, Scale Models as Guide to Interpretation of": Parker, T. J. and McDowell, A. N. *Bull.*, AAPG (1951), v. 35, no. 9, pp. 2076-2086.

304. "Salt Dome Field, Coastal Louisiana, Directional Drilling as Development Aid in": Williams, Neil, *Oil and Gas Jour.* (1944), v. 43, no. 31, pp. 66-68.

535. "Salt-Dome Formation, Gulf Coast, History of Concepts of": Nettleton, L. L., *Bull.*, AAPG (1955), v. 39, no. 12, pp. 2373-2383.

832. "Salt Dome Formation, Recent Experimental and Geophysical Evidence of Mechanics of": Nettleton, L. L., *Bull.*, AAPG (1943), v. 27, no. 1, pp. 51-63; (abs.) v. 26, no. 5, pp. 903-904.

399. "Salt Dome Geochemistry, A Contribution to": Stuart, Murray, *Jour. Inst. Pet.* (1931), v. 17, pp. 338-345.

833. "Salt Dome Geology May Enter New Phase": Halbouty, Michel T. and Hardin, George C., Jr., *Oil and Gas Jour.* (1954), v. 53, no. 26, pp. 93-98.

531. "Salt Dome Geology, New Look at, May Increase Gulf Coast Reserves": Sovinsky, V. N., *World Oil,* Part I (1958), v. 147, no. 5, pp. 180-181; Part II (1958), v. 147, no. 6, pp. 111-114.

834. "Salt Dome Geology in Past and Future Oil Exploration, Significance of": Halbouty, Michel T. and Hardin, George C., Jr., *The Oil Forum,* Special Oil Finders' Issue (April, 1955), pp. 129-131, 152.

835. "Salt Dome Graben Structures, Role of Concurrent Deposition and Deformation of Sediments in Development of": Currie, J. B., *Bull.,* AAPG (1956), v. 40, no. 1, pp. 1-16.

836. "Salt Dome in the Gulf Coast, Discovery by Geophysical Methods of the New" (abs.): DeGolyer, E. L., *Bull.*, GSA (1925), v. 36, p. 161; *Pan Am. Geologist,* v. 43, no. 2.

536. "Salt Dome, Gulf Coast, Interest Centers on": Eby, J. B., *World Oil* (1956), v. 143, no. 5, pp. 143-150; *Proc.,* International Geol. Cong. (1956).

837. "Salt Dome and Its Peculiarities as a Geologic Structure and as a Cause of Localizing Oil Deposits, The" (abs.): Weaver, Paul, *Oil* (1941), v. 1, no. 10, p. 24.

126. "Salt Dome Materials, Secondary, of Coastal Plain of Texas and Louisiana": Hanna, Marcus A., *Bull.,* AAPG (1930), v. 14, no. 11, pp. 1469-1475.

838. "Salt Dome Mechanics, Modern Views as to": Weaver, Paul, Unpublished Paper, AAPG Reg. Mtg. (1948), Houston, Texas.

347d. *Salt Dome of Elmoralar, Geological Report No. 191 on the:* Nolthenius, Tutien, A. B., Archive Petroleos Mexicanos (1922).

451. *Salt Dome Oil Fields, Geology of:* Moore, R. C., (ed.) American Association of Petroleum Geologists (1926), 797 pp.

504. "Salt Dome Oil and Gas Pools, Possibility of Using Gravity Anomalies in the Search for": Shaw, E. W., *Science* (1917), new ser. v. 46, pp. 553-556.

306. "Salt Dome Oil Production, Directional Drilling for": Joynt, K. R. and Massad, A. H., *World Oil* (1956), v. 142, no. 7, pp. 192, 194, 199, 202.

730. "Salt Dome Overhang, Oil Found Under Huge": *World Oil* (1955), v. 140, no. 6, p. 97.

839. "Salt Dome Overhang, A Suggested Method of Approach for Determination of": Lester, O. C., *Paper* 2, Soc. Pet. Geophy. (1937); *Early Geophysical Papers,* SEG (1947), p. 11.

840. "Salt Dome, Petroliferous, Height of Increasing": Thacker, R. B., *Pet. Age* (1924), v. 11, p. 530.

370. Salt Dome, Piercement, Better Concept of Faulting Patterns Aids Development": Kornfeld, M. M., *Oil Weekly* (1941), v. 100, no. 10, pp. 19-20.

841. "Salt Dome Possibilities": Steinmayer, R. A., *Bull.* 22, La. Geol. Svy. (1933), pp. 17-30.

842. "Salt Dome Problem, Contribution to": Van Tuyl, F. M., *Bull.,* AAPG (1930), v. 14, no. 8, pp. 1041-1047; (abs.) *Pan Am. Geologist,* v. 53, no. 3, p. 221.

843. "Salt Dome Problems, American, in the Light of the Rumanian and German Salt Domes": Barton, D. C., *Bull.,* AAPG (1925), v. 9, no. 9, pp. 1227-1268; *Geology of Salt Dome Oil Fields,* AAPG (1926), pp. 167-208.

843a. "Salt Dome Prospects," McGuirt, J., *Bull* 6, La. Geol. Svy. (1935), pp. 167-179.

844. "Salt Dome, Reconnaissance of, by Fan Shooting and a Comparison of Seismic Refraction Depth Formulae": Peters, J. W., *Compass* (1938), v. 18, no. 4, pp. 211-217.

348. "Salt Dome Region, Emba, U. S. S. R. and Some Comparisons with Other Salt Dome Regions": Sanders, C. W., *Bull.,* AAPG (1939), v. 23, no. 4, pp. 492-516.

845. "Salt Dome, Shallow, Note on Wave-Guide Propagation Over a": Howell, Lynn G. and Kean, C. H., *Geophysics* (1953), v. 18, no. 2, pp. 338-339.

846. "Salt Dome Statistics": Patrick, W. W., *Guidebook,* AAPG-SEPM-SEG Jt. Ann. Mtg. (1953), Houston, Texas, pp. 13-20.

847. "Salt Dome Statistics": Sawtelle, George, *Bull.,* AAPG (1936), v. 20, no. 6, pp. 726-735; *Gulf Coast Oil Fields,* AAPG (1936), pp. 109-118.

848. "Salt Dome Stratigraphy—Lower Gulf Coast" (abs.): Lowman, Shepard, W., *Oil and Gas Jour.* (1955), v. 53, no. 48, p. 212.

849. "Salt Dome Structure (Preliminary Notice)": Balk, Robert, *Bull.,* AAPG (1947), v. 31, no. 7, pp. 1295-1299.

482. "Salt Dome Structure, Relation of Geophysics to": Eby, J. B. and Clark, R. P., *Bull.,* AAPG (1935), v. 19, no. 3, pp. 356-377; *Gulf Coast Oil Fields,* AAPG (1936), pp. 170-191.

483. "Salt Dome Structure (with discussion by J. B. Eby and R. P. Clark), Relation of Geophysics to": Barret, Wm. M., *Bull.,* AAPG (1935), v. 19, no. 7, pp. 1069-1073.

850. "Salt Dome Structures, Experiments Relating to": Link, T. A., *Bull.,* AAPG (1930), v. 14, no. 4, pp. 483-508; (abs.) *Pan Am. Geologist,* v. 53, p. 221.

851. "Salt Dome Structures in the Texas-Louisiana Gulf Coast, New Geological Studies Result in Discoveries of Large Gas and Oil Reserves from": Halbouty, Michel T. and Hardin, George C., Jr., *Proc.,* Fourth World Pet. Cong. (1955), Rome, Italy, sec. 1, pp. 83-101.

400. "Salt Dome Studies by Geo-electrical Methods": Sundberg, K., *Jour. Inst. Pet.* (1931), v. 17, pp. 376-380.

852. "Salt Dome Sulphur Mining": Wolf, A. G., *Guidebook,* AAPG-SEPM-SEG Jt. Ann. Mtg. (1953), Houston Texas, pp. 39-40.

704. "Salt Dome Tectonics, Model Structures of": Parker, T. J., *PhD Dissertation,* Tex. U. (1952), Dept. of Geol.

705. "Salt Dome Tectonics, Model Studies of" McDowell, A. N., and Parker, T. J., *Bull.,* AAPG (1955), v. 39, no. 12, pp. 2384-2470; Review by W. T. Born, *Geophysics* (1955), v. 36, no. 44, p. 1121.

853. "Salt Dome Terminology": Taylor, R. E., *Oil and Gas Jour.* (1938), v. 36, no. 44, p. 58.

854. "Salt Dome Test in Louisiana, Union Sulphur Drills 9,250 Feet in": Williams, Neil, *Oil and Gas Jour.* (1931), v. 29, no. 52, p. 143.

855. "Salt Dome Theory, Moot Points in": Owens, L., *Jour. Inst. Pet.* (1931), v. 17, pp. 334-337.

856. "Salt Dome Waters, Chemical Relation of": Minor, H. E., *Bull.,* AAPG (1925), v. 9, no. 1, pp. 38-41; *Geology of Salt Dome Oil Fields,* AAPG (1926), pp. 777-780.

857. "Salt Dome Waters, Hydraulics of": Pennington, H., *Oil Weekly* (1929), v. 52, no. 7, pp. 27-29.

858. "Salt Domes": Brown, R. V., *Jour. Inst. Pet.* (1934), v. 20, pp. 73-93.

859. "Salt Domes": Knoy, M. F., *Sci. Am.* (1931), v. 144, p. 308.

12. "Salt Domes, American, Origin of the Anhydrite Cap Rock of": Goldman, M. I., *Prof. Paper* 175, USGS (1933), pp. 83-114; Review by Marcus

A. Hanna, *Econ. Geol.* (1936), v. 31, no. 6, pp. 642-644.

860. "Salt Domes and Anticlines": Hallam, A. H., *Oil Eng. and Finance* (1923), v. 3, p. 119.

27. "Salt Domes of Ascension and Iberville Parishes, Louisiana": Howe, H. V. and McGuirt, J. H., *Bull. 13,* La. Geol. Svy. (1938), pp. 87-187.

52. "Salt Domes of Bienville Parish, Louisiana" (abs.): Russell, R. D., *Bull.,* AAPG (1942), v. 26, no. 5, p. 904.

92. "Salt Domes of Cameron and Vermilion Parishes": Howe, H. V. and McGuirt, J. H., *Bull. 6,* La. Geol. Svy. (1935), pp. 73-166.

103. "Salt Domes in the Carpathian Region of Rumania, Geology of the": Voitesti, I. P., *Bull.,* AAPG (1925), v. 9, no. 8, pp. 1165-1206.

861. "Salt Domes and Their Ceramic Deposits": Steinmayer, R. A., *Bull.,* Am. Ceramic Soc. (1938), v. 17, no. 6, pp. 260-262.

300. "Salt Domes, Coastal, Wildcat Developments on": Williams, Neil, *Oil and Gas Jour.* (1938), v. 37, no. 12, pp. 33-34.

128a. "Salt Domes, Colorado-Utah": *Bull.* AAPG (1927), v. 11, no. 2, pp. 111-133.

5. "Salt Domes, Deep Seated, Aerial Photos of Multiple Surface Faults May Locate": Desjardins, Louis, *Oil and Gas Jour.* (1952), v. 51, no. 13, pp. 82-84.

697. "Salt Domes, Deep Seated, in the Northeast Portion of the Mississippi Salt Basin, Faulting Associated With": Hughes, Dudley, J., *Trans., GCAGS* (1960), v. 10, pp. 154-173.

862. "Salt Domes in Depth, Distribution of" (abs.): Rosaire, E. E., and Stiles, M. E., *Pan Am. Geologist* (1932), v. 57, no. 4, p. 316.

863. "Salt Domes, Discussion of Thrust Faults on": Link, T. A., *Bull.,* AAPG (1954), v. 38, no. 12, p. 2506.

864. "Salt Domes of East Texas Basin Flavored with Oil": Krusekopf, H. H., Jr., *Oil and Gas Jour.* (1959), v. 57, no. 19, pp. 143-147.

865. "Salt Domes in East Texas, Recently Discovered": Renick, B. C., *Bull.,* AAPG (1928), v. 12, no. 5, pp. 527-547.

346. "Salt Domes, Economic Importance of": Barton, D. C., *Bull. 2801,* Tex. U. (1928), pp. 7-53.

772. "Salt Domes, Effect of, on the Accumulation of Petroleum": Barton, D. C., *Bull.,* AAPG (1931), v. 15, no. 1, pp. 61-66.

866. "Salt Domes, Experimental Study of the Origin of": Torrey, P. D. and Fralich, C. E.,

Jour. Geol. (1926), v. 34, no. 3, pp. 224-234; (abs.) *Oil and Gas Jour.* (1925), v. 23, no. 45, p. 133.

867. "Salt Domes, Experiments in Connection with": Escher, B. G. and Kuehner, P. H., *Leidsche Geol. Mededeel.* (1929), Deel 3, Afl. 3, pp. 151-182.

744. "Salt Domes, Favorite Home for Oil": Hanna, Marcus A., *Oil and Gas Jour.* (1959), v. 57, no. 6, pp. 138-142.

382. "Salt Domes, Fluid Mechanics of": Nettleton, L. L., *Bull.,* AAPG (1934), v. 18, no. 9, pp. 1175-1204; *Gulf Coast Oil Fields,* AAPG (1936), pp. 79-108.

672. "Salt Domes Genetically Related to Zones of Crustal Megashearing, Are?": Keith, B. A., *Oil Weekly* (1942), v. 108, no. 3, p. 24.

868. "Salt Domes—A Geological Enigma": Gardner, Frank J., *Oil and Gas Jour.* (1955), v. 54, no. 14, p. 155.

537. "Salt Domes, Gulf Coast": Hill, R. T., *Econ. Geol.* (1919), v. 14, no. 8, pp. 643-644.

538. "Salt Domes, Gulf Coast": Wolf, A. G., *Magazine,* Colorado School of Mines (1920), v. 10, no. 9, pp. 171-177.

542. "Salt Domes, Gulf Coast, Their Distribution, Description and Origin": Wojciechowski, W. A., *MS Thesis,* Mich. U. (1952), Dept. of Geol.

337. "Salt Domes, Gulf Coast, Drilling Play Reflects Activity Near": *Oil and Gas Jour.* (1940), v. 38, no. 50, pp. 92, 95, 102.

754. "Salt Domes, Gulf Coast, Intrusive Origin of": Rogers, G. S., *Econ. Geol.* (1918), v. 13, pp. 447-485; (discussion), v. 14, pp. 178-180.

755. "Salt Domes, Gulf Coast, Intrusive Origin of the, Its Bearing on the Accumulation of Oil": Jones, W. A., *Econ. Geol.* (1918), v. 13, no. 8, pp. 621-622.

631. "Salt Domes, Gulf Coast, Louann Salt and Its Relationship to": Andrews, Donald I., *Trans., GCAGS* (1960), v. 10, pp. 215-240.

565. "Salt Domes, Gulf Coast, Occurrence of Gypsum in": Barton, D. C., *Econ. Geol.* (1922), v. 17, no. 2, pp. 141-143.

539. "Salt Domes of the Gulf Coast, Origin of": Rogers, G. S., *Jour.,* Washington Acad. Sci. (1919), v. 9, no. 10, pp. 291-292.

95. "Salt Domes, Gulf Coast, Origin of the Cap Rock of the": DeGolyer, E. L., (discussion) *Econ. Geol.* (1918), v. 13, pp. 616-620.

789. "Salt Domes on the Gulf Coast, Plastic Flow Theory in Explanation of": Smiley, T. F., *Oil and Gas Jour.* (1936), v. 34, no. 40, p. 48.

530. "Salt Domes of the Gulf Coast Region": Hanna, Marcus A., *Oil* (1944), v. 4, no. 4, pp. 29-30.

408. "Salt Domes in the Gulf Coast Region, A Review of Geological Concepts and Economic Significance of": Halbouty, Michel T., *Bull.*, Houston Geol. Soc. (1959), v. 2, no. 2.

543. "Salt Domes of the Gulf Coast and Their Relation to Petroleum": Hare, J. E., *MS Thesis*, Yale U. (1922), Dept. of Geol.

541. "Salt Domes in Gulf Coast Still Reign": Ingalls, Philip C., *Oil and Gas Jour.* (1953), v. 52, no. 7, p. 357.

869. "Salt Domes, Gulf Coast, Tectonics of" (abs.): Hanna, Marcus A., *Trans.*, GCAGS (1958), v. 8, p. 100.

544. "Salt Domes, Gulf Coast, Where are Those?" *Oil and Gas Jour.* (1952), v. 51, no. 14, pp. 130-134.

551. "Salt Domes of Gulf Coastal Plain, Genesis of": Halbouty, Michel T. and Hardin, George C. Jr., *Bull.*, AAPG (1956), v. 40, no. 4, pp. 737-746.

757. "Salt Domes, Gulf Coastal Plain, Secondary Intrusive Origin of": Matteson, W. G. and Coste, E., *Trans.*, AIME (1921), v. 65, pp. 295-334; preprints, nos. 1048, 1073, 1088; (abs.) *Mining and Metallurgy*, no. 170, p. 37.

870. "Salt Domes, Gulf Coastal Plain, Subsidence in": Sellards, E. H., *Bull. 3001*, Tex. U. (1930), Bur. Econ. Geol., pp. 9-36.

553. "Salt Domes of the Gulf Coastal Plain of the United States, Origin of the": DeGolyer, E. L., *Jour. Inst. Pet.* (1931), v. 17, pp. 331-333.

562. "Salt Domes, Gulf, Do All Have Vents?", Thacker, R. B., *Eng. and Mining Jour.* (1926), v. 121, no. 17, pp. 684-686.

365. "Salt Domes of the Gulf Region of the United States, Exploration Techniques on": Halbouty, Michel T. and Hardin, George C., Jr., *Oil and Gas Jour.* (1959), v. 57, no. 24, pp. 134-137.

364. "Salt Domes of the Gulf Region of the United States, A Geological Appraisal of Present and Future Exploration Techniques on": Halbouty, Michel T. and Hardin, George C., Jr., *Paper 5*, Fifth World Pet. Cong. (1959), sec. 1, pp. 1-13; *Oil* (1959), v. 19, no. 8, pp. 33-42.

609. "Salt Domes of the Isthmus of Tehauntepec": Ver Wiebe, W. A., *Pan Am. Geologist* (1926), v. 45, no. 5, pp. 349-358.

628. "Salt Domes, Limestone Cap Rock of, A Theory for the Formation of": McLeod, Richard R., *Trans.*, GCAGS (1960), v. 10, pp. 151-153.

96. "Salt Domes, Louisiana, Origin of the Cap Rock of": Taylor, R. E., *Bull. 11*, La. Geol. Svy. (1938), Dept. of Conserv., 191 pp.; *PhD Dissertation*, LSU, Dept. of Geol; Review of by R. E. Janssen, *Jour. Geol.* (1939), v. 47, p. 222.

657. "Salt Domes of Louisiana and Texas": Harris, G. D., *Science* (1908), new ser., v. 27, pp. 347-348.

871. "Salt Domes, Manner of Salt Flowage in": Jones, R. A., *Oil Weekly* (1932), v. 66, no. 7, pp. 31-32, 35-36.

385. "Salt Domes, Mechanics of Formation of, With Special Reference to Gulf Coast Salt Domes of Texas and Louisiana": Barton, D. C., *Bull.*, AAPG (1933), v. 17, no. 9, pp. 1025-1083; *Gulf Coast Oil Fields*, AAPG (1936), pp. 20-78.

872. "Salt Domes, Meteor Craters, and Crypto-Volcanic Structures": Washburne, C. W., *Bull.*, AAPG (1937), v. 21, no. 5, pp. 629-630.

873. "Salt Domes; Their Nature, Origin, and Composition": Spaulding, W. M., *MS Thesis*, Mich. U. (1952), Dept. of Geol.

721. "Salt Domes of North America, Notes on the" (abs.): DeGolyer, E. L., *Bull.*, GSA (1923), v. 34, p. 66.

723. "Salt Domes, North American, Origin of": DeGolyer, E. L., *Bull.*, AAPG (1925), v. 9, no. 5, pp. 831-874; *Geology of Salt Dome Oil Fields*, AAPG (1926), pp. 1-44.

874. "Salt Dome's North Flank Its Best Prospect, Is a?" Shead, W. C. and Allen, Edwin R., *World Oil* (1956), v. 142, no. 5, pp. 158-160.

634. "Salt Domes, North Louisiana, Tabulation of": Blanpied, B. W., *Guidebook*, 1960 Spring Field Trip, Shreveport Geol. Soc., pp. 57-60

875. "Salt Domes of Northeastern Texas": Cheney, C. A., *Oil and Gas Jour.* (1922), v. 20, no. 32, pp. 82-83.

486. "Salt Domes of Northern Germany": Ramanes, James, *Jour. Inst. Pet.* (1931), v. 17, pp. 252-259.

726. "Salt Domes, Oil Concentration About": Harris, G. D., *Science* (1912), new ser., v. 35, pp. 546-547.

876. "Salt Domes and Old Fields, Comb Coastal Louisiana for Overlooked Reserves in": Williams, Neil, *Oil and Gas Jour.* (1936), v. 35, no. 27, pp. 11-12.

877. "Salt Domes, The Origin of": Wolf, A. G., *Eng. and Mining Jour.* (1923), v. 115, no. 9, pp. 412-414.

98. "Salt Domes, The Origin of the Cap Rock of": Hackford, J. E., *Oil Eng. and Finance* (1924), v. 5, no. 101, p. 512.

795. "Salt Domes, Outer Rings of Production Should Surround": Carroll, Don L., *Oil Weekly* (1943), v. 111, no. 9, p. 14.

878. "Salt Domes of Permian and Pennsylvanian Age in Southeastern Utah and Their Influence on Oil Accumulation": Crum, H. E. and Prommel, H. W. C., *Bull.*, AAPG (1927), v. 11, no. 4, pp. 373-393.

763. "Salt Domes in Persia": Harrison, J. V., *Jour. Inst. Pet.* (1931), v. 17, pp. 300-320.

879. "Salt Domes, Piercement, in South Louisiana, Unconformity Traps Around" (abs.): Jackson, J. Roy, Jr.; (abs.) *Oil and Gas Jour.* (1956), v. 54, no. 53, pp. 142-144.

476. "Salt Domes, Piercement Type, Application of Geophysical Technique to Finding New Flank Production on": Weaver, Paul, *Oil and Gas Jour.* (1952), v. 51, no. 7, pp. 90-94.

880. "Salt Domes, Piercement Type, Strategic Location of Wells in Flank Sands on": Anonymous, *Oil Weekly* (1942), v. 104, no. 10, pp. 17-20.

788. "Salt Domes of Plaquemines and St. Barnard Parishes": Howe, H. V. and McGuirt, J. H., *Bull. 8,* La. Geol. Svy. (1936), pp. 200-278.

803. "Salt Domes, Refraction Surveying of": Wolf, Alexander, *World Oil* (1947), v. 127, no. 7, pp. 120-125.

702. "Salt Domes Related to Mississippi Submarine Trough": Shepard, F. P., *Bull.*, GSA (1937), v. 48, pp. 1349-1361; (abs.) *Proc.* (1936), pp. 101-202; *Geophysics,* v. 2, no. 2, p. 169.

881. "Salt Domes, Reply to Thrust Faults on": Halbouty, Michel T. and Hardin, George C., Jr., *Bull.*, AAPG (1954), v. 38, no. 12, p. 2566.

882. "Salt Domes, the Significance of, to Petroleum Occurrence": Lloyd, J. J., *Geol. Rev.*, Geol. Soc. Coll. (1944), New York, v. 4, no. 1, pp.24-28.

645. *Salt Domes of South Louisiana, Vol. I:* Stipe, Jack C. (ed), New Orleans Geol. Soc. (1960), 145 pp.; *Vol. II:* Spillers, James P. (ed.), New Orleans Geol. Soc. (1962), 107 pp.; *Vol. I (first revision):* Raymond, J. P., Jr. (ed.), New Orleans Geol. Soc. (1963), 133 pp.

646. "Salt Domes, South Louisiana, Field Trip to": Taylor, R. E., *Guides to Southeastern Geology,* GSA and Assoc. Soc. (1955), pp. 538-548.

883. "Salt Domes of South Texas": Barton, D. C., *Bull.*, AAPG (1925), v. 9, no. 3, pp. 536-589;

Geology of Salt Dome Oil Fields, AAPG (1926), pp. 718-771.

650. "Salt Domes, Southern Louisiana, Nature of Growth of and Its Effect on Petroleum Accumulation": Atwater, Gordon and Forman, McLain J., *Bull.*, AAPG (1959), v. 43, no. 11, pp. 2592-2622; (abs.) *Trans.*, GCAGS (1958), v. 8, pp. 20-21.

651. "Salt Domes, Southern Louisiana, Present Activities Among" (abs.): Ames, E. R., *Pan Am. Geologist*, v. 53, no. 3, pp. 220-221.

884. "Salt Domes, Stratigraphy of the Gulf Coastal Plain as Related to": Shaw, E. W., *Jour.*, Washington Acad. Sci. Jour. (1919), v. 9, no. 10, pp. 289-291.

885. "Salt Domes and Structures, East **Texas,** Promise Oil": Logan, Jack, *Oil Weekly* (Aug. 7, 1931), pp. 17-20.

65. "Salt Domes in Texas, (Boggy Creek and Moss Bluff Domes), Two New": Pratt W. E., *Bull.*, AAPG (1926), v. 10, no. 11, pp. 1171-1172.

886. "Salt Domes, Texas, Electrical Surveys of Some Shallow": Lewis, Wm. Bradley, *Geophysics* (1948), v. 13, no. 4, pp. 595-599.

140. "Salt Domes of Texas, Gulf Coast, First Authentic Cretaceous Formation Found on": Morrison, T. E., *Bull.*, AAPG (1929), v. 13, no. 8, pp. 1065-1069.

725. "Salt Domes, Texas Gulf Piercement Type, Factors Affecting Quantity of Oil Accumulation Around Some": Halbouty, Michel T. and Hardin, George C., Jr., *Bull.*, AAPG (1955), v. 39, no. 5, pp. 697-711.

656. "Salt Domes of Texas and Louisiana": Deussen, Alexander, *Oil Weekly* (1922), v. 24, no. 4, pp. 11, 16, 18.

632. "Salt Domes of Texas and Louisiana Gulf Coast": Clapp, F. G., *Jour. Inst. Pet.* (1931), v. 17, pp. 281-299.

6a. "Salt Domes in Texas, Louisiana, Mississippi, Alabama and Offshore Tidelands: A Survey": Hawkins, Murphy E. and Jirik, C. J., *Inf. Circ.*, U. S. Dept. of the Interior, Bur. of Mines (in press, 1966).

756. "Salt Domes, The Theory of Volcanic Origin of": DeGolyer, E. L., *Bull. 137*, AIME (1918), pp. 987-1000; discussion by J. A. Udden, *Bull. 139*, AIME (1918), p. 1147; *Trans.*, AIME (1918), v. 61, pp. 456-477.

574. "Salt Domes, Three New Reported, All in Harris County, Texas": Williams, Neil, *Oil and Gas Jour.* (1928), v. 27, no. 14, p. 32.

887. "Salt Domes of the United States": Hanna, Marcus A., *Bull.,* GSA (1932), v. 43, p. 160; *Pan Am. Geologist,* v. 57, no. 1, pp. 75-76.

888. *Salt, An Essay on, Containing Notices of Its Origin, Formation, Geological Position and Principal Localities, Embracing a Particular Description of the American Salines:* Van Rennselaer, Jeremiah (1823), New York, 80 pp.

889. "Salt—Depositional and Deformation Problems": Lees, G. M., *Jour. Inst. Pet.* (1931), v. 17, pp. 259-280.

366a. "Salt and Fault Map of South Louisiana (1966 Edition)": Wallace, W. E., Jr. (ed.), *Trans.,* GCAGS (1966), v. 16.

871. "Salt Flowage in Salt Domes, Manner of": Jones, R. A., *Oil Weekly* (1932), v. 66, no. 7, pp. 31-32, 35-36.

26. "Salt Formation, Artesian": Willis, B., *Bull.,* AAPG (1948), v. 32, no. 7, pp. 1227-1264.

515a. "Salt in Gulf Coast Domes, Structure of": Kupfer, Donald H., *Symposium on Salt,* Northern Ohio Geol. Soc., Inc. (1963), Cleveland, Ohio, pp. 104-123.

642. "Salt in Louisiana, With Special Reference to Its Geologic Occurrence": Harris, G. D., *Bull.,* La. Geol. Svy. (1908), v. 7, pp. 5-59.

487. "Salt Masses of Germany, The Upthrust of the": Stille, H., *Bull.,* AAPG (1925), v. 9, no. 3, pp. 417-441; *Geology of Salt Dome Oil Fields,* AAPG (1926), pp. 142-146.

802. "Salt Masses, Outlining of, by Refraction Methods": Musgrove, A. W., Woolley, W. C. and Gray, Helen, *Geophysics* (1960), v. 25, no. 1, pp. 141-167.

485. "Salt Migration in Northern Germany, on the Mechanism of": Trusheim, F., *Bull.,* AAPG (1960), v. 44, no. 9, pp. 1519-1540.

29. "Salt Mine, Avery Island, and the Joseph Jefferson Salt Deposit": Lucas, A. F., *Eng. and Mining Jour.* (1896), v. 62, pp. 463-464.

32. "Salt Mines of Avery's Island": Romeyn, H., *Mines and Min.* (1900), v. 20, pp. 438-439.

31. "Salt in Mine on Avery's Island, Salt Inclusion in": Heald, K. C., *Bull.,* AAPG (1924), v. 8, no. 5, pp. 674-676.

11. "Salt Mines of Central Kansas, Anhydrite and Associated Minerals from": Rogers, A. F., *Am. Jour. Sci.* (1910), ser. 4, v. 29, pp. 258-261.

347b. "Salt Mines, Electrical Resistivity Surveys in": Scharon, LeRoy, *Symposium on Salt,* Northern Ohio Geol. Soc., Inc. (1963), Cleveland, Ohio, pp. 379-389.

496. "Salt Mines of Grand Cote Island, A Piece of Difficult Shaft Sinking in Developing the": Hazelhurst, J. N., *Eng. News* (Nov. 7, 1901).

643. "Salt Mines, Louisiana, Their Operation and Output": Wooten, P., *Min. World* (1912), v. 36, pp. 401-402.

36. "Salt and Overhanging Cap Rock at Barbers Hill, Chambers County, Texas": Judson, Sidney A., Murphy, P. C. and Stamey, R. A., *Bull.,* AAPG (1932), v. 16, no. 5, pp. 469-482.

371. "Salt Ridge Hypothesis on Origin of Texas Gulf Coast Type of Faulting": Quarles, Miller, Jr., *Bull.,* AAPG (1953), v. 37, no. 3, pp. 489-508.

890. "Salt in Smackover Field, Union County, Arkansas": Spooner, W. C., *Bull.,* AAPG (1932), v. 16, no. 6, pp. 601-608.

890a. "Salt Solution Cavities for Underground Storage, Use of": Bays, Carl A., *Symposium on Salt* (1963), Northern Ohio Geol. Soc., Inc., pp. 564-578.

699. "Salt in Southern Mississippi, Seismograph Evidence on the Depth of the": Swartz, Charles A., *Geophysics* (1943), v. 8, no. 1, pp. 1-2.

545. "Salt Stock, Evidence of Erosion of, in Gulf Coast Salt Plug in Late Oligocene": Hanna, Marcus A., *Bull.,* AAPG (1939), v. 23, no. 4, pp. 604-607; corrections, p. 1576; v. 27, no. 1, pp. 85-86.

486a. "Salt Stock Families in Northwestern Germany" (abs.): Sannemann, D., *Bull.,* AAPG (1965), v. 49, no. 3, p. 357.

555a. "Salt Structure of Gulf of Mexico Basin— A Review": Murray, G. E., *Bull.,* AAPG (1966), v. 50, no. 3, pp. 439-478.

612. "Salt Structure of Jefferson Island Salt Dome, Iberia and Vermilion Parishes, Louisiana": Balk, Robert, *Bull.,* AAPG (1953), v. 37, no. 11, pp. 2455-2474.

771. "Salt Structures in Their Relation to Petroleum Deposits" (abs.): Stahl, A. F. V., *Jour. Inst. Pet.* (1929), v. 15, pp. 315A-316A.

639. "Salt and Sulphur in Louisiana, Resume of": Murray, G. E., *Proc.,* Southeastern Mineral Symposium (1950); *Spec. Pub. 1,* Ky. Geol. Svy. (1953), pp. 48-68.

125. "Salt and Sulphur Valuable Deposits in Coastal Fields": McGreal, P. L., *Oil and Gas Jour.* (1927), v. 25, no. 35, p. 107.

891. *Salt, Symposium on:* Bersticker, A. C. (ed.), Northern Ohio Geol. Soc., Inc. (1963), Cleveland, Ohio, 661 pp.

892. "Salt, A Theory on the Occurrence of":

Shrewsbury, R. D., *Oil Weekly* (1946), v. 122, no. 1, pp. 36-39.

540. "Salt Volume of Gulf Coast Salt Domes": Hammer, Sigmund, *Trans.,* AAPG-SEPM-SEG Jt. Ann. Mtg. (1953), Houston, Texas, p. 9, unpublished ms. (Courtesy Sigmund Hammer and Gulf Research and Development Company).

342. "Salt Water Injection for Pressure Maintenance in East Hackberry Field, Louisiana": Euwer, M. L., *Oil and Gas Jour.* (1945), v. 44, no. 21, pp. 100-102, 131.

893. "Saltillo-Galeana Areas, Coahuila and Nuevo Leon, Mesozoic Stratigraphy and Structure": *Guidebook,* 1959 Field Trip, So. Tex. Geol. Soc., pp. 11-13.

423a. "Salzhorste, Zur Geologie der Nordhannoverschen": Harbort, E., *Monatsber. d. Deutsch. Geol. Ges.,* 62 (1910), p. 326.

893a. "Salzmassen, Studien Uber den Bau von": Lachmann, R., *Kali* (1910a), Heft 9, p. 188.

893b. *Salzstock-Familien, Zur Entwicklung von:* Sannemann, D., (1960).

28a. "Salzgebirges, Das Aufsteigen der": Stille, H., *Zeitschr. f. Prakt. Geologie,* 19 (1911), p. 91.

385b. "Salzvorkommen, Zur Frage der Aufpressungsvorgilange und des Alters der Nordwestdeutschen": Harbort, E., *Kali* (1913), Heft 5, p. 112.

80. "San Felipe (Brookshire) Field, Walker County, Texas": Davies, W. J., *Guidebook,* AAPG-SEPM-SEG Jt. Ann. Mtg. (March, 1953), Houston, Texas, pp. 97-99.

505. "San Luis Pass Dome, Brazoria County, Texas, Submarine Gravity Detailing": Nettleton, L. L., *Geophysics* (1957), v. 22, no. 2, pp. 348-358.

505a. "San Marcos Arch, Texas, Stratigraphic-Trap Possibilities in Upper Jurassic Rocks": Halbouty, Michel T., *Bull.,* AAPG (1966), v. 50, no. 1, pp. 3-24.

681. "Santa Ana: Mexico's No. 2 Field?": Lawrence, Carl, *Oil and Gas Jour.* (1961), v. 59, no. 35, pp. 80-82.

42. "Saratoga and Batson Oil Fields, Further Notes on Barite Pisolites from the": Barton, D. C. and Mason, S. L., *Bull.,* AAPG (1925), v. 9, no. 9, pp. 1294-1295.

894. "Saratoga Dome, Repressuring Test at": Williams, Neil, *Oil and Gas Jour.* (1930), v. 29, no. 15, pp. 39, 146-147.

895. "Saratoga Oil Field, Hardin County, Texas" Suman, J. R., *Bull.,* AAPG (1925), v. 9, no. 2,

pp. 263-285; *Geology of Salt Dome Oil Fields,* AAPG (1926), pp. 501-523.

749. "Saratoga Oil Field, Texas, Oolitic and Pisolitic Barite from the": Moore, E. S., *Bull.,* GSA (1914), v. 25, pp. 77-79.

896. "Saratoga Salt Dome, Hardin County, Texas, Drilling for Steeply Dipping Oil Producing Sands": Vittrup, L. J., *Bull.,* AAPG (1947), v. 31, no. 11, pp. 2041-2044.

897. "Saratoga, Second Compressor Unit for Repressuring at": Williams, Neil, *Oil and Gas Jour.* (1932), v. 30, no. 38, p. 67.

898. "Scale Models, Geologic Notes on the Construction of": McDowell, A. N. and Parker, Travis J., *Mines Mag.* (1950), v. 40, no. 10, pp. 75-79.

405. "Scale Models, Theory of, as Applied to the Study of Geologic Structures": Hubbert, M. K., *PhD Dissertation,* Chicago U. (1937), Dept. of Geol.; *Bull.,* GSA (1937), v. 48, pp. 1459-1519.

684. "Scanlon or Midway Dome, Lamar County, Mississippi": Munroe, D. J., *Bull.,* AAPG (1938), v. 22, no. 7, pp. 816-822; (abs.) *Oil and Gas Jour.* (1938), v. 36, no. 44, pp. 58, 62; *World Pet.,* v. 9, no. 10, p. 70.

899. "Section 28 Salt Dome, St. Martin Parish, Louisiana": Donoghue, D., *Bull.,* AAPG (1925), v. 9, no. 9, pp. 1290-1293; *Geology of Salt Dome Oil Fields,* AAPG (1926), pp. 352-355.

900. "Sections, Geologic, in Texas and Adjoining States": Thompson, W. C., *Bull.,* AAPG (1937), v. 21, no. 8, pp. 1083-1087.

900a. *Sedimentary Rocks:* Pettijohn, F. J., Harper & Brothers (1957), Second Edition, New York, 484 pp.

762a. "Sedimentation in Permian Castile Sea": King, R. H., *Bull.,* AAPG (1947), v. 31, no. 3, pp. 470-477.

559. "Sediments from Gulf of Mexico": Levorsen, A. I., *Bull.,* AAPG (1939), v. 23, no. 7, p. 1123.

728. "Sediments of Late Geological Age, Oil Fields of Gulf Coast Area Found in": Woodruff, E. G., *Oil and Gas Jour.* (1935), v. 33, no. 64, pp. 38-39, 149.

311a. "Seepage Refluxion, Dolomitization by": Adams, J. E. and Rhodes, M. L., *Bull.,* AAPG (1960), v. 44, no. 12, pp. 1912-1920.

550. "Seismic and Gravity Exploration in the Gulf Coast Through 1936, The Amount and Distribution of": Rosaire, E. E. and Ransone, K., *Geophysics* (1937), v. 2, no. 1, pp. 1-16.

901. "Seismic Prospecting, The History and De-

velopment of": Weatherby, B. B., *Geophysical Case Histories,* SEG (1948), v. 1, pp. 7-20; *Geophysics* (1940), v. 5, no. 3, pp. 215-230.

826. "Seismograph Determination of Salt Dome Boundary Using Well Detector Deep on Dome Flank": Gardner, L. W., *Geophysics* (1949), v. 14, no. 1, pp. 29-38; (abs.) *Oil and Gas Jour.* (1948), v. 46, no. 52, p. 115.

711. "Seismograph Evidence on Depth of Salt Column, Moss Bluff Dome, Texas": Hoylman, H. Wayne, *Geophysics* (1946), v. 11, no. 2, pp. 128-134.

824. "Seismograph Evidence on the Depth of the Salt in Southeast Texas": Hoylman, H. Wayne, *Geophysics* (1945), v. 10, no. 3, p. 450.

902. "Seismological Discovery and Partial Detail of Vermilion Bay Salt Dome, Louisiana": Rosaire, E. E. and Lester, O. C., Jr., *Bull.,* AAPG (1932), v. 16, no. 12, pp. 1221-1229; *Geophysical Case Histories,* SEG (1948), v. 1, no. 1, pp. 135-143; *Trans.,* Soc. Pet. Geophy. (1933), v. 3, pp. 51-59; *Early Geophysical Papers,* SEG (1947), pp. 381-389.

818a. "Senegal Salt Basin, The": Aymé, J. M., *Salt Basins Around Africa* (1965), The Institute of Petroleum, London, pp. 83-90.

903. "Ship Shoals Dome off Louisiana Coast, Oil Found on": Kornfeld, J. A., *Oil and Gas Jour.* (1951), v. 49, no. 36, p. 58.

102. "Siderite in Cap Rock at Carlos Dome, Grimes County, Texas, Occurrence of": Rolshausen, F. W., *Bull.,* AAPG (1934), v. 18, no. 4, pp. 543-546, *Gulf Coast Oil Fields,* AAPG (1936), pp. 133-135.

566. "Sierra del Fraile, State of Nuevo Leon, Mexico, Preliminary Report on Instrusive Gypsum": Murray, G. E. and Wall, J. R., *Guidebook,* 1959 Field Trip, So. Tex. Geol. Soc., pp. DI-D7; Spanish Trans. by P. E. Narvarte, pp. D8-D12.

673b. *Sierra Madre Oriental de Mexico, entre Torreon y Monterrey, Tectonica de la:* Cserna, Zoltan de, 20th Congreso Geologico Internacional (1956).

627a. *Sismologico de Refraccion en el Area de Chinameca, Ver., Levantamiento:* Del Castillo, G. L. and Beutelspacher, S. R., Inedito, Archivo Consejo de Recursos Naturales no Renovables (1961).

147. "Sismologico de Refraccion en la Cuenca Salina del Istmo, El Metodo": Basurto Garcia, Jesus and Islas Leal, Juventino, *Bol.,* Asoc. Mex. Geol. Petrol. (1950), v. 2, no. 7, pp. 461-472.

890. "Smackover Field, Union County, Arkansas, Salt in": Spooner, W. C., *Bull.,* AAPG (1932), v. 16, no. 6, pp. 601-608.

24a. "Smackover Limestone in South Arkan-

sas, Northeast Texas, and North Louisiana, Notes on the Stratigraphy of Formations Which Underlie the": Hazzard, R. T., Spooner, W. C. and Blanpied, B. W., *1945 Ref. Rept.,* v. 2, Shreveport Geol. Soc. (1947), pp. 483-503.

904. "Sorrento Dome, Fourth Test Opened": Williams, Neil, *Oil and Gas Jour.* (1928), v. 26, no. 44, pp. 34, 92.

905. "Sorrento Dome Notable Achievement": Williams, Neil, *Oil and Gas Jour.* (1928), v. 26, no. 43, pp. 33, 86.

772b. *Source Beds of Petroleum:* Rept. of investigation supported jointly by the API and the Geol. Svy. of the U. S. Dept. of Interior from 1931 to 1941, Trask, P. D. and Patnode, H. W., AAPG (1942), 561 pp.

906. "South Dayton Salt Dome, Liberty County, Texas": Bowman, W. F., *Bull.,* AAPG (1925), v. 9, no. 3, pp. 655-666; *Geology of Salt dome Oil Fields,* AAPG (1926), pp. 558-559.

302. "South Gillock, Dickinson and Gillock Fields, Galveston County, Texas": Gahagan, Donald I., *Guidebook,* AAPG-SEPM-SEG Jt. Ann. Mtg., (March, 1953), Houston, Texas, pp. 110-113.

470. "South Houston Salt Dome and Oil Field, Harris County, Texas, Geophysical History of": Eby, J. B., *Bull.,* AAPG (1945), v. 29, no. 2, pp. 210-214; *Geophysical Case Histories,* SEG (1948), v. 1, pp. 43-47.

907. "South Liberty Field, Liberty County, Texas": Halbouty, Michel T., *Typical Oil and Gas Fields of Southeast Texas,* Houston Geol. Soc. (1962), pp. 200-206.

460. "South Liberty Salt Dome, Liberty County, Texas, Types of Hydrocarbon Accumulation and Geology of": Halbouty, Michel T. and Hardin, George C., Jr., *Bull.,* AAPG (1951), v. 35, no. 9, pp. 1939-1977.

908. "South Pass Block 27 Field, Offshore, Plaquemines Parish, Louisiana, Geology of": Smith, Derrell, A., *Bull.,* AAPG (1960), v. 45, no. 1, pp. 51-71.

602b. "South Thornwell Field, Jefferson Davis and Cameron Parishes, Louisiana, Intrusive Shale Dome in": Roach, C. B., *Bull.,* AAPG (1962), v. 46, no. 12, pp. 2121-2132.

909. "South Tyler Field, Smith County, Texas": Weirich, T. E., *Bull.,* AAPG (1944), v. 28, no. 11, pp. 1646-1647.

910. *Spindletop:* Clark, James A. and Halbouty, Michel T., Random House Inc. (1952), New York, 306 pp.

911. "*Spindletop* by James A. Clark and Michel T. Halbouty, Review of": Steenland, Nelson C., *Geophysics* (1953), v. 18, no. 1, p. 236.

912. "Spindletop, Captain Lucas—Titan of": *World Oil* (1951), v. 132, no. 1, p. 254.

913. "Spindletop, First and Among Best of Gulf Coast Fields": Logan, L. J., *World Oil* (1951), v. 132, no. 1, pp. 228-230.

914. "Spindletop Given High Place in History of Industry": *World Oil* (1951), v. 132, no. 1, pp. 225-227.

915. "Spindletop, Homage Paid to, as Discovery of Petroleum Epoch": Norman, Stanley, *Oil and Gas Jour.* (1941), v. 40, no. 22, pp. 14-15.

916. "Spindletop — Its Roar Echoed Around the World": Ingram, Robert, *Oil and Gas Jour.* (1941), v. 39, no. 49, pp. 42-46.

917. "Spindletop, Jefferson County, Texas, Variation and Migration of Crude Oil at": Barton, D. C., *Bull.*, AAPG (1935), v. 19, no. 5, pp. 618-643; *Gulf Coast Oil Fields*, AAPG (1936), pp. 309-334.

918. "Spindletop Offers Opportunity for Prolonged Productive Life": Williams, Neil, *Oil and Gas Jour.* (1941), v. 40, no. 22, pp. 16-17.

919. *Spindletop Oil Field, A History of Its Discovery and Development*: Johnson, Thelma, et al, Neches Printing Co. (1927), Beaumont, Texas.

920. "Spindletop Oil Field, Jefferson County, Texas": Halbouty, Michel T. and Eby, J. B., *Bull.*, AAPG (1937), v. 21, no. 4, pp. 475-490.

921. "Spindletop, Opening with Lucas Gusher; a Lesson in Perseverance": McBeth, R. S., *Nat'l Pet. News* (1921), v. 13, pp. 51-52.

922. "Spindletop's Production Peaks: 1902 and 1927": *World Oil* (1951), v. 132, no. 1, p. 232.

762. "Spindletop, Revival of, Recalls the Dream of Patillo Higgins": *Oil and Gas Jour.* (1926), v. 25, no. 8, pp. 41, 107.

811. "Spindletop, Rotary System of Drilling Pioneered at": Kastrop, J. E., *World Oil* (1951), v. 132, no. 1, pp. 233-234, 238, 240, 244, 246, 248, 252.

923. "Spindletop Salt Dome and Oil Field, Jefferson County, Texas": Barton, D. C. and Paxson, R. B., *Bull.*, AAPG (1925), v. 9, no. 3, pp. 594-612; *Geology of Salt Dome Oil Fields*, AAPG (1926), pp. 478-496.

924. "Spindletop's Second Fifty Years": Halbouty, Michel T. and Clark, James A., *The Texas Preview* (Jan., 1953), pp. 26-28.

925. "Spindletop Section": *Oil and Gas Jour.* (1926), v. 25, no. 14, pp. 76A-76P.

926. "Spindletop Wells Worked Over by Stanolind to Control Water": Williams, Neil, *Oil and Gas Jour.* (1936), v. 35, no. 26, pp. 89, 91.

927. "Starks Dome is Making Oil History": Williams, Neil, *Oil and Gas Jour.* (1927), v. 26, no. 19, pp. 184-185.

570. "Starks Field, Calcasieu Parish, Louisiana, Hackberry Foraminiferal Zonation of": Kornfeld, M. M., *Bull.*, AAPG (1939), v. 23, no. 12, pp. 1835-1836.

846. "Statistics, Salt Dome": Patrick, W. W., *Guidebook*, AAPG-SEPM-SEG Jt. Ann. Mtg. (1953), Houston, Texas, pp. 13-20.

847. "Statistics, Salt Dome": Sawtelle, George, *Bull.*, AAPG (1936), v. 20, no. 6, pp. 726-735; *Gulf Coast Oil Fields*, AAPG (1936), pp. 109-118.

80. "Steen, Brooks, and Grand Saline Salt Domes, Smith and Van Zandt Counties, Texas": Powers, Sidney and Hopkins, O. B., *Bull.* 736, USGS (1922), pp. 179-239.

621. "Steinsalz and Kalisalze, Geology by Franz Lotze, Review of": Reed, R. D., *Bull.*, AAPG (1939), v. 23, no. 2, pp. 254-256.

689a. "Storage of Radioactive Waste in Mine Cavities" (abs.): Struxness, E. G., *Symposium on Salt*, Northern Ohio Geol. Soc., Inc. (1963), p. 412.

505a."Stratigraphic-Trap Possibilities in Upper Jurassic Rocks, San Marcos Arch, Texas": Halbouty, Michel T., *Bull.*, AAPG (1966), v. 50, no. 1, pp. 3-24.

546. "Stratigraphic Traps on Gulf Coast, Probably Undiscovered": Halbouty, Michel T., *World Pet.* (1938), v. 9, no. 6, pp. 27-39.

547. "Stratigraphic Variations, Shallow, over Gulf Coast Structures": Rosaire, E. E., *Geophysics* (1938), v. 3, no. 2, pp. 96-115; (discussion), pp. 115-121.

390. "Stratigraphy of the Frio Formation, Jefferson and Orange Counties, Texas": Reedy, M. F., Jr., *Bull.*, AAPG (1949), v. 33, no. 11, pp. 1830-1858; (abs.) *Bull.*, AAPG (1949), v. 33, no. 1, pp. 108-109; *Oil and Gas Jour.* (1949), v. 47, no. 32, p. 104.

452. "Stratigraphy and the Geology of the Port Barre Salt Dome": Crain, H. F., *Thesis*, Kan. U. (1947), Dept. of Geol.

884. "Stratigraphy of the Gulf Coastal Plain, as Related to Salt Domes"(abs.): Shaw E. W.,

Jour., Washington Acad. Sci. (1919), v. 9, no. 10, pp. 289-291.

575. "Stratigraphy of Harris and Waller Counties, Texas": Beckelhymer, R., L., *Bull.*, AAPG (1946), v. 30, no. 1, pp. 52-62.

848. "Stratigraphy, Salt Dome-Lower Gulf Coast" (abs.): Lowman, Shepard W., *Oil and Gas Jour.* (1955), v. 53, no. 48, p. 212.

677a. "Stratigraphy of Southeast Mexico, Notes on the": Nuttall, W. L. F., *Geol. Rept. 192* (March, 1929) (inedito).

893. "Stratigraphy and Structure, Mesozoic, Saltillo-Galeana Areas, Coahuila and Nuevo Leon": *Guidebook*, 1959 Field Trip, So. Tex. Geol. Soc., pp. 11-13.

600. "Stratigraphy, Tertiary, and Interior Salt Domes of North Louisiana": Lambert, Ernest H., Jr., *Guidebook*, 1960, Spring Field Trip, Shreveport Geol. Soc., 147 pp.

928. "Stratigraphy, Wilcox (Eocene), A Key to Production (of Oil and Gas)": Echols, D. A. J. and Malkin, D. S., *Bull.*, AAPG (1948), v. 32, no. 1, pp. 11-33; corrections, p. 310.

929. "Stratton Ridge Salt Dome, Brazoria County, Texas": Applin, P. L., *Bull.*, AAPG (1925), v. 9, no. 1, pp. 1-34; *Geology of Salt Dome Oil Fields*, AAPG (1926), pp. 644-677.

682. "Structural Correlation of Micromagnetic and Reflection Data": Jenny, W. P., *Oil Weekly* (1946), v. 124, no. 3, pp. 32-33.

123. "Structural Depression over Gulf Coast Salt Domes, The Origin of the, with Particular Reference to Clay Creek Dome, Washington County, Texas": McDowell, A. N., *MS Thesis*, Tex. A & M U. (1951), Dept. of Geol.

513. "Structural Features in the Gulf Coast Area, Changing Conception of": Clark, R. P., *Oil and Gas Jour.* (1937), v. 35, no. 48, pp. 87-88; (abs.) *World Pet.*, v. 8, p. 106.

461b. *Structural Geology for Petroleum Geologists:* Russell, William L., McGraw-Hill Book Co., Inc. (1955), New York, N. Y.

669. *Structural Map of Texas*, Third Ed.: Sellards, E. H. and Hendricks, L. C., Tex. U. (1946), Bur. Econ. Geol.

685. "Structural Theory for Oil and Gas Migration and Accumulation, Present Interpretations of the": McCoy, Alex, W. and Keyte, W. Ross, *Problems of Petroleum Geology*, AAPG (1934), p. 276.

930. "Structure, Complex, of Wilcox Trend Being Unraveled": Todd, John D., *Oil Weekly* (1940), v. 99, no. 3, pp. 52-57; (abs.) World Pet., v. 12, no. 4, p. 104.

328. "Structure Elements of Domes": Balk, Robert, *Bull.*, AAPG (1936), v. 20, no. 1, pp. 51-67; (abs.) v. 19, no. 1, p. 136; *World Pet.*, v. 7, no. 3, p. 150.

501. "Structure of Grand Saline Salt Dome, Van Zandt County, Texas": Balk, Robert, *Bull.*, AAPG (1949), v. 33, no. 11, pp. 1791-1829.

931. "Structure of Morton Salt Co. Mine, Weeks Island Salt Dome Louisiana": Kupfer, Donald H., *Bull.*, AAPG (1962), v. 46, no. 8, pp. 1460-1467.

635. "Structure, North Louisiana Surface, Evidence is Small": Easton, H. D., Jr., *Oil Weekly* (1935), v. 77, no. 2, pp. 35-38.

728a. *Structure of Typical American Oil Fields*, Vol. I: Teas, L. P., et al, American Association of Petroleum Geologists (1929), Tulsa, Oklahoma, 510 pp.

728b. *Structure of Typical American Oil Fields*, Vol. II: Spooner, W. C., et al, American Association of Petroleum Geologists (1929), Tulsa, Oklahoma, 780 pp.

728c. *Structure of Typical American Oil Fields*, Vol. III: Howell, J. V. (ed.), American Association of Petroleum Geologists (1948), Tulsa, Oklahoma, 516 pp.

932. "Structure of Winnfield Salt Dome, Winn Parish, Louisiana": Hoy, R. B., Foose, R. M. and O'Neill, B. J., Jr., *Bull.*, AAPG (1962), v. 46, no. 8, pp. 1444-1459.

933. "Structure of Winnfield Salt Dome,, Winn Parish, Louisiana": Hoy, R. B. and Kuhn, Robert, *Bull.*, AAPG (1964), v. 48, no. 3, pp. 360-361.

934. "Structure of the Woodlawn Field, Jefferson Davis Parish, Louisiana": Pyle, G. T. and Babisak, Julius, *Trans.*, GCAGS (1951), v. 1, pp. 200-210.

3. "Structures Controlling Accumulation", Olcott, Perry, *Guidebook*, AAPG-SEPM-SEG Jt. Ann. Mtg. (March, 1953), Houston, Texas, pp. 33-36.

935. "Structures, Multiple Sands and Deep Producing Possibilities, Numerous Types of, Outstanding Features of South Texas Geology": Pinkley, G. R., *Oil Weekly* (1936), v. 83, no. 3, pp. 51-53, 56, 58, 60.

936. "Structures, Oil Field, Three Dimensional Method for Solution of": Currie, J. B., *Bull.*, AAPG (1952), v. 36, no. 5, pp. 889-890.

658. "Structures, Where Are the, Off Louisiana and Texas": *Oil and Gas Jour.* (1959), v. 57, no. 24, p. 107.

870. "Subsidence in Gulf Coastal Plain Salt Domes": Sellards, E. H., *Bull. 3001,* Tex. U. (1930), Bur. Econ. Geol., pp. 9-36.

493. "Subsidence of the Surface in the Goose Creek Field, Texas, Some Questions on the Cause to the": Pratt, W. E., *Bull.,* AAPG (1927), v. 11, no. 8, pp. 887-889.

617. "Subsurface Study of Jennings Field, Acadia Parish, Louisiana": Roach, C. B., *Bull.,* AAPG (1943), v. 27, no. 8, pp. 1102-1122; (abs). *Bull.,* AAPG (1941), v. 25, no. 5, p. 929; *Oil and Gas Jour.* (1941), v. 39, no. 47, p. 56.

937. "Sugarland Field, Fort Bend County, Texas": Grinstaad, Fred E., *Typical Oil and Gas Fields of Southeast Texas,* Houston Geol. Soc. (1962), pp. 219, 220.

938. "Sugarland Oil Field, Fort Bend County, Texas": McCarter, W. B. and O'Bannon, P. H., *Bull.,* AAPG (1933), v. 17, no. 11, pp. 1362-1386; *Gulf Coast Oil Fields,* AAPG (1936), pp. 709-733.

939. "Sugarland Oil Field, Fort Bend County, Texas": Pollack, J. M., *Guidebook,* AAPG-SEPM-SEG Jt. Ann. Mtg. (March, 1953), Houston, Texas, pp. 153-156.

940. "Sugarland, Repressuring Successful at": Williams, Neil, *Oil and Gas Jour.* (1930), v. 29, no. 12, pp. 31, 112, 114.

940a. "Sulfates, The Problem of the Natural Reduction of": Bastin, Edson S., *Bull.,* AAPG (1926), v. 10, no. 12, pp. 1270-1299.

811b. "Sulphur Cycle, The Distribution of S34 in Nature and the": Szabo, A., Tudge, A., Macnamara, J. and Thode, H. G., *Science* (1950), v. 111, pp. 464-465.

497. "Sulphur Deposit, Grand Ecaille, Development of the": Lundy, W. T., *Tech. Pub. 553,* AIME (1925), pp. 3-18.

753. "Sulphur Deposits, Gulf Coast Salt Dome, Origin of": Feely, H. W. and Kulp, J. L., *Bull.,* AAPG (1957), v. 41, no. 8, pp. 1802-1853.

941. "Sulphur Deposits, Salt Dome, of Texas Gulf Coast": Barton, D. C., *Pan Am. Geologist* (1925), v. 44, no. 1, pp. 59-60.

395a. "Sulphur Deposits of the U.S.S.R., Genesis of Some": Murzaiev, P. M., *Econ. Geol.* (1937), v. 32, pp. 69-103.

942. "Sulphur Dome, Calcasieu Parish, Louisi-ana": Bauernschmidt, A. J., Jr., *Bull,* AAPG (1930), v. 14, no. 8, pp. 1079-1086.

942a. "Sulphur: Its Occurrence, Production and Economics": Myers, John C., *Bull. 4,* Society of Independent Professional Earth Scientists (July 22, 1964), Houston, Texas, 9 pp.

68. "Sulphur Mine at Boling Dome": Rainwater, E. H. and Zingula, R. P. (ed.), *Field Excursion No. 7,* Geology of the Gulf Coast and Central Texas and Guidebook of Excursions, Houston Geol. Soc. (1962), Houston, Texas, pp. 278-280.

659. "Sulphur Mines, Louisiana's": Moresi, C. K., *Review,* La. Conserv. (1934), v. 4, no. 1, pp. 44-48.

852. "Sulphur Mining, Salt Dome": Wolf, A. G., *Guidebook,* AAPG-SEPM-SEG Jt. Ann. Mtg. (1953), Houston, Texas, pp. 39-40.

805. "Sulfur Recovery, The Reservoir Mechanism of": Rayne, John R., Craft, B. C. and Hawkins, Murray F., Jr., *Trans.,* AIME (1956), v. 207, pp. 246-251; *Tech. Paper 4385; Jour. of Pet. Tech.* (1956), v. 8, no. 11, pp. 246-251.

942b. "Sulfur Resources and Production in Texas, Louisiana, Missouri, Oklahoma, Arkansas and Mississippi, and Markets for the Sulfur": Netzeband, F. F., Early, Thomas R., Ryan, J. P. and Miller, W. C., *Inf. Circ. 8222,* U. S. Dept. of the Interior, Bur. of Mines (1964), 77 pp.

943. "Sulphur Salt Dome, Louisiana": Kelly, P. K., *Bull.,* AAPG (1925), v. 9, no. 3, pp. 479-496; *Geology of Salt Dome Oil Fields,* AAPG (1926), pp. 452-469.

563. "Sulphur Salt Dome, Louisiana, Deformation, Metamorphism, and Mineralization in Gypsum-Anhydrite Cap Rock": Goldman, M. I., *Memior 50,* GSA (1952), 169 pp.

639. "Sulphur and Salt in Louisiana, Resume of": Murray, G. E., *Proc.,* Southwestern Mineral Symposium (1950); *Spec. Pub. 1,* Ky. Geol. Svy. (1953), pp. 48-68.

125. "Sulphur and Salt Valuable Deposits in Coastal Fields": McGreal, P. L., *Oil and Gas Jour.* (1927), v. 25, no. 35, p. 107.

456. "Sulphur and Sulphur Oil Deposits of the Coastal Plain, Geology of the": Lucas, A. F., *Indus. and Chem. Eng. Jour.* (1912), v. 4, pp. 140-143.

326. "Sulphur Supply, The Gulf Coast Domes in Relation to": Thomas, Kirby, *Eng. and Mining Jour.* (1918), v. 106, no. 1, p. 7.

549. "Sulphur Waters, Occurrence of, in the Gulf Coast of Texas and Louisiana, and Their Significance

in Locating New Domes": Henninger, W. F., *Bull.,* AAPG (1925), v. 9, no. 1, pp. 35-37; *Geology of Salt Dome Oil Fields,* AAPG (1926), pp. 774-776.

128. "Surface Formations, Post-Fleming, of Coastal Southeast Texas and South Louisiana": Doering, John, *Bull.,* AAPG (1935), v. 19, no. 5, pp. 651-688; *Gulf Coast Oil Fields,* AAPG (1936), pp. 432-469.

944. "Surface Fracture System of South Texas": Barton, D. C., *Bull.,* AAPG (1933), v. 17, no. 10, pp. 1194-1212; *Gulf Coast Oil Fields,* AAPG (1936), pp. 251-269.

945. "Swamps and Marshlands, Coastal Louisiana": Gould, H. R. and Morgan, J. P., *Field Trip No. 9,* Geology of the Gulf Coast and Central Texas and Guidebook of Excursions, Houston Geol. Soc. (1962), pp. 287-341.

670. "Sweet Lake Field in Coastal Louisiana Is Good Example of Maritime Drilling Operations": Williams, Neil, *Oil and Gas Jour.* (1934), v. 32, no. 48, pp. 15-16.

891. *Symposium on Salt:* Bersticker, A. C. (ed.), Northern Ohio Geol. Soc., Inc. (1963), Cleveland, Ohio, 661 pp.

113. "Tabasco y Chiapas, Resena Acerca de la Geologia de": Bose, E., *Bol.,* Inst., Mexico, num 20, 116, pp. 9 lams.

357a. "Tanzania, Southern, Evaporite Basin in": Kent, P. E., *Salt Basins Around Africa,* The Institute of Petroleum (1965), London, pp. 41-54.

946. "Tatum Salt Dome, Lamar County, Mississippi": Morgan, C. L., *Bull.,* AAPG (1941), v. 25, no. 3, p. 424.

675. "Tectonic Framework of Northeast Mexico": Humphrey, W. E., *Trans.,* GCAGS (1956), v. 6, pp. 25-35.

670. "Tectonic Map of the United States": Longwell, C. R., *et al,* AAPG and USGS (1944).

673b. *Tectonica de la Sierra Madre Oriental de Mexico, entre Torreon y Monterrey:* Cserna, Zoltan de, 20th Congreso Geologico Internacional (1956).

548. "Tectonics, Gulf Coast": Bornhauser, Max, *Bull.,* AAPG (1958), v. 42, no. 2, pp. 339-370.

869. "Tectonics of Gulf Coast Salt Domes" (abs.): Hanna, Marcus A., *Trans.,* GCAGS (1958), v. 8, p. 100.

679. "Tectonics of Mexico": Alvarez, Manuel, Jr., *Bull.,* AAPG (1949), v. 33, no. 8, pp. 1319-1335; *Bol.,* Soc. Geol. Mex. (1949), Tomo 14.

673a. "Tectonics, Regional, and Oil Prospects of

Eastern Mexico": Trumpy, D., *Geological Report No. 247* (1932), Archivo de Petroleos Mexicanos.

680. "Tehuantepec Oil Domes May Mark Potential Oil Territory for Mexico": Gutierrez, Gil and Yzaguirre, Lauro A., *Oil and Gas Jour.* (1960), v. 58, no. 8, pp. 150-161.

747. "Temperature as Affecting Oil Well Drilling and Production": Halbouty, Michel T., *Symposium on Temperatures,* Am. Inst. of Physics (1940), New York, pp. 1039-1057.

748. "Temperature Effects on Oil Well Drilling, Part I": Halbouty, Michel T., *Oil Weekly* (1939), v. 96, no. 2, pp. 10-16; "Temperature Affecting Crude Oil Producing, Part II": (1939), v. 96, no. 2, pp. 15-19.

947. "Temperature Gradients": Van Orstrand, C. E., *Problems of Petroleum Geology,* AAPG (1934), pp. 989-1021.

948. "Temperature Well-Logging": Guyod, H. C., *Oil Weekly* (1946), "Part I, Heat Conductions": v. 123, no. 8, pp. 35-39; "Part II, Salt Intrusions"; no. 9, pp. 33-42; "Part III, Temperature Distribution in the Ground": no. 10, pp. 32-39; "Part IV, Wells in Thermal Equilibrium": no. 11, pp. 50-53; "Part V, Wells Not in Thermal Equilibrium; A, Rotary Holes": v. 124, no. 1, pp. 26-30, 32-34; "Part VI": no. 2, pp. 36-40; "Part VII, Conclusion": no. 3, pp. 38-40.

949. "Tepetate Oil Field, Acadia Parish, Louisiana, Geology of": Bornhauser, Max and Bates, F. W., *Bull.,* AAPG (1938), v. 22, no. 3, pp. 285-305.

510. "Tepetate on Very Deep Salt Dome, Acadia Parish, Louisiana, Gravity Minimum at": Barton, D. C., *Geophysical Case Histories,* SEG (1948), v. 1, pp. 175-183; *Tech. Pub. 1760,* AIME; *Pet. Tech.* (1944), v. 7, no. 6, pp. 15-22.

853. "Terminology, Salt Dome" (abs.): Taylor, R. E., *Oil and Gas Jour.* (1938), v. 36, no. 44, p. 58.

950. "Tertiary-Cretaceous Growth of the East Basin": Coon, L. A., *Trans.,* GCAGS (1956), v. 6, pp. 85-90.

737a. "Tertiary Formations of the West Gulf Coast, Oil and Gas Fields of the Upper Cretaceous and": Adams, G. I., *Bull.,* USGS (1901), pp. 37-62.

640. "Tertiary Stratigraphy of Louisiana, Review of": Howe, H. V., *Bull.,* AAPG (1933), v. 17, no. 6, pp. 613-655; *Gulf Coast Oil Fields,* AAPG (1936), pp. 383-424.

900. "Texas and Adjoining States, Geologic Sections in": Thompson, W. C., *Bull.,* AAPG (1937), v. 21, no. 8, pp. 1083-1087.

689a. "Texas Coastal Plain, Mineral Resources of the": Perkins, J. M. and Lonsdale, J. T., *Bur. Econ. Geol.* (1955), Tex. U., Min. Res. Circ. 38, 49 pp.

330. "Texas Domes, Origin of the": Dumble, E. T., *Bull.*, AIME (1918), v. 142, pp. 1629-1636.

864. "Texas, East, Basin, Salt Domes of, Flavored with Oil": Krusekopf, H. H., Jr., *Oil and Gas Jour.* (1959), v. 57, no. 19, pp. 143-147.

950. "Texas, East, Basin, Tertiary-Cretaceous Growth of the": Coon, L. A., *Trans.*, GCAGS (1956), v. 6, pp. 85-90.

429. "Texas, East, the Geology of": Dumble, E. T., *Bull. 1869,* Tex. U. (1918), 388 pp.

597. "Texas, East, Interior Salt Domes of" (abs.): Clark, G. C., *Bull.*, AAPG (1949), v. 33, no. 12, pp. 2067-2068; *Oil and Gas Jour.* (1949), v. 48, no. 25, p. 87.

817. "Texas, East, and Louisiana Salines, the Origin of the": Norton, E. G., *Bull.*, AIME (1915), no. 97, pp. 93-102; no. 101, pp. 1120-1122; *Trans.*, v. 15, pp. 502-513.

660. "Texas, East, Lower Claiborne of, With Special Reference to Mount Sylvan Dome and Salt Movements": Wendlandt, E. A. and Knebel, G. M., *Bull.*, AAPG (1929), v. 13, no. 10, pp. 1347-1375.

865. "Texas, East, Salt Domes in, Recently Discovered": Renick, B. C., *Bull.*, AAPG (1928), v. 12, no. 5, pp. 527-547.

885. "Texas, East, Salt Domes and Structures Promise Oil": Logan, Jack, *Oil Weekly* (Aug. 7, 1931), pp. 17-20.

420. *Texas, Geological Survey of, First Annual Report of the:* Dumble, E. T. (1889), 410 pp.

457. "Texas, Geology of, Thirty-five Years of Progress in the Knowledge of the" Deussen, Alexander, *Bull. 3501,* Tex. U., pp. 37-57.

458. "Texas, Geology of: Volume 1, Stratigraphy": Sellards, E. H., Adkins, W. S. and Plummer, F. B., *Bull. 3232,* Tex. U. (1933), Bur. Econ. Geol., 1007 pp.

459. "Texas, Geology of: Volume 2, Structural and Economic Geology": Sellards, E. H. and Baker, C. L., *Bull. 3401,* Tex. U. (1934), Bur. Econ. Geol., 884 pp.

941. "Texas Gulf Coast, Salt Dome Sulphur Deposits of": Barton, D. C., *Pan. Am. Geologist* (1925), v. 44, no. 1, pp. 59-60.

951. "Texas Gulf Coast, Velocities in the Local Areal Distribution of": Swan, B. G., *Geophysics* (1942), v. 7, no. 4, pp. 367-392.

729. "Texas Gulf Coastal Region, Relation of Topography to the Oil Fields of the": Wolf, A. G., *Eng. Mechanics Jour.* (1921), v. 111, pp. 474-475.

601. "Texas, Interior Salt Domes of": Powers, Sidney, *Bull.*, AAPG (1926), v. 10, no. 1, pp. 1-60; *Geology of Salt Dome Oil Fields*, AAPG (1926), pp. 209-268.

14. "Texas, Laminated Anhydrite in": Uden, J. A., *Bull.*, AAPG (1924), v. 35, no. 2, pp. 347-354.

815. "Texas-Louisiana Coastal Plain, Minerals of the Saline Domes of the": Hawkins, A. C., *Am. Mineralogist* (1918), v. 3, pp. 189-192.

463. "Texas and Louisiana, Current Geophysical Activity in": Barton, D. C., *Trans.*, Am. Geophys. Union (1936), 17th Ann. Mtg. (1936), pt. 1, pp. 76-77; *Earthquake Notes*, no. 8, p. 76.

472. "Texas and Louisiana, Geophysical Investigations Carried Out in Salt Dome Areas of": Schmidt, C., *Jour. Inst. Pet.* (1931), v. 17, pp. 381-383.

632. "Texas and Louisiana Gulf Coast, Salt Domes of": Clapp, F. G., *Jour. Inst. Pet.* (1931), v. 17, pp. 281-299.

6a. Texas, Louisiana, Mississippi, Alabama and Offshore Tidelands, Salt Domes in; A Survey": Jirik, C. J. and Hawkins, Murphy E., *Inf. Circ.*, U. S. Dept. of Interior, Bur. of Mines (in press, 1966).

602. "Texas, Louisiana and Mississippi, Interior Salt Domes of": Clark, G. C., *Guidebook,* 1960 Spring Field Trip, Shreveport Geol. Soc., pp. 3-16; (abs.) *Bull.*, AAPG (1959), v. 43, no. 7, pp. 1776-1777.

654. "Texas and Louisiana, Oil Producing Horizons of Gulf Coast in": Deussen, Alexander, *Bull.*, AAPG (1934), v. 18, no. 4, pp. 500-518; *Gulf Coast Oil Fields,* AAPG (1936), pp. 1-19.

655. "Texas and Louisiana, Salt Dome Cap Rock Minerals": Hanna, Marcus A. and Wolf, A. G., *Bull.*, AAPG (1934), v. 18, no. 2, pp. 212-225; *Gulf Coast Oil Fields,* AAPG (1936), pp. 119-132.

656. "Texas and Louisiana, Salt Domes of": Deussen, Alexander, *Oil Weekly* (1922), v. 24, no. 4, pp. 11, 16, 18.

657. "Texas and Louisiana, Salt Domes of": Harris, G. D., *Science* (1908), new ser., v. 27, pp. 347-348.

658. "Texas and Louisiana, Where the Struc-

tures Are Off": *Oil and Gas Jour.* (1959), v. 57, no. 24, p. 107.

806. "Texas, Mineral Resources of": Sellards, E. H., *Tex. Geol. Mag.* (1944), v. 8, no. 2, pp. 19-30.

807. "Texas, Mineral Resources of, by Counties, Index to": Sellards, E. H. and Evans, G. L., *Min. Res. Circ. 29,* Tex U. (1944), 21 pp.

683. "Texas, Northeast, Midway Limestone of": Thompson, W. C., *Bull.,* AAPG (1922), v. 6, no. 4, pp. 323-332.

738. "Texas, Northeast, Occurrence of Oil and Gas in": Herald, F. A., (ed.) *Pub. 5116,* Tex. U. (1951), 449 pp.

455. "Texas, Northeast, Resume of Subsurface Geology of, with Emphasis on Salt Structures": Eaton, R. W., *Trans.,* GCAGS (1956), v. 6, pp. 79-84.

24a. "Texas, Northeast, South Arkansas, and North Louisiana, Notes on the Stratigraphy of Formations Which Underlie the Smackover Limestone in": Hazzard, R. T., Spooner, W. C. and Blanpied, B. W., *1945 Ref. Rept.,* v. 2, Shreveport Geol. Soc. (1947), pp. 483-503.

875. "Texas, Northeastern, Salt Domes of": Cheney, C. A., *Oil and Gas Jour.* (1922), v. 20, no. 32, pp. 82-83.

741. "Texas, Occurrence of Oil and Gas in": Sellards, E. H. and Hendricks, L. C., *Pub. 4301,* Tex. U. (1946), pp. 179-190.

952. "Texas, Oil Bearing Formations in": Udden, J. A., *Bull.,* AAPG (1919), v. 3, no. 1, 82-98.

886. "Texas, Shallow Salt Domes, Electrical Surveys of Some": Lewis, Wm. Bradley, *Geophysics* (1948), v. 13, no. 4, pp. 595-599.

935. "Texas, South, Geology, Numerous Types of Structures, Multiple Sands, and Deep Producing Possibilities Outstanding Features of": Pinkley, G. R., *Oil Weekly* (1936), v. 83, no. 3, pp. 51-53, 56, 58, 60.

953. "Texas, South, 1937-1938, Activities in": Mossom, D. S., *Bull.,* AAPG (1938), v. 22, no. 6, pp. 750-757; (abs.) *Oil and Gas Jour.* (1938), v. 36, no. 44, p. 56; v. 37, no. 24, p. 52.

794. "Texas, South, Problem of Pre-Trinity Deposits in": Getzendaner, F. M., *Bull.,* AAPG (1943), v. 27, no. 9, pp. 1228-1244; (abs.), v. 26, no. 5, pp. 904-905.

883. "Texas, South, Salt Domes of": Barton, D. C. *Bull.,* AAPG (1925), v. 9, no. 3, pp. 536-589; *Geology of Salt Dome Oil Fields,* AAPG (1926), pp. 718-771.

944. "Texas, South, Surface Fracture System of": Barton, D. C., *Bull.,* AAPG (1933), v. 17, no. 10, pp. 1194-1212; *Gulf Coast Oil Fields,* AAPG (1936), pp. 251-269.

653. "Texas, Southeast, and Louisiana, Southwest, Torsion Balance Surveys in": Barton, D. C., *Trans.,* Am. Geophys. Union, 13th Ann. Mtg. (1932), pp. 40-42.

737. *Texas, Southeast, Typical Oil and Gas Fields of*: Dunham, R. L. (ed.), Houston Geol. Soc. (1962), 243 pp.

801. "Texas, Upper Gulf Coast, 1939 Reference Report": *Lockwood's, C. D. Oil Report,* (March, 1939), Houston, Texas.

158a. "Texas, West, Delaware Basin and Southeastern New Mexico, Upper Permian Ochoa Series of": Adams, J. E., *Bull.,* AAPG (1944), v. 28, no. 11, pp. 1598-1625.

954. "Thompson Field, Fort Bend County, Texas": Behrman, R. G., Jr., *Guidebook,* AAPG-SEPM-SEG Jt. Ann. Mtg. (March, 1953), Houston, Texas, pp. 157-160.

936. "Three Dimensional Method for Solution of Oil Field Structures": Currie, J. B., *Bull.,* AAPG (1952), v. 36, no. 5, pp. 889-890.

955. "Third Try — Success": Van London, Wilma, *Oil and Gas Jour.* (1953), v. 51, no. 37, p. 63.

71. "Thrust Fault at Boling Salt Dome, Wharton County, Texas, New Exploration Possibilities on Piercement Type Salt Domes Established by": Halbouty, Michel T. and Hardin, George C., Jr., *Bull.,* AAPG (1954), v. 38, no. 8, pp. 1725-1740.

863. "Thrust Faults on Salt Domes, Discussion of": Link, T. A., *Bull.,* AAPG (1954), v. 38, no. 12, p. 2506.

881. "Thrust Faults on Salt Domes, Reply to": Halbouty, Michel T. and Hardin, George C., Jr., *Bull.,* AAPG (1954), v. 38, no. 12, p. 2566.

956. "Tigre Lagoon—An Example of Structural Development in Relation to Salt Dome Growth": Reichert, H. C., *Trans.,* GCAGS (1955), v. 5, pp. 199-208.

957. "Timbalier Bay Field, An Engineering Challenge—Development of South Louisiana's Giant": Lipari, C. A., *Jour. of Pet. Tech.* (1963), v. 15, no. 2, pp. 127-132.

383. "Timbalier Bay, Louisiana, A Seasonal Ecological Study of Foraminifera from" (abs.):

Waldron, Robert P., *Trans.,* CGAGS (1962), v. 12, p. 302.

638b. "Topographical Survey of Louisiana, Report of": Lockett, S. H., *Rept. of Supt. for* 1870, LSU (1871), pp. 16-26.

356. "Torsion Balance Survey at Esperson": Barton, D. C., *Oil and Gas Jour.* (1930), v. 28, no. 46, pp. 38, 141.

355. "Torsion Balance Survey of Esperson Salt Dome, Liberty County, Texas": Barton, D. C., *Bull.,* AAPG (1930), v. 14, no. 9, pp. 1129-1143.

653. "Torsion Balance Surveys in Southwest Louisiana and Southeast Texas": Barton, D. C., *Trans.,* Am. Geophys. Union, 13th Ann. Mtg. (1932), pp. 40-42.

6b. "Traissic Salt in the Algerian Sahara, The": Demaison, G. J., *Salt Basins Around Africa,* The Institute of Petroleum (1965), London, pp. 91-100.

374a. "Trinity Group of the Comanchean Cretaceous of the Gulf Coastal Plain, A Correlation and Regional Stratigraphic Analysis of the Formation of the; and the Genesis and Petrography of the Ferry Lake Anhydrite": Forgotson, J. M., Jr., *Trans.,* GCAGS (1956), v. 6, pp. 91-105.

737. *Typical Oil and Gas Fields of Southeast Texas:* Dunham, R. L. (ed.), Houston Geol. Soc. (1962), 243 pp.

958. "Uber Autoplaste (Nichttektonische) Formelemente in Bau der Salzgesteine Norddeutschlands": Lachmann, R., *Monatsber. d. Deutsch. Geol. Ges.,* Bd. 62. (1910b), pp. 113-116.

739. "Unconformities in the Mid-Continent Region, Relation of Oil and Gas Pools to": Levorsen, A. I., *Problems of Petroleum Geology,* AAPG (1934) 780 pp.

879. "Unconformity Traps Around Piercement Salt Domes in South Louisiana" (abs.): Jackson, J. Roy, Jr., *Oil and Gas Jour.* (1956), v. 54, no. 53, pp. 142-143.

710a. "Underground Storage Caverns at Texas Eastern's Mont Belvieu, Texas, Terminal": Cozad, D. J., *Symposium on Salt,* Northern Ohio Geol. Soc., Inc. (1963), Cleveland, Ohio, pp. 634-661.

890a. "Underground Storage, Use of Salt Solution Cavities for": Bays, Carl, *Symposium on Salt,* Northern Ohio Geol. Soc., Inc. (1963), pp. 564-578.

93. "United States of America and Canada, Salt Deposits of the": Ward, Thomas, *Trans.,* Manchester Geol. Soc. (1890), v. 20, pp. 471-498.

887. "United States, Salt Domes of the":

Hanna, Marcus A., *Bull.,* GSA (1932), v. 43, p. 160; *Pan. Am. Geologist,* v. 57, no. 1, pp. 75-76.

737a. "Upper Cretaceous and Tertiary Formations of the West Gulf Coast, Oil and Gas Fields of the": Adams, G. I., *Bull.,* USG S (1901), pp. 37-62.

505a. "Upper Jurassic Rocks, San Marcos Arch, Texas, Stratigraphic-Trap Possibilities in": Halbouty, Michel T., *Bull.,* AAPG (1966), v. 50, no. 1, pp. 3-24.

158a. "Upper Permian Ochoa Series of Delaware Basin, West Texas and Southeastern New Mexico": Adams, J. E., *Bull.,* AAPG (1944), v. 28, no. 11, pp. 1598-1625.

395a. "U.S.S.R., Genesis of Some Sulphur Deposits of the": Murzaiev, P. M., *Econ. Geol.* (1937), v. 32, pp. 69-103.

128a. "Utah-Colorado Salt Domes": *Bull.,* AAPG (1927), v. 11, no. 2, pp. 111-133.

959. "Valentine (La Rose) Dome, Louisiana, Discovery of": Buchanan, G. S., *Bull.,* AAPG (1934), v. 18, no. 4, p. 543; *Gulf Coast Oil Fields,* AAPG (1936), p. 1040.

960. "Van Zandt Dome (Texas)": Morgan, Aubrey, *Compass* (1940), v. 20, no. 3, pp. 166-170.

951. "Velocities, Local Areal Distribution of, in the Texas Gulf Coast": Swan, B. G., *Geophysics* (1942), v. 7, no. 4, pp. 367-392.

961. "Venice Field, Plaquemines Parish, Louisiana, Drilling and Producing Report": Rose, Walter, *Oil and Gas Jour.* (1952), v. 51, no. 11, pp. 62-64.

962. "Venice Field's Circular Waterway Outlines an Oil Rich Structure, Field Operations in Louisiana's Marshes": *Oil and Gas Jour.* (1955), v. 54, no. 10, pp. 122-123.

902. "Vermilion Bay Salt Dome, Louisiana, Seismological Discovery and Partial Detail of": Rosaire, E. E. and Lester, O. C., Jr., *Bull.,* AAPG (1932), v. 16, no. 12, pp. 1221-1229; *Geophysical Case Histories,* SEG (1948), v. 1, no. 1, pp. 135-143; *Trans.,* Soc. Pet. Geophy. (1933), v. 3, pp. 51-59; *Early Geophysical Papers,* SEG (1947), pp. 381-389.

90a. "Vermilion and Cameron Parishes, A Partial List of Maps Dealing with": McGuirt, J. H., *Bull.* 6, La. Geol. Svy. (1935), pp. 197-203.

91. "Vermilion and Cameron Parishes, Reports on the Geology of": Howe, H. V., Russell, R. J., McGuirt, J. H., Craft, B. C. and Stephenson, M. B., *Bull.* 6, La. Geol. Svy. (1935), 242 pp. Includes: "Physiography of Coastal Southwest Louisiana": Howe, H. V., Russell, R. J. and McGuirt, J. H.,

pp. 1-68; "Salt Domes of Cameron and Vermilion Parishes": Howe, H. V. and McGuirt, J. H., pp. 73-166; "Salt Dome Prospects": McGuirt, J. H., pp. 167-179; "Mineral Development": Craft, B. C., pp. 181-186; "Some Microfossils of the Potamides Matsoni Zone of Louisiana": Stephenson, M. B., pp. 187-188; "A Partial List of Maps Dealing with Cameron and Vermilion Parishes": McGuirt, J. H., pp. 197-203.

92. "Vermilion and Cameron Parishes, Salt Domes of": Howe, H. V. and McGuirt, J. H., *Bull.* 6, La., Geol. Svy. (1935), pp. 73-166.

963. "Vicksburg Formation in Deep Test, Acadia Parish, Louisiana": Halbouty, Michel T., *Bull.,* AAPG (1932), v. 16, no. 6, pp. 609-610.

964. "Vinton, Louisiana Oil Field, The": Wrather, W. E., *Bull.,* AAPG (1921), v. 5, no. 2, pp. 339-480.

965. "Vinton Salt Dome, Louisiana": Thompson, S. A. and Eichelberger, O. H., *Bull.,* AAPG (1928), v. 12, no. 4, pp. 385-394.

575. "Waller and Harris Counties, Texas, Stratigraphy of": Beckelhymer, R. L., *Bull.,* AAPG (1946), v. 30, no. 1, pp. 52-62.

809. "Water-Insoluble Residues in Rock Salt of Louisiana Salt Plugs": Taylor, R. E., *Bull.,* AAPG (1937), v. 21, no. 10, pp. 1268-1310; corrections, v. 21, pp. 1494, 1496; (abs.) *World Pet.,* v. 9, no. 1, pp. 60-61.

652. "Waters, Formation, in Southwest Louisiana": Timm, B. C. and Maricelli, J. J., *Bull.,* AAPG (1953), v. 37, no. 2, pp. 394-409.

552. "Waters, Oil Field, of the Gulf Coastal Plain": Minor, H. E., *Problems of Petroleum Geology,* AAPG (1934), pp. 891-905.

856. "Waters, Salt Dome, Chemical Relation of": Minor, H. E., *Bull.,* AAPG (1925), v. 9, no. 1, pp. 38-41; *Geology of Salt Dome Oil Fields,* AAPG (1926), pp. 777-780.

857. "Waters, Salt Dome, Hydraulics of": Pennington, H., *Oil Weekly* (1929), v. 52, no. 7, pp. 27-29.

845. "Wave-Guide Propagation Over a Shallow Salt Dome, Note on": Howell, Lynn G. and Kean, C. H., *Geophysics* (1953), v. 18, no. 2, pp. 338-339.

461. "Webster Parish, Geology of": Martin, James L., Hough, Leo W., Raggio, David L. and Sandberg, Adolph E., *Bull.* 29, La. Geol. Svy. (1954), Dept. of Conserv., 252 pp.

965a. "Weeks Island": Pittman, J. W. and

Sheeler, J. E. R., *The Petroleum Engineer* (March, 1952), pp. B-7 - B-10.

966. "Weeks Island Field, High Pressure Gas Lift System Restores Deep Wells to Production in": Wickizer, C. L., *Oil and Gas Jour.* (1963), v. 61, no. 37, pp. 106-115.

931. "Weeks Island Salt Dome, Louisiana, Structure of Morton Salt Company Mine": Kupfer, Donald H., *Bull.,* AAPG (1962), v. 46, no. 8, pp. 1460-1467.

967. "Weeks Island Salt Dome Operation, Louisiana": Williams, Neil, *Oil and Gas Jour.* (1948), v. 47, no. 18, pp. 58-60, 89.

968. "Well Data and Apparent Faulting, Relations Between Kinds of": Suter, H. H., *Bull.,* AAPG (1946), v. 30, no. 11, pp. 1910-1917.

969. "Wells, Historic, in the American Fields": *Oil and Gas Jour.* (1923), v. 22, no. 27, pp. 84, 86, 96.

633. "Wells, Interesting Wildcat, Drilled in North Louisiana in 1942": Blanpied, B. W. and Hazzard, R. T., *Bull.,* AAPG (1944), v. 28, no. 4, pp. 554-561.

142. "Wells in Mississippi, Significance of Upper Cretaceous Fossils from": Stephenson, L. W., *Bull.,* AAPG (1945), v. 29, no. 7, pp. 1008-1018.

24. "Wells, Tabulation of, Which Have Encountered Salt or Cap Rock in North Louisiana and South Arkansas": Lambert, Ernest H., Jr., *Guidebook,* 1960 Spring Field Trip, Shreveport Geol. Soc., pp. 61-69.

970. "Welsh, Louisiana Oil Field": Reed, L. C., AAPG (1925), v. 9, no. 3, pp. 464-478; *Geology of Salt Dome Oil Fields,* AAPG (1926), pp. 437-451.

971. "West Columbia Field, Brazoria County, Texas": Hackbarth, R. E., *Guidebook,* AAPG-SEPM-SEG Jt. Ann. Mtg. (March, 1953), Houston, Texas, pp. 161-162.

972. "West Columbia Field, Brazoria County, Texas, Well Spacing and Production Interference in": Miller, John C., *Bull.,* AAPG (1942), v. 26, no. 9, pp. 1441-1466.

973. "West Columbia Field, Deeper Drilling in, Revives Brazoria County": Williams, Neil, *Oil and Gas Jour.* (1934), v. 33, no. 20, pp. 11, 44.

974. "West Columbia Oil Field, Brazoria County, Texas": Barton, D. C., *Bull.,* AAPG (1921), v. 5, no. 2, pp. 212-251.

975. "West Columbia Salt Dome and Oil Field, Brazoria County, Texas": Carlton, D. P., *Struc-*

ture of Typical American Oil Fields, AAPG (1929), v. 2, pp. 451-469.

976. "West Point, Texas Salt Dome, Freestone County": DeGolyer, E. L., *Jour. Geol.* (1919), v. 27, no. 8, pp. 647-663.

928. "Wilcox (Eocene), Stratigraphy, A Key to Production (of Oil and Gas)": Echols, D. A. J. and Malkin, D. S., *Bull.,* AAPG (1948), v. 32, no. 1, pp. 11-33; corrections, p. 310.

930. "Wilcox Trend Being Unraveled, Complex Structure of": Todd, John D., *Oil Weekly* (1940), v. 99, no. 3, pp. 52-57; (abs.) *World Pet.,* v. 12, no. 4, p. 104.

88. "Winn and Caldwell Parishes, Louisiana, Geology of": Huner, John, Jr., *Bull.* 15, La. Geol. Svy. (1939), 356 pp.

99. "Winnfield Salt Dome, Louisiana, Metallic Minerals in Cap Rock": Barnes, V. E., *Am. Mineralogist* (1933), v. 18, pp. 335-340.

977. "Winnfield Salt Dome, Winn Parish, Louisiana": Belchic, Harriet Cameron, *Guidebook,* 1960 Spring Field Trip, Shreveport Geol. Soc., pp. 29-47.

933. "Winnfield Salt Dome, Winn Parish, Louisiana, Structure of": Hoy, R. B. and Kuhn, Robert., *Bull.,* AAPG (1964), v. 48, no. 3, pp. 360-361.

932. "Winnfield Salt Dome, Winn Parish, Louisiana, Structure of": Hoy, R. B., Foose, R. M. and O'Neill, B. J., Jr., *Bull.,* AAPG (1962), v. 46, no. 8, pp. 1444-1459.

461a. "Winnfield Sheet, Notes on the Geology of the": Harris, G. D., *Rept. of 1907,* Geol. Svy. of La. (1907), Bull. 5.

825. "Woodbine Sand Waters, East Texas, Salt Diffusion in": Horton, C. W., *Bull.,* AAPG (1944), v. 28, no. 11, pp. 1635-1641.

934. "Woodlawn Field, Jefferson Davis Parish, Louisiana, Structure of the": Pyle, G. T. and Babisak, Julius, *Trans.,* GCAGS (1951), v. 1, pp. 200-210.

33f. *Yacimientos de Azufre, Sintesis de la Morfologia de las Masas de Sal del Istmo de Tehuantepec en Relacion con los:* Gibson, B. Juan, Inedito, Archivo Consejo de Recursos Naturales no Renovables (1957).

661. "Yacimientos Petroliferos en la, Region de Macuspana, Tabasco": Gutierrez, Gil R., *Bol.,* Asoc. Mex. Geol. Petrol. (1950), v. 2, no. 8, pp. 499-510.

Salt Domes of Texas

Alphabetical Listing
(Alternate Name in Parentheses)

Dome	County	Dome	County
Allen	Brazoria	(DeWalt) Sugarland	Fort Bend
Arriola	Hardin	Dilworth Ranch	McMullen
Barbers Hill (Mont Belvieu)	Chambers	East Tyler (Tyler)	Smith
Batson	Hardin	Elkhart	Anderson
(Bessie Heights) Port Neches	Orange	Esperson (Sheeks)	Liberty
Bethel	Anderson	Fannett	Jefferson
Big Creek	Fort Bend	(Ferguson) Clay Creek	Washington
Big Hill	Jefferson	Ferguson Crossing (Carlos)	Brazos and Grimes
(Big Hill) Gulf	Matagorda	(Freeport) Bryan Mound	Brazoria
Block 144	Galveston - Offshore	(Friendswood) Webster	Harris
		(Gay Hill) Clay Creek	Washington
Blue Ridge	Fort Bend	(Graddy) Butler	Freestone
Boggy Creek	Anderson and Cherokee	Grand Saline	Van Zandt
		(Grubbles) Thompson	Fort Bend
Boling (Newgulf)	Fort Bend and Wharton	Gulf (Big Hill)	Matagorda
		Gyp Hill (Las Cuevas, Loma Blanca)	Brooks
Brenham (Millcreek)	Austin and Washington	Hainesville	Wood
Brooks	Smith	Hankamer	Liberty
(Brookshire) San Felipe	Austin and Waller	Hawkinsville	Matagorda
Brushy Creek (Purt)	Anderson	High Island	Galveston
(Bryan Heights) Bryan Mound	Brazoria	(Hinkle's Ferry) Clemens	Brazoria
		Hockley	Harris
Bryan Mound (Bryan Heights, Freeport)	Brazoria	Hoskins Mound	Brazoria
		Hull	Liberty
Bullard	Smith	Humble	Harris
Butler (Graddy, West Point)	Freestone	(Ives Creek) Raccoon Bend	Austin
(Carlos) Ferguson Crossing	Brazos and Grimes	(Ives Crossing) Clay Creek	Washington
Cedar Point	Chambers	(Jefferson Coast) McFaddin Beach	Jefferson
Clam Lake	Jefferson		
Clay Creek (Gay Hill, Ives Crossing, Ferguson)	Washington	Keechi	Anderson
		(Kiser Hill) West Columbia	Brazoria
Clemens (Hinkle's Ferry)	Brazoria	Kittrell (Trinity)	Houston
(Clemville) Markham	Matagorda	La Rue	Henderson
(Cockburn) Sugarland	Fort Bend	(Las Cuevas) Gyp Hill	Brooks
Concord	Anderson	(Liberty) South Liberty	Liberty
(Cove) Lost Lake	Chambers	(Lockwood) Thompson	Fort Bend
(Cow Bayou) Orange	Orange	(Loma Blanca) Gyp Hill	Brooks
Damon Mound	Brazoria	Long Point (Pathfinder)	Fort Bend
Danbury	Brazoria	Lost Lake (Cove)	Chambers
Davis Hill	Liberty	(Mansfield Ferry) Port Neches	Orange
Day	Madison	Manvel	Brazoria

Dome	County	Dome	County
Markham (Clemville)	Matagorda	San Felipe (Brookshire, Sealy)	Austin and Waller
McFaddin Beach (Jefferson Coast)	Jefferson - Offshore	San Luis Pass	Brazoria and Galveston- Offshore
(Millcreek) Brenham	Austin and Washington	Saratoga	Hardin
Millican	Brazos	(Sealy) San Felipe	Austin and Waller
Moca	Webb	(Sheeks) Esperson	Liberty
(Mont Belvieu) Barbers Hill	Chambers	Sour Lake	Hardin
(Moore) Orchard	Fort Bend	(South Dayton) South Liberty	Liberty
Moss Bluff	Liberty	South Houston	Harris
Mount Sylvan	Smith	South Liberty (South Dayton, Liberty)	Liberty
Mykawa	Harris		
Nash	Brazoria and Fort Bend	Spindletop	Jefferson
		Steen	Smith
(Newgulf) Boling	Wharton and Fort Bend	Stewart Beach	Galveston- Offshore
North Dayton	Liberty	Stratton Ridge	Brazoria
Oakwood	Leon and Freestone	Sugarland (DeWalt, Cockburn)	Fort Bend
Orange (Cow Bayou)	Orange	Thompson (Rabb's Ridge, Lockwood, Grubbles)	Fort Bend
Orchard (Moore)	Fort Bend	(Trinity) Kittrell	Houston
Palangana	Duval	(Tyler) East Tyler	Smith
Palestine	Anderson	Webster (Friendswood)	Harris
(Pathfinder) Long Point	Fort Bend	West Columbia (Kiser Hill)	Brazoria
Pescadito	Webb	(West Point) Butler	Freestone
Piedras Pintas	Duval	Whitehouse	Smith
Pierce Junction	Harris		
Port Neches (Mansfield Ferry, Bessie Heights)	Orange		
(Purt) Brushy Creek	Anderson		
(Rabb's Ridge) Thompson	Fort Bend		
Raccoon Bend (Ives Creek)	Austin		
Red Fish Reef	Chambers		

Offshore

Block 144
McFaddin Beach
San Luis Pass
Stewart Beach

By County

Anderson County
Bethel
Boggy Creek
Brushy Creek (Purt)
Concord
Elkhart
Keechi
Palestine

Austin County
Brenham (Millcreek)

Austin County (cont.)
Raccoon Bend (Ives Creek)
San Felipe (Brookshire, Sealy)

Brazoria County
Allen
Bryan Mound (Bryan Heights, Freeport)
Clemens (Hinkle's Ferry)
Damon Mound
Danbury
Hoskins Mound

Brazoria County (cont.)
Manvel
Nash
San Luis Pass - Offshore
Stratton Ridge
West Columbia (Kiser Hill)

Brazos County
Ferguson Crossing (Carlos)
Millican

Brooks County
Gyp Hill (Las Cuevas, Loma Blanca)

Chambers County
Barbers Hill (Mont Belvieu)
Cedar Point
Lost Lake (Cove)
Red Fish Reef

Cherokee County
Boggy Creek

Duval County
Palangana
Piedras Pintas

Fort Bend County
Big Creek
Blue Ridge
Boling (Newgulf)
Long Point (Pathfinder)
Nash
Orchard (Moore)
Sugarland (DeWalt, Cockburn)
Thompson (Rabbs Ridge, Lockwood, Grubbles)

Freestone County
Butler (Graddy, West Point)
Oakwood

Galveston County
Block 144 - Offshore
High Island
San Luis Pass - Offshore
Stewart Beach - Offshore

Grimes County
Ferguson Crossing (Carlos)

Hardin County
Arriola
Batson
Saratoga
Sour Lake

Harris County
Hockley
Humble
Mykawa
Pierce Junction
South Houston
Webster (Friendswood)

Henderson County
La Rue

Houston County
Kittrell (Trinity)

Jefferson County
Big Hill
Clam Lake
Fannett
McFadden Beach (Jefferson Coast) - Offshore
Spindletop

Leon County
Oakwood

Liberty County
Davis Hill
Esperson (Sheeks)
Hankamer
Hull
Moss Bluff
North Dayton
South Liberty (South Dayton, Liberty)

Madison County
Day

Matagorda County
Gulf (Big Hill)
Hawkinsville
Markham (Clemville)

McMullen County
Dilworth Ranch

Orange County
Orange (Cow Bayou)
Port Neches (Mansfield Ferry, Bessie Heights)

Smith County
Brooks
Bullard
East Tyler (Tyler)
Mount Sylvan

Salt Dome Index

Allen, Brazoria County:

6a.   *BMIC*
944.   *Bull.*, v. 17, no. 10, p. 1206; *GC*, p. 263
329.   *Bull.*, v. 17, no. 12, pp. 1494-1497; *GC*, pp.
       143-146
329.   *Bull.*, v. 17, no. 12, pp. 1516-1517;
       OW, v. 71, no. 13, pp. 18, 20-24;
       GC, pp. 165-166; *OGJ*, v. 32, no.
       25, pp. 16, 18
847.   *Bull.*, v. 20, no. 6, p. 729; *GC*, p. 112
832.   *Bull.*, v. 27, no. 1, p. 59
260.   *Bull.*, v. 29, no. 6, pp. 828-829
291.   *Bull.*, v. 38, no. 6, pp. 1215, 1219
705.   *Bull.*, v. 39, no. 12, p. 2417
293.   *Bull.*, v. 40, no. 6, pp. 1243, 1245
298.   *Bull.*, v. 46, no. 6, p. 924
 96.   *Bull.*, La. Geol. Svy., no. 11, p. 53
427.   *GAGC*, p. 271
363.   *Geophysics*, v. 1, no. 1, Fig. 3 (between **pp.**
       142-143), Fig. 8 (between pp. 146-147)
846.   *Guidebook*, AAPG-SEPM-SEG (1953),
       p. 15
801.   *Lockwood's* (Texas 1939), Sec. 4, p. 3,
       Sec. 5, p. 12, 29
478.   *OGJ*, v. 27, no. 25, pp. 35, 91
515.   *OGJ*, v. 28, no. 49, p. 118
474.   *OGJ*, v. 28, no. 50, p. 143
321.   *OGJ*, v. 29, no. 22, pp. 30-31, 107
854.   *OGJ*, v. 29, no. 52, p. 143
484.   *OGJ*, v. 32, no. 20, p. 11
337.   *OGJ*, v. 38, no. 50, p. 102
520.   *OGJ*, v. 39, no. 49, p. 140
316.   *OGJ*, v. 60, no. 40, pp. 113-114
524.   *OW*, v. 90, no. 7, pp. 143, 144
161.   *OW*, v. 123, no. 3, p. 85

Allen, Brazoria County: (cont.)

409.   *OW*, v. 123, no. 3, p. 110
434.   *PROB.*, pp. 631-632, 637
410.   *WO*, v. 130, no. 7, p. 60

Arriola, Hardin County:

6a.   *BMIC*
385.   *Bull.*, v. 17, no. 9, p. 1049; *GC*, p. 45
847.   *Bull.*, v. 20, no. 6, p. 729; *GC*, p. 112
286.   *Bull.*, v. 33, no. 6, p. 972
288.   *Bull.*, v. 35, no. 6, p. 1330
291.   *Bull.*, v. 38, no. 6, pp. 1209, 1216
725.   *Bull.*, v. 39, no. 5, pp. 700-701, 705, 709-
       710
292.   *Bull.*, v. 39, no. 6, p. 980
427.   *GAGC*, p. 271
363.   *Geophysics*, v. 1, no. 1, Fig. 3 (between pp.
       142-143), Fig. 8, (between pp. 146-
       147)
846.   *Guidebook*, AAPG-SEPM-SEG (1953),
       p. 15
801.   *Lockwood's* (Texas 1939), Sec. 4, p. 3,
       Sec. 5, p. 12
478.   *OGJ*, v. 27, no. 25, p. 35
515.   *OGJ*, v. 28, no. 49, p. 118
484.   *OGJ*, v. 32, no. 20, p. 11
365.   *OGJ*, v. 57, no. 24, p. 136
719.   *OGJ*, v. 60, no. 24, pp. 140-141
376.   *OW*, v. 82, no. 10, p. 14
524.   *OW*, v. 90, no. 7, p. 168
161.   *OW*, v. 123, no. 3, p. 85
409.   *OW*, v. 123, no. 3, p. 121
364.   *Paper 5*, Fifth World Pet. Cong., sec 1,
       p. 6; *Oil*, v. 19, no. 8, p. 38
410.   *WO*, v. 130, no. 7, p. 72

Barbers Hill, Chambers County: (Mont Belvieu)

6a. *BMIC*
127. *Bull.*, v. 1, no. 1, p. 47
549. *Bull.*, v. 9, no. 1, p. 35-36; *SD*, pp. 774-775
906. *Bull.*, v. 9, no. 3, pp. 656, 664; *SD*, pp. 559, 567
40. *Bull.*, v. 9, no. 6, pp. 958-973; *SD*, pp. 530-545
589. *Bull.*, v. 9, no. 7, pp. 1032, 1035; *SD*, pp. 571, 574
843. *Bull.*, v. 9, no. 9, pp. 1263; *SD*, pp. 203
35. *Bull.*, v. 14, no. 6, pp. 719-741; (abs.) *Pan-Am Geologist*, v. 53, no. 3, p. 221
36. *Bull.*, v. 16, no. 5, pp. 469-482
385. *Bull.*, v. 17, no. 9, pp. 1051, 1059, 1072, 1080-1081; *GC*, pp. 46, 54, 67, 75-76
944. *Bull.*, v. 17, no. 10, p. 1206; *GC*, p. 263
329. *Bull.*, v. 17, no. 12, pp. 1492-1500, 1502, 1513-1516; *GC*, pp. 141-147, 149, 151, 162-165; *OW*, v. 71, no. 11, pp. 18-24; no. 12, pp. 18-22; no. 13, pp. 18, 20-24; *OGJ*, v. 32, no. 21, pp. 16, 30; no. 22, pp. 18, 22; no. 25, pp. 16, 18; no. 27, p. 18; (abs.) *Pan-Am Geologist*, v. 59, no. 3, p. 230
654. *Bull.*, v. 18, no. 4, p. 510; *GC*, p. 11
37. *Bull.*, v. 19, no. 1, pp. 25-36; *EGP*, pp. 685-696; *Trans.* SEG, v. 5, pp. 25-36
433. *Bull.*, v. 19, no. 9, p. 1323; *GC*, p. 976
847. *Bull.*, v. 20, no. 6, p. 729; *GC*, p. 112
462. *Bull.*, v. 20, no. 11, p. 1422
900. *Bull.*, v. 21, no. 8, p. 1086
287. *Bull.*, v. 34, no. 6, pp. 1185, 1189
288. *Bull.*, v. 35, no. 6, p. 1329
290. *Bull.*, v. 37, no. 6, p. 1433
71. *Bull.*, v. 38, no. 8, p. 1740
881. *Bull.*, v. 38, no. 12, p. 2566
725. *Bull.*, v. 39, no. 5, pp. 698-703, 705-706, 708, 711
292. *Bull.*, v. 39, no. 6, p. 984
293. *Bull.*, v. 40, no. 6, pp. 1240, 1244, 1246, 1248, 1251
294. *Bull.*, v. 41, no. 6, p. 1185
96. *Bull.*, La. Geol. Svy., no. 11, p. 50
115. *Chron. Hist.*, pp. 119, 157
427. *GAGC*, p. 271
717. *GAS*, pp. 685, 691, 707, 739
4. *GC*, pp. 17-22
354. *GCH*, v. 1, pp. 48, 64
402. *GCH*, v. 1, pp. 272-273, 275

Barbers Hill, Chambers County: (Mont Belvieu) (Cont.)

363. *Geophysics*, v. 1, no. 1, Fig. 2 (between pp. 142-143), Fig. 7 (between pp. 146-147)
846. *Guidebook*, AAPG-SEPM-SEG (1953), p. 15
801. *Lockwood's* (Texas 1939), sec. 4, p. 4; sec. 5, pp. 13, 29
532. *OGJ*, v. 25, no. 40, p. 152
515. *OGJ*, v. 28, no. 49, pp. 42-43
321. *OGJ*, v. 29, no. 22, pp. 30-31, 107
854. *OGJ*, v. 29, no. 52, p. 143
105. *OGJ*, v. 31, no. 5, pp. 49-50
728. *OGJ*, v. 33, no. 64, p. 149
520. *OGJ*, v. 39, no. 49, pp. 64, 133, 135, 138
311. *OGJ*, v. 39, no. 49, p. 84
39. *OGJ*, v. 41, no. 13, pp. 42-43
450. *OGJ*, v. 46, no. 4, p. 136
833. *OGJ*, v. 53, no. 26, p. 93
41. *OGJ*, v. 55, no. 34, pp. 72-73
744. *OGJ*, v. 57, no. 6, p. 140
365. *OGJ*, v. 57, no. 24, pp. 135-136
526. *OGJ*, v. 59, no. 31, p. 255
722. *OFNA*, pp. 134, 147, 151
871. *OW*, v. 66, no. 7, pp. 31-32
527. *OW*, v. 69, no. 1, p. 16
758. *OW*, v. 69, no. 1, p. 59
376. *OW*, v. 82, no. 10, p. 14
524. *OW*, v. 90, no. 7, p. 150
370. *OW*, v. 100, no. 10, p. 20
161. *OW*, v. 123, no. 3, pp. 83-85
170. *OW*, v. 123, no. 3, p. 87
409. *OW*, v. 123, no. 3, p. 114
364. *Paper 5*, Fifth World Pet. Cong., sec. 1, pp. 4, 6; *Oil*, v. 19, no. 8, pp. 35, 37-38
449. *Pet. Geol.*, pp. 258, 275
434. *PROB.*, pp. 632-633, 642, 663-664
552. *PROB.*, pp. 894-895
851. *Proc.*, Fourth World Pet. Cong., sec. 1, pp. 85, 95
983. *SOS*, pp. 539-545
984. *SOS*, pp. 634-661
583. *Trans.*, GCAGS, v. 9, p. 62
410. *WO*, v. 130, no. 7, p. 62
335. *WO*, v. 142, no. 7, p. 158
38. *WP*, v. 10, no. 1, pp. 40-55
581. *WP* (May, 1936), pp. 271-272

Batson, Hardin County:

6a. *BMIC*
127. *Bull.*, v. 1, no. 1, p. 46
973. *Bull.*, v. 5, no. 2, pp. 243
895. *Bull.*, v. 9, no. 2, p. 278; *SD*, 516

Batson, Hardin County: (cont.)

906.   *Bull.,* v. 9, no. 3, p. 656; *SD,* p. 559
 44.   *Bull.,* v. 9, no. 9, pp. 1277-1282; *SD,* pp. 524-529
618.   *Bull.,* v. 10, no. 1, pp. 87, 92; *SD,* pp. 412, 418
944.   *Bull.,* v. 17, no. 10, p. 1206; *GC,* p. 263
655.   *Bull.,* v. 18, no. 2, p. 222; *GC,* p. 129
654.   *Bull.,* v. 18, no. 4, p. 502; *GC,* p. 3
847.   *Bull.,* v. 20, no. 6, p. 729; *GC,* p. 112
285.   *Bull.,* v. 32, no. 6, p. 1028
286.   *Bull.,* v. 33, no. 6, pp. 972, 977
287.   *Bull.,* v. 34, no. 6, p. 1185
288.   *Bull.,* v. 35, no. 6, pp. 1330, 1335
725.   *Bull.,* v. 39, no. 5, pp. 700-701, 705-706, 709-710
294.   *Bull.,* v. 41, no. 6, p. 1186
753.   *Bull.,* v. 41, no. 8, p. 1848
297.   *Bull.,* v. 45, no. 6, p. 873
 96.   *Bull.,* La. Geol. Svy., no. 11, p. 115
427.   *GAGC,* p. 271
717.   *GAS,* pp. 685, 695, 708
846.   *Guidebook,* AAPG-SEPM-SEG (1953), p. 15
  3.   *Guidebook,* AAPG-SEPM-SEG (1953), p. 33
801.   *Lockwood's* (Texas 1939), sec. 4, p. 4; sec. 5, pp. 13, 29-30
 43.   *HGS,* pp. 8-13
722.   *OFNA,* pp. 146-147, 152
968.   *OGJ,* v. 22, no. 27, p. 86
300.   *OGJ,* v. 37, no. 12, p. 33
311.   *OGJ,* v. 39, no. 49, p. 84
520.   *OGJ,* v. 39, no. 49, pp. 133, 135, 138
365.   *OGJ,* v. 57, no. 24, p. 136
376.   *OW,* v. 82, no. 10, p. 14
524.   *OW,* v. 90, no. 7, p. 168
161.   *OW,* v. 123, no. 3, pp. 84-85
409.   *OW,* v. 123, no. 3, p. 121
364.   *Paper 5,* Fifth World Pet. Cong., sec. 1, p. 6; *Oil,* v. 19, no. 8, p. 38
146.   *PROB.,* p. 116
434.   *PROB.,* pp. 632-633, 661
851.   *Proc.,* Fourth World Pet. Cong., sec. 1, pp. 86, 96
410.   *WO,* v. 130, no. 7, p. 72

Bessie Heights, Orange County: (see Port Neches)

Bethel, Anderson County:

 6a.   *BMIC*
865.   *Bull.,* v. 12, no. 5, pp. 530, 535
309.   *Bull.,* v. 13, no. 6, p. 613
660.   *Bull.,* v. 13, no. 10, p. 1356

Bethel, Anderson County: (cont.)

329.   *Bull.,* v. 17, no. 12, pp. 1495-1496, 1518-1520; *OW,* v. 71, no. 11, pp. 18-24; no. 12, pp. 18-22; no. 13, pp. 18, 20-24; *OGJ,* v. 32, no. 21, pp. 16, 30; no. 23, pp. 18, 28; no. 25, pp. 16, 18; no. 27, p. 18; *GC,* pp. 144-145, 167-169; *(abs.) Pan-Am Geologists,* v. 59, no. 3, p. 230
203.   *Bull.,* v. 41, no. 6, pp. 1174-1175, 1178
204.   *Bull.,* v. 42, no. 6, pp. 1289, 1293, 1295
205.   *Bull.,* v. 43, no. 6, pp. 1296-1297, 1299
427.   *GAGC,* p. 271
602.   *Guidebook,* Shreveport Geol. Soc. (1960), pp. 5, 9-13
831.   *OGJ,* v. 56, no. 10, pp. 248, 250
 86.   *OGJ,* v. 56, no. 30, p. 263
864.   *OGJ,* v. 57, no. 19, pp. 143-144, 146
318.   *OGJ,* v. 58, no. 7, p. 157
325.   *OGJ,* v. 61, no. 52, pp. 210-212, 214
885.   *OW* (Aug. 7, 1931), p. 19
364.   *Paper 5,* World Pet. Cong., sec. 1, pp. 3, 8-10; *Oil,* v. 19, no. 8, pp. 34, 39-40
434.   *PROB.,* pp. 632-633, 669
455.   *Trans.,* GCAGS, v. 6, p. 84
950.   *Trans.,* GCAGS, v. 6, p. 90

Big Creek, Fort Bend County:

 6a.   *BMIC*
315.   *Bull.,* v. 6, no. 3, p. 253
883.   *Bull.,* v. 9, no. 3, p. 569; *SD,* p. 751
385.   *Bull.,* v. 17, no. 9, p. 1056; *GC,* p. 51
847.   *Bull.,* v. 20, no. 6, p. 729; *GC,* p. 112
283.   *Bull.,* v. 30, no. 6, pp. 995, 997
286.   *Bull.,* v. 33, no. 6, p. 972
287.   *Bull.,* v. 34, no. 6, p. 1185
294.   *Bull.,* v. 41, no. 6, p. 1185
427.   *GAGC,* p. 271
717.   *GAS,* pp. 685, 709
363.   *Geophysics,* v. 1, no. 1, Fig. 2 (between pp. 142-143), Fig. 7 (between pp. 146-147)
846.   *Guidebook,* AAPG-SEPM-SEG (1953), p. 15
801.   *Lockwood's* (Texas 1939), sec. 4, p. 4; sec. 5, p. 13
125.   *OGJ,* v. 25, no. 35, p. 107
520.   *OGJ,* v. 39, no. 49, p. 138
376.   *OW,* v. 82, no. 10, p. 14
524.   *OW,* v. 90, no. 7, p. 154
161.   *OW,* v. 123, no. 3, pp. 85, 88
409.   *OW,* v. 123, no. 3, p. 117
434.   *PROB.,* pp. 631-632
410.   *WO,* v. 130, no. 7, p. 68

Big Hill, Jefferson County:

6a. *BMIC*
127. *Bull.,* v. 1, no. 1, p. 47
57. *Bull.,* v. 9, no. 3, pp. 590-593; *SD,* pp. 497-500
58. *Bull.,* v. 9, no. 4, pp. 711-737
589. *Bull.,* v. 9, no. 7, pp. 1032, 1035; *SD,* pp. 571, 574
843. *Bull.,* v. 9, no. 9, p. 1263; *SD,* p. 203
385. *Bull.,* v. 17, no. 9, pp. 1048, 1072; *GC,* pp. 43, 67
847. *Bull.,* v. 20, no. 6, p. 729; *GC,* p. 112
775. *Bull.,* v. 33, no. 7, p. 1253
287. *Bull.,* v. 34, no. 6, p. 1186
290. *Bull.,* v. 37, no. 6, pp. 1433, 1437-1438, 1440
291. *Bull.,* v. 38, no. 6, pp. 1209, 1213, 1216, 1218
292. *Bull.,* v. 39, no. 6, pp. 981, 983
293. *Bull.,* v. 40, no. 6, p. 1246
427. *GAGC,* pp. 228, 271
717. *GAS,* p. 709
363. *Geophysics,* v. 1, no. 1, Fig. 2 (between pp. 142-143), Fig. 7 (between pp. 146-147)
846. *Guidebook,* AAPG-SEPM-SEG (1953), p. 15
3. *Guidebook,* AAPG-SEPM-SEG (1953), p. 35
801. *Lockwood's* (Texas 1939), sec. 5, pp. 13, 30
722. *OFNA,* p. 134
515. *OGJ,* v. 28, no. 49, p. 42
59. *OGJ,* v. 33, no. 41, pp. 26, 61
300. *OGJ,* v. 37, no. 12, p. 34
337. *OGJ,* v. 38, no. 50, p. 102
520. *OGJ,* v. 39, no. 49, pp. 133, 138
541. *OGJ,* v. 52, no. 7, p. 357
526. *OGJ,* v. 59, no. 31, p. 256
524. *OW,* v. 90, no. 7, p. 177
409. *OW,* v. 123, no. 3, p. 126
434. *PROB.,* pp. 632-633
410. *WO,* v. 130, no. 7, p. 76
581. *WP* (May, 1936), pp. 271-272

Big Hill, Matagorda County: (See Gulf)

Block 144, Galveston County: (see Offshore)

Blue Ridge, Fort Bend County:

6a. *BMIC*
63. *Bull.,* v. 9, no. 2, pp. 304-316; *SD,* pp. 600-612
883. *Bull.,* v. 9, no. 3, p. 569; *SD,* p. 751
938. *Bull.,* v. 17, no. 11, p. 1379; *GC,* p. 726
382. *Bull.,* v. 18, no. 9, p. 1197; *GC,* p. 101
847. *Bull.,* v. 20, no. 6, p. 729; *GC,* p. 112
282. *Bull.,* v. 29, no. 6, p. 789

Blue Ridge, Fort Bend County: (cont.)

286. *Bull.,* v. 33, no. 6, p. 972
288. *Bull.,* v. 35, no. 6, p. 1329
289. *Bull.,* v. 36, no. 6, p. 1207
290. *Bull.,* v. 37, no. 6, pp. 1436, 1440
291. *Bull.,* v. 38, no. 6, pp. 1209-1210, 1216, 1218
725. *Bull.,* v. 39, no. 5, pp. 700-701, 705-706, 708-709
292. *Bull.,* v. 39, no. 6, pp. 980, 982, 984
293. *Bull.,* v. 40, no. 6, p. 1246
294. *Bull.,* v. 41, no. 6, p. 1185
427. *GAGC,* pp. 213, 268, 271
786. *GCH,* v. 2, p. 155
363. *Geophysics,* v. 1, no. 1, Fig. 2 (between pp. 142-143), Fig. 7 (between pp. 146-147)
547. *Geophysics,* v. 3, no. 2, p. 99
846. *Guidebook,* AAPG-SEPM-SEG (1953), p. 15
61. *Guidebook,* AAPG-SEPM-SEG (1953), pp. 82-85
68. *Guidebook,* HGS (1962), p. 278
801. *Lockwood's* (Texas 1939), sec. 4, p. 5; sec. 5, pp. 14, 30
125. *OGJ,* v. 25, no. 35, p. 107
532. *OGJ,* v. 25, no. 40, p. 152
790. *OGJ,* v. 30, no. 37, p. 76
520. *OGJ,* v. 39, no. 49, p. 138
62. *OGJ,* v. 49, no. 34, pp. 52-55
745. *OGJ,* v. 54, no. 23, p. 321
365. *OGJ,* v. 57, no. 24, p. 136
364. *Paper 5,* Fifth World Pet. Cong., sec. 1, p. 6; *Oil,* v. 19, no. 8, p. 38
434. *PROB.,* pp. 632-633
552. *PROB.,* p. 905
947. *PROB.,* p. 1018
851. *Proc.,* Fourth World Pet. Cong., sec. 1, pp. 92-93, 96
857. *OW,* v. 52, no. 7, p. 28
376. *OW,* v. 82, no. 10, p. 14
524. *OW,* v. 90, no. 7, p. 158
161. *OW,* v. 123, no. 3, pp. 85, 87-88
409. *OW,* v. 123, no. 3, p. 118
410. *WO,* v. 130, no. 7, p. 68

Boggy Creek, Anderson and Cherokee Counties:

6a. *BMIC*
65. *Bull.,* v. 10, no. 11, pp. 1171-1172
865. *Bull.,* v. 12, no. 5, p. 528
309. *Bull.,* v. 13, no. 6, pp. 613, 615
66. *Bull.,* v. 16, no. 6, pp. 584-600; (abs.) *Pan-Am. Geologist,* v. 57, no. 4, p. 308

Boggy Creek, Anderson and Cherokee Counties:
(cont.)

385. *Bull.,* v. 17, no. 9, pp. 1049, 1074, 1076, 1078; *GC,* pp. 44, 69, 71, 73
825. *Bull.,* v. 28, no. 11, p. 1640
201. *Bull.,* v. 38, no. 6, p. 1197
203. *Bull.,* v. 41, no. 6, p. 1174
204. *Bull.,* v. 42, no. 6, p. 1295
96. *Bull.,* La. Geol. Svy., no. 11, pp. 22-23, 25-26
427. *GAGC,* pp. 216-217
394. *GAS,* pp. 665, 677
901. *GCH,* v. 1, p. 13; *Geophysics,* v. 5, no. 3, p. 221
361. *Geophysics,* v. 3, no. 1, p. 32
23. *Geophysics,* v. 16, no. 3, p. 405
602. *Guidebook,* Shreveport Geol. Soc. (1960), p. 5
722. *OFNA,* p. 135
831. *OGJ,* v. 56, no. 10, pp. 248, 250
864. *OGJ,* v. 57, no. 19, pp. 143-144
318. *OGJ,* v. 58, no. 7, p. 157
325. *OGJ,* v. 61, no. 52, pp. 210-211, 214
885. *OW* (Aug. 7, 1931), pp. 17, 19-20
364. *Paper 5,* Fifth World Pet. Cong., sec. 1, pp. 3, 8; *Oil,* v. 19, no. 8, pp. 34, 38
449. *Pet. Geol.,* pp. 406, 410
685. *PROB.,* p. 276
742. *PROB.,* pp. 315, 330
686. *PROB.,* p. 422
731. *PROB.,* p. 579
434. *PROB.,* pp. 632-633, 639, 659-661, 669
739. *PROB.,* p. 780
947. *PROB.,* p. 1018
64. *Pub. 5116,* Tex. U., pp. 29-34
455. *Trans.,* GCAGS, v. 6, p. 84

Boling, Fort Bend and Wharton Counties: (New-
gulf)

6a. *BMIC*
385. *Bull.,* v. 17, no. 9, pp. 1056, 1072; *GC,* pp. 51, 67
655. *Bull.,* v. 18, no. 2, pp. 216-221, 223; *GC,* pp. 123-128, 130
847. *Bull.,* v. 20, no. 6, p. 729; *GC,* p. 112
462. *Bull.,* v. 20, no. 11, p. 1422
283. *Bull.,* v. 30, no. 6, pp. 995-996, 998
285. *Bull.,* v. 32, no. 6, p. 1028
286. *Bull.,* v. 33, no. 6, pp. 972, 976
288. *Bull.,* v. 35, no. 6, p. 1334
289. *Bull.,* v. 36, no. 6, p. 1209
290. *Bull.,* v. 37, no. 6, pp. 1433, 1437-1438, 1441
291. *Bull.,* v. 38, no. 6, pp. 1210, 1213

Boling, Fort Bend and Wharton Counties: (New-
gulf) (cont.)

71. *Bull.,* v. 38, no. 8, pp. 1725-1740
881. *Bull.,* v. 38, no. 12, p. 2566
725. *Bull.,* v. 39, no. 5, pp. 700-701, 705-706, 708-710
705. *Bull.,* v. 39, no. 12, p. 2388
293. *Bull.,* v. 40, no. 6, p. 1248
753. *Bull.,* v. 41, no. 8, pp. 1809, 1816-21, 1828-33, 1839-41, 1843, 1844, 1851
295. *Bull.,* v. 42, no. 6, p. 1305
96. *Bull.,* La. Geol. Svy., no. 11, pp. 15, 22, 50, 75, 118
942a. *Bull. 4,* SIPES, p. 5, Figs. 1, 3
427. *GAGC,* pp. 217, 228, 241, 249, 271
717. *GAS,* pp. 702-703
363. *Geophysics,* v. 1, no. 1, Fig. 2 (between pp. 142-143), Fig. 7 (between pp 146-147)
846. *Guidebook,* AAPG-SEPM-SEG (1953), p. 15
70. *Guidebook,* AAPG-SEPM-SEG (1953), pp. 87-96
69. *Guidebook,* International Geol. Cong., 16th Session, v. 6, pp. 86-90
68. *Guidebook,* HGS (1962), pp. 279-280
801. *Lockwood's* (Texas 1939), sec. 4, p. 5; sec. 5, pp. 14, 30
67. *Magazine,* Colorado School of Mines, v. 19, no. 7, pp. 20-22
722. *OFNA,* p. 152
532. *OGJ,* v. 25, no. 40, pp. 151, 155
520. *OGJ,* v. 39, no. 49, p. 138
833. *OGJ,* v. 53, no. 26, pp. 93-94, 96-98
745. *OGJ,* v. 54, no. 23, p. 324
365. *OGJ,* v. 57, no. 24, pp. 135-136
376. *OW,* v. 82, no. 10, p. 14
524. *OW,* v. 90, no. 7, p. 198
161. *OW,* v. 123, no. 3, pp. 85, 88
409. *OW,* v. 123, no. 3, p. 133
364. *Paper 5,* Fifth World Pet. Cong., sec. 1, pp. 2, 6; *Oil,* v. 19, no. 8, pp. 36, 38
449. *Pet. Geol.,* pp. 412-413
434. *PROB.,* pp. 631-632
857. *Proc.,* Fourth World Pet. Cong., sec. 1, pp. 89-90, 92, 96
583. *Trans.,* GCAGS, v. 9, p. 62
631. *Trans.,* GCAGS, v. 10, p. 218
410. *WO,* v. 130, no. 7, p. 89
536. *WO,* v. 143, no. 5, p. 150

Brenham, Austin and Washington Counties:
(Millcreek)

6a. *BMIC*

Brenham, Austin and Washington Counties: (Millcreek) (cont.)

883. *Bull.,* v. 9, no. 3, p. 572; *SD,* p. 754
723. *Bull.,* v. 9, no. 5, pp. 869, 871; *SD,* pp. 39, 41
78. *Bull.,* v. 19, no. 9, pp. 1330-1338; *GC,* pp. 780-788
847. *Bull.,* v. 20, no. 6, p. 729; *GC,* p. 112
462. *Bull.,* v. 20, no. 11, p. 1422
96. *Bull.,* La. Geol. Svy., no. 11, p. 53
77. *Bull. 661,* USGS, pp. 271-280
427. *GAGC,* p. 271
717. *GAS,* pp. 684-685
363. *Geophysics,* v. 1, no. 1, Fig. 2 (between pp. 142-143), Fig. 7 (between pp. 146-147)
846. *Guidebook,* AAPG-SEPM-SEG (1953), p. 15
801. *Lockwood's* (Texas 1939), sec. 4, p. 5; sec. 5, pp. 14, 30
76. *HGS,* pp. 28-29
532. *OGJ,* v. 25, no. 40, p. 152
520. *OGJ,* v. 39, no. 49, pp. 65, 138
476. *OGJ,* v. 51, no. 7, pp. 90, 94
524. *OW,* v. 90, no. 7, p. 197
161. *OW,* v. 123, no. 3, p. 85
409. *OW,* v. 123, no. 3, p. 110
434. *PROB.,* pp. 631-632
410. *WO,* v. 130, no. 7, p. 89

Brooks, Smith County:

6a. *BMIC*
601. *Bull.,* v. 10, no. 1, pp. 4, 14, 29-30, 33, 35-36; *SD,* pp. 212-222, 237-238, 241, 243-244
208. *Bull.,* v. 46, no. 6, pp. 916, 918-919
429. *Bull.* 1869, Tex. U, p. 26
427. *GAGC,* p. 271
831. *OGJ,* v. 56, no. 10, p. 248
864. *OGJ,* v. 57, no. 19, p. 143
885. *OW* (Aug. 7, 1931), pp. 17, 19
434. *PROB.,* pp. 632-633

Brookshire, Austin and Waller Counties: (see San Felipe)

Brushy Creek, Anderson County: (Purt)

6a. *BMIC*
209. *Bull.,* v. 47, no. 6, pp. 1074, 1078
427. *GAGC,* p. 271
831. *OGJ,* v. 56, no. 10, p. 248
325. *OGJ,* v. 61, no. 52, pp. 211-212, 214
434. *PROB.,* pp. 632-633

Bryan Heights, Brazoria County: (see Bryan Mound)

Bryan Mound, Brazoria County: (Bryan Heights, Freeport)

6a. *BMIC*
127. *Bull.,* v. 1, no. 1, p. 44
952. *Bull.,* v. 3, no. 1, p. 87
929. *Bull.,* v. 9, no. 1, pp. 4, 5; *SD,* pp. 647-648
82. *Bull.,* v. 9, no. 3, pp. 613-625; *SD,* pp. 678-690
58. *Bull.,* v. 9, no. 4, p. 732; *SD,* p. 712
589. *Bull.,* v. 9, no. 7, p. 1032; *SD,* p. 571
385. *Bull.,* v. 17, no. 9, pp. 1049, 1072; *GC,* pp. 45, 67
591. *Bull.,* v. 20, no. 2, pp. 157, 173; *GC,* pp. 835, 851
847. *Bull.,* v. 20, no. 6, p. 729; *GC,* p. 112
287. *Bull.,* v, 34, no. 6, p. 1184
291. *Bull.,* v. 38, no. 6, pp. 1215, 1219
96. *Bull.,* La. Geol. Svy., no. 11, pp. 15, 50, 60, 71, 118
942a. *Bull. 4,* SIPES, p. 1, Figs. 1, 3
403. *EGP,* pp. 341, 346, 349
427. *GAGC,* p. 271
717. *GAS,* pp. 685, 709
402. *GCH,* v. 1, pp. 252-256, 271
363. *Geophysics,* v. 1, no. 1, Fig. 2 (between pp. 142-143), Fig. 7 (between pp. 146-147)
846. *Guidebook,* AAPG-SEPM-SEG (1953), p. 15
801. *Lockwood's* (Texas 1939), sec. 5, pp. 14, 30
722. *OFNA,* p. 134
300. *OGJ,* v. 37, no. 12, p. 34
337. *OGJ,* v. 38, no. 50, p. 102
520. *OGJ,* v. 39, no. 49, pp. 133, 138
524. *OW,* v. 90, no. 7, p. 144
161. *OW,* v. 123, no. 3, p. 85
409. *OW,* v. 123, no. 3, p. 110
449. *Pet. Geol.,* pp. 412-413
434. *PROB.,* pp. 631-632
410. *WO,* v. 130, no. 7, p. 60

Bullard, Smith County:

6a. *BMIC*
865. *Bull.,* v. 12, no. 5, p. 540
309. *Bull.,* v. 13, no. 6, p. 613
427. *GAGC,* p. 271
125. *OGJ,* v. 25, no. 35, p. 107
831. *OGJ,* v. 56, no. 10, p. 248
864. *OGJ,* v. 57, no. 19, p. 143
885. *OW* (Aug. 7, 1931), p. 19
434. *PROB.,* pp. 632-633, 673

Butler, Freestone County: (Graddy, West Point)

6a.   *BMIC*

84.   *Am. Jour. of Sci.,* v. 49, pp. 133-136

683. *Bull.,* v. 6, no. 4, p. 329

601. *Bull.,* v. 10, no. 1, pp. 14, 47, 54-56, 59; *SD,*
         pp. 222, 255, 262-265, 267

753. *Bull.,* v. 41, no. 8, pp. 1828-1830

204. *Bull.,* v. 42, no. 6, pp. 1289, 1293

205. *Bull.,* v. 43, no. 6, p. 1302

206. *Bull.,* v. 44, no. 6, p. 811

429. *Bull.* 1869, Tex. U., pp. 299, 308

427. *GAGC,* p. 271

831. *OGJ,* v. 56, no. 10, pp. 248, 250

864. *OGJ,* v. 57, no. 19, p. 143

318. *OGJ,* v. 58, no. 7, p. 157

885. *OW* (Aug. 7, 1931), p. 19

434. *PROB.,* pp. 632-633

Carlos, Brazos and Grimes Counties: (see Ferguson Crossing)

Cedar Point, Chambers County:

6a.   *BMIC*

107. *Bull.,* v. 22, no. 11, pp. 1601-1602

210. *Bull.,* v. 23, no. 6, p. 880

286. *Bull.,* v. 33, no. 6, pp. 971, 977

288. *Bull.,* v. 35, no. 6, p. 1329

290. *Bull.,* v. 37, no. 6, p. 1436

801. *Lockwood's* (Texas 1939), sec. 4, p. 5; sec.
         5, pp. 15, 31

722. *OFNA,* p. 151

162. *OGJ,* v. 39, no. 49, p. 96

524. *OW,* v. 90, no. 7, p. 150

161. *OW,* v. 123, no. 3, p. 85

409. *OW,* v. 123, no. 3, p. 114

410. *WO,* v. 130, no. 7, p. 62

Clam Lake, Jefferson County:

6a.   *BMIC*

217. *Bull.,* v. 22, no. 6, p. 741

800. *Bull.,* v. 30, no. 8, p. 1307

427. *GAGC,* p. 271

846. *Guidebook,* AAPG-SEPM-SEG (1953),
         p. 15

118. *HGS,* pp. 34-37

801. *Lockwood's* (Texas 1939), sec. 4, p. 6;
         sec. 5, pp. 15, 31

722. *OFNA,* p. 148

524. *OW,* v. 90, no. 7, p. 178

161. *OW,* v. 123, no. 3, p. 85

409. *OW,* v. 123, no. 3, p. 126

838. *Paper* (unpublished) by L. D. Hillyer,
         GCAGS First Ann. Mtg. (1951)

Clam Lake, Jefferson County: (cont.)

291. *Trans.,* GCAGS, v. 11, p. 226

410. *WO,* v. 130, no. 7, p. 76

Clay Creek, Washington County: (Gay Hill, Ives Crossing, Ferguson)

6a.   *BMIC*

121. *Bull.,* v. 15, no. 1, pp. 43-60; (abs.) *Pan-
         Am Geologist,* v. 53, no. 3, p. 226

122. *Bull.,* v. 15, no. 3, pp. 279-283

94.   *Bull.,* v. 15, no. 9, pp. 1105-1113

385. *Bull.,* v. 17, no. 9, pp. 1025-1026, 1050,
         1067-1069, 1073-1079, 1082-1083;
         GC, pp. 20-21, 45, 62-64, 68-74,
         77-78

944. *Bull.,* v. 17, no. 10, p. 1206; *GC,* p. 263

120. *Bull.,* v. 20, no. 1, pp. 68-90; *GC,* pp. 757-779;
         (abs.) *World Pet.,* v. 7, no. 3, p. 150

847. *Bull.,* v. 20, no. 6, p. 729; *GC,* p. 112

928. *Bull.,* v. 32, no. 1, pp. 11, 23

288. *Bull.,* v. 35, no. 6, pp. 13, 34

708. *Bull.,* v. 35, no. 9, pp. 2085-2086

96.   *Bull.,* La. Geol. Svy., no. 11, pp. 23, 25-
         26, 51, 57, 90

427. *GAGC,* p. 271

717. *GAS,* pp. 684-685, 690, 706

363. *Geophysics,* v. 1, no. 1, Fig. 2, (between
         pp. 142-143), Fig. 7 (between pp.
         146-147)

550. *Geophysics,* v. 2, no. 1, p. 14

846. *Guidebook,* AAPG-SEPM-SEG (1953),
         p. 16

801. *Lockwood's* (Texas 1939), sec. 4, p. 6;
         sec. 5, pp. 15, 31

515. *OGJ,* v. 28, no. 49, p. 118

524. *OW,* v. 90, no. 7, p. 197

161. *OW,* v. 123, no. 3, p. 85

409. *OW,* v. 123, no. 3, p. 133

449. *Pet. Geol.,* pp. 413, 415

434. *PROB.,* pp. 631-632

123. *Thesis,* Tex. A & M, Dept. of Geol.
         (A. N. McDowell, 1951)

410. *WO,* v. 130, no. 7, p. 89

Clemens, Brazoria County: (Hinkle's Ferry)

6a.   *BMIC*

944. *Bull.,* v. 17, no. 10, p. 1206; *GC,* p. 263

847. *Bull.,* v. 20, no. 6, p. 729; *GC,* p. 112

288. *Bull.,* v. 35, no. 6, p. 1328

96.   *Bull.,* La. Geol. Svy., no. 11, p. 118

942a. *Bull.* 4, SIPES, Figs. 1, 3

427. *GAGC,* p. 271

Clemens, Brazoria County: (Hinkle's Ferry) (cont.)

463. *Geophysics,* v. 1, no. 1, Fig. 2 (between pp. 142-143), Fig. 7 (between pp. 146-147)
846. *Guidebook,* AAPG-SEPM-SEG (1953), p. 16
801. *Lockwood's* (Texas 1939), sec. 5, p. 15
532. *OGJ,* v. 25, no. 40, p. 97
478. *OGJ,* v. 27, no. 25, pp. 35, 91
515. *OGJ,* v. 28, no.49, p. 118
474. *OGJ,* v. 28, no. 50, p. 143
484. *OGJ,* v. 32, no. 20, p. 11
300. *OGJ,* v. 37, no. 12, p. 34
337. *OGJ,* v. 38, no. 50, p. 102
520. *OGJ,* v. 39, no. 49, p. 140
524. *OW,* v. 90, no. 7, p. 144
434. *PROB.,* pp. 631-632
631. *Trans.,* GCAGS, v. 10, p. 218

Clemville, Matagorda County: (see Markham)

Cockburn, Fort Bend County: (see Sugarland)

Concord, Anderson County:

6a. *BMIC*
191. *Bull.,* v. 27, no. 6, p. 784
129. *Bull.,* v. 28, no. 10, pp. 1537-1538
207. *Bull.,* v. 45, no. 6, pp. 862, 865
427. *GAGC,* p. 271
602. *Guidebook,* Shreveport Geol. Soc. (1960), p. 5
831. *OGJ,* v. 56, no. 10, pp. 248, 250
864. *OGJ,* v. 57, no. 19, pp. 143-144
318. *OGJ,* v. 58, no. 7, p. 157
325. *OGJ,* v. 61, no. 52, pp. 210-212, 214
455. *Trans.,* GCAGS, v. 6, p. 84

Cove, Chambers County: (see Lost Lake)

Cow Bayou, Orange County: (see Orange)

Damon Mound, Brazoria County:

6a. *BMIC*
952. *Bull.,* v. 3, no. 1, p. 87
973. *Bull.,* v. 5, no. 2, p. 212
315. *Bull.,* v. 6, no. 3, p. 253
929. *Bull.,* v. 9, no. 1, pp. 4, 5, 25, 30; *SD,* pp. 647-648, 668, 673
549. *Bull.,* v. 9, no. 1, p. 36; *SD,* p. 775
769. *Bull.,* v. 9, no. 1, p. 78; *SD,* p. 86
152. *Bull.,* v. 9, no. 3, pp. 505-535; *SD,* pp. 613-642
883. *Bull.,* v. 9, no. 3, pp. 560, 573; *SD,* pp. 742, 755

Damon Mound, Brazoria County: (cont.)

923. *Bull.,* v. 9, no. 3, p. 607; *SD,* p. 491
58. *Bull.,* v. 9, no. 4, p. 723; *SD,* p. 703
785. *Bull.,* v. 9, no. 4, pp. 745, 752; *SD,* pp. 426, 433
723. *Bull.,* v. 9, no. 5, pp. 843-844, 852-853, 855, 860, 862; *SD,* pp. 13, 14, 22-23, 25, 30
589. *Bull.,* v. 9, no. 7, pp. 1032, 1035; *SD,* 571, 574
843. *Bull.,* v. 9, no. 9, pp. 1230, 1263; *SD,* 170, 203
618. *Bull.,* v. 10, no. 1, p. 80; *SD,* p. 405
385. *Bull.,* v. 17, no. 9, pp. 1050, 1059; *GC,* pp. 45, 54
944. *Bull.,* v. 17, no. 10, p. 1206; *GC,* p. 263
329. *Bull.,* v. 17, no. 12, p. 1496; *GC,* p. 145
611. *Bull.,* v. 17, no. 11, p. 1324; *GC,* p. 501
938. *Bull.,* v. 17, no. 11, p. 1378; *GC,* p. 725
654. *Bull.,* v. 18, no. 4, pp. 505, 509-510; *GC,* pp. 6, 10-11
847. *Bull.,* v. 20, no. 6, p. 729; *GC,* p. 112
286. *Bull.,* v. 33, no. 6, p. 970
287. *Bull.,* v. 34, no. 6, p. 1184
289. *Bull.,* v. 36, no. 6, p. 1207
740. *Bull.,* v. 36, no. 8, p. 1513
290. *Bull.,* v. 37, no. 6, pp. 1433, 1440
291. *Bull.,* v. 38, no. 6, pp. 1210, 1213, 1217
725. *Bull.,* v. 39, no. 5, pp. 700-701, 703-705, 706, 708-710
292. *Bull.,* v. 39, no. 6, p. 984
293. *Bull.,* v. 40, no. 6, p. 1248
96. *Bull.,* La. Geol. Svy., no. 11, p. 25
942a. *Bull. 4,* SIPES, Figs. 1, 3
429. *Bull.* 1869, Tex. U., p. 261
427. *GAGC,* pp. 217, 271
717. *GAS,* pp. 685-686, 694, 708
154. *GCH,* v. 1, pp. 35-42
420. *Geol. Svy. of Tex.,* First Ann. Svy., p. XXXII
363. *Geophysics,* v. 1, no. 1, Fig. 2 (between pp. 142-143), Fig. 7 (between pp. 146-147)
846. *Guidebook,* AAPG-SEPM-SEG (1953), p. 16
3. *Guidebook,* AAPG-SEPM-SEG (1953), p. 35
151. *Guidebook,* AAPG-SEPM-SEG (1953), pp. 107-109
801. *Lockwood's* (Texas 1939), sec. 4, p. 7; sec. 5, pp. 17,32
150. *Min. Res. Circ.* 31, Texas U., p. 3
722. *OFNA,* pp. 134, 145-146, 153
728. *OGJ,* v. 33, no. 64, p. 149

Damon Mound, Brazoria County: (cont.)

520.   *OGJ,* v. 39, no. 49, pp. 64, 65, 133, 138;
              Oil, v. 19, no. 8, p. 38
745.   *OGJ,* v. 54, no. 23, p. 324
365.   *OGJ,* v. 57, no. 24, p. 136
376.   *OW,* v. 82, no. 10, p. 14
524.   *OW,* v. 90, no. 7, p. 144
370.   *OW,* v. 100, no. 10, p. 20
161.   *OW,* v. 123, no. 3, p. 85
409.   *OW,* v. 123, no. 3, p. 112
364.   ***Paper 5,*** **Fifth World Pet. Cong., sec. 1, p. 6**
449.   *Pet. Geol.,* pp. 271, 274, 413-414
146.   *PROB.,* p. 116
434.   *PROB.,* pp. 631-632
947.   *PROB.,* p. 1018
857.   *Proc.,* Fourth World Pet. Cong., sec. 1, p. 92
154.   *Tech. Pub.* 1760, AIME; *Pet. Tech.,* v.
              7, no. 6, pp. 2-9
583.   *Trans.,* GCAGS, v. 9, pp. 59-60, 62
153.   *Trans.,* GCAGS, v. 11, pp. 213-223
410.   *WO,* v. 130, no. 7, p. 61

Danbury, Brazoria County:

6a.   *BMIC*
511.   *Bull.,* v. 19, no. 1, p. 24; *Trans.,* SEG, v. 5,
              p. 24; *EGP,* p. 684
847.   *Bull.,* v. 20, no. 6, p. 729; *GC,* p. 112
285.   *Bull.,* v. 32, no. 6, p. 1028
286.   *Bull.,* v. 33, no. 6, pp. 970, 977
287.   *Bull.,* v. 34, no. 6, pp. 1184, 1189
288.   *Bull.,* v. 35, no. 6, p. 1328
290.   *Bull.,* v. 37, no. 6, pp. 1433, 1436, 1440
291.   *Bull.,* v. 38, no. 6, pp. 1209, 1213, 1216, 1219
294.   *Bull.,* v. 41, no. 6, p. 1185
427.   *GAGC,* p. 271
717.   *GAS,* pp. 685, 695
363.   *Geophysics,* v. 1, no. 1, Fig. 3 (between pp.
              142-143), Fig. 8 (between pp. 146-
              147)
846.   *Guidebook,* AAPG-SEPM-SEG (1953),
              p. 16
801.   *Lockwood's* (Texas 1939), sec. 4, p. 7; sec.
              5, pp. 17, 32
722.   *OFNA,* p. 153
515.   *OGJ,* v. 28, no. 49, p. 118
484.   *OGJ,* v. 32, no. 20, p. 11
337.   *OGJ,* v. 38, no. 50, p. 102
524.   *OW,* v. 90, no. 7, p. 144
161.   *OW,* v. 123, no. 3, p. 85
409.   *OW,* v. 123, no. 3, p. 112
146.   *PROB.,* p. 115
434.   *PROB.,* pp. 631-632
155.   *Trans.,* GCAGS, v. 2, p. 7
410.   *WO,* v. 130, no. 7, p. 61

Davis Hill, Liberty County:

6a.   *BMIC*
906.   *Bull.,* v. 9, no. 3, p. 656; *SD,* p. 559
385.   *Bull.,* v. 17, no. 9, pp. 1059, 1072; *GC,* pp.
              54, 67
128.   *Bull.,* v. 19, no. 5, p. 669; *GC,* p. 441
847.   *Bull.,* v. 20, no. 6, p. 729
462.   *Bull.,* v. 20, no. 11, p. 1422
725.   *Bull.,* v. 39, no. 5, pp. 697, 700-701, 705-706,
              709-710
292.   *Bull.,* v. 39, no. 6, p. 986
293.   *Bull.,* v. 40, no. 6, pp. 1245, 1248
427.   *GAGC,* p. 271
717.   *GAS,* pp. 685-686
363.   *Geophysics,* v. 1, no. 1, Fig. 2 (between
              pp. 142-143), Fig. 7 (between pp.
              146-147)
846.   *Guidebook,* AAPG-SEPM-SEG (1953), p. 16
801.   *Lockwood's* (Texas 1939), sec. 5, p. 17
478.   *OGJ,* v. 27, no. 25, pp. 35, 91
300.   *OGJ,* v. 37, no. 12, p. 34
337.   *OGJ,* v. 38, no. 50, p. 102
520.   *OGJ,* v. 39, no. 49, p. 138
868.   *OGJ,* v. 54, no. 14, p. 155
365.   *OGJ,* v. 57, no. 24, p. 136
524.   *OW,* v. 90, no. 7, p. 179
364.   *Paper* 5, Fifth World Pet. Cong., sec. 1,
              p. 6; *Oil,* v. 19, no. 8, p. 38
434.   *PROB.,* pp. 632-633

Day, Madison County:

6a.   *BMIC*
286.   *Bull.,* v. 33, no. 6, pp. 967, 969, 975
287.   *Bull.,* v. 34, no. 6, p. 1187
291.   *Bull.,* v. 39, no. 6, p. 983
364.   *Paper 5,* Fifth World Pet. Cong., sec. 1, p.
              3; *Oil,* v. 19, no. 8, p. 34
410.   *WO,* v. 130, no. 7, p. 80

DeWalt, Fort Bend County: (see Sugarland)

Dilworth Ranch, McMullen County:

6a.   *BMIC*
427.   *GAGC,* p. 271
846.   *Guidebook,* AAPG-SEPM-SEG (1953),
              p. 16
764.   *OGJ,* v. 55, no. 26, p. 189

East Tyler, Smith County: (Tyler)

6a.   *BMIC*
865.   *Bull.,* v. 12, no. 5, p. 537
309.   *Bull.,* v. 13, no. 6, p. 611

East Tyler, Smith County: (Tyler) (cont.)

660. *Bull.,* v. 13, no. 10, pp. 1348, 1351; *GC,* pp. 1042, 1045
427. *GAGC,* p. 271
831. *OGJ,* v. 56, no. 10, p. 248
864. *OGJ,* v. 57, no. 19, p. 143
885. *OW* (Aug. 7, 1931), p. 19
434. *PROB.,* pp. 632-633

Elkhart, Anderson County:

6a. *BMIC*
186. *Bull.,* v. 22, no. 6, pp. 728-730
189. *Bull.,* v. 25, no. 6, p. 1086
202. *Bull.,* v. 39, no. 6, pp. 967, 972
427. *GAGC,* p. 271

Esperson, Liberty County: (Sheeks)

6a. *BMIC*
355. *Bull.,* v. 14, no. 9, pp. 1129-1143
385. *Bull.,* v. 17, no. 9, pp. 1050, 1079-1080; *GC,.* pp. 45, 74-75
352. *Bull.,* v. 18, no. 12, pp. 1632-1654; *GC,* pp. 857-879
511. *Bull.,* v. 19, no. 1, pp. 19-20; *Trans.,* SEG, v. 5, pp. 19-20, *EGP,* pp. 679-680
847. *Bull.,* v. 20, no. 6, p. 730; *GC,* p. 113
900. *Bull.,* v. 21, no. 8, p. 1086, Plate C
211. *Bull.,* v. 24, no. 6, p. 1089
215. *Bull.,* v. 28, no. 6, p. 855
285. *Bull.,* v. 32, no. 6, p. 1028
286. *Bull.,* v. 33, no. 6, p. 974
287. *Bull.,* v. 34, no. 6, p. 1186
288. *Bull.,* v. 35, no. 6, pp. 1331, 1335
289. *Bull.,* v. 36, no. 6, p. 1208
290. *Bull.,* v. 37, no. 6, pp. 1436-1437, 1439-1440
725. *Bull.,* v. 39, no. 5, pp.700-701, 705-706, 709
293. *Bull.,* v. 40, no. 6, pp. 1240, 1244
296. *Bull.,* v. 43, no. 6, p. 1310
555a. *Bull.,* v. 50, no 3, p. 469
96. *Bull.,* La. Geol. Svy., no. 11, p. 51
429. *Bull. 1869,* Tex. U., p. 297
427. *GAGC,* pp. 218, 254, 271
717. *GAS,* pp. 685, 695, 718, 728, 738
354. *GCH,* v. 1, pp. 48-65
510. *GCH,* v. 1, p. 182
402. *GCH,* v. 1, pp. 274-276
363. *Geophysics,* v. 1, no. 1, Fig. 3, (between pp. 142-143, Fig. 8 (between pp. 146-147)
846. *Guidebook,* AAPG-SEPM-SEG (1953), p. 16
353. *Guidebook,* AAPG-SEPM-SEG (1953), pp. 115-116

Esperson, Liberty County: (Sheeks) (cont.)

351. *HGS,* pp. 47-52
801. *Lockwood's* (Texas 1939), sec. 4, p. 8; sec. 5, pp. 17, 33
722. *OFNA,* p. 153
356. *OGJ,* v. 28, no. 46, pp. 38, 141
515. *OGJ,* v. 28, no. 49, pp. 43, 118
474. *OGJ,* v. 28, no. 50, p. 143
484. *OGJ,* v. 32, no. 20, p. 11
39. *OGJ,* v. 41, no. 13, pp. 42-43
365. *OGJ,* v. 57, no. 24, p. 136
871. *OW,* v. 66, no. 7, p. 35
527. *OW,* v. 69, no. 1, pp. 16-17
524. *OW,* v. 90, no. 7, pp. 179, 182
370. *OW,* v. 100, no. 10, p. 20
161. *OW,* v. 123, no. 3, pp. 83-85
170. *OW,* v. 123, no. 3, pp. 87-88
409. *OW,* v. 123, no. 3, p. 128
364. *Paper* 5, Fifth World Pet. Cong., sec. 1, p. 6; *Oil,* v. 19, no. 8, p. 38
449. *Pet. Geol.,* p. 413
146. *PROB.,* p. 115
686. *PROB.,* p. 418
434. *PROB.,* pp. 632-633
410. *WO,* v. 130, no. 7, p. 78

Fannett, Jefferson County:

6a. *BMIC*
385. *Bull.,* v. 17, no. 9, p. 1064; *GC,* p. 59
329. *Bull.,* v. 17, no. 12, p. 1496; *GC,* p. 145
511. *Bull.,* v. 19, no. 1, p. 19; Trans., *SEG,* v. 5, p. 19; *EGP,* p. 679
482. *Bull.,* v. 19, no. 3, pp. 357, 362-364; *GC,* pp. 171, 176-178
847. *Bull.,* v. 20, no. 6, p. 730; *GC,* p. 113
462. *Bull.,* v. 20, no. 11, p. 1422
211. *Bull.,* v. 24, no. 6, p. 1089
212. *Bull.,* v. 25, no. 6, p. 1010
283. *Bull.,* v. 30, no. 6, pp. 995, 997
286. *Bull.,* v. 33, no. 6, p. 973
390. *Bull.,* v. 33, no. 11, pp. 1830, 1844
291. *Bull.,* v. 38, no. 6, p. 1218
725. *Bull.,* v. 39, no. 5, pp. 700-701, 705-706, 708-711
292. *Bull.,* v. 39, no. 6, p. 980
705. *Bull.,* v. 39, no. 12, pp. 2421-2422
942a. *Bull.* 4, SIPES, Figs. 1, 3
360. *EGP,* pp. 259, 262; *Jour.,* Soc. of Pet. Geophysicists, v. 6, no. 1, pp. 15, 18
427. *GAGC,* p. 271
363. *Geophysics,* v. 1, no. 1, Fig. 3 (between pp. 142-143), Fig. 8 (between pp. 146-147)

Fannett, Jefferson County: (cont.)
361. *Geophysics,* v. 3, no. 1, p. 32
846. *Guidebook,* AAPG-SEPM-SEG (1953),
p. 16
801. *Lockwood's* (Texas 1939), sec. 4, p. 9;
sec. 5, pp. 18- 33
478. *OGJ,* v. 27, no. 25, pp. 35, 91
515. *OGJ,* v. 28, no. 49, p. 118
484. *OGJ,* v. 32, no. 20, p. 11
337. *OGJ,* v. 38, no. 50, p. 102
520. *OGJ,* v. 39, no. 49, p. 140
366. *OGJ,* v. 47, no. 30, p. 93
745. *OGJ,* v. 54, no. 23, pp. 321, 324
365. *OGJ,* v. 57, no. 24, p. 136
376. *OW,* v. 82, no. 10, p. 14
524. *OW,* v. 90, no. 7, p. 178
370. *OW,* v. 100, no. 10, p. 20
161. *OW,* v. 123, no. 3, pp. 83-85
409. *OW,* v. 123, no. 3, p. 126
364. *Paper* 5, Fifth World Pet. Cong., sec. 1,
p. 6; *Oil,* v. 19, no. 8, p. 38
434. *PROB.,* pp. 632-633
851. *Proc.,* Fourth World Pet. Cong., sec. 1, p.
94
583. *Trans.,* GCAGS, v. 9, p. 62
631. *Trans.,* GCAGS, v. 10, p. 218
410. *WO,* v. 130, no. 7, p. 76
335. *WO,* v. 142, no. 7, p. 158

Ferguson, Washington County: (see Clay Creek)

Ferguson Crossing, Brazos and Grimes Counties:
(Carlos)
6a. *BMIC*
102. *Bull.,* v. 18, no. 4, pp. 543-546; *GC,* pp.
133-135
847. *Bull.,* v. 20, no. 6, p. 730; *GC,* p. 113
374. *Bull.,* v. 23, no. 7, pp. 1092-1093
297. *Bull.,* v. 45, no. 6, p. 873
96. *Bull.,* La. Geol. Svy., no. 11, p. 70
427. *GAGC,* p. 271
363. *Geophysics,* v. 1, no. 1, Fig. 3 (between pp.
142-143), Fig. 8 (between pp.
146-147)
846. *Guidebook,* AAPG-SEPM-SEG (1953),
p. 16
524. *OW,* v. 90, no. 7, p. 168

Freeport, Brazoria County: (see Bryan Mound)

Friendswood, Harris County: (see Webster)

Gay Hill, Washington County: (see Clay Creek)

Graddy, Freestone County: (see Butler)

Grand Saline, Van Zandt County:
6a. *BMIC*
723. *Bull.,* v. 9, no. 5, pp. 839, 842, 859; *SD,* pp.
9, 12, 29
601. *Bull.,* v. 10, no. 1, pp. 4, 7, 14-15, 17-23,
36; *SD,* pp. 212, 215, 222-223, 225-
231, 244
655. *Bull.,* v. 18, no. 2, pp. 214, 215; *GC,* pp. 121-
122
849. *Bull.,* v. 31, no. 7, pp. 1295-1296
501. *Bull.,* v. 33, no. 11, pp. 1791-1829
705. *Bull.,* v. 39, no. 12, p. 2389
753. *Bull.,* v. 41, no. 8, pp. 1828-30, 1848
206. *Bull.,* v. 44, no. 6, p. 817
932. *Bull.,* v. 46, no. 8, pp. 1454-1455, 1457, 1459
931. *Bull.,* v. 46, no. 8, pp. 1460, 1465
555a. *Bull.,* v. 50, no. 3, pp. 451, 455-456, 459-460
96. *Bull.,* La. Geol. Svy., no.11, pp. 25, 49, 55
429. *Bull. 1869,* Tex. U., p. 20
80. *Bull. 736,* USGS, pp. 179-239
427. *GAGC,* pp. 209, 211-212, 264, 271
499. *GCH,* v. 1, pp. 105-120; *Geophysics,* v. 10,
no. 3, pp. 376-391
420. *Geol. Svy. of Tex.,* First Ann. Rept., pp. 33,
35
502. *Geophysics,* v. 17, no. 3, pp. 544-549
498. *Guidebook,* HGS (1962), pp. 266-267, 272-
276
831. *OGJ,* v. 56, no. 10, p. 248
864. *OGJ,* v. 57, no. 19, p. 143
325. *OGJ,* v. 61, no. 52, pp. 210-211, 214
449. *Pet. Geol.,* p. 407
434. *PROB.,* pp. 632-633, 641, 651-652
947. *PROB.,* pp. 996, 1018
865. *RI 38,* Tex. U., Bur. Econ. Geol., pp. 23-24
515a. *SOS,* pp. 104-106, 111, 113-119
347b. *SOS,* pp. 379-389
631. *Trans.,* GCAGS, v. 10, pp. 217-218, 236
885. *OW* (Aug. 7, 1931), p. 19

Grubbles, Fort Bend County: (see Thompson)

Gulf, Matagorda County: (Big Hill)
6a. *BMIC*
929. *Bull.,* v. 9, no. 1, pp. 4, 5; *SD,* pp. 647-648
769. *Bull.,* v. 9, no. 1, p. 71, *SD,* p. 79
58. *Bull.,* v. 9, no. 4, pp. 711-737; *SD,* pp.
691-717
589. *Bull.,* v. 9, no. 7, p. 1032; *SD,* p. 571
655. *Bull.,* v. 18, no. 2, pp. 215, 217, 219-223;
GC, pp. 122, 124, 126-130
137. *Bull.,* v. 20, no. 2, p. 183; *GC,* p. 1030

Gulf, Matagorda County: (Big Hill) (cont.)

847. *Bull.,* v. 20, no. 6, p. 729; *GC,* p. 112
753. *Bull.,* v. 41, no. 8, p. 1848
 96. *Bull.,* La. Geol. Svy., no. 11, pp. 15, 25,
        49, 51, 60, 69, 70-71, 75, 102, 118
942a. *Bull. 4,* SIPES, Figs. 1, 3
427. *GAGC,* p. 271
717. *GAS,* pp. 685, 708
363. *Geophysics,* v. 1, no. 1, Fig. 2 (between
        pp. 142-143), Fig. 7 (between pp.
        146-147)
846. *Guidebook,* AAPG-SEPM-SEG (1953),
        p. 16
801. *Lockwood's* (Texas 1939), sec. 5, pp. 13, 30
722. *OFNA,* p. 134
125. *OGJ,* v. 25, no. 35, p. 107
300. *OGJ,* v. 37, no. 12, p. 34
337. *OGJ,* v. 38, no. 50, p. 102
520. *OGJ,* v. 39, no. 49, pp. 133, 135, 138
524. *OW,* v. 90, no. 7, p. 184
161. *OW,* v. 123, no. 3, p. 85
409. *OW,* v. 123, no. 3, p. 129
434. *PROB.,* pp. 631-632, 640
410. *WO,* v. 130, no. 7, p. 82

**Gyp Hill, Brooks County: (Las Cuevas, Loma
Blanca)**

 6a. *BMIC*
883. *Bull.,* v. 9, no. 3, pp. 577-581, 586; *SD,*
        pp. 759-763, 768
785. *Bull.,* v. 9, no. 4, p. 745; *SD,* p. 426
847. *Bull.,* v. 20, no. 6, pp. 731, 733; *GC,* pp.
        114, 117
495. *Bull.,* v. 28, no. 4, p. 547
250. *Bull.,* v. 30, no. 6, p. 974
 96. *Bull.,* La. Geol. Svy., no. 11, pp. 5, 49, 77,
        113
427. *GAGC,* pp. 228, 271
363. *Geophysics,* v. 1, no. 1, Fig. 2 (between
        pp. 142-143), Fig. 7 (between pp.
        146-147)
846. *Guidebook,* AAPG-SEPM-SEG (1953),
        p. 17
722. *OFNA,* p. 148
337. *OGJ,* v. 38, no. 50, p. 102
691. *OGJ,* v. 52, no. 7, pp. 358, 360
764. *OGJ,* v. 55, no. 26, p. 189
298. *Bull.,* v. 46, no. 6, p. 924
942a. *Bull. 4,* SIPES, Figs. 1, 3
427. *GAGC,* p. 271
717. *GAS,* pp. 685-686, 710
363. *Geophysics,* v. 1, no. 1, Fig. 2 (between
        pp. 142-143), Fig. 7 (between pp.
        146-147)

**Gyp Hill, Brooks County: (Las Cuevas, Loma
Blanca) (cont.)**

846. *Guidebook,* AAPG-SEPM-SEG (1953),
        p. 17
801. *Lockwood's* (Texas 1939), sec. 4, p. 11;
        sec. 5, pp. 19, 35
722. *OFNA,* p. 147
532. *OGJ,* v. 25, no. 40, p. 152
790. *OGJ,* v. 30, no. 37, p. 76
359. *OGJ,* v. 34, no. 8, p. 42
520. *OGJ,* v. 39, no. 49, pp. 133, 138, 140
526. *OGJ,* v. 59, no. 31, p. 255
527. *OW,* v. 69, no. 1, p. 16
756. *OW,* v. 69, no. 1, p. 59
376. *OW,* v. 82, no. 10, p. 14
524. *OW,* v. 90, no. 7, p. 166
170. *OW,* v. 123, no. 3, pp. 83-85
161. *OW,* v. 123, no. 3, p. 87
409. *OW,* v. 123, no. 3, p. 118
449. *Pet. Geol.,* pp. 268-269, 274, 413-415
851. *Proc.,* Fourth World Pet. Cong., sec. 1,
        pp. 85, 90
146. *PROB.,* p. 115
434. *PROB.,* pp. 632-633
631. *Trans.,* GCAGS, v. 10, p. 218
410. *WO,* v. 130, no. 7, p. 70
581. *WP* (May 1936), pp. 271-273

Hainesville, Wood County:

 6a. *BMIC*
203. *Bull.,* v. 41, no. 6, pp. 1174-1175, 1177-1178
206. *Bull.,* v. 43, no. 6, p. 1302
427. *GAGC,* p. 271
467. *Geophysics,* v. 13, no. 3, pp. 387-403
602. *Guidebook,* Shreveport Geol. Soc. (1950),
        pp. 5-9, 13
818. *OGJ,* v. 55, no. 22, p. 167
831. *OGJ,* v. 56, no. 10, pp. 248, 250
 86. *OGJ,* v. 56, no. 30, p. 263
864. *OGJ,* v. 57, no. 19, pp. 143-144, 146-147
318. *OGJ,* v. 58, no. 7, p. 157
325. *OGJ,* v. 61, no. 52, pp. 210-212, 214
885. *OW* (Aug. 7, 1931), p. 19
364. *Paper 5,* Fifth World Pet. Cong., sec. 1,
        pp. 3, 8; *Oil,* v. 19, no. 8, pp. 34, 39
434. *PROB.,* pp. 632-633
455. *Trans.,* GCAGS, v. 6, p. 84
950. *Trans.,* GCAGS, v. 6, pp. 85-90

Hankamer, Liberty County:

 6a. *BMIC*
511. *Bull.,* v. 19, no. 1, pp. 19-20, 24; *Trans.,*
        SEG, v. 5, pp. 19-20, 24; *EGP,* pp.
        679-680, 684

Hankamer, Liberty County: (cont.)

847.   *Bull.*, v. 20, no. 6, p. 730; *GC*, p. 113
285.   *Bull.*, v. 32, no. 6, p. 1028
286.   *Bull.*, v. 33, no. 6, p. 974
287.   *Bull.*, v. 34, no. 6, pp. 1186-1187
288.   *Bull.*, v. 35, no. 6, pp. 1331, 1335
290.   *Bull.*, v. 37, no. 6, p. 1440
292.   *Bull.*, v. 39, no. 6, p. 983
96.   *Bull.*, La. Geol. Svy., no. 11, p. 51
427.   *GAGC*, p. 271
717.   *GAS*, pp. 685, 729
363.   *Geophysics*, v. 1, no. 1, Fig. 3 (between
           pp. 142-143), Fig. 8 (between pp.
           146-147)
846.   *Guidebook*, AAPG-SEPM-SEG (1953),
           p. 17
572.   *HGS*, pp. 74-75
801.   *Lockwood's* (Texas 1939), sec. 4, p. 10; sec.
           5, pp. 19, 34
478.   *OGJ*, v. 27, no. 25, p. 35
515.   *OGJ*, v. 28, no. 49, pp. 43, 118
474.   *OGJ*, v. 28, no. 50, p. 143
484.   *OGJ*, v. 32, no. 20, p. 11
376.   *OW*, v. 82, no. 10, p. 14
524.   *OW*, v. 90, no. 7, p. 182
161.   *OW*, v. 123, no. 3, p. 85
409.   *OW*, v. 123, no. 3, p. 128
434.   *PROB*, pp. 632-633
410.   *WO*, v. 130, no. 7, pp. 78-80

Hawkinsville, Matagorda County:

6a.   *BMIC*
385.   *Bull.*, v. 17, no. 9, pp. 1056, 1072; *GC*,
           pp. 51, 67
847.   *Bull.*, v. 20, no. 6, p. 730; *GC*, p. 113
545.   *Bull.*, v. 23, no. 4, pp. 604-605
96.   *Bull.*, La. Geol. Svy., no. 11, p. 55
360.   *EGP*, pp. 259, 262; *Jour.*, Soc. of Pet.
           Geophysicists, v. 6, no. 1, pp. 15, 18
427.   *GAGC*, p. 271
363.   *Geophysics*, v. 1, no. 1, Fig. 3 (between
           pp. 142-143), Fig. 8 (between pp.
           146-147)
361.   *Geophysics*, v. 3, no. 1, p. 32
845.   *Geophysics*, v. 18, no. 2, pp. 338-339
846.   *Guidebook*, AAPG-SEPM-SEG (1953),
           p. 17
801.   *Lockwood's* (Texas 1939), sec. 4, p. 11;
           sec. 5, pp. 19, 35
478.   *OGJ*, v. 27, no. 25, pp. 35, 91
515.   *OGJ*, v. 28, no. 49, p. 118
484.   *OGJ*, v. 32, no. 20, p. 11
300.   *OGJ*, v. 37, no. 12, p. 34
337.   *OGJ*, v. 38, no. 50, p. 102

Hawkinsville, Matagorda County: (cont.)

524.   *OW*, v. 90, no. 7, p. 186
161.   *OW*, v. 123, no. 3, p. 85
409.   *OW*, v. 123, no. 3, p. 129
434.   *PROB.*, pp. 631-632, 651, 655
410.   *WO*, v. 130, no. 7, p. 82

High Island, Galveston County:

6a.   *BMIC*
127.   *Bull.*, v. 1, no. 1, p. 46
952.   *Bull.*, v. 3, no. 1, p. 87
723.   *Bull.*, v. 9, no. 5, p. 844; *SD*, p 14
589.   *Bull.*, v. 9, no. 7, p. 1032; *SD*, p. 571
585.   *Bull.*, v. 16, no. 7, pp. 701-702
329.   *Bull.*, v. 17, no. 12, pp. 1493-1497, 1502,
           1511-1513; *GC*, pp. 142-146, 151,
           160-162; *OW*, v. 71, no. 12, pp. 18-
           22; *OGJ*, v. 32, no. 25, pp. 16, 18
433.   *Bull.*, v. 19, no. 9, p. 1323; *GC*, p. 976
432.   *Bull.*, v. 20, no. 5, pp. 560-611; *GC*, pp.
           909-960; (abs.) *WP*, v. 7, no. 8, p. 404
847.   *Bull.*, v. 20, no. 6, p. 729; *GC*, p. 112
283.   *Bull.*, v. 30, no. 6, p. 995
285.   *Bull.*, v. 32, no. 6, p. 1028
286.   *Bull.*, v. 33, no. 6, p. 972
775.   *Bull.*, v. 33, no. 7, p. 1253
287.   *Bull.*, v. 34, no. 6, p. 1185
288.   *Bull.*, v. 35, no. 6, p. 1335
290.   *Bull.*, v. 37, no. 6, p. 1436
293.   *Bull.*, v. 40, no. 6, pp. 1243, 1246
753.   *Bull.*, v. 41, no. 8, p. 1848
283.   *Bull.*, v. 30, no. 6, pp. 995-997
849.   *Bull.*, v. 31, no. 7, p. 1295
285.   *Bull.*, v. 32, no. 6, p. 1028
286.   *Bull.*, v. 33, no. 6, p. 973
287.   *Bull.*, v. 34, no. 6, p. 1186
725.   *Bull.*, v. 39, no. 5, pp. 700-701, 705-706, 709
292.   *Bull.*, v. 39, no. 6, p. 986
705.   *Bull.*, v. 39, no. 12, p. 2417
96.   *Bull.*, La. Geol. Svy., no. 11, pp. 38, 49-50,
           55, 61-62, 70, 90, 112
429.   *Bull. 1869*, Tex. U., p. 261
427.   *GAGC*, pp. 218, 240, 268, 271
499.   *GCH*, v. 1, p. 120; *Geophysics*, v. 10, no.
           3, p. 391
363.   *Geophysics*, v. 1, no. 1, Fig. 2 (between
           pp. 142-143), Fig. 7 (between pp.
           146-147)
307.   *Geophysics*, v. 3, no. 3, p. 194
507.   *Geophysics*, v. 20, no. 4, pp. 829-840
846.   *Guidebook*, AAPG-SEPM-SEG (1953),
           p. 17

High Island, Galveston County: (cont.)

587. *HGS,* pp. 76-79; *Guidebook,* AAPG-SEPM-SEG (1953), pp. 125-128
801. *Lockwood's* (Texas 1939), sec. 5, p. 19
722. *OFNA,* p. 152
574. *OGJ,* v. 27, no. 14, p. 32
478. *OGJ,* v. 27, no. 25, p. 35
515. *OGJ,* v. 28, no. 49, p. 42
300. *OGJ,* v. 37, no. 12, p. 34
337. *OGJ,* v. 38, no. 50, p. 102
520. *OGJ,* v. 39, no. 49, p. 138
745. *OGJ,* v. 54, no. 23, pp. 322, 324
365. *OGJ,* v. 57, no. 24, p. 136
857. *OW,* v. 52, no. 7, pp. 28-29
524. *OW,* v. 90, no. 7, p. 172
161. *OW,* v. 123, no. 3, p. 85
170. *OW,* v. 123, no. 3, p. 87
409. *OW,* v. 123, no. 3, p. 122
364. *Paper 5,* Fifth World Pet. Cong., sec. 1, p. 6; *Oil,* v. 19, no. 8, p. 38
434. *PROB.,* pp. 631-632, 637-639, 642, 650-651, 655, Plates 1-3
851. *Proc.,* Fourth World Pet. Cong., sec. 1, pp. 95-96
568. *Pub. 4301,* Tex. U., Bur. Econ. Geol., pp. 207-226
515a. *SOS,* pp. 105-106
631. *Trans.,* GCAGS, v. 10, p. 218
410. *WO,* v. 130, no. 7, p. 74

Hinkle's Ferry, Brazoria County: (see Clemens)

Hockley, Harris County:

6a. *BMIC*
127. *Bull.,* v. 1, no. 1, pp. 45
588. *Bull.,* v. 7, no. 3, pp. 297-299
549. *Bull.,* v. 9, no. 1, p. 36; *SD,* p. 775
769. *Bull.,* v. 9, no. 1, p. 57; *SD,* p. 65
883. *Bull.,* v. 9, no. 3, p. 542; *SD,* p. 724
785. *Bull.,* v. 9, no. 4, pp. 741, 745; *SD,* pp. 422, 426
723. *Bull.,* v. 9, no. 5, p. 869; *SD,* p. 39
589. *Bull.,* v. 9, no. 7, pp. 1031-1060; *SD,* pp. 570-599
590. *Bull.,* v. 15, no. 4, pp. 465-469; *GC,* pp. 136-140
385. *Bull.,* v. 17, no. 9, pp. 1048, 1072; *GC,* pp. 43, 67
944. *Bull.,* v. 17, no. 10, p. 1206; *GC,* p. 263
611. *Bull.,* v. 17, no. 11, p. 1331; *GC,* p. 507
655. *Bull.,* v. 18, no. 2, pp. 214-216; *GC,* pp. 121-123
847. *Bull.,* v. 20, no. 6, p. 730; *GC,* p. 113
462. *Bull.,* v. 20, no. 11, pp. 1416, 1433

Hoskins Mound, Brazoria County:

6a. *BMIC*
127. *Bull.,* v. 1, no. 1, pp. 44, 80
929. *Bull.,* v. 9, no. 1, pp. 4-5, 24; *SD,* pp. 647-648, 667
769. *Bull.,* v. 9, no. 1, pp. 70-71, 73; *SD,* pp. 78-79, 81
589. *Bull.,* v. 9, no. 7, p. 1032; *SD,* p. 571
82. *Bull.,* v. 9, no. 3, pp. 616, 624; *SD,* pp. 681, 689
385. *Bull.,* v. 17, no. 9, p. 1051; *GC,* p. 46
655. *Bull.,* v. 18, no. 2, p. 220; *GC,* p. 127
591. *Bull.,* v. 20, no. 2, pp. 155-178; *GC,* pp. 833-855
847. *Bull.,* v. 20, no. 6, p. 730; *GC,* p. 113
753. *Bull.,* v. 41, no. 8, pp. 1844, 1848
96. *Bull.,* La. Geol. Svy., no. 11, pp. 13, 15, 35, 38, 40, 49-50, 53, 60, 67-68, 71, 75, 118
942a. *Bull. 4,* SIPES, Figs. 1, 3
403. *EGP,* pp. 341, 346, 349
427. *GAGC,* pp. 228, 271
402. *GCH,* v. 1, pp. 255-257, 259, 271
363. *Geophysics,* v. 1, no. 1, Fig. 2 (between pp. 142-143), Fig. 7 (between pp. 146-147)
592. *Geophysics,* v. 6, no. 3, pp. 259-263
846. *Guidebook,* AAPG-SEPM-SEG (1953), p. 17
805. *JPT,* v. 8, no. 11; *Trans.,* AIME, v. 207, p. 247
801. *Lockwood's* (Texas 1939), sec. 5, p. 20
722. *OFNA,* p. 146
125. *OGJ,* v. 25, no. 35, p. 107
300. *OGJ,* v. 37, no. 12, p. 34
337. *OGJ,* v. 38, no. 50, p. 102
520. *OGJ,* v. 39, no. 49, p. 138
524. *OW,* v. 90, no. 7, p. 146
161. *OW,* v. 123, no. 3, p. 85
409. *OW,* v. 123, no. 3, p. 112
449. *Pet. Geol.,* pp. 412-413
434. *PROB.,* pp. 631-632
410. *WO,* v. 130, no. 7, p. 61

Hull, Liberty County:

6a. *BMIC*
973. *Bull.,* v. 5, no. 2, p. 233
883. *Bull.,* v. 9, no. 3, p. 543; *SD,* p. 724
329. *Bull.,* v. 17, no. 12, pp. 1494-1497, 1510; *GC,* pp. 143-146, 159-160; *OW,* v. 71, no. 12, pp. 18-22; *OGJ,* v. 32, no. 25, pp. 16, 18
654. *Bull.,* v. 18, no. 4, p. 510; *GC,* p. 11
847. *Bull.,* v. 20, no. 6, p. 730; *GC,* p. 113

Hull, Liberty County: (cont.)

462. *Bull.*, v. 20, no. 11, p. 1422
286. *Bull.*, v. 33, no. 6, pp. 974-975
287. *Bull.*, v. 34, no. 6, pp. 1187, 1189
288. *Bull.*, v. 35, no. 6, pp. 1332, 1335
289. *Bull.*, v. 36, no. 6, p. 1208
290. *Bull.*, v. 37, no. 6, p. 1433
291. *Bull.*, v. 38, no. 6, pp. 1209-1210, 1216
725. *Bull.*, v. 39, no. 5, pp. 697-698, 700-701, 705-706, 709
292. *Bull.*, v. 39, no. 6, pp. 980-981
294. *Bull.*, v. 41, no. 6, p. 1187
295. *Bull.*, v. 42, no. 6, p. 1304
297. *Bull.*, v. 45, no. 6, p. 874
115. *Chron. Hist.*, p. 118
427. *GAGC*, pp. 217, 246, 271
717. *GAS*, p. 705
363. *Geophysics*, v. 1, no. 1, Fig. 2 (between pp. 142-143), Fig. 7 (between pp. 146-147)
846. *Guidebook*, AAPG-SEPM-SEG (1953), p. 17
3. *Guidebook*, AAPG-SEPM-SEG (1953), p. 33
801. *Lockwood's* (Texas 1939), sec. 4, p. 11; sec. 5, pp. 20, 35
722. *OFNA*, pp. 147, 151
125. *OGJ*, v. 25, no. 35, p. 107
593. *OGJ*, v. 32, no. 25, pp. 21-22
337. *OGJ*, v. 38, no. 50, p. 102
311. *OGJ*, v. 39, no. 49, p. 84
520. *OGJ*, v. 39, no. 49, p. 138
450. *OGJ*, v. 46, no. 4, p. 136
476. *OGJ*, v. 51, no. 7, p. 94
868. *OGJ*, v. 54, no. 14, p. 155
744. *OGJ*, v. 57, no. 6, p. 140
365. *OGJ*, v. 57, no. 24, pp. 135-136
526. *OGJ*, v. 59, no. 31, p. 255
376. *OW*, v. 82, no. 10, p. 14
524. *OW*, v. 90, no. 7, pp. 182, 184
161. *OW*, v. 123, no. 3, pp. 81, 83-85
409. *OW*, v. 123, no. 3, p. 128
364. *Paper 5,* Fifth World Pet. Cong., sec. 1, pp. 2, 6; *Oil*, v. 19, no. 8, pp. 36, 38
434. *PROB.*, pp. 632-633, 673
552. *PROB.*, pp. 899-900
851. *Proc.*, Fourth World Pet. Cong., sec. 1, pp. 88, 90, 96
525. *WO*, v. 130, no. 7, p. 58
410. *WO*, v. 130, no. 7, p. 80
581. *WP* (May, 1936), pp. 271-272

Humble, Harris County:

6a. *BMIC*

Humble, Harris County: (cont.)

906. *Bull.*, v. 9, no. 3, p. 656; *SD*, p. 559
618. *Bull.*, v. 10, no. 1, p. 79; *SD*, p. 404
944. *Bull.*, v. 17, no. 10, p. 1206; *GC*, p. 263
654. *Bull.*, v. 18, no. 4, pp. 502, 504-505, 513; *GC*, pp. 3, 5-6, 11, 14
128. *Bull.*, v. 19, no. 5, p. 682; *GC*, p. 463
847. *Bull.*, v. 20, no. 6, p. 730; *GC*, p. 113
462. *Bull.*, v. 20, no. 11, p. 1422
282. *Bull.*, v. 29, no. 6, p. 789
285. *Bull.*, v. 32, no. 6, p. 1028
287. *Bull.*, v. 34, no. 6, pp. 1186, 1189
288. *Bull.*, v. 35, no. 6, p. 1331
291. *Bull.*, v. 38, no. 6, p. 1210
725. *Bull.*, v. 39, no. 5, pp. 700-701, 705-706, 709
293. *Bull.*, v. 40, no. 6, pp. 1240, 1244, 1248
96. *Bull.*, La. Geol. Svy., no. 11, pp. 25, 115
429. *Bull. 1869,* Tex. U., pp. 262, 294, 297
115. *Chron. Hist.*, pp. 84-85
427. *GAGC*, p. 271
717. *GAS*, pp. 685, 705-706, 738
363. *Geophysics*, v. 1, no. 1, Fig. 2 (between pp. 142-143), Fig. 7 (between pp. 146-147)
361. *Geophysics*, v. 3, no. 1, p. 31
547. *Geophysics*, v. 3, no. 2, pp. 107, 110
307. *Geophysics*, v. 3, no. 3, pp. 191, 194
512. *Geophysics*, v. 22, no. 3, p. 633
846. *Guidebook*, AAPG-SEPM-SEG (1953), p. 17
801. *Lockwood's* (Texas 1939), sec. 4, p. 11; sec. 5, pp. 20, 35
722. *OFNA*, pp. 146-147, 151-152
574. *OGJ*, v. 27, no. 14, p. 32
515. *OGJ*, v. 28, no. 49, pp. 42-43
790. *OGJ*, v. 30, no. 37, p. 73
728. *OGJ*, v. 33, no. 46, p. 149
300. *OGJ*, v. 37, no. 12, p. 33
337. *OGJ*, v. 38, no. 50, p. 102
594. *OGJ*, v. 39, no. 5, pp. 61, 64
311. *OGJ*, v. 39, no. 49, p. 84
520. *OGJ*, v. 39, no. 49, pp. 135, 138
744. *OGJ*, v. 57, no. 6, p. 140
365. *OGJ*, v. 57, no. 24, p. 136
526. *OGJ*, v. 59, no. 31, p. 255
857. *OW*, v. 52, no. 7, p. 29
376. *OW*, v. 82, no. 10, p. 14
524. *OW*, v. 90, no. 7, pp. 172, 174
169. *OW*, v. 99, no. 3, p. 47
161. *OW*, v. 123, no. 3, pp. 81, 83-85
409. *OW*, v. 123, no. 3, p. 122
364. *Paper 5,* World Pet. Cong., sec. 1, p. 6; *Oil*, v. 19, no. 8, p. 38
449. *Pet. Geol.*, pp. 274-275

Humble, Harris County: (cont.)

146. *PROB.*, p. 115
434. *PROB.*, pp. 632-633, 671
947. *PROB.*, pp. 996, 1018-1019
525. *WO*, v. 130, no. 7, p. 58
410. *WO*, v. 130, no. 7, p. 74

Ives Creek, Austin County: (see Raccoon Bend)

Ive's Crossing, Washington County: (see Clay Creek)

Jefferson Coast, Jefferson County: (see McFaddin Beach)

Keechi, Anderson County:

6a. *BMIC*
127. *Bull.*, v. 1, no. 1, p. 75
683. *Bull.*, v. 6, no. 4, p. 329
883. *Bull.*, v. 9, no. 3, p. 564; *SD*, p. 746
723. *Bull.*, v. 9, no. 5, pp. 839, 871; *SD*, pp. 9, 36, 41
843. *Bull.*, v. 9, no. 9, p. 1230; *SD*, p. 170
601. *Bull.*, v. 10, no. 1, pp. 4, 14, 35-45, 53, 57; *SD*, pp. 212, 222, 243-253, 261, 265
309. *Bull.*, v. 13, no. 6, p. 613
329. *Bull.*, v. 17, no. 12, pp. 1495-1496, 1517-1518; *GC*, pp. 144-145, 166-167; *OW*, v. 71, no. 12, pp. 18-22; *OGJ*, v. 32, no. 25, pp. 16, 18
429. *Bull. 1869*, Tex. U., pp. 26, 300-302, 308
427. *GAGC*, p. 271
831. *OGJ*, v. 56, no. 10, p. 248
864. *OGJ*, v. 57, no. 19, p. 143
885. *OW* (Aug. 7, 1931), pp. 17, 19
449. *Pet. Geol.* p. 258
434. *PROB.*, pp. 632-633

Kiser Hill, Brazoria County: (see West Columbia)

Kittrell, Houston County: (Trinity)

6a. *BMIC*
847. *Bull.*, v. 20, no. 6, p. 730; *GC*, p. 113
900. *Bull.*, v. 21, no. 8, p. 1086
928. *Bull.*, v. 32, no. 1, p. 11
203. *Bull.*, v. 41, no. 6, p. 1174
427. *GAGC*, p. 271
363. *Geophysics*, v. 1, no. 1, Fig. 2 (between pp. 142-143), Fig. 7 (between pp. 146-147)
846. *Guidebook*, AAPG-SEPM-SEG (1953), p. 17
602. *Guidebook*, Shreveport Geol. Soc. (1960), p. 5

Kittrell, Houston County: (Trinity) (cont.)

801. *Lockwood's* (Texas 1939), sec. 4, p. 12; sec. 5, pp. 20, 35
364. *Paper* 5, Fifth World Pet. Cong., sec. 1, p. 3; *Oil*, v. 19, no. 8, p. 34
455. *Trans.*, GCAGS, v. 6, p. 84

LaRue, Henderson County:

6a. *BMIC*
250. *Bull.*, v. 30, no. 6, pp. 973-974
705. *Bull.*, v. 39, no. 12, p. 2417
548. *Bull.*, v. 42, no. 2, pp. 362-364
427. *GAGC*, pp. 211, 271
831. *OGJ*, v. 56, no. 10, p. 248
864. *OGJ*, v. 57, no. 19, p. 143
885. *OW* (Aug. 7, 1931), p. 19
434. *PROB.*, pp. 632-633

Las Cuevas, Brooks County: (see Gyp Hill)

Liberty, Liberty County: (see South Liberty)

Lockwood, Fort Bend County: (see Thompson)

Loma Blanca, Brooks County: (see Gyp Hill)

Long Point, Fort Bend County: (Pathfinder)

6a. *BMIC*
847. *Bull.*, v. 20, no. 6, p. 730; *GC*, p. 113
288. *Bull.*, v. 35, no. 6, p. 1329
289. *Bull.*, v. 36, no. 6, p. 1207
291. *Bull.*, v. 38, no. 6, p. 1216
725. *Bull.*, v. 39, no. 5, pp. 697, 699-701, 705-708, 710
294. *Bull.*, v. 41, no. 6, p. 1185
299. *Bull.*, v. 47, no. 6, p. 1084
96. *Bull.*, La. Geol. Svy., no. 11, pp. 25, 50, 118
942a. *Bull.* 4, SIPES, p. 1, Figs. 1, 3
427. *GAGC*, p. 271
154. *GCH*, v. 1, pp. 36-37
363. *Geophysics*, v. 1, no. 1, Fig. 3 (between pp. 142-143), Fig. 8 (between pp. 146-147)
479. *Geophysics*, v. 5, no. 3, p. 250
886. *Geophysics*, v. 13, no. 4, pp. 597-598
846. *Guidebook*, AAPG-SEPM-SEG (1953), p. 17
801. *Lockwood's* (Texas 1939), sec. 5, p. 21
722. *OFNA*, p. 146
478. *OGJ*, v. 27, no. 25, pp. 35, 91
515. *OGJ*, v. 28, no. 49, p. 118
474. *OGJ*, v. 28, no. 50, p. 143
484. *OGJ*, v. 32, no. 20, p. 11
300. *OGJ*, v. 37, no. 12, p. 34
337. *OGJ*, v. 38, no. 50, p. 102

Long Point, Fort Bend County:
  (Pathfinder) (cont.)

520. *OGJ*, v. 39, no. 49, p. 140
365. *OGJ*, v. 57, no. 24, p. 136
524. *OW*, v. 90, no. 7, p. 162
161. *OW*, v. 123, no. 3, p. 86
364. *Paper 5,* Fifth World Pet. Cong., sec. 1,
      pp. 5-6; *Oil*, v. 19, no. 8, pp. 37-38
434. *PROB.,* pp. 631-632
947. *PROB.,* pp. 996, 1019
631. *Trans.,* GCAGS, v. 10, p. 218

Lost Lake, Chambers County: (Cove)
  6a. *BMIC*
630. *Bull.,* v. 11, no. 6, p. 633
944. *Bull.,* v. 17, no. 10, p. 1208; *GC,* p. 265
511. *Bull.,* v. 19, no. 1, p. 24; *Trans.,* SEG, v.
      5, p. 24; *EGP,* p. 684
847. *Bull.,* v. 20, no. 6, p. 730; *GC,* p. 113
296. *Bull.,* v. 38, no. 6, p. 1219
725. *Bull.,* v. 39, no. 5, pp. 700-706, 708-711
294. *Bull.,* v. 41, no. 6, p. 1188
 96. *Bull.,* La. Geol. Svy., no. 11, p. 55
360. *EGP,* p. 260; *Jour.,* Soc. of Pet. Geophysi-
      cists, v. 6, no. 1, p. 16
427. *GAGC,* p. 271
717. *GAS,* pp. 685, 695, 717
510. *GCH,* v. 1, p. 182
363. *Geophysics,* v. 1, no. 1, Fig. 3 (between
      pp. 142-143), Fig. 8 (between pp.
      146-147)
362. *Geophysics,* v. 4, no. 3, p. 158
846. *Guidebook,* AAPG-SEPM-SEG (1953),
      p. 18
801. *Lockwood's* (Texas 1939), sec. 4, p. 13;
      sec. 5, p. 21
722. *OFNA,* p. 153
478. *OGJ*, v. 27, no. 25, pp. 35, 91
515. *OGJ*, v. 28, no. 49, p. 118
474. *OGJ*, v. 28, no. 50, p. 143
484. *OGJ*, v. 32, no. 20, p. 11
520. *OGJ*, v. 39, no. 49, p. 138
365. *OGJ*, v. 57, no. 24, pp. 135-136
334. *OW,* v. 69, no. 1, p. 65
524. *OW,* v. 90, no. 7, p. 150
161. *OW,* v. 123, no. 3, p. 85
409. *OW,* v. 123, no. 3, p. 112
364. *Paper 5,* Fifth World Pet. Cong., sec. 1,
      pp. 4, 6; *Oil,* v. 19, no. 8, pp. 35,
      37-38
434. *PROB.,* pp. 632-633, 651
851. *Proc.,* Fourth World Pet. Cong., sec. 1,
      p. 95
410. *WO,* v. 130, no. 7, p. 64

Mansfield Ferry, Orange County: (see Port
  Neches)

Manvel, Brazoria County:
  6a. *BMIC*
511. *Bull.,* v. 19, no. 1, pp. 19-20; *Trans.,*
      SEG, v. 5, pp. 19-20; *EGP,* pp.
      679-680
751. *Bull.,* v. 20, no. 5, p. 547; *GC,* p. 896
847. *Bull.,* v. 20, no. 6, p. 730; *GC,* p. 113
285. *Bull.,* v. 32, no. 6, p. 1028
286. *Bull.,* v. 33, no. 6, p. 970
287. *Bull.,* v. 34, no. 6, pp. 1184, 1189
290. *Bull.,* v. 37, no. 6, p. 1436
717. *GAS,* pp. 685, 729
409. *GCH,* v. 1, p. 74
466. *GCH,* v. 2, pp. 157-159, 161-162
363. *Geophysics,* v. 1, no. 1, Fig. 3 (between
      pp. 142-143), Fig. 8 (between pp.
      146-147)
361. *Geophysics,* v. 3, no. 1, pp. 30, 33-34
547. *Geophysics,* v. 3, no. 2, p. 101
362. *Geophysics,* v. 4, no. 3, p. 166
951. *Geophysics,* v. 7, no. 4, p. 386
846. *Guidebook,* AAPG-SEPM-SEG (1953),
      p. 18
662. *Guidebook,* AAPG-SEPM-SEG (1953),
      pp. 136-137
801. *Lockwood's* (Texas 1939), sec. 4, p. 14;
      sec. 5, pp. 22, 37
722. *OFNA,* p. 151
515. *OGJ*, v. 28, no. 49, p. 118
790. *OGJ*, v. 30, no. 37, p. 71
473. *OGJ*, v. 31, no. 8, p. 16
484. *OGJ*, v. 32, no. 20, p. 11
663. *OGJ*, v. 33, no. 41, pp. 77-79
664. *OGJ*, v. 39, no. 9, pp. 57-64
520. *OGJ*, v. 39, no. 49, p. 140
744. *OGJ*, v. 57, no. 6, p. 140
526. *OGJ*, v. 59, no. 31, p. 255
527. *OW,* v. 69, no. 1, pp. 16-18
524. *OW,* v. 90, no. 7, p. 146
161. *OW,* v. 123, no. 3, pp. 83-85
409. *OW,* v. 123, no. 3, p. 112
410. *WO,* v. 130, no. 7, p. 61
430. *WO* (Sept., 1937), p. 43

Markham, Matagorda County: (Clemville)
  6a. *BMIC*
792. *Bull.,* v. 9, no. 2, pp. 348-349; *SD,* p. 781
883. *Bull.,* v. 9, no. 3, p. 569; *SD,* p. 751
723. *Bull.,* v. 9, no. 5, pp 861, 867, 870-871;
      SD, pp. 31, 37, 40-41
843. *Bull.,* v. 9, no. 9, p. 1229; *SD,* p. 169

Markham, Matagorda County:
  (Clemville) (cont.)
601. *Bull.,* v. 10, no. 1, p. 10; *SD,* p. 218
618. *Bull.,* v. 10, no. 1, p. 80; *SD,* p. 405
385. *Bull.,* v. 17, no. 9, pp. 1027; 1047-1049;
        GC, pp. 22, 42-44
611. *Bull.,* v. 17, no. 11, pp. 1321; 1324;
        GC, pp. 498, 501
511. *Bull.,* v. 19, no. 1, p. 24; *Trans.,* SEG, v.
        5, p. 24; *EGP,* p. 684
847. *Bull.,* v. 20, no. 6, p. 730; *GC,* p. 113
285. *Bull.,* v. 32, no. 6, p. 1028
290. *Bull.,* v. 37, no. 6, p. 1441
291. *Bull.,* v. 38, no. 6, pp. 1209-1210, 1216,
        1218
292. *Bull.,* v. 39, no. 6, p. 983
293. *Bull.,* v. 40, no. 6, p. 1248
 96. *Bull.,* La. Geol. Svy., no. 11, p. 21
427. *GAGC,* p. 271
717. *GAS,* pp. 703-705
363. *Geophysics,* v. 1, no. 1, Fig. 2 (between
        pp. 142-143), Fig. 7 (between pp.
        146-147)
846. *Guidebook,* AAPG-SEPM-SEG (1953),
        p. 18
801. *Lockwood's* (Texas 1939), sec. 4, p. 14;
        sec. 5, 22, 37
532. *OGJ,* v. 25, no. 40, p. 152
474. *OGJ,* v. 28, no. 50, p. 143
790. *OGJ,* v. 30, no. 37, pp. 73, 76
520. *OGJ,* v. 39, no. 49, pp. 135, 138
376. *OW,* v. 82, no. 10, p. 14
524. *OW,* v. 90, no. 7, p. 186
161. *OW,* v. 123, no. 3, p. 85
409. *OW,* v. 123, no. 3, p. 129
434. *PROB.,* pp. 631-632, 639, 666
631. *Trans.,* GCAGS, v. 10, pp. 217, 226
410. *WO,* v. 130, no. 7, p. 82

McFaddin Beach, Jefferson County: (see Offshore)

Millcreek, Austin and Washington Counties: (see Brenham)

Millican, Brazos County:
 6a. *BMIC*
282. *Bull.,* v. 29, no. 6, p. 789
928. *Bull.,* v. 32, no. 1, p. 20
288. *Bull.,* v. 35, no. 6, p. 1329
708. *Bull.,* v. 35, no. 9, pp. 2083-2084, 2086
294. *Bull.,* v. 41, no. 6, p. 1185
427. *GAGC,* p. 271
846. *Guidebook,* AAPG-SEPM-SEG (1953),
        p. 18
161. *OW,* v. 123, no. 3, p. 88

Millican, Brazos County: (cont.)
409. *OW,* v. 123, no. 3, p. 110
525. *WO,* v. 130, no. 7, p. 59
410. *WO,* v. 130, no. 7, p. 62

Moca, Webb County:
 6a. *BMIC*
427. *GAGC,* p. 271
846. *Guidebook,* AAPG-SEPM-SEG (1953),
        p. 18
691. *OGJ,* v. 52, no. 7, pp. 358, 360
764. *OGJ,* v. 55, no. 26, p. 189

Mont Belvieu, Chambers County: (see Barber's Hill)

Moore, Fort Bend County: (see Orchard)

Moss Bluff, Liberty County:
 6a. *BMIC*
 65. *Bull.,* v. 10, no. 11, pp. 1171-1172
713. *Bull.,* v. 11, no. 3, p. 308
511. *Bull.,* v. 19, no. 1, pp. 20, 24; *Trans.,*
        SEG, v. 5, pp. 20, 24; *EGP,* pp.
        680, 684
482. *Bull.,* v. 19, no. 3, pp. 357-361; *GC,*
        pp. 171-175
847. *Bull.,* v. 20, no. 6, p. 730; *GC,* p. 113
288. *Bull.,* v. 35, no. 6, p. 1332
289. *Bull.,* v. 36, no. 6, p. 1208
290. *Bull.,* v. 37, no. 6, pp. 1436, 1441
725. *Bull.,* v. 39, no. 5, pp. 699-702, 705-706,
        708, 710-711
705. *Bull.,* v. 39, no. 12, pp. 2387, 2417
753. *Bull.,* v. 41, no. 8, pp. 1816, 1820-23,
        1828-33, 1836, 1839-41, 1844, 1851
295. *Bull.,* v. 42, no. 6, p. 1306
298. *Bull.,* v. 46, no. 6, p. 927
942a. *Bull.,* 4, SIPES, Figs. 1, 3
360. *EGP,* p. 259; *Jour.,* Soc. of Pet. Geo-
        physicists, v. 6, no. 1, p. 15
427. *GAGC,* pp. 241, 249, 271
363. *Geophysics,* v. 1, no. 1, Fig. 3 (between
        pp. 142-143), Fig. 8 (between pp.
        146-147)
711. *Geophysics,* v. 11, no. 2, pp. 128-134
505. *Geophysics* v. 22, no. 2, p. 348
846. *Guidebook,* AAPG-SEPM-SEG (1953),
        p. 18
801. *Lockwood's* (Texas 1939), sec. 5, pp. 22
        37
722. *OFNA,* p. 152
125. *OGJ,* v. 25, no. 35, p. 107

Moss Bluff, Liberty County: (cont.)

532.   *OGJ*, v. 25, no. 40, p. 97
478.   *OGJ*, v. 27, no. 25, pp. 35, 91
515.   *OGJ*, v. 28, no. 49, p. 118
790.   *OGJ*, v. 30, no. 37, p. 76
484.   *OGJ*, v. 32, no. 20, p. 11
300.   *OGJ*, v. 37, no. 12, p. 34
337.   *OGJ*, v. 38, no. 50, p. 102
712.   *OGJ*, v. 49, no. 30, pp. 45-46
365.   *OGJ*, v. 57, no. 24, pp. 135-136
524.   *OW*, v. 90, no. 7, p. 184
161.   *OW*, v. 123, no. 3, p. 85
409.   *OW*, v. 123, no. 3, p. 128
364.   *Paper* 5, Fifth World Pet. Cong., sec. 1, pp. 4, 6; *Oil*, v. 19, no. 8, pp. 35, 37-38
434.   *PROB.*, pp. 632-633
631.   *Trans.*, GCAGS, v. 10, p. 218
153.   *Trans.*, GCAGS, v. 11, p. 214
410.   *WO*, v. 130, no. 7, p. 80

Mount Sylvan, Smith County:

6a.   *BMIC*
865.   *Bull.*, v. 12, no. 5, p. 540
660.   *Bull.*, v. 13, no. 10, pp. 1347, 1361-1367
365.   *Bull.*, v. 17, no. 9, p. 1079; *GC*, p. 74
385.   *Bull.*, v. 39, no. 12, p. 2417
427.   *GAGC*, p. 270
717.   *GC*, pp. 1041-1049
831.   *OGJ*, v. 56, no. 10, p. 248
864.   *OGJ*, v. 57, no. 19, pp. 143-144
885.   *OW* (Aug. 7, 1931), p. 19
434.   *PROB.*, pp. 632-633

Mykawa, Harris County:

6a.   *BMIC*
611.   *Bull.*, v. 17, no. 11, p. 1324; *GC*, p. 501
654.   *Bull.*, v. 18, no. 4, p. 518; *GC*, p. 13
511.   *Bull.*, v. 19, no. 1, p. 19; *Trans.*, SEG, v. 5, p. 19; *EGP*, p. 679
482.   *Bull.*, v. 19, no. 3, pp. 357-358, 365, 372; *GC*, pp. 170-171, 179, 186
847.   *Bull.*, v. 20, no. 6, p. 730; *GC*, p. 113
292.   *Bull.*, v. 39, no. 6, p. 980
294.   *Bull.*, v. 41, no. 6, p. 1186
295.   *Bull.*, v. 42, no. 6, p. 1304
427.   *GAGC*, p. 271
717.   *GAS*, pp. 685, 695-696, 718, 727-728, 737-738
470.   *GCH*, v. 1, p. 45
388.   *GCH*, v. 1, pp. 74, 76, 79
466.   *GCH*, v. 2, p. 158

Mykawa, Harris County: (cont.)

363.   *Geophysics*, v. 1, no. 1, Fig. 3 (between pp. 142-143), Fig. 8 (between pp. 146-147)
307.   *Geophysics*, v. 3, no. 3, pp. 191, 194
951.   *Geophysics*, v. 7, no. 4, p. 386
846.   *Guidebook*, AAPG-SEPM-SEG (1953), p. 18
801.   *Lockwood's* (Texas 1939), sec. 4, p. 14; sec. 5, pp. 22, 37
722.   *OFNA*, p. 153
574.   *OGJ*, v. 27, no. 14, p. 32
478.   *OGJ*, v. 27, no. 25, p. 35
515.   *OGJ*, v. 28, no. 49, pp. 43, 118
473.   *OGJ*, v. 31, no. 8, p. 16
393.   *OGJ*, v. 32, no. 7, p. 36
484.   *OGJ*, v. 32, no. 20, p. 11
524.   *OW*, v. 90, no. 7, p. 174
161.   *OW*, v. 123, no. 3, p. 85
409.   *OW*, v. 123, no. 3, p. 122
434.   *PROB.*, pp. 632-633
410.   *WO*, v. 130, no. 7, p. 74

Nash, Brazoria and Fort Bend Counties:

6a.   *BMIC*
382.   *Bull.*, v. 18, no. 9, p. 1197; *GC*, p. 101
847.   *Bull.*, v. 20, no. 6, p. 730; *GC*, p. 113
283.   *Bull.*, 30, no. 6, pp. 995-996
287.   *Bull.*, v. 34, no. 6, p. 1185
288.   *Bull.*, v. 35, no. 6, p. 1330
290.   *Bull.*, v. 37, no. 6, pp. 1436, 1440
725.   *Bull.*, v. 39, no. 5, pp. 699-701, 703, 705-708, 710
293.   *Bull.*, v. 40, no. 6, p. 1246
299.   *Bull.*, v. 47, no. 6, p. 1084
942a.   *Bull.* 4, SIPES, Figs. 1, 3
115.   *Chron. Hist.*, p. 150
477.   *EGP*, pp. 247-248; *Jour.*, Soc. of Pet. Geophysicists, v. 6, no. 1, pp. 3-4
360.   *EGP*, pp. 258, 262; *Jour.*, Soc. of Pet. Geophysicists, v. 6, no. 1, pp. 14, 18
427.   *GAGC.* p. 271
901.   *GCH*, v. 1, pp. 12, 16; *Geophysics*, v. 5, no. 3, pp. 220, 226
509.   *GCH*, v. 1, pp. 21, 24; *Geophysics*, v. 5, no. 3, pp. 231, 234
363.   *Geophysics*, v. 1, no. 1, Fig. 3 (between pp. 142-143), Fig. 8 (between pp. 146-147
479.   *Geophysics*, v. 5, no. 3, p. 250
480.   *Geophysics*, v. 22, no. 2, p. 225
846.   *Guidebook*, AAPG-SEPM-SEG (1953), p. 18
716.   *HGS*, pp. 134-137

Nash, Brazoria and Fort Bend Counties: (cont.)
801. *Lockwood's* (Texas 1939), sec. 4, p. 14; sec. 5, pp. 22, 37
722. *OFNA,* p. 146
532. *OGJ,* v. 25, no. 40, p. 151
478. *OGJ,* v. 27, no. 25, pp. 35, 91
515. *OGJ,* v. 28, no. 49, p. 118
474. *OGJ,* v. 28, no. 50, p. 143
484. *OGJ,* v. 32, no. 20, pp. 11, 34
337. *OGJ,* v. 38, no. 50, p. 102
520. *OGJ,* v. 39, no. 49, pp. 138, 140
450. *OGJ,* v. 46, no. 4, p. 141
365. *OGJ,* v. 57, no. 24, p. 136
376. *OW,* v. 82, no. 10, p. 14
524. *OW,* v. 90, no. 7, p. 162
161. *OW,* v. 123, no. 3, pp. 85-86
170. *OW,* v. 123, no. 3, p. 87
409. *OW,* v. 123, no. 3, p. 118
364. *Paper* 5, Fifth World Pet. Cong., sec. 1, p. 6; *Oil,* v. 19, no. 8, p. 38
434. *PROB.,* pp. 631-632, 670
154. *Tech. Pub. 1760,* AIME, Pet. Tech., v. v. 7, no. 6, pp. 2-9; *GCH* v. 1, pp. 35-42
583. *Trans.,* GCAGS, v. 9, pp. 59-62
153. *Trans.,* GCAGS, v. 11, pp. 214, 216, 218, 222
410. *WO,* v. 130, no. 7, p. 70

Newgulf, Fort Bend and Wharton Counties: (see Boling)

North Dayton, Liberty County:
6a. *BMIC*
549. *Bull.,* v. 9, no. 1, p. 35; *SD,* p. 774
883. *Bull.,* v. 9, no. 3, pp. 542, 561, 570; *SD,* pp. 724, 743, 752
906. *Bull.,* v. 9, no. 3, p. 656; *SD,* p. 559
618. *Bull.,* v. 10, no. 1, p. 79; *SD,* p. 404
944. *Bull.,* v. 17, no. 10, p. 1208; *GC,* p. 265
847. *Bull.,* v. 20, no. 6, p. 730; *GC,* p. 113
286. *Bull.,* v. 33, no. 6, pp. 975, 977
287. *Bull.,* v. 34, no. 6, p. 1187
288. *Bull.,* v. 35, no. 6, pp. 1332, 1335
290. *Bull.,* v. 37, no. 6, p. 1437
291. *Bull.,* v. 38, no. 6, pp. 1210, 1218
725. *Bull.,* v. 39, no. 5, pp. 700-701, 703-706, 709-710
292. *Bull.,* v. 39, no. 6, p. 983
427. *GAGC,* p. 271
717. *GAS,* pp. 685, 709
154. *GCH,* v. 1, p. 42
354. *GCH,* v. 1, pp. 48, 64

North Dayton, Liberty County: (cont.)
363. *Geophysics,* v. 1, no. 1, Fig. 2 (between pp. 142-143), Fig. 7 (between pp. 146-147)
846. *Guidebook,* AAPG-SEPM-SEG (1953), p. 18
801. *Lockwood's* (Texas 1939), sec. 4, p. 14; sec. 5, pp. 23, 38
722. *OFNA,* p. 152
474. *OGJ,* v. 28, no. 50, pp. 142-143
520. *OGJ,* v. 39, no. 49, pp. 135, 138
868. *OGJ,* v. 54, no. 14, p. 155
365. *OGJ,* v. 57, no. 24, p. 136
376. *OW,* v. 82, no. 10, p. 14
524. *OW,* v. 90, no. 7, p. 184
161. *OW,* v. 123, no. 3, p. 85
409. *OW,* v. 123, no. 3, p. 128
364. *Paper* 5, Fifth World Pet. Cong., sec. 1, p. 6; *Oil,* v. 19, no. 8, p. 38
146. *PROB.,* p. 116
434. *PROB.,* pp. 632-633
410. *WO,* v. 130, no. 7, p. 80

Oakwood, Leon and Freestone Counties:
6a. *BMIC*
865. *Bull.,* v. 12, no. 5, p. 537
309. *Bull.,* v. 13, no. 6, pp. 611-612
205. *Bull.,* v. 43, no. 6, pp. 1296-1297, 1299
427. *GAGC,* p. 271
722. *OFNA,* p. 148
478. *OGJ,* v. 27, no. 25, p. 35
831. *OGJ,* v. 56, no. 10, p. 248
86. *OGJ,* v. 56, no. 30, p. 263
864. *OGJ,* v. 57, no. 19, pp. 143-144
318. *OGJ,* v. 58, no. 7, p. 157
325. *OGJ,* v. 61, no. 52, pp. 210-212, 214
885. *OW* (Aug. 7, 1931), p. 19
364. *Paper* 5, Fifth World Pet. Cong., sec. 1, pp. 3, 8; *Oil,* v. 19, no. 8, pp. 34, 39

Orange, Orange County: (Cow Bayou)
6a. *BMIC*
856. *Bull.,* v. 9, no. 9, p. 39; *SD,* p. 778
969. *Bull.,* v. 9, no. 3, p. 470; *SD,* p. 443
347. *Bull.,* v. 9, no. 3, p. 499; *SD,* p. 472
589. *Bull.,* v. 9, no. 7, p. 1032; *SD,* p. 571
385. *Bull.,* v. 17, no. 9, p. 1082; *GC,* p. 77
654. *Bull.,* v. 18, no. 4, pp. 506-508, 510; *GC,* pp. 7-9, 11
751. *Bull.,* v. 20, no. 5, pp. 531-559; *GC,* pp. 880-908
847. *Bull.,* v. 20, no. 6, p. 730; *GC,* p. 113
750. *Bull.,* v. 23, no. 4, pp. 602-603

Orange, Orange County: (Cow Bayou) (cont.)

285. *Bull.*, v. 32, no. 6, p. 1028
286. *Bull.*, v. 33, no. 6, p. 976
390. *Bull.*, v. 33, no. 11, pp. 1830, 1844, 1847
287. *Bull.*, v. 34, no. 6, p. 1188
290. *Bull.*, v. 37, no. 6, p. 1441
291. *Bull.*, v. 38, no. 6, pp. 1209-1210, 1213
292. *Bull.*, v. 39, no. 6, p. 984
705. *Bull.*, v. 39, no. 12, p. 2417
427. *GAGC*, p. 271
717. *GAS*, pp. 685, 695, 697, 718, 729-730, 737, 739
363. *Geophysics*, v. 1, no. 1, Fig. 2 (between pp. 142-143), Fig. 7 (between pp. 146-147), pp. 144, 147
846. *Guidebook*, AAPG-SEPM-SEG (1953), p. 19
801. *Lockwood's* (Texas 1939), sec. 4, p. 15; sec. 5, pp. 23, 38
722. *OFNA*, pp. 147, 151, 153
968. *OGJ*, v. 22, no. 27, p. 86
125. *OGJ*, v. 25, no. 35, p. 107
515. *OGJ*, v. 28, no. 49, pp. 42-43
337. *OGJ*, v. 38, no. 50, p. 102
311. *OGJ*, v. 39, no. 49, p. 84
520. *OGJ*, v. 39, no. 49, p. 138
527. *OW*, v. 69, no. 1, pp. 16, 18
376. *OW*, v. 82, no. 10, p. 14
524. *OW*, v. 90, no. 7, p. 194
370. *OW*, v. 100, no. 10, p. 20
161. *OW*, v. 123, no. 3, pp. 83-85
409. *OW*, v. 123, no. 3, p. 130
146. *PROB.*, pp. 115-116, 146-148
686. *PROB.*, p. 418
434. *PROB.*, pp. 632-633
851. *Proc.*, Fourth World Pet. Cong., sec. 1, p. 96
494. *SD*, p. 554
791. *Trans.*, GCAGS, v. 11, pp. 226, 232
410. *WO*, v. 130, no. 7, p. 84

Orchard, Fort Bend County: (Moore)

6a. *BMIC*
392. *Bull.*, v. 13, no. 4, pp. 384-385
385. *Bull.*, v. 17, no. 9, p. 1074; *GC*, p. 69
944. *Bull.*, v. 17, no. 10, p. 1206; *GC*, p. 263
329. *Bull.*, v. 17, no. 12, pp. 1494-1496, 1517, 1519; *GC*, pp. 143-145, 166, 168; *OW*, v. 71, no. 11, pp. 18-24; no. 13, pp. 18, 20-24; *OGJ*, v. 32, no. 21, pp. 16, 30; no. 27, p. 18
128. *Bull.*, v. 19, no. 5, p. 682; *GC*, p. 463
847. *Bull.*, v. 20, no. 6, p. 731; *GC*, p. 114
545. *Bull.*, v. 23, no. 4, pp. 604-605
287. *Bull.*, v. 34, no. 6, p. 1185

Orchard, Fort Bend County: (Moore) (cont.)

288. *Bull.*, v. 35, no. 6, pp. 1330, 1335
289. *Bull.*, v. 36, no. 6, p. 1207
705. *Bull.*, v. 39, no. 12, pp. 2417, 2421
293. *Bull.*, v. 40, no. 6, p. 1251
294. *Bull.*, v. 41, no. 6, p. 1185
96. *Bull.*, La. Geol. Svy., no. 11, pp. 118-119
942a. *Bull. 4*, SIPES, Figs. 1, 3
477. *EGP*, p. 248; *Jour.*, Soc. of Pet. Geophysicists, v. 6, no. 1, p. 4
360. *EGP*, pp. 259, 262; *Jour.*, Soc. of Pet. Geophysicists, v. 6, no. 1, pp. 15, 18
427. *GAGC*, p. 271
717. *GAS*, pp. 685, 710
901. *GCH*, v. 1, p. 11; *Geophysics*, v. 5, no. 3, p. 220
363. *Geophysics*, v. 1, no. 1, Fig. 3 (between pp. 142-143), Fig. 8 (between pp. 146-147)
361. *Geophysics*, v. 3, no. 1, p. 32
479. *Geophysics*, v. 5, no. 3, p. 250
480. *Geophysics*, v. 22, no. 2, p. 225
846. *Guidebook*, AAPG-SEPM-SEG (1953), p. 19.
801. *Lockwood's* (Texas 1939), sec. 4, p. 16; sec. 5, pp. 23, 38
722. *OFNA*, p. 146
532. *OGJ*, v. 25, no. 40, p. 151
478. *OGJ*, v. 27, no. 25, pp. 35, 91
515. *OGJ*, v. 28, no. 49, p. 118
484. *OGJ*, v. 32, no. 20, p. 11
752. *OGJ*, v. 34, no. 51, pp. 46, 48
758. *OW*, v. 69, no. 1, p. 59
376. *OW*, v. 82, no. 10, p. 14
524. *OW*, v. 90, no. 7, p. 162
161. *OW*, v. 123, no. 3, pp. 85-86
409. *OW*, v. 123, no. 3, p. 118
434. *PROB.*, pp. 631-632
631. *Trans.*, GCAGS, v. 10, p. 218
410. *WO*, v. 130, no. 7, p. 68

Palangana, Duval County:

6a. *BMIC*
973. *Bull.*, v. 5, no. 2, p. 218
769. *Bull.*, v. 9, no. 1, p. 57; *SD*, p. 65
883. *Bull.*, v. 9, no. 3, pp. 536-550, 555, 557-559, 569, 573, 580, 586, 587; *SD*, pp. 718-732, 737, 739-741, 751, 755, 762, 768, 769
944. *Bull.*, v. 17, no. 10, pp. 1194-1195, 1198-1202, 1205, 1208, 1210; *GC*, pp. 251-252, 255-259, 262, 265, 267
655. *Bull.*, v. 18, no. 2, pp. 219-220, 222; *GC*, pp. 126-127, 129

Palangana, Duval County: (cont.)

847. *Bull.,* v. 20, no. 6, p. 731; *GC,* p. 114
96. *Bull.,* La. Geol. Svy., no. 11, pp. 70, 118
942a. *Bull. 4,* SIPES, Figs. 1, 3
427. *GAGC,* p. 271
846. *Guidebook,* AAPG-SEPM-SEG (1953), p. 19
300. *OGJ,* v. 37, no. 12, p. 34
337. *OGJ,* v. 38, no. 50, p. 102
691. *OGJ,* v. 52, no. 7, pp. 358, 360
764. *OGJ,* v. 55, no. 26, p. 189
449. *Pet. Geol.,* pp. 417-418
434. *PROB.,* pp. 631-632

Palestine, Anderson County:

6a. *BMIC*
683. *Bull.,* v. 6, no. 4, p. 329
883. *Bull.,* v. 9, no. 3, pp. 560, 564, 587; *SD,* pp. 742, 746, 769
723. *Bull.,* v. 9, no. 5, pp. 839, 865-866: *SD,* pp. 9, 35-36
601. *Bull.,* v. 10, no. 1, pp. 4-5, 8, 14, 19, 45-53; *SD,* pp. 212-213, 216, 222, 227, 253-261
753. *Bull.,* v. 41, no. 8, pp. 1828-30
429. *Bull. 1869,* Tex. U., pp. 20, 25-27, 143, 299-302, 307
760. *Bull. 661,* USGS, pp. 253-270; (abs.) *Washington Acad. Sci. Jour.,* v. 8, p. 173
427. *GAGC,* p. 271
420. *Geol. Svy. of Tex.,* First Ann. Rept., pp. 33-34
498. *Guidebook,* HGS (1962), pp. 266-272
831. *OGJ,* v. 56, no. 10, pp. 248, 250
864. *OGJ,* v. 57, no. 19, p. 143
885. *OW* (Aug. 7, 1931), pp. 17, 19
434. *PROB.,* pp. 632-633

Pathfinder Fort Bend County: (see Long Point)

Pescadito, Webb County:

6a. *BMIC*
259. *Bull.,* v. 42, no. 6, pp. 1283, 1286
427. *GAGC,* pp. 217, 244, 271
364. *Paper 5,* Fifth World Pet. Cong., sec. 1, pp. 3, 11; *Oil,* v. 19, no. 8, pp. 34, 40-41
764. *OGJ,* v. 55, no. 26, p. 189
86. *OGJ,* v. 56, no. 30, p. 263

Piedras Pintas, Duval County:

6a. *BMIC*
127. *Bull.,* v. 1, no. 1, p. 49

Piedras Pintas, Duval County: (cont.)

883. *Bull.,* v. 9, no. 3, pp. 536-538, 540, 543, 545-547, 553-555, 557-559, 586; *SD,* pp., 718-720, 722-725, 727-729, 735-737, 739-741, 768
944. *Bull.,* v. 17, no. 10, pp. 1195, 1198-1202, 1208, 1210; *GC,* pp. 252-253, 259, 265, 267
847. *Bull.,* v. 20, no. 6, p. 731; *GC,* p. 114
427. *GAGC,* p. 271
846. *Guidebook,* AAPG-SEPM-SEG (1953), p. 19
125. *OGJ,* v. 25, no. 35, p. 107
532. *OGJ,* v. 25, no. 40, p. 155
691. *OGJ,* v. 52, no. 7, pp. 358, 360
764. *OGJ,* v. 55, no. 26, p. 189
434. *PROB.,* pp. 631-632

Pierce Junction, Harris County:

6a. *BMIC*
127. *Bull.,* v. 1, no. 1, p. 49
929. *Bull.,* v. 9, no. 1, pp. 25, 30; *SD,* pp. 668, 673
883. *Bull.,* v. 9, no. 3, pp. 542, 569; *SD,* pp. 724, 751
391. *Bull.,* v. 17, no. 4, pp. 438-443
654. *Bull.,* v. 18, no. 4, p. 507; *GC,* p. 8
847. *Bull.,* v. 20, no. 6, p. 731; *GC,* p. 114
285. *Bull.,* v. 32, no. 6, p. 1028
286. *Bull.,* v. 33, no. 6, p. 973
287. *Bull.,* v. 34, no. 6, pp. 1186, 1189
725. *Bull.,* v. 39, no. 5, pp. 700-701, 705-706, 708-709
293. *Bull.,* v. 40, no. 6, pp. 1240, 1244, 1246, 1248, 1251
294. *Bull.,* v. 41, no. 6, p. 1186
297. *Bull.,* v. 45, no. 6, p. 873
96. *Bull.,* La. Geol. Svy., no. 11, p. 25
403. *EGP,* p. 345; *Trans.,* SEG, v. 3, p. 17
427. *GAGC,* pp. 213, 217, 245, 271
717. *GAS,* pp. 694, 697, 700-702
388. *GCH,* v. 1, p. 74
363. *Geophysics,* v. 1, no. 1, Fig. 2 (between pp. 142-143), Fig. 7 (between pp. 146-147)
307. *Geophysics,* v. 3, no. 3, pp. 191, 194
846. *Guidebook,* AAPG-SEPM-SEG (1953), p. 19
780. *Guidebook,* AAPG-SEPM-SEG (1953), pp. 147-150
68. *Guidebook,* HGS (1962), p. 278
801. *Lockwood's* (Texas 1939), sec. 4, p. 16; sec. 5, pp. 24, 38
722. *OFNA,* pp. 147, 151, 153

Pierce Junction, Harris County: (cont.)

968. *OGJ*, v. 22, no. 27, p. 86
125. *OGJ*, v. 25, no. 35, p. 107
532. *OGI*, v. 25, no. 40, pp. 152, 155
574. *OGJ*, v. 27, no. 14, p. 32
473. *OGJ*, v. 31, no. 8, p. 16
337. *OGJ*, v. 38, no. 50, p. 102
520. *OGJ*, v. 39, no. 49, pp. 138, 140
782. *OGJ*, v. 54, no. 63, pp. 166, 169
727. *OGJ*, v. 55, no. 2, p. 73
744. *OGJ*, v. 57, no. 6, p. 140
365. *OGJ*, v. 57, no. 24, p. 136
526. *OGJ*, v. 59, no. 31, p. 255
783. *OW*, v. 46, no. 11, pp. 95-98
857. *OW*, v. 52, no. 7, p. 29
527. *OW*, v. 69, no. 1, p. 16
308. *OW*, v. 78, no. 10, p. 22
376. *OW*, v. 82, no. 10, p. 14
524. *OW*, v. 90, no. 7, p. 174
161. *OW*, v. 123, no. 3, pp. 83-85
170. *OW*, v. 123, no. 3, p. 88
409. *OW*, v. 123, no. 3, p. 122
364. *Paper 5*, Fifth World Pet. Cong., sec. 1,
        p. 6; *Oil*, v. 19, no. 8, p. 38
434. *PROB.*, pp. 632-633
947. *PROB.*, p. 1019
851. *Proc.*, Fourth World Pet. Cong., sec. 1,
        p. 90
410. *WO*, v. 130, no. 7, p. 76
335. *WO*, v. 142, no. 7, pp. 158, 160

Port Neches, Orange County: (Mansfield Ferry, Bessie Heights)

6a. *BMIC*
751. *Bull.*, v. 20, no. 5, p. 539; *GC*, p. 888
847. *Bull.*, v. 20, no. 6, p. 731; *GC*, p. 114
800. *Bull.*, v. 30, no. 8, p. 1307
286. *Bull.*, v. 33, no. 6, pp. 976-977
390. *Bull.*, v. 33, no. 11, pp. 1830, 1840-1842,
        1844, 1847
288. *Bull.*, v. 35, no. 6, pp. 1334-1335
290. *Bull.*, v. 37, no. 6, p. 1437
705. *Bull.*, v. 39, no. 12, pp. 2417, 2421-2422
427. *GAGC*, p. 271
717. *GAS*, pp. 685, 730
363. *Geophysics*, v. 1, no. 1, Fig. 3 (between 142-
        143), Fig. 8 (between pp. 146-147)
547. *Geophysics*, v. 3, no. 2, p. 99
846. *Guidebook*, AAPG-SEPM-SEG (1953),
        p. 19
801. *Lockwood's* (Texas 1939), sec. 4, pp. 16-
        17; sec. 5, pp. 24, 39
722. *OFNA*, pp. 148, 152

Port Neches, Orange County: (Mansfield Ferry, Bessie Heights) (cont.)

515. *OGJ*, v. 28, no. 49, pp. 43, 118
484. *OGJ*, v. 32, no. 20, p. 11
520. *OGJ*, v. 39, no. 49, p. 64
526. *OGJ*, v. 59, no. 31, p. 256
527. *OW*, v. 69, no. 1, pp. 16-17
524. *OW*, v. 90, no. 7, p. 194
376. *OW*, v. 82, no. 10, p. 14
161. *OW*, v. 123, no. 3, p. 85
409. *OW*, v. 123, no. 3, p. 130
146. *PROB.*, p. 115
434. *PROB.*, pp. 632-633
791. *Trans.*, GCAGS, v. 11, pp. 226, 232
410. *WO*, v. 30, no. 7, p. 84

Purt, Anderson County: (see Brushy Creek)

Rabb's Ridge, Fort Bend County: (see Thompson)

Raccoon Bend, Austin County: (Ives Creek)

6a. *BMIC*
944. *Bull.*, v. 17, no. 10, p. 1206; *GC*, p. 263
611. *Bull.*, v. 17, no. 11, p. 1324; *GC*, p. 501
799. *Bull.*, v. 17, no. 12, pp. 1459-91; *GC*, pp.
        676-708
654. *Bull.*, v. 18, no. 4, pp. 514-518; *GC*, pp.
        15-19
751. *Bull.*, v. 20, no. 5, p. 547; *GC*, p. 896
847. *Bull.*, v. 20, no. 6, p. 731; *GC*, p. 114
462. *Bull.*, v. 20, no. 11, p. 1418
800. *Bull.*, v. 30, no. 8, pp. 1306-1307
287. *Bull.*, v. 34, no. 6, pp. 1184, 1188-1189
288. *Bull.*, v. 35, no. 6, p. 1328
708. *Bull.*, v. 35, no. 9, pp. 2082, 2086
289. *Bull.*, v. 36, no. 6, p. 1207
291. *Bull.*, v. 38, no. 6, p. 1210
292. *Bull.*, v. 39, no. 6, p. 984
705. *Bull.*, v. 39, no. 12, pp. 2431, 2453
293. *Bull.*, v. 40, no. 6, p. 1246
115. *Chron. Hist.*, p. 167
360. *EGP*, p. 256; *Jour.*, Soc. of Pet. Geophysi-
        cists, v. 6, no. 1, p. 12
427. *GAGC*, p. 271
717. *GAS*, pp. 684-685, 691, 695, 718-724, 738
154. *GCH*, v. 1, p. 36
363. *Geophysics*, v. 1, no. 1, Fig. 2 (between
        pp. 142-143), Fig. 7 (between pp.
        146-147)
361. *Geophysics*, v. 3, no. 1, p. 34
846. *Guidebook*, AAPG-SEPM-SEG (1953),
        p. 19
801. *Lockwood's* (Texas 1939), sec. 4, p. 17; sec.
        5, pp. 24, 39

Raccoon Bend, Austin County: (Ives Creek) (cont.)

722. *OFNA*, pp. 147-148, 151, 153
515. *OGJ*, v. 28, no. 49, p. 43
520. *OGJ*, v. 39, no. 49, pp. 138, 140
764. *OGJ*, v. 55, no. 26, p. 189
744. *OGJ*, v. 57, no. 6, p. 140
526. *OGJ*, v. 59, no. 31, p. 255
527. *OW*, v. 69, no. 1, pp. 16, 18
524. *OW*, v. 90, no. 7, p. 143
161. *OW*, v. 123, no. 3, pp. 83-86
409. *OW*, v. 123, no. 3, p. 110
449. *Pet. Geol.*, pp. 413-415
434. *PROB.*, pp. 632-633
631. *Trans.*, GCAGS, v. 10, pp. 217, 236
410. *WO*, v. 130, no. 7, p. 60

Red Fish Reef, Chambers County:

6a. *BMIC*
162. *OGJ*, v. 39, no. 49, p. 96
161. *OW*, v. 123, no. 3, p. 85
409. *OW*, v. 123, no. 3, p. 114
410. *WO*, v. 130, no. 7, p. 64

San Felipe, Austin and Waller Counties: (Brookshire, Sealy)

6a. *BMIC*
944. *Bull.*, v. 17, no. 10, p. 1206; *GC*, p. 263
847. *Bull.*, v. 20, no. 6, p. 729; *GC*, p. 112
462. *Bull.*, v. 20, no. 11, p. 1417
928. *Bull.*, v. 32, no. 1, p. 20
288. *Bull.*, v. 35, no. 6, p. 1326
290. *Bull.*, v. 37, no. 6, p. 1437
71. *Bull.*, v. 38, no. 8, pp. 1735-1736
725. *Bull.*, v. 39, no. 5, pp. 697, 700-701, 705-706, 709-710
292. *Bull.*, v. 39, no. 6, p. 980
705. *Bull.*, v. 39, no. 12, p. 2417
555a. *Bull.*, v. 50, no. 3, p. 468
427. *GAGC*, pp. 214, 271
717. *GAS*, pp. 685, 739
363. *Geophysics*, v. 1, no. 1, Fig. 3 (between pp. 142-143), Fig. 8 (between pp. 146-147)
886. *Geophysics*, v. 13, no. 4, pp. 597-599
846. *Guidebook*, AAPG-SEPM-SEG (1953), p. 19
81. *Guidebook*, AAPG-SEPM-SEG (1953), pp. 97-99
801. *Lockwood's* (Texas 1939), sec. 4, p. 5; sec. 5, pp. 14, 30
478. *OGJ*, v. 27, no. 25, p. 35
515. *OGJ*, v. 28, no. 49, p. 118
484. *OGJ*, v. 32, no. 20, p. 11

San Felipe, Austin and Waller Counties: (Brookshire, Sealy) (cont.)

541. *OGJ*, v. 52, no. 7, p. 357
365. *OGJ*, v. 57, no. 24, p. 136
524. *OW*, v. 90, no. 7, p. 197
161. *OW*, v. 123, no. 3, p. 85
409. *OW*, v. 123, no. 3, p. 133
364. *Paper 5*, Fifth World Pet. Cong., sec. 1, p. 6; *Oil*, v. 19, no. 8, p. 38
434. *PROB.*, pp. 631-632
851. *Proc.*, Fourth World Pet. Cong., sec. 1, p. 95
410. *WO*, v. 130, no. 7, p. 60

San Luis Pass, Brazoria and Galveston Counties: (See Offshore)

Saratoga, Hardin County:

6a. *BMIC*
127. *Bull.*, v. 1, no. 1, p. 46
895. *Bull.*, v. 9, no. 2, pp. 263-285; *SD*, pp. 501-523
906. *Bull.*, v. 9, no. 3, pp. 656, 664; *SD*, pp. 559, 567
42. *Bull.*, v. 9, no. 9, pp. 1294-1295
944. *Bull.*, v. 17, no. 10, p. 1208; *GC*, p. 265
654. *Bull.*, v. 18, no. 4, p. 504; *GC*, p. 5
847. *Bull.*, v. 20, no. 6, p. 731; *GC*, p. 114
283. *Bull.*, v. 30, no. 6, pp. 995-997
896. *Bull.*, v. 31, no. 11, pp. 2041-2044
285. *Bull.*, v. 32, no. 6, p. 1028
286. *Bull.*, v. 33, no. 6, p. 972
287. *Bull.*, v. 34, no. 6, pp. 1185, 1189
288. *Bull.*, v. 35, no. 6, p. 1335
290. *Bull.*, v. 37, no. 6, p. 1433
291. *Bull.*, v. 38, no. 6, pp. 1209, 1216
725. *Bull.*, v. 39, no. 5, pp. 700-701, 705-706, 709-710
292. *Bull.*, v. 39, no. 6, pp. 981-982
293. *Bull.*, v. 40, no. 6, pp. 1240, 1244
749. *Bull.*, GSA, v. 25, pp. 77-79
429. *Bull. 1869*, Tex. U., pp. 261, 294, 296
427. *GAGC*, p. 271
717. *GAS*, pp. 706-707
363. *Geophysics*, v. 1, no. 1, Fig. 2 (between pp. 142-143), Fig. 7 (between pp. 146-147)
846. *Guidebook*, AAPG-SEPM-SEG (1953), p. 19
801. *Lockwood's* (Texas 1939), sec. 4, p. 17; sec. 5, pp. 24-25, 39
722. *OFNA*, pp. 145-147, 152
968. *OGJ*, v. 22, no. 27, pp. 84, 86
894. *OGJ*, v. 29, no. 15, pp. 39, 146-147
897. *OGJ*, v. 30, no. 38, p. 67

South Houston, Harris County: (cont.)

307. *Geophysics,* v. 3, no. 3, pp. 191, 194
481. *Geophysics,* v. 4, no. 3, p. 151
362. *Geophysics,* v. 4, no. 3, p. 164
508. *Geophysics,* v. 23, no. 4, p. 694
846. *Guidebook,* AAPG-SEPM-SEG (1953), p. 20
801. *Lockwood's* (Texas 1939), sec. 4, p. 18; sec. 5, pp. 25, 40-41
338. *OGJ,* v. 34, no. 21, p. 15
524. *OW,* v. 90, no. 7, p. 174
161. *OW,* v. 123, no. 3, pp. 83-85
409. *OW,* v. 123, no. 3, p. 122
410. *WO,* v. 130, no. 7, p. 76

South Liberty, Liberty County: (South Dayton, Liberty)

6a. *BMIC*
127. *Bull.,* v. 1, no. 1, p. 45
906. *Bull.,* v. 9, no. 3, pp. 655-666; *SD,* pp. 558-569
385. *Bull.,* v. 17, no. 9, pp. 1048, 1079; *GC,* pp. 43, 74
944. *Bull.,* v. 17, no. 10, p. 1208; *GC,* p. 265
519. *Bull.,* v. 17, no. 12, p. 1449; *GC,* p. 195
654. *Bull.,* v. 18, no. 4, pp. 509-510; *GC,* pp. 10-11
847. *Bull.,* v. 20, no. 6, p. 731; *GC,* p. 114
462. *Bull.,* v. 20, no. 11, p. 1422
800. *Bull.,* v. 30, no. 8, p. 1307
285. *Bull.,* v. 32, no. 6, p. 1028
286. *Bull.,* v. 33, no. 6, pp. 974, 977
436. *Bull.,* v. 34, no. 3, p. 367
287. *Bull.,* v. 34, no. 6, pp. 1187, 1189
288. *Bull.,* v. 35, no. 6, pp. 1332, 1335
460. *Bull.,* v. 35, no. 9, pp. 1939-1977
289. *Bull.,* v. 36, no. 6, p. 1208
290. *Bull.,* v. 37, no. 6, pp. 1433, 1438, 1441
291. *Bull.,* v. 38, no. 6, pp. 1209-1210, 1216, 1218
725. *Bull.,* v. 39, no. 5, pp. 700-701, 705-706, 709-710
292. *Bull.,* v. 39, no. 6, p. 984
293. *Bull.,* v. 40, no. 6, pp. 1240, 1244, 1248, 1251
294. *Bull.,* v. 41, no. 6, pp. 1187-1188
372. *Bull.,* v. 45, no. 2, p. 239
403. *EGP,* p. 345; *Trans.,* SEG, v. 3, p. 17
427. *GAGC,* p. 271
717. *GAS,* pp. 685, 687, 710
154. *GCH,* v. 1, p. 36
354. *GCH,* v. 1, pp. 48, 64
363. *Geophysics,* v. 1, no. 1, Fig. 2 (between pp. 142-143), Fig. 7 (between pp. 146-147)
512. *Geophysics,* v. 22, no. 3, p. 633

South Liberty, Liberty County: (South Dayton, Liberty) (cont.)

846. *Guidebook,* AAPG-SEPM-SEG (1953), 20
907. *HGS,* pp. 200-206
801. *Lockwood's* (Texas 1939), sec. 4, p. 18; sec. 5, pp. 26, 41
722. *OFNA.* pp. 148, 151
532. *OGJ,* v. 25, no. 40, p. 152
473. *OGJ,* v. 31, no. 8, p. 16
520. *OGJ,* v. 39, no. 49, pp. 138, 140
745. *OGJ,* v. 54, no. 23, pp. 321-322, 324
365. *OGJ,* v. 57, no. 24, pp. 135-136
857. *OW,* v. 52, no. 7, p. 27
871. *OW,* v. 66, no. 7, p. 35
527. *OW,* v. 69, no. 1, p. 16
376. *OW,* v. 82, no. 10, p. 14
524. *OW,* v. 90, no. 7, p. 184
161. *OW,* v. 123, no. 3, p. 85
170. *OW,* v. 123, no. 3, p. 88
409. *OW,* v. 123, no. 3, p. 128
364. *Paper 5,* Fifth World Pet. Cong., sec. 1, pp. 2, 6; *Oil,* v. 19, no. 8, pp. 36, 38
146. *PROB.,* pp. 123-124, 126, 144
434. *PROB.,* pp. 632-633
851. *Proc.,* Fourth World Pet. Cong., sec. 1, pp. 87, 90-92, 94
631. *Trans.,* GCAGS, v. 10, pp. 217, 236
410. *WO,* v. 130, no. 7, p. 80

Spindletop, Jefferson County:

6a. *BMIC*
423. *Bol.,* v. 2, no. 7, p. 453
127. *Bull.,* v. 1, no. 1, p. 47
952. *Bull.,* v. 3, no. 1, p. 87
973. *Bull.,* v. 5, no. 2, pp. 212, 245, 333
895. *Bull.,* v. 9, no. 2, p. 278; *SD,* p. 516
969. *Bull.,* v. 9, no. 3, p. 474; *SD,* p. 447
923. *Bull.,* v. 9, no. 3, pp. 594-612; *SD,* pp. 478-496
723. *Bull.,* v. 9, no. 5, pp. 841-844
589. *Bull.,* v. 9, no. 7, pp. 1032, 1035; *SD,* pp. 571, 574
618. *Bull.,* v. 10, no. 1, pp. 79, 80, 87-88; *SD,* pp. 404-405, 412-413
385. *Bull.,* v. 17, no. 9, p. 1080; *GC,* p. 75
328. *Bull.,* v. 17, no. 12, p. 1512; *GC,* p. 161
654. *Bull.,* v. 18, no. 4, p. 502; *GC,* p. 3
917. *Bull.,* v. 19, no. 5, pp. 618-643; *GC,* pp. 309-334
751. *Bull.,* v. 20, no. 5, p. 526
847. *Bull.,* v. 20, no. 6, p. 731; *GC,* p. 114
920. *Bull.,* v. 21, no. 4, pp. 475-490

Spindletop, Jefferson County: (cont.)

536. *WO,* v. 143, no. 5, pp. 144, 150
581. *WP* (May, 1936), pp. 271-272

Steen, Smith County:

6a. *BMIC*
601. *Bull.,* v. 10, no. 1, pp. 14, 23-26, 28;
        SD, pp. 212, 222, 231-234
429. *Bull. 1869,* Tex. U., pp. 25-26
831. *OGJ,* v. 56, no. 10, p. 248
864. *OGJ,* v. 57, no. 19, p. 143
885. *OW* (Aug. 7, 1931), pp. 17, 19
434. *PROB.,* pp. 632-633
631. *Trans.,* GCAGS, v. 10, p. 217

Stewart Beach, Galveston County: (see Offshore)

Stratton Ridge, Brazoria County:

6a. *BMIC*
127. *Bull.,* v. 1, no. 1, p. 44
973. *Bull.,* v. 5, no. 2, p. 218
929. *Bull.,* v. 9, no. 1, pp. 1-34; *SD,* pp. 644-677
883. *Bull.,* v. 9, no. 3, p. 569; *SD,* p. 751
 82. *Bull.,* v. 9, no. 3, pp. 616, 624; *SD,*
        pp. 681, 689
906. *Bull.,* v. 9, no. 3, p. 664; *SD,* p. 567
618. *Bull.,* v. 10, no. 1, p. 79; *SD,* p. 404
944. *Bull.,* v. 17, no. 10, p. 1208; *GC,* p. 265
591. *Bull.,* v. 20, no. 2, p. 170; *GC,* p. 848
847. *Bull.,* v. 20, no. 6, p. 731; *GC,* p. 114
462. *Bull.,* v. 20, no. 11, p. 1422
283. *Bull.,* v. 30, no. 6, pp. 995-996
285. *Bull.,* v. 32, no. 6, p. 1028
292. *Bull.,* v. 39, no. 6, pp. 980, 982
295. *Bull.,* v. 42, no. 6, p. 1306
427. *GAGC,* p. 271
363. *Geophysics,* v. 1, no. 1, Fig. 2 (between
        pp. 142-143), Fig. 7 (between pp.
        146-147)
846. *Guidebook,* AAPG-SEPM-SEG (1953),
        p. 20
801. *Lockwood's* (Texas 1939), sec. 5, pp.
        26, 41
515. *OGJ,* v. 28, no. 49, p. 42
484. *OGJ,* v. 32, no. 20, p. 11
300. *OGJ,* v. 37, no. 12, p. 34
337. *OGJ,* v. 38, no. 50, p. 102
520. *OGJ,* v. 39, no. 49, p. 138
524. *OW,* v. 90, no. 7, p. 148
161. *OW,* v. 123, no. 3, p. 85
170. *OW,* v. 123, no. 3, p. 87
409. *OW,* v. 123, no. 3, p. 112
434. *PROB.,* pp. 631-632
552. *PROB.,* p. 896

Stratton Ridge, Brazoria County: (cont.)

583. *Trans.,* GCAGS, v. 9, p. 62
410. *WO,* v. 130, no. 7, p. 61

Sugarland, Fort Bend County: (DeWalt, Cockburn)

6a. *BMIC*
385. *Bull.,* v. 17, no. 9, p. 1050; *GC,* p. 45
938. *Bull.,* v. 17, no. 11, pp. 1362-1386; *GC,*
        pp. 709-733
654. *Bull.,* v. 18, no. 4, p. 510; *GC,* p. 11
382. *Bull.,* v. 18, no. 9, p. 1197; *GC,* p. 101
511. *Bull.,* v. 19, no. 1, pp. 19-20; *EGP,* pp.
        679-680; *Trans.,* SEG, v. 5, pp.
        19-20
482. *Bull.,* v. 19, no. 3, pp. 357, 364, 366-368;
        GC, pp. 171, 178, 180-182
847. *Bull.,* v. 20, no. 6, p. 731; *GC,* p. 114
290. *Bull.,* v. 37, no. 6, p. 1436
 96. *Bull.,* La. Geol. Svy., no. 11, p. 53
115. *Chron. Hist.,* p. 164
427. *GAGC,* p. 271
717. *GAS,* pp. 685, 695, 697, 713-717, 736,
        738
510. *GCH,* v. 1, p. 182
363. *Geophysics,* v. 1, no. 1, Fig. 3 (between
        pp. 142-143), Fig. 8 (between pp.
        146-147)
362. *Geophysics,* v. 4, no. 3, p. 158
 68. *Guidebook,* HGS (1962), p. 278
846. *Guidebook,* AAPG-SEPM-SEG (1953),
        p. 20
939. *Guidebook,* APG-SEPM-SEG (1953),
        pp. 153-156
937. *HGS,* pp. 219, 220
801. *Lockwood's* (Texas 1939), sec. 5, pp. 26,
        41
772. *OFNA,* pp. 147, 151, 153
574. *OGJ,* v. 27, no. 14, p. 32
478. *OGJ,* v. 27, no. 25, pp. 35, 91
515. *OGJ,* v. 28, no. 49, pp. 43, 118
474. *OGJ,* v. 28, no. 50, p. 143
484. *OGJ,* v. 32, no. 20, pp. 10-11
311. *OGJ,* v. 39, no. 49, p. 84
520. *OGJ,* v. 39, no. 49, pp. 140, 164
744. *OGJ,* v. 57, no. 6, p. 140
526. *OGJ,* v. 59, no. 31, p. 255
834. *Oil Forum,* Special Oil Finders' Issue
        (April, 1955), p. 130
527. *OW,* v. 69, no. 1, pp. 16-17
376. *OW,* v. 82, no. 10, p. 14
524. *OW,* v. 90, no. 7, p. 162
161. *OW,* v. 123, no. 3, pp. 81, 83-85
409. *OW,* v. 123, no. 3, p. 118

Sugarland, Fort Bend County: (DeWalt, Cockburn) (cont.)

434. *PROB.,* pp. 631-632, 709
552. *PROB.,* p. 898
851. *Proc.,* Fourth World Pet. Cong., sec. 1, p. 97
525. *WO,* v. 130, no. 7, p. 59
410. *WO,* v. 130, no. 7, p. 70

Thompson, Fort Bend County: (Rabbs Ridge, Lockwood, Grubbles)

6a. *BMIC*
511. *Bull.,* v. 19, no. 1, pp. 19-20; *Trans.,* SEG, v. 5, pp. 19-20; *EGP,* pp. 679-680
751. *Bull.,* v. 20, no. 5, p. 547; GC, p. 896
847. *Bull.,* v. 20, no. 6, p. 731; *GC,* p. 114
211. *Bull.,* v. 24, no. 6, p. 1089
396. *Bull.,* v. 24, no. 8, p. 1411
212. *Bull.,* v. 25, no. 6, p. 1010
291. *Bull.,* v. 38, no. 6, pp. 1209, 1216
294. *Bull.,* v. 41, no. 6, p. 1185
  7. *Bull.,* v. 42, no. 12, p. 2949
115. *Chron. Hist.,* p. 169
360. *EGP,* p. 259; *Jour.,* Soc. of Pet. Geophysicists, v. 6, no. 1, p. 15
427. *GAGC,* pp. 218, 255, 271
717. *GAS,* pp. 685, 695-697, 718, 726, 736-739
154. *GCH,* v. 1, pp. 36-37
363. *Geophysics,* v. 1, no. 1, Fig. 3 (between pp. 142-143), Fig. 8 (between pp. 146-147)
547. *Geophysics,* v. 3, no. 2, p. 101
846. *Guidebook,* AAPG-SEPM-SEG (1953), p. 20
954. *Guidebook,* AAPG-SEPM-SEG (1953), pp. 157-160
801. *Lockwood's* (Texas 1939), sec. 4, pp. 18, 19; sec. 5, pp. 27, 41
722. *OFNA,* pp. 147, 151, 153
790. *OGJ,* v. 30, no. 37, p. 70
393. *OGJ,* v. 32, no. 7, pp. 8, 36
484. *OGJ,* v. 32, no. 20, p. 11
520. *OGJ,* v. 39, no. 49, p. 140
744. *OGJ,* v. 57, no. 6, p. 140
526. *OGJ,* v. 59, no. 31, p. 255
797. *OW,* v. 67, no. 13, pp. 10-12, 40-42
527. *OW,* v. 69, no. 1, pp. 16-18
524. *OW,* v. 90, no. 7, pp. 162, 166
169. *OW,* v. 99, no. 3, p. 48
370. *OW,* v. 100, no. 10, p. 20
161. *OW,* v. 123, no. 3, pp. 83-86
409. *OW,* v. 123, no. 3, p. 118
449. *Pet. Geol.,* pp. 413-414

Thompson, Fort Bend County: (Rabbs Ridge, Lockwood, Grubbles) (cont.)

434. *PROB.,* pp. 632-633
410. *WO,* v. 130, no. 7, p. 70

Trinity, Houston County: (see Kittrell)

Tyler, Smith County: (see East Tyler)

Webster, Harris County: (Friendswood)

6a. *BMIC*
217. *Bull.,* v. 22, no. 6, p. 741
381. *Bull.,* v. 22, no. 11, pp. 1602
396. *Bull.,* v. 24, no. 8, pp. 1422
212. *Bull.,* v. 25, no. 6, p. 1010
 71. *Bull.,* v. 38, no. 8, p. 1725
725. *Bull.,* v. 39, no. 5, p. 698
294. *Bull.,* v. 41, no. 6, pp. 1184, 1186
115. *Chron. Hist.,* p. 194
427. *GAGC,* p. 251
388. *GCH,* v. 1, pp. 74-84
466. *GCH,* v. 2, p. 158
361. *Geophysics,* v. 3, no. 1, pp. 30-31, 33-34
307. *Geophysics,* v. 3, no. 3, pp. 191, 194
397. *Geophysics,* v. 4, no. 3, pp. 217-218
846. *Guidebook,* AAPG-SEPM-SEG (1953), p. 20
  3. *Guidebook,* AAPG-SEPM-SEG (1953), pp. 33, 35
801. *Lockwood's* (Texas 1939), sec. 4, p. 19; sec. 5, pp. 27, 42
722. *OFNA,* pp. 147, 151
386. *OGJ,* v. 36, no. 13, p. 43
450. *OGJ,* v. 46, no. 4, p. 136
833. *OGJ,* v. 53, no. 26, p. 93
744. *OGJ,* v. 57, no. 6, p. 140
526. *OGJ,* v. 59, no. 31, p. 255
834. *Oil Forum,* Special Oil Finders Issue (April, 1955), p. 130
524. *OW,* v. 90 ,no. 7, p. 172
161. *OW,* v. 123, no. 3, pp. 83-86
409. *OW,* v. 123, no. 3, p. 122
351. *Proc.,* Fourth World Pet. Cong., sec. 1, p. 86
525. *WO,* v. 130, no. 7, p. 58
410. *WO,* v. 130, no. 7, p. 76
430. *WP* (Sept., 1937), pp. 36, 43

West Columbia, Brazoria County: (Kiser Hill)

6a. *BMIC*
974. *Bull.,* v. 5, no. 2, pp. 212-251
315. *Bull.,* v. 6, no. 3, p. 253
929. *Bull.,* v. 9, no. 1, pp. 4-5, 25, 30; *SD,* pp. 647-648, 668, 673

West Columbia, Brazoria County: (Kiser Hill)
  (cont.)

923. *Bull.,* v. 9, no. 3, p. 611; *SD,* p. 495
 58. *Bull.,* v. 9, no. 4, p. 723; *SD,* p. 703
589. *Bull.,* v. 9, no. 7, p. 1032; *SD,* p. 571
618. *Bull.,* v. 10, no. 1, pp. 88, 90, 93; *SD,*
       pp. 413, 415, 418
385. *Bull.,* v. 17, no. 9, p. 1080; *GC,* p. 75
944. *Bull.,* v. 17, no. 10, p. 1206; *GC,* p. 263
611. *Bull.,* v. 17, no. 11, p. 1324; *GC,* p. 501
938. *Bull.,* v. 17, no. 11, p. 1378; *GC,* p. 725
654. *Bull.,* v. 18, no. 4, pp. 504-505; *GC,*
       pp. 5-6
591. *Bull.,* v. 20, no. 2, p. 170; *GC,* p. 848
847. *Bull.,* v. 20, no. 6, p. 731; *GC,* p. 114
486. *Bull.,* v. 22, no. 6, p. 742
971. *Bull.,* v. 26, no. 9, pp. 1441-1466
285. *Bull.,* v. 32, no. 6, pp. 1028, 1030
286. *Bull.,* v. 33, no. 6, pp. 970-971, 977
287. *Bull.,* v. 34, no. 6, p. 1184
292. *Bull.,* v. 39, no. 6, pp. 982, 984
293. *Bull.,* v. 40, no. 6, p. 1246
115. *Chron. Hist.,* pp. 115, 126
427. *GAGC,* pp. 217, 245, 271
717. *GAS,* pp. 685, 691, 694, 697, 709
154. *GCH,* v. 1, pp. 36-37
363. *Geophysics,* v. 1, no. 1, Fig. 2 (between
       pp. 142-143), Fig. 7 (between pp.
       146-147)
547. *Geophysics,* v. 3, no. 2, p. 112
846. *Guidebook,* AAPG-SEPM-SEG (1953), p. 20
  3. *Guidebook,* AAPG-SEPM-SEG (1953), p. 33
971. *Guidebook,* AAPG-SEPM-SEG (1953),
       pp. 161-162
602. *Guidebook,* Shreveport Geol. Soc. (1960),
       p. 16
801. *Lockwood's* (Texas 1939), sec. 4, p. 19
       sec. 5, pp. 27, 42
722. *OFNA,* pp. 146-147, 151
968. *OGJ,* v. 22, no. 27, p. 86
518. *OGJ,* v. 25, no. 30, p. 92
972. *OGJ,* v. 33, no. 20, pp. 11, 44
728. *OGJ,* v. 33, no. 64, p. 149
300. *OGJ,* v. 37, no. 12, p. 33
311. *OGJ,* v. 39, no. 49, p. 84
520. *OGJ,* v. 39, no. 49, pp. 133, 138
744. *OGJ,* v. 57, no. 6, p. 140
365. *OGJ,* v. 57, no. 24, p. 136
526. *OGJ,* v. 59, no. 31, p. 255
376. *OW,* v. 82, no. 10, pp. 14-15
524. *OW,* v. 90, no. 7, p. 148
169. *OW,* v. 99, no. 3, p. 47
370. *OW,* v. 100, no. 10, p. 20
161. *OW,* v. 123, no. 3, pp. 83-85

West Columbia, Brazoria County: (Kiser Hill)
  (cont.)

517. *OW,* v. 123, no. 3, p. 89
409. *OW,* v. 123, no. 3, p. 112
364. *Paper 5,* Fifth World Pet. Cong., sec. 1, p.
       6; *Oil,* v. 19, no. 8, p. 38
743. *PROB.,* pp. 340-341
686. *PROB.,* p. 418
434. *PROB.,* pp. 631-632, 675-676
974. *STR.,* v. 2, pp. 451-469
583. *Trans.,* GCAGS, v. 9, pp. 59, 62
525. *WO,* v. 130, no. 7, p. 58
410. *WO,* v. 130, no. 7, pp. 61-62

West Point, Freestone County: (see Butler)

Whitehouse, Smith County:
  6a. *BMIC*
865. *Bull.,* v. 12, no. 5, pp. 537-539
309. *Bull.,* v. 13, no. 6, p. 611
427. *GAGC,* p. 271
831. *OGJ,* v. 56, no. 10, p. 248
864. *OGJ,* v. 57, no. 19, p. 143
885. *OW* (Aug. 7, 1931) p. 19
434. *PROB.,* pp. 632-633

Offshore

Block 144, Galveston County:
  6a. *BMIC*
427. *GAGC,* p. 271

McFaddin Beach, Jefferson County: (Jefferson
  Coast)
  6a. *BMIC*
671. *Bull.,* v. 23, no. 3, pp. 339-342
860. *Bull.,* v. 30, no. 8, p. 1307
436. *Bull.,* v. 34, no. 3, p. 367
294. *Bull.,* v. 41, no. 6, pp. 1184, 1186
115. *Chron. Hist.,* p. 194
427. *GAGC,* p. 271
846. *Guidebook,* AAPG-SEPM-SEG (1953),
       p. 18
801. *Lockwood's* (Texas 1939), sec. 5, p. 37
722. *OFNA,* p. 148
300. *OGJ,* v. 37, no. 12, p. 34
337. *OGJ,* v. 38, no. 50, p. 102
162. *OGJ,* v. 39, no. 49, p. 96
631. *Trans.,* GCAGS, v. 10, p. 236

San Luis Pass, Brazoria and Galveston Counties:
  6a. *BMIC*
505. *Geophysics,* v. 22, no. 2, pp. 348-358

Stewart Beach, Galveston County:
  6a. *BMIC*

Salt Domes of Louisiana

Alphabetical Listing

(Alternate name in Parenthesis)

Dome	Parish	Dome	Parish
Anse la Butte	St. Martin	(Choctaw) Bayou Choctaw	Iberville
Arcadia	Bienville	Clovelly (Scully)	Lafourche
Ashwood (Somerset)	Tensas	(Cockrell) Potash	Plaquemines
Avery Island (Petit Anse)	Iberia	Coleman (South Coleman)	Madison
Barataria	Jefferson	(Convent) Hester	St. James
Bay de Chene	Jefferson and	Coochie Brake	Winn
	Lafourche	Coon Point (Ship Shoal	
Bay Junop	Terrebonne	Block 38-Offshore)	Terrebonne
Bay Marchand	Lafourche	(Coon Road) Bay St. Elaine	Terrebonne
Bay St. Elaine (Coon Road)	Terrebonne	Cote Blanche Island	St. Mary
(Bayou Alabama)		Creole (West Cameron	
Bayou des Glaise	Iberville	Block 2)	Cameron
Bayou Blue	Iberville	Crowley (South Crowley)	Acadia
Bayou Bouillon	St. Martin	Crowville	Franklin
(Bayou Chicot) Pine Prarie	Evangeline	Cut Off	Lafourche
Bayou Choctaw (Choctaw,		Darrow	Ascension
Grosse Tete, Plaquemines)	Iberville	Delta Duck Club	Plaquemines
Bayou Couba		Dog Lake	Terrebonne
(N. Lake Salvador)	St. Charles	Drake's	Winn
Bayou des Allemands	St. Charles	Duck Port	Madison
Bayou des Glaise (Bayou		East Hackberry (Kelso Bayou)	Cameron
Alabama)	Iberville	(East Tallulah) Walnut	
(Bayou St. Denis) Lafitte	Jefferson	Bayou	Madison
(Bayou Wikoff) North		Edgerly	Calcasieu
Crowley	Acadia	(Evangeline) Jennings	Acadia
Belle Isle	St. Mary	Fausse Point (Loureauville)	Iberia and
Big Lake	Cameron		St. Martin
Bistineau	Webster	Foules	Catahoula
Black Bayou	Cameron	Four Isle	Terrebonne
Bosco	Acadia	Garden Island Bay	Plaquemines
Bully Camp	Lafourche	Gibsland	Bienville
(Bunkie) Cheneyville	Rapides	Gilbert	Franklin
Caillou Island	Terrebonne	Golden Meadow	Lafourche
Calcasieu Lake	Cameron	Good Hope	St. Charles
Cameron Meadows	Cameron	(Grand Cote) Weeks Island	Iberia
Cedar Creek	Winn	(Grand Ecaille) Lake	
Chacahoula (Thibodeaux)	Lafourche	Washington	Plaquemines
Charenton	St. Mary	(Grosse Tete) Bayou Choctaw	Iberville
Cheneyville (Bunkie)	Rapides	Gueydan	Vermilion
(Chester) Lonnie	Winn	(Hackberry) West Hackberry	Cameron
Chestnut	Natchitoches	(Hager-Martin) Section 28	St. Martin
		(Harang) Valentine	Lafourche

Dome	Parish
Hester (Hester-Vacherie, Convent)	St. James
(Hester-Vacherie) Hester	St. James
Iberia (Little Bayou, New Iberia)	Iberia
Iowa (Iowa Junction)	Jefferson Davis
(Iowa Junction) Iowa	Jefferson Davis
Jeanerette	St. Mary
Jefferson Island (Lake Peigneur)	Iberia
Jennings (Evangeline)	Acadia
(Kelso Bayou) East Hackberry	Cameron
(Killens Ferry) Snake Bayou	Tensas
King's	Bienville
Lafitte (Bayou St. Denis)	Jefferson
Lake Barre	Terrebonne
Lake Chicot	St. Martin
Lake Hermitage	Plaquemines
Lake Mongoulis	St. Martin
(Lake Peigneur) Jefferson Island	Iberia
Lake Pelto	Terrebonne
Lake Salvador	St. Charles
Lake Washington (Grand Ecaille, Myrtle Grove)	Plaquemines
(La Rose) Valentine	Lafourche
Leeville	Lafourche
(Little Bayou) Iberia	Iberia
Lockport	Calcasieu
Lonnie (Chester)	Winn
(Loureauville) Fausse Point	Iberia and St. Martin
Milam	Winn
Minden	Webster
(Myrtle Grove) Lake Washington	Plaquemines
Napoleonville	Assumption
Newellton	Tensas
(New Iberia) Iberia	Iberia
North Crowley (Bayou Wikoff)	Acadia
(North Lake Salvador) Bayou Couba	St. Charles
North Mallard Bay	Cameron
North Starks	Calcasieu
North Tallulah (Tallulah)	Madison
Packton	Winn
Paradis	St. Charles
(Petit Anse) Avery Island	Iberia
Pine Prairie (Bayou Chicot)	Evangeline
(Plaquemines) Bayou Choctaw	Iberville
Plumb Bob	St. Martin

Dome	Parish
Port Barre	St. Landry
Potash (Cockrell)	Plaquemines
Price's	Winn
Prothro	Bienville
Rabbit Island	Iberia
Raceland	Lafourche
Rayburn's	Bienville
Roanoke	Jefferson Davis
(Rose) Venice	Plaquemines
St. Gabriel	Iberville
St. Martinville	St. Martin
(Scully) Clovelly	Lafourche
Section 28 (Hager Martin)	St. Martin
Sikes	Winn
Singer	Madison
Snake Bayou (Killens Ferry)	Tensas
(Somerset) Ashwood	Tensas
Sorrento	Ascension
(South Coleman) Coleman	Madison
(South Crowley) Crowley	Acadia
South Section 28	St. Martin
South Tallulah	Madison
South Tigre Lagoon	Iberia
(Spanish Pass) Venice	Plaquemines
Starks	Calcasieu
Stella	Plaquemines
(Sulphur) Sulphur Mines	Calcasieu
Sulphur Mines (Sulphur)	Calcasieu
Sweet Lake	Cameron
(Tallulah) North Tallulah	Madison
(Thibodeaux) Chacahoula	Lafourche
Timbalier Bay	Lafourche
Vacherie	Bienville and Webster
Valentine (Harang, La Rose)	Lafourche
Venice (Rose, Spanish Pass)	Plaquemines
Vermilion Bay	Iberia
Vinton	Calcasieu
Walnut Bayou (East Tallulah)	Madison
Weeks Island (Grande Cote)	Iberia
Welsh	Jefferson Davis
West Bay	Plaquemines
(West Cameron Block 2) Creole	Cameron
West Cote Blanche Bay	St. Mary
West Hackberry (Hackberry)	Cameron
White Castle	Iberville
Winnfield	Winn
Woodlawn	Jefferson Davis

Offshore

East Cameron Area

Block 115 (Block 104)
Block 118

East Cameron Area (cont.)

Block 126
Block 139
Block 151
Block 152
Block 155
Block 160
Block 187 (Block 194)
Block 189

Eugene Island Area

Block 32
Block 77
Block 110
Block 126
Block 128
Block 175
Block 184
Block 188
Block 205
Block 208
Block 231
Block 238
Block 292

Grand Isle Area

Block 16
Block 18
Block 72

Main Pass Area

Block 46

Ship Shoal Area

Block 32
(Block 38) Coon Point
Block 72
Block 113 (Block 114)
Block 154
Block 208
Block 230

South Marsh Island Area

Block 6
Block 7
Block 8
Block 38
Block 41
Block 48
Block 57
Block 66
Block 73
Block 79

South Pass Area

Block 27

South Pelto Area

Block 20

South Timbalier Area

Block 54
Block 86
Block 131
Block 135
Block 176

Vermilion Area

Block 102
Block 111
Block 120
Block 162
Block 164
Block 190 (Block 191)
Block 203
Block 245

West Cameron Area

(Block 2) Creole
Block 386

West Delta Area

Block 30
Block 133

By Parish

Acadia Parish

Bosco
Crowley

Acadia Parish (cont.)
Jennings (Evangeline)
Lawson
North Crowley (Bayou Wikoff)

Ascension Parish
Darrow
Sorrento

Assumption Parish
Napoleonville

Bienville Parish
Arcadia
Gibsland
King's
Prothro
Rayburn's
Vacherie

Calcasieu Parish
Edgerly
Lockport
North Starks
Starks
Sulphur Mines (Sulphur)
Vinton

Cameron Parish
Big Lake
Black Bayou
Calcasieu Lake
Cameron Meadows
Creole (West Cameron Blk. 2)
East Hackberry (Kelso Bayou)
North Mallard Bay
Sweet Lake
West Hackberry (Hackberry)

Catahoula Parish
Foules

Evangeline Parish
Pine Prairie (Bayou Chicot)

Franklin Parish
Crowville
Gilbert

Iberia Parish
Avery Island (Petit Anse)
Fausse Point (Loureauville)
Iberia (Little Bayou, New Iberia)
Jefferson Island (Lake Peigneur)
Rabbit Island
South Tigre Lagoon
Vermilion Bay
Weeks Island (Grand Cote)

Iberville Parish
Bayou Blue
Bayou Choctaw (Choctaw, Grosse
    Tete, Plaquemines)
Bayou des Glaises (Bayou Alabama)
St. Gabriel
White Castle

Jefferson Parish
Barataria
Bay de Chene
Lafitte (Bayou St. Denis)

Jefferson Davis Parish
Iowa (Iowa Junction)
Roanoke
Welsh
Woodlawn

Lafourche Parish
Bay de Chene
Bay Marchand
Bully Camp
Chacahoula (Thibodeaux)
Clovelly (Scully)
Cut Off
Golden Meadow
Leeville
Raceland
Timbalier Bay
Valentine (Harang, La Rose)

Madison Parish
Coleman (South Coleman)
Duck Port
North Tallulah (Tallulah)
Singer
South Tallulah
Walnut Bayou (East Tallulah)

Natchitoches Parish
Chestnut

Plaquemines Parish
Delta Duck Club
Garden Island Bay
Lake Hermitage
Lake Washington (Grand Ecaille, Myrtle Grove)
Potash (Cockrell)
Stella
Venice (Rose, Spanish Pass)
West Bay

Rapides Parish
Cheneyville (Bunkie)

Saint Charles Parish
Bayou Couba (N. Lake Salvador)
Bayou des Allemands
Good Hope
Lake Salvador
Paradis

Saint James Parish
Hester (Convent, Hester-Vacherie)

Saint Landry Parish
Port Barre

Saint Martin Parish
Anse la Butte
Bayou Bouillon
Fausse Point (Loureaville)
Lake Chicot
Lake Mongoulois
Plumb Bob
Saint Martinville
Section 28 (Hager-Martin)
South Section 28

Saint Mary Parish
Belle Isle
Charenton
Cote Blanche Island
Franklin
Jeanerette
West Cote Blanche Bay

Tensas Parish
Ashwood (Somerset)
Newellton
Snake Bayou (Killens Ferry)

Terrebonne Parish
Bay Junop
Bay Saint Elaine (Coon Road)
Caillou Island
Coon Point - Offshore (Ship Shoal Blk. 38)
Dog Lake
Four Isle
Lake Barre
Lake Pelto

Vermillion Parish
Gueydan

Webster Parish
Bistineau

Webster Parish (cont.)
Minden
Vacherie

Winn Parish
Cedar Creek
Chester
Coochie Brake
Drake's
Lonnie (Chester)
Milam
Packton
Price's
Sikes
Winnfield

Offshore

East Cameron Area
Block 115 (Block 104)
Block 118
Block 126
Block 139
Block 151
Block 152
Block 155
Block 160
Block 187 (Block 194)
Block 189

Eugene Island Area
Block 32
Block 77
Block 110
Block 126
Block 128
Block 175
Block 184
Block 188
Block 205
Block 208
Block 231
Block 238
Block 292

Grand Isle Area
Block 16
Block 18
Block 72

Main Pass Area
Block 46

Salt Dome Index

Anse la Butte, St. Martin Parish: (cont.)
851. *Proc.,* Fourth World Pet. Cong., sec. 1, pp. 86, 95
17. *Trans.,* GCAGS, v. 5, pp. 65-82
8. *Trans.,* GCAGS, v. 7, p. 235
583. *Trans.,* GCAGS, v. 9, p. 62
373. *Trans.,* GCAGS, v. 11, pp. 146-147
153. *Trans.,* GCAGS, v. 11, p. 222
410. *WO,* v. 130, no. 7, p. 114

Arcadia, Bienville Parish:
6a. *BMIC*
601. *Bull.,* v. 10, no. 1, p. 6, 14; *SD,* pp. 214, 222
598. *Bull.,* v. 10, no. 3, pp. 222-226, 228; *SD,* pp. 274-278
427. *GAGC,* p. 269
22. *Guidebook,* Shreveport Geol. Soc. (1960), pp. 48-56.
634. *Guidebook* Shreveport Geol. Soc. (1960), p. 57
24. *Guidebook,* Shreveport Geol. Soc. (1960), p. 64
421. *Guidebook,* Shreveport Geol. Soc. (1960), Plate A-55, p. 98; Plate A-60, p. 99
434. *PROB.,* pp. 632-633

Ashwood dome, Tensas Parish: (Somerset)
6a. *BMIC*
427. *GAGC,* p. 269
634. *Guidebook* Shreveport Geol. Soc. (1960), p. 59
24. *Guidebook,* Shreveport Geol. Soc. (1960), p. 68

Avery Island, Iberia Parish: (Petit Anse)
6a. *BMIC*
31. *Bull.,* v. 8, no. 5, pp. 674-676; *Econ. Geol.,* v. 13, no. 6, pp. 471-472
723. *Bull.,* v. 9, no. 5, pp. 836-838, 840-842; *SD,* pp. 6-8, 10-12
777. *Bull.,* v. 9, no. 2, p. 348; *SD,* p. 781
883. *Bull.,* v. 9, no. 3, pp. 561, 564-565, 567; *SD,* pp. 743, 746-747, 749
380. *Bull.,* v. 9, no. 4, pp. 761-775; *SD,* pp. 361-375
601. *Bull.,* v. 10, no. 1, p. 16; *SD,* p. 224
618. *Bull.,* v. 10, no. 1, p. 79; *SD,* p. 405
385. *Bull.,* v. 17, no. 9, pp. 1047, 1051; *GC,* pp. 42, 46
54. *Bull.,* v. 19, no. 5, p. 649; *GC,* p. 1038
847. *Bull.,* v. 20, no. 6, p. 731; *GC,* p. 115
214. *Bull.,* v. 27, no. 6, pp. 732, 735-736
218. *Bull.,* v. 29, no. 6, p. 801
219. *Bull.,* v. 30, no. 6, p. 1004

Avery Island, Iberia Parish: (Petit Anse) (cont.)
436. *Bull.,* v. 34, no. 3, pp. 365-368
224. *Bull.,* v. 35, no. 6, p. 1343
230. *Bull.,* v. 41, no. 6, p. 1194
30. *Bull.,* v. 43, no. 5, pp. 944-957
554. *Bull.,* v. 47, no. 1, p. 180
96. *Bull. 11,* La. Geol. Svy., pp. 9, 32, 38, 42, 110, 159, 161
29. *Eng. & Min. Jour.,* v. 62, pp. 463-464
403. *EGP,* p. 343
427. *GAGC,* pp. 222, 236, 270
363. *Geophysics,* v. 1, no. 1, Fig. 2 (between pp. 142-143), Fig. 7 (between pp. 146-147)
945. *Guidebook,* HGS (1962), pp. 314-318
647. *Lockwood's* (Louisiana 1940), pp. 30-31, 329
32. *Mines & Min.,* v. 20, pp. 438-439
645. *NOGS,* v. 2, pp. 28-29
722. *OFNA,* pp. 134, 136
327. *OGJ,* v. 28, no. 45, p. 159
300. *OGJ,* v. 37, no. 12, pp. 33-34
337. *OGJ,* v. 38, no. 50, pp. 95, 102
520. *OGJ,* v. 39, no. 49, pp. 65, 129-130
476. *OGJ,* v. 51, no. 7, p. 94
879. *OGJ,* v. 54, no. 53, p. 144
524. *OW,* v. 90, no. 7, p. 214
161. *OW,* v. 123, no. 3, pp. 82, 84-85
409. *OW,* v. 123, no. 3, p. 144
434. *PROB.,* pp. 632-633, 636
515a. *SOS,* pp. 105-106, 111, 113, 117, 121
28b. *SOS,* pp. 367-378
314a. *SOS,* p. 390
136. *Trans.,* GCAGS, v. 5, pp. 173-174
701. *Trans.,* GCAGS, v. 10, p. 2
631. *Trans.,* GCAGS, v. 10, pp. 217-218
410. *WO,* v. 130, no. 7, p. 100

Barataria, Jefferson Parish:
6a. *BMIC*
211. *Bull.,* v. 24, no. 6, pp. 1088-1089
34. *Bull.,* v. 25, no. 2, pp. 322-323
324. *Bull.,* v. 28, no. 9, pp. 1259, 1262-1263, 1303
219. *Bull.,* v. 30, no. 6, p. 1004
800. *Bull.,* v. 30, no. 8, p. 1307
221. *Bull.,* v. 32, no. 6, p. 1038
234. *Bull.,* v. 45, no. 6, p. 886
235. *Bull.,* v. 46, no. 6, pp. 934, 936
427. *GAGC,* p. 270
647. *Lockwood's* (Louisiana 1940), pp. 36-37
645. *NOGS,* v. 2, pp. 42-43
722. *OFNA,* p. 148
478. *OGJ,* v. 27, no. 25, p. 35

Barataria, Jefferson Parish: (cont.)

520. *OGJ,* v. 39, no. 49, pp. 65, 164
524. *OW,* v. 90, no. 7, p. 216
161. *OW,* v. 123, no. 3, pp. 85, 88
409. *OW,* v. 123, no. 3, p. 147
616. *Trans.,* GCAGS, v. 8, pp. 105-106, 109-110, 115
378. *Trans.,* GCAGS, v. 11, p. 141
410. *WO,* v. 130, no. 7, p. 104

Bay de Chene, Jefferson and Lafourche Parishes:
6a. *BMIC*
221. *Bull.,* v. 32, no. 6, p. 1037
223. *Bull.,* v. 34, no. 6, p. 1196
224. *Bull.,* v. 35, no. 6, p. 1343
225. *Bull.,* v. 36, no. 6, p. 1217
827. *Bull.,* v. 42, no. 3, p. 538
234. *Bull.,* v. 45, no. 6, p. 886
427. *GAGC,* pp. 222, 270
645. *NOGS,* v. 2, pp. 44-45
409. *OW,* v. 123, no. 3, p. 147
503. *Trans.,* GCAGS, v. 9, pp. 112-117, 119-120
410. *WO,* v. 130, no. 7, p. 104

Bay Junop, Terrebonne Parish:
6a *BMIC*
847. *Bull.,* v. 20, no. 6, p. 731; *GC,* p. 115
222. *Bull.,* v. 33, no. 6, pp. 981-983
227. *Bull.,* v. 38, no. 6, p. 1230
96. *Bull. 11,* La. Geol. Svy., p. 51
427. *GAGC,* pp. 226, 270
363. *Geophysics,* v. 1, no. 1, Fig. 3 (between pp. 142-143), Fig. 8 (between pp. 146-147)
645. *NOGS,* v. 1, pp. 96-97; v. 1, first rev. pp. 84-85
327. *OGJ,* v. 28, no. 45, p. 160
515. *OGJ,* v. 28, no. 49, p. 118
484. *OGJ,* v. 32, no. 20, p. 10
300. *OGJ,* v. 37, no. 12, p. 34
337. *OGJ,* v. 38, no. 50, p. 102
955. *OGJ,* v. 51, no. 37, p. 63
524. *OW,* v. 90, no. 7, p. 226
434. *PROB.,* pp. 632-633
410. *WO,* v. 130, no. 7, p. 116

Bay Marchand, Lafourche Parish:
6a. *BMIC*
223. *Bull.,* v. 34, no. 6, p. 1197
224. *Bull.,* v. 35, no. 6, p. 1344
229. *Bull.,* v. 40, no. 6, p. 1259
230. *Bull.,* v. 41, no. 6, p. 1196
650. *Bull.,* v. 43, no. 11, pp. 2601-2602
555a. *Bull.,* v. 50, no. 3, pp. 441, 444

Bay Marchand, Lafourche Parish: (cont.)
96. *Bull. 11,* La. Geol. Svy., p. 110
427. *GAGC,* pp. 222-223, 238, 260, 270
934. *JPT,* v. 15, no. 2, p. 127
647. *Lockwood's* (Louisiana 1940), pp. 44-45
645. *NOGS,* v. 2, pp. 46-47
327. *OGJ,* v. 28, no. 45, p. 160
515. *OGJ,* v. 28, no. 49, p. 118
300. *OGJ,* v. 37, no. 12, p. 34
337. *OGJ,* v. 38, no. 50, p. 102
311. *OGJ,* v. 39, no. 49, p. 97
637. *OGJ,* v. 57, no. 48, pp. 126, 128
524. *OW,* v. 90, no. 7, p. 218
644. *Trans.,* GCAGS, v. 9, pp. 78, 84
410. *WO,* v. 130, no. 7, p. 106
45. *WO,* v. 132, no. 7, pp. 167-172, 174

Bay St. Elaine, Terrebonne Parish: (Coon Road)
6a. *BMIC*
847. *Bull.,* v. 20, no. 6, p. 731; *GC,* p. 115
218. *Bull.,* v. 29, no. 6, p. 799
222. *Bull.,* v. 33, no. 6, p. 984
224. *Bull.,* v. 35, no. 6, pp. 1343-1344
225. *Bull.,* v. 36, no. 6, p. 1217
407. *Bull.,* v. 37, no. 2, p. 419
227. *Bull.,* v. 38, no. 6, p. 1229
228. *Bull.,* v. 39, no. 6, p. 993
229. *Bull.,* v. 40, no. 6, p. 1258
827. *Bull.,* v. 42, no. 3, p. 548
231. *Bull.,* v. 42, no. 6, p. 1314
46. *Bull.,* v. 43, no. 10, pp. 2470-2480
96. *Bull. 11,* La. Geol. Svy., p. 119
942a. *Bull. 4,* SIPES, Figs. 1, 3
427. *GAGC,* pp. 227, 270
717. *GAS,* pp. 685, 710-711, 738
363. *Geophysics,* v. 1, no. 1, Fig. 3 (between pp. 142-143, Fig. 8 (between pp 146-147)
647. *Lockwood's* (Louisiana 1940), pp. 46-47
645. *NOGS,* v. 2, pp. 76-77
327. *OGJ,* v. 28, no. 45, p. 160
515. *OGJ,* v. 28, no. 49, p. 118
484. *OGJ,* v. 32, no. 20, p. 10
879. *OGJ,* v. 54, no. 53, p. 144
334. *OW,* v. 69, no. 1, p. 68
524. *OW,* v. 90, no. 7, pp. 224, 226
161. *OW,* v. 123, no. 3, p. 85
409. *OW,* v. 123, no. 3, p. 156
434. *PROB.,* pp. 632-633
410. *WO,* v. 130, no. 7, p. 116

Bayou Alabama, Iberville Parish:
(see **Bayou des Glaise**)

Bayou Blue, Iberville Parish:

  6a. *BMIC*
- 847. *Bull.,* v. 20, no. 6, p. 731; *GC,* p. 115
- 218. *Bull.,* v. 29, no. 6, p. 799
- 219. *Bull.,* v. 30, no. 6, p. 1004
- 221. *Bull.,* v. 33, no. 6, p. 984
- 225. *Bull.,* v. 36, no. 6, p. 1217
- 229. *Bull.,* v. 40, no. 6, p. 1257
- 47. *Bull.,* v. 41, no. 9, pp. 1915-1951
- 234. *Bull.,* v. 45, no. 6, p. 885
- 555a. *Bull.,* v. 50, no. 3, pp. 450, 468
- 96. *Bull. 11,* La. Geol. Svy., pp. 32-38
- 27. *Bull. 13,* La. Geol. Svy., pp. 2, 61, 88, 173-183
- 427. *GAGC,* pp. 217, 226, 270
- 363. *Geophysics,* v. 1, no. 1, Fig. 3 (between pp. 142-143), Fig. 8 (between pp 146-147)
- 647. *Lockwood's* (Louisiana 1940), pp. 48-49
- 645. *NOGS,* v. 1, pp. 30-31; v. 1, first rev. pp. 18-19
- 478. *OGJ,* v. 27, no. 25, p. 35
- 515. *OGJ,* v. 28, no. 49, p. 118
- 336. *OGJ,* v. 29, no. 14, pp. 42, 146
- 484. *OGJ,* v. 32, no. 20, p. 10
- 337. *OGJ,* v. 38, no. 50, p. 92
- 311. *OGJ,* v. 39, no. 49, p. 82
- 524. *OW,* v. 90, no. 7, p. 216
- 370. *OW,* v. 100, no. 10, p. 20
- 161. *OW,* v. 123, no. 3, pp. 85, 87-88
- 409. *OW,* v. 123, no. 3, p. 147
- 434. *PROB.,* pp. 632-633
- 8. *Trans.,* GCAGS, v. 7, p. 234
- 583. *Trans.,* GCAGS, v. 9, p. 62
- 373. *Trans.,* GCAGS, v. 11, pp. 141-142, 145, 147
- 410. *WO,* v. 130, no. 7, p. 102

Bayou Bouillon, St. Martin:

  6a. *BMIC*
- 127. *Bull.,* v. 1, no. 1, p. 45
- 48. *Bull.,* v. 9, no. 9, pp. 1283-1289; *SD,* pp. 345-351
- 640. *Bull.,* v. 17, no. 6, pp. 634, 642; *GC,* pp. 404, 412
- 847. *Bull.,* v. 20, no. 6, p. 731; *GC,* p. 115
- 225. *Bull.,* v. 36, no. 6, p. 1218
- 555a. *Bull.,* v. 50, no. 3, pp. 461-462, 473
- 96. *Bull. 11,* La. Geol. Svy., pp. 49, 55, 183
- 427. *GAGC,* pp. 225, 270
- 717. *GAS,* pp. 685, 739
- 363. *Geophysics,* v. 1, no. 1, Fig. 2 (between pp. 142-143), Fig. 7 (between pp. 146-147)

Bayou Bouillon, St. Martin: (cont.)

- 647. *Lockwood's* (Louisiana 1940), pp. 50-51
- 645. *NOGS,* v. 2, pp. 66-67
- 75. *OGJ,* v. 26, no. 44, pp. 51, 122
- 478. *OGJ,* v. 27, no. 25, pp. 35, 91
- 327. *OGJ,* v. 28, no. 45, p. 159
- 300. *OGJ,* v. 37, no. 12, p. 34
- 520. *OGJ,* v. 39, no. 49, p. 138
- 524. *OW,* v. 90, no. 7, p. 223
- 161. *OW,* v. 123, no. 3, p. 85
- 434. *PROB.,* pp. 632-633
- 8. *Trans.,* GCAGS, v. 7, p. 235
- 410. *WO,* v. 130, no. 7, p. 114

Bayou Chicot, Evangeline Parish: (see Pine Prairie)

Bayou Choctaw, Iberville Parish: (Plaquemines, Choctow, Grosse Tete)

  6a. *BMIC*
- 847. *Bull.,* v. 20, no. 6, p. 731; *GC,* p. 115
- 753. *Bull.,* v. 41, no. 8, pp. 1828-1830
- 236. *Bull.,* v. 47, no. 6, p. 1093
- 555a. *Bull.,* v. 50, no. 3, p. 445
- 96. *Bull. 11,* La. Geol. Svy., pp. 30, 32, 38-39, 41, 43, 49, 53, 55, 119, 158, 160
- 27. *Bull. 13,* La. Geol. Svy., pp. 2, 88-89, 154-172
- 427. *GAGC,* p. 270
- 717. *GAS,* pp. 685, 712
- 363. *Geophysics,* v. 1, no. 1, Fig. 3 (between pp. 142-143), Fig. 8 (between pp. 146-147)
- 647. *Lockwood's* (Louisiana 1940), pp. 52-53
- 645. *NOGS,* v. 1, pp. 20-21; v. 1, first rev., pp. 32-33
- 478. *OGJ,* v. 27, no. 25, p. 35
- 327. *OGJ,* v. 28, no. 45, p. 159
- 515. *OGJ,* v. 28, no. 49, p. 118
- 790. *OGJ,* v. 30, no. 37, p. 71
- 484. *OGJ,* v. 32, no. 20, p. 10
- 49. *OGJ,* v. 52, no. 7, pp. 277-281
- 376. *OW,* v. 82, no. 10, p. 14
- 525. *OW,* v. 90, no. 7, p. 216
- 161. *OW,* v. 123, no. 3, p. 85
- 409. *OW,* v. 123, no. 3, p. 147
- 434. *PROB.,* pp. 632-633
- 8. *Trans.,* GCAGS, v. 7, p. 234
- 410. *WO,* v. 130, no. 7, p. 102

Bayou Couba, St. Charles Parish: (North Lake Salvador)

  6a. *BMIC*
- 214. *Bull.,* v. 27, no. 6, p. 736
- 221. *Bull.,* v. 32, no. 6, p. 1037

Belle Isle, St. Mary Parish: (cont.)

363. *Geophysics.* v. 1, no. 1, Fig. 2 (between pp. 142-143), Fig. 7 (between pp. 146-147)
647. *Lockwood's* (Louisiana 1940), pp. 64-65
645. *NOGS,* v. 1, pp. 86-87; v. 1, first rev. pp. 74-75
722. *OFNA,* pp. 134, 316
327. *OGJ,* v. 28, no. 45, p. 159
300. *OGJ,* v. 37, no. 12, pp. 33-34
337. *OGJ,* v. 38, no. 50, pp. 95, 102
520. *OGJ,* v. 39, no. 49, p. 130
524. *OW,* v. 90, no. 7, p. 224
161. *OW,* v. 123, no. 3, pp. 85, 87
409. *OW,* v. 123, no. 3, p. 156
686. *PROB.,* p. 418
434. *PROB.,* pp. 632-633
515a. *SOS,* pp. 105-106
314a. *SOS,* p. 390
136. *Trans.,* GCAGS, v. 5, pp. 173-174
701. *Trans.,* GCAGS, v. 10, p. 2
631. *Trans.,* GCAGS, v. 10, pp. 217-218
410. *WO,* v. 130, no. 7, p. 116

Big Lake, Cameron Parish:

6a. *BMIC*
847. *Bull.,* v. 20, no. 6, p. 731; *GC,* p. 115
227. *Bull.,* v. 38, no. 6, p. 1226
228. *Bull.,* v. 39, no. 6, p. 994
229. *Bull.,* v. 40, no. 6, p. 1256
236. *Bull.,* v. 47, no. 6, p. 1093
555a. *Bull.,* v. 50, no. 3, p. 473
427. *GAGC,* pp. 222, 270, 274
363. *Geophysics,* v. 1, no. 1, Fig. 3 (between pp. 142-143), Fig. 8 (between pp. 146-147)
647. *Lockwood's* (Louisiana 1940), pp. 66-67
645. *NOGS,* v. 2, pp. 10-11
79. *OGJ,* v. 36, no. 34, pp. 48-49
422. *OGJ,* v. 54, no. 59, p. 222
524. *OW,* v. 90, no. 7, p. 208
161. *OW,* v. 123, no. 3, p. 85
409. *OW,* v. 123, no. 3, p. 142
8. *Trans.,* GCAGS, v. 7, p. 234
410. *WO,* v. 130, no. 7, p. 98

Bistineau, Webster Parish:

6a. *BMIC*
723. *Bull.,* v. 9, no. 5, p. 837; *SD,* p. 7
601. *Bull.,* v. 10, no. 1, pp. 4, 14; *SD,* pp. 212, 222
598. *Bull.,* v. 10, no. 3, pp. 217, 222-224, 251-255; *SD,* pp. 269, 274-276, 303-307
640. *Bull.,* v. 17, no. 6, p. 614; *GC,* p. 384

Bistineau, Webster Parish: (cont.)

177. *Bull.,* v. 37, no. 6, p. 1454
461. *Bull. 29,* La. Geol. Svy., pp. 73, 81, 108, 111-117, 225
427. *GAGC,* p. 269
634. *Guidebook,* Shreveport Geol. Soc. (1960), p. 57
24. *Guidebook,* Shreveport Geol. Soc. (1960), p. 63
434. *PROB.,* pp. 632-633

Black Bayou, Cameron Parish:

6a. *BMIC*
640. *Bull.,* v. 17, no. 6, p. 642; *GC,* p. 412
847. *Bull.,* v. 20, no. 6, p. 731; *GC,* p. 115
218. *Bull.,* v. 29, no. 6, p. 792
652. *Bull.,* v. 37, no. 2, p. 404
227. *Bull.,* v. 38, no. 6, p. 1227
91. *Bull. 6,* La. Geol. Svy., pp. 122-134, 182, 185-186, 205, 213, 221
96. *Bull. 11,* La. Geol. Svy., pp. 50, 115, 119
427. *GAGC,* p. 270
717. *GAS,* pp. 685, 711
363. *Geophysics,* v. 1, no. 1, Fig. 3 (between pp. 142-143), Fig. 8 (between pp. 146-147)
647. *Lockwood's* (Louisiana 1940), pp. 68-69
645. *NOGS,* v. 2, pp. 12-13
478. *OGJ,* v. 27, no. 25, pp. 35, 91
327. *OGJ,* v. 28, no. 45, p. 42
515. *OGJ,* v. 28, no. 49, p. 118
484. *OGJ,* v. 32, no. 20, p. 10
524. *OW,* v. 90, no. 7, p. 208
161. *OW,* v. 123, no. 3, p. 85
409. *OW,* v. 123, no. 3, p. 142
434. *PROB.,* pp. 632-633
8. *Trans.,* GCAGS, v. 7, p. 234
410. *WO,* v. 130, no. 7, p. 98
335. *WO,* v. 142, no. 7, p. 158

Bosco, Acadia Parish:

6a. *BMIC*
847. *Bull.,* v. 20, no. 6, p. 731; *GC,* p. 115
357. *Bull. 31,* La. Geol. Svy., pp. 77, 79, 91, 94-96, 159-168
1. *Bull. 36,* La. Geol. Svy., pp. 49-52, 55, 74-76
363. *Geophysics,* v. 1, no. 1, Fig. 3 (between pp. 142-143), Fig. 8 (between pp. 146-147)
647. *Lockwood's* (Louisiana 1940), pp. 70-72
645. *NOGS,* v. 2, pp. 2-3
74. *OGJ,* v. 33, no. 3, p. 8
72. *OGJ,* v. 33, no. 6, p. 16

Bosco, Acadia Parish: (cont.)

79. *OGJ*, v. 36, no. 34, p. 48
520. *OGJ*, v. 39, no. 49, p. 140
73. *OW*, v. 76, no. 11, pp. 66-67
524. *OW*, v. 90, no. 7, p. 201
161. *OW*, v. 123, no. 3, pp. 82, 84-85
409. *OW*, v. 123, no. 3, p. 134
410. *WO*, v. 130, no. 7, p. 92

Bully Camp, Lafourche Parish:

6a. *BMIC*
218. *Bull.*, v. 29, no. 6, p. 796
221. *Bull.*, v. 32, no. 6, p. 1037
223. *Bull.*, v. 34, no. 6, p. 1196
227. *Bull.*, v. 38, no. 6, p. 1228
228. *Bull.*, v. 39, no. 6, p. 992
229. *Bull.*, v. 40, no. 6, p. 1257
235. *Bull.*, v. 46, no. 6, p. 934
427. *GAGC*, p. 270
645. *NOGS*, v. 2, pp. 48-49
515. *OGJ*, v. 28, no. 49, p. 118
879. *OGJ*, v. 54, no. 53, p. 144
524. *OW*, v. 90, no. 7, p. 218
161. *OW*, v. 123, no. 3, p. 85
409. *OW*, v. 123, no. 3, p. 148
373. *Trans.*, GCAGS, v. 11, p. 147
410. *WO*, v. 130, no. 7, p. 106

Bunkie, Rapides Parish: (see Cheneyville)

Caillou Island, Terrebonne Parish:

6a. *BMIC*
847. *Bull.*, v. 20, no. 6, p. 731; *GC*, p. 115 ,
223. *Bull.*, v. 34, no. 6, pp. 1195-1196
225. *Bull.*, v. 36, no. 6, p. 1217
227. *Bull.*, v. 38, no. 6, p. 1230
228. *Bull.*, v. 39, no. 6, p. 994
229. *Bull.*, v. 40, no. 6, pp. 1258-1259, 1262
230. *Bull.*, v. 41, no. 6, p. 1196
827. *Bull.*, v. 42, no. 3, pp. 548, 553, 555
231. *Bull.*, v. 42, no. 6, pp. 1314, 1317
232. *Bull.*, v. 43, no. 6, p. 1320
650. *Bull.*, v. 43, no. 11, pp. 2601-2602
234. *Bull.*, v. 45, no. 6, p. 886
85. *Bull.*, v. 45, no. 10, pp. 1701-1702, 1706
158. *Bull.*, v. 47, no. 12, p. 2014
555a. *Bull.*, v. 50, no. 3, pp. 441, 444, 467
96. *Bull. 11*, La. Geol. Svy., p. 51
115. *Chron. Hist.*, p. 163
427. *GAGC*, pp. 217, 222-223, 247, 270
901. *GCH*, v. 1, p. 13; *Geophysics*, v. 5, no. 3, p. 221

Caillou Island, Terrebonne Parish: (cont.)

363. *Geophysics*, v. 1, no. 1, Fig. 3 (between pp. 142-143), Fig. 8 (between pp. 146-147)
957. *JPT*, v. 15, no. 2, p. 127
647. *Lockwood's* (Louisiana 1940), pp. 74-75
645. *NOGS*, v. 2, pp. 78-79
722. *OFNA*, pp. 134, 138
478. *OGJ*, v. 27, no. 25, p. 35
327. *OGJ*, v. 28, no. 45, p. 160
515. *OGJ*, v. 28, no. 49, p. 118
484. *OGJ*, v. 32, no. 20, p. 10
79. *OGJ*, v. 36, no. 34, pp. 46, 48, 50
337. *OGJ*, v. 38, no. 50, p. 102
311. *OGJ*, v. 39, no. 49, p. 84
637. *OGJ*, v. 57, no. 48, pp. 126, 128
334. *OW*, v. 69, no. 1, p. 68
376. *OW*, v. 82, no. 10, p. 14
524. *OW*, v. 90, no. 7, p. 226
161. *OW*, v. 123, no. 3, pp. 84-85
409. *OW*, v. 123, no. 3, p. 156
644. *Trans.*, GCAGS, v. 9, pp. 78, 84
410. *WO*, v. 130, no. 7, p. 118

Calcasieu Lake, Cameron Parish:

6a. *BMIC*
385. *Bull.*, v. 17, no. 9, p. 1048; *GC*, p. 43
847. *Bull.*, v. 20, no. 6, p. 731; *GC*, p. 115
218. *Bull.*, v. 29, no. 6, p. 801
232. *Bull.*, v. 43, no. 6, pp. 1312, 1314-1315
555a. *Bull.*, v. 50, no. 3, p. 448
91. *Bull. 6*, La. Geol. Svy., pp. 144-145, 147, 150, 205, 211-212, 215
96. *Bull. 11*, La. Geol. Svy., pp. 53, 55, 77
427. *GAGC*, pp. 220-222, 228, 270
363. *Geophysics*, v. 1, no. 1, Fig. 3 (between pp. 142-143), Fig. 8 (between pp. 146-147), p. 143
647. *Lockwood's* (Louisiana 1940), pp. 76-77
645. *NOGS*, v. 2, pp. 14-15
478. *OGJ*, v. 27, no. 25, pp. 35, 91
327. *OGJ*, v. 28, no. 45, p. 42
515. *OGJ*, v. 28, no. 49, p. 118
484. *OGJ*, v. 32, no. 20, p. 10
300. *OGJ*, v. 37, no. 12, p. 34
337. *OGJ*, v. 38, no. 50, pp. 95, 102
86. *OGJ*, v. 56, no. 30, p. 263
637. *OGJ*, v. 57, no. 48, p. 130
524. *OW*, v. 90, no. 7, p. 208
434. *PROB.*, pp. 632-633
851. *Proc.*, Fourth World Pet. Cong., sec. 1, p. 95
87. *Trans.*, GCAGS, v. 3, pp. 71-81
644. *Trans.*, GCAGS, v. 9, p. 81
724. *WO*, v. 144, no. 7, p. 179

Cameron Meadows, Cameron Parish:

  6a. *BMIC*

  90. *Bull.,* v. 16, no. 3, pp. 255-256

511. *Bull.,* v. 19, no. 1, pp. 19, 21; *EGP,* pp. 679, 681; *Trans.,* SEG, v. 5, pp. 19, 21

847. *Bull.,* v. 20, no. 6, p. 731; *GC,* p. 115

221. *Bull.,* v. 32, no. 6, p. 1037

223. *Bull.,* v. 34, no. 6, p. 1195

652. *Bull.,* v. 37, no. 2, pp. 404-405

227. *Bull.,* v. 38, no. 6, p. 1227

555a. *Bull.,* v. 50, no. 3, p. 468

  91. *Bull. 6,* La. Geol. Svy., pp. 3, 13, 15, 135-136, 138-143, 182, 186, 205, 215, 221

427. *GAGC,* pp. 215, 270

717. *GAS,* pp. 685, 734

363. *Geophysics,* v. 1, no. 1, Fig. 3 (between pp. 142-143), Fig. 8 (between pp. 146-147)

  89. *Geophysics,* v. 10, no. 1, pp. 1-16; *GCH,* v. 1, pp. 161-174; *OW,* v. 118, no. 12, pp. 46-52; *Dallas Digest* (1948), p. 98

647. *Lockwood's* (Louisiana 1940), pp. 78-79

645. *NOGS,* v. 2, pp. 16-17

515. *OGJ,* v. 28, no. 49, p. 118

790. *OGJ,* v. 30, no. 37, p. 71

484. *OGJ,* v. 32, no. 20, p. 10

311. *OGJ,* v. 39, no. 49, p. 84

520. *OGJ,* v. 39, no. 49, p. 138

527. *OW,* v. 69, no. 1, pp. 16-17

524. *OW,* v. 90, no. 7, p. 208

161. *OW,* v. 123, no. 3, p. 85

409. *OW,* v. 123, no. 3, p. 142

434. *PROB.,* pp. 632-633

  8. *Trans.,* GCAGS, v. 7, p. 234

410. *WO,* v. 130, no. 7, p. 98

Cedar Creek, Winn Parish:

  6a. *BMIC*

601. *Bull.,* v. 10, no. 1, pp. 4, 7, 14; *SD,* pp. 212, 215, 222

598. *Bull.,* v. 10, no. 3, pp. 222-223, 282-287; *SD,* pp. 274-275, 334-338

  88. *Bull. 15,* La. Geol. Svy., pp. 61, 70, 194, 244-252, 269-270, 293-294, 309

427. *GAGC,* pp. 269, 273

634. *Guidebook,* Shreveport Geol. Soc. (1960), p. 58

  24. *Guidebook,* Shreveport Geol. Soc. (1960), p. 65

600. *Guidebook,* Shreveport Geol. Soc. (1960), Plate A-170

434. *PROB.,* pp. 632-633

Chacahoula, Lafourche Parish: (Thibodeaux)

  6a. *BMIC*

847. *Bull.,* v. 20, no. 6, p. 731; *GC,* p. 115

210. *Bull.,* v. 23, no. 6, p. 886

222. *Bull.,* v. 33, no. 6, p. 984

223. *Bull.,* v. 34, no. 6, p. 1196

225. *Bull.,* v. 36, no. 6, pp. 1217-1218

407. *Bull.,* v. 37, no. 2, p. 419

230. *Bull.,* v. 41, no. 6, p. 1195

555a. *Bull.,* v. 50, no. 3, p. 449

  96. *Bull. 11,* La. Geol. Svy., p. 119

942a. *Bull. 4,* SIPES, Figs. 1, 3

427. *GAGC,* p. 270

363. *Geophysics,* v. 1, no. 1, Fig. 3 (between pp. 142-143), Fig. 8 (between pp. 146-147)

647. *Lockwood's* (Louisiana 1940), pp. 82-83

645. *NOGS,* v. 2, pp. 50-51

484. *OGJ,* v. 32, no. 20, p. 10

300. *OGJ,* v. 37, no. 12, p. 34

108. *OGJ,* v. 54, no. 77, p. 172; *GCH,* v. 2, p. 113

109. *Oil,* v. 1, pp. 16-18

524. *OW,* v. 90, no. 7, p. 218

161. *OW,* v. 123, no. 3, p. 85

409. *OW,* v. 123, no. 3, p. 148

434. *PROB.,* pp. 632-633

631. *Trans.,* GCAGS, v. 10, p. 218

373. *Trans.,* GCAGS, v. 11, p. 142

410. *WO,* v. 130, no. 7, p. 106

Charenton, St Mary Parish:

  6a. *BMIC*

225. *Bull.,* v. 36, no. 6, p. 1217

226. *Bull.,* v. 37, no. 6, p. 1447

431. *Geophysics,* v. 2, no. 1, p. 66

547. *Geophysics,* v. 3, no. 2, pp. 101, 113

514. *JPT,* v. 4, no. 9, p. 16

647. *Lockwood's* (Louisiana 1940), pp. 86-87

645. *NOGS,* v. 1, pp. 88-89; v. 1, first rev., pp. 76-77

111. *OGJ,* v. 37, no. 17, pp. 26-27

  52. *OW,* v. 90, no. 7, p. 224

161. *OW,* v. 123, no. 3, pp. 82, 84-85

409. *OW,* v. 123, no. 3, p. 156

851. *Proc.,* Fourth World Pet. Cong., sec. 1, p. 95

410. *WO,* v. 130, no. 7, p. 116

Cheneyville, Rapides Parish: (Bunkie)

  6a. *BMIC*

847. *Bull.,* v. 20, no. 6, p. 731; *GC,* p. 115

  96. *Bull. 11,* La. Geol. Svy., p. 51

427. *GAGC,* p. 270

647. *Lockwood's* (Louisiana 1940), pp. 88-89

Cote Blanche Island, St. Mary Parish: (cont.)

722. *OFNA,* p. 134
300. *OGJ,* v. 37, no. 12, pp. 33-34
520. *OGJ,* v. 39, no. 49, p. 130
337. *OGJ,* v. 39, no. 50, pp. 95, 102
524.   *OW,* v. 90, no. 7, p. 224
434. *PROB.,* pp. 632-633
515a. *SOS,* pp. 105-106
314a. *SOS,* p. 390
136. *Trans.,* GCAGS, v. 5, pp. 173-179
701. *Trans.,* GCAGS, v. 10, p. 2
410. *WO,* v. 130, no. 7, p. 116
730. *WO,* v. 140, no. 6, p. 97
649. *WO,* v. 142, no. 7, p. 218
536. *WO,* v. 143, no. 5, p. 150

Creole, Cameron Parish: (West Cameron, Blk. 2)

6a. *BMIC*
210. *Bull.,* v. 23, no. 6, p. 883
234. *Bull.,* v. 45, no. 6, p. 887
235. *Bull.,* v. 46, no. 6, p. 936
115. *Chron. Hist.,* pp. 193, 197
647. *Lockwood's* (Louisiana 1940), pp. 96-97
645. *NOGS,* v. 2, pp. 18-19
437. *OGJ,* v. 47, no. 8, p. 250
524. *OW,* v. 90, no. 7, p. 210
161. *OW,* v. 123, no. 3, pp. 81, 85
409. *OW,* v. 123, no. 3, p. 142
449. *Pet. Geol.,* pp. 280, 284, 436, 444, 615
138. *STR,* v. 3, pp. 281-298
525. *WO,* v. 130, no. 7, p. 59
410. *WO,* v. 130, no. 7, p. 98

Crowley, Acadia Parish (South Crowley)

Crowville, Franklin Parish:

6a. *BMIC*
144. *Bull.,* v. 31, no. 11, pp. 2049-2050
172. *Bull.,* v. 32, no. 6, p. 1044
427. *GAGC,* p. 269
634. *Guidebook,* Shreveport Geol. Soc. (1960),
         p. 59
24. *Guidebook,* Shreveport Geol. Soc. (1960),
         p. 68

Cut Off, Lafourche Parish:

6a.   *BMIC*
227. *Bull.,* v. 38, no. 6, p. 1224
427. *GAGC,* p. 270
645. *NOGS,* v. 1, pp. 52-53; v. 1, first rev.,
         pp. 40-41
776. *Trans.,* GCAGS, v. 12, pp. 232-236

Darrow, Ascension Parish:

6a. *BMIC*
511. *Bull.,* v. 19, no. 1, p. 19; *EGP,* p. 679;
         Trans., SEG, v. 5, p. 19
847. *Bull.,* v. 20, no. 6, p. 731; *GC,* p. 115
157. *Bull.,* v. 22, no. 10, pp. 1412-1422; (abs.)
         OGJ, v. 36, no. 44, pp. 51, 53; World
         Pet., v. 9, no. 13, p. 54
236. *Bull.,* v. 47, no. 6, p. 1093
555a. *Bull.,* v. 50, no. 3, p. 449
  96. *Bull. 11,* La. Geol. Svy., pp. 32, 38, 49, 53, 55
  27. *Bull. 13,* La. Geol. Svy., pp. 1-2, 88, 92-114,
         150
360. *EGP,* p. 253; *Jour.,* Soc. of Pet. Geophysi-
         cists, v. 6, no. 1, p. 9
427. *GAGC,* pp. 234, 270
901. *GCH,* v. 1, p. 17; *Geophysics,* v. 5, no. 3,
         p. 225
156. *GCH,* v. 1, pp. 144-152; *Tech. Pub. 1495,*
         AIME; Pet. Tech., v. 5, p. 8; *Trans.,*
         v. 151, pp. 253-260
363. *Geophysics,* v. 1, no. 1, Fig. 3 (between pp.
         142-143), Fig. 8 (between pp. 146-
         147)
475. *Geophysics,* v. 1, no. 3, p. 310
361. *Geophysics,* v. 3, no. 1, p. 32
647. *Lockwood's* (Louisiana 1940), pp. 98-99
645. *NOGS,* v. 1, pp. 14-15; v. 1, first rev., pp.
         2-3
478. *OGJ,* v. 27, no. 25, p. 35
327. *OGJ,* v. 28, no. 45, p. 159
515. *OGJ,* v. 28, no. 49, p. 118
484. *OGJ,* v. 32, no. 20, p. 10
524. *OW,* v. 90, no. 7, p. 202
161. *OW,* v. 123, no. 3, p. 85
409. *OW,* v. 123, no. 3, p. 137
449. *Pet. Geol.,* pp. 436, 443
  8. *Trans.,* GCAGS, v. 7, p. 234
410. *WO.* v. 130, no. 7, p. 94

Delta Duck Club, Plaquemines Parish:

6a. *BMIC*
218. *Bull.,* v. 29, no. 6, p. 797
219. *Bull.,* v. 30, no. 6, pp. 1004, 1006
436. *Bull.,* v. 34, no. 3, p. 382
227. *Bull.,* v. 38, no. 6, p. 1228
427. *GAGC,* p. 270
645. *NOGS,* v. 1, pp. 58-59; v. 1, first rev.,
         pp. 46-47
437. *OGJ,* v. 47, no. 8, p. 250
161. *OW,* v. 123, no. 3, p. 85
409. *OW,* v. 123, no. 3, p. 149
410. *WO,* v. 130, no. 7, p. 108

Dog Lake, Terrebonne Parish:

6a. *BMIC*

847. *Bull.,* v. 20, no. 6, p. 731; *GC,* p. 115
221. *Bull.,* v. 32, no. 6, p. 1037
223. *Bull.,* v. 34, no. 6, p. 1196
225. *Bull.,* v. 36, no. 6, p. 1217
227. *Bull.,* v. 38, no. 6, 1230
231. *Bull.,* v. 42, no. 6, p. 1314
232. *Bull.,* v. 43, no. 6, p. 1317
363. *Geophysics,* v. 1, no. 1, Fig. 3 (between pp. 142-143), Fig. 8 (between pp. 146-147)
647. *Lockwood's* (Louisiana 1940), pp. 104-105
645. *NOGS,* v. 1, pp. 100-101; v. 1, first rev., pp. 88-89
327. *OGJ,* v. 28, no. 45, p. 160
515. *OGJ,* v. 28, no. 49, p. 118
484. *OGJ,* v. 32, no. 20, p. 10
334. *OW,* v. 69, no. 1, pp. 67-68
524. *OW,* v. 90, no. 7, p. 226
161. *OW,* v. 123, no. 3, p. 85
409. *OW,* v. 123, no. 3, p. 156
146. *PROB.,* p. 115
434. *PROB.,* pp. 632-633
410. *WO,* v. 130, no. 7, p. 118

Drake's, Winn Parish:

6a. *BMIC*

723. *Bull.,* v. 9, no. 5, p. 837; *SD,* p. 7
601. *Bull.,* v. 10, no. 1, pp. 4, 14; *SD,* pp. 212, 222
598. *Bull.,* v. 10, no. 3, pp. 222-223, 271-276; *SD,* pp. 274-275, 323-328
96. *Bull. 11,* La. Geol. Svy., p. 50
88. *Bull. 15,* La. Geol. Svy., pp. 35, 49, 65, 70, 186, 190-191, 224-236, 238, 247, 252, 255, 270, 277, 288, 294-295, 309, 347-348
429. *Bull. 1869,* Tex. U., pp. 20, 25
427. *GAGC,* p. 269
634. *Guidebook,* Shreveport Geol. Soc. (1960), p. 58
24. *Guidebook,* Shreveport Geol. Soc. (1960), p. 65
421. *Guidebook,* Shreveport Geol. Soc. (1960), Plate A-130+, p. 106; Plate A-140
434. *PROB.,* pp. 632-633

Duck Port, Madison Parish:

6a. *BMIC*

East Cameron Area Blocks: (see Offshore)

East Hackberry, Cameron Parish: (Kelso Bayou)

6a. *BMIC*

345. *Bull.,* v. 15, no. 3, pp. 247-256
847. *Bull.,* v. 20, no. 6, p. 731; *GC,* p. 115
652. *Bull.,* v. 37, no. 2, p. 404
407. *Bull.,* v. 37, no. 2, p. 419
227. *Bull.,* v. 38, no. 6, p. 1227
555a. *Bull.,* v. 50, no. 3, pp. 441, 443, 473
440. *Bull. 1,* Gulf Coast and So. La. Oil Scouts Assn., pp. 124-125
91. *Bull. 6,* La. Geol. Svy., pp. 77, 88-89, 103-121, 182-186, 209, 212, 215, 220
96. *Bull. 11,* La. Geol. Svy., pp. 26, 32, 38, 49, 51, 53, 111, 158
427. *GAGC,* pp. 222, 238, 269, 270, 274
717. *GAS,* pp. 685, 717-718
363. *Geophysics,* v. 1, no. 1, Fig. 3 (between pp. 142-143), Fig. 8 (between pp. 146-147)
793. *JPT,* v. 4, no. 7, pp. 16-17
647. *Lockwood's* (Louisiana 1940), pp. 138-141
645. *NOGS,* v. 2, pp. 20-21
478. *OGJ,* v. 27, no. 25, pp. 35, 91
327. *OGJ,* v. 28, no. 45, p. 42
515. *OGJ,* v. 28, no. 49, p. 118
790. *OGJ,* v. 30, no. 37, p. 73
484. *OGJ,* v. 32, no. 20, p. 10
337. *OGJ,* v. 38, no. 50, pp. 92, 95
311. *OGJ,* v. 39, no. 49, p. 84
520. *OGJ,* v. 39, no. 49, p. 140
342. *OGJ,* v. 44, no. 21, pp. 100-102, 131
527. *OW,* v. 69, no. 1, pp. 16-17
376. *OW,* v. 82, no. 10, p. 14
524. *OW,* v. 90, no. 7, p. 210
344. *OW,* v. 119, no. 6, pp. 46, 49-51
161. *OW,* v. 123, no. 3, pp. 82, 84-85
409. *OW,* v. 123, no. 3, p. 142
146. *PROB.,* p. 115
434. *PROB.,* pp. 632-633, 659, 661
8. *Trans.,* GCAGS, v. 7, p. 234
410. *WO,* v. 130, no. 7, p. 98

East Tallulah, Madison Parish: (see Walnut Bayou)

Edgerly, Calcasieu Parish:

6a. *BMIC*

856. *Bull.,* v. 9, no. 1, pp. 38-41; *SD,* pp. 777-780
347. *Bull.,* v. 9, no. 3, pp. 497-504; *SD,* pp. 470-477
847. *Bull.,* v. 20, no. 6, p. 731; *GC,* p. 115
219. *Bull.,* v. 30, no. 6, p. 1004
222. *Bull.,* v. 33, no. 6, p. 984
223. *Bull.,* v. 34, no. 6, p. 1195

Four Isle, Terrebonne Parish: (cont.)

363. *Geophysics,* v. 1, no. 1, Fig. 3 (between pp. 142-143), Fig. 8 (between pp. 146-147)
647. *Lockwood's* (Louisiana 1940), pp. 118-119
645. *NOGS,* v. 1, pp. 102-103; v. 1, first rev., pp. 90-91
327. *OGJ,* v. 28, no. 45, p. 160
515. *OGJ,* v. 28, no. 49, p. 118
484. *OGJ,* v. 32, no. 20, p. 10
334. *OW,* v. 69, no. 1, p. 68
524. *OW,* v. 90, no. 7, p. 226
161. *OW,* v. 123, no. 3, p. 85
409. *OW,* v. 123, no. 3, p. 156
434. *PROB.,* pp. 632-633
410. *WO,* v. 130, no. 7, p. 118
335. *WO,* v. 142, no. 7, p. 157

Garden Island Bay, Plaquemines Parish:

6a. *BMIC*
847. *Bull.,* v. 20, no. 6, p. 731; *GC,* p. 115
221. *Bull.,* v. 32, no. 6, p. 1037
222. *Bull.,* v. 33, no. 6, p. 984
436. *Bull.,* v. 34, no. 3, p. 382
234. *Bull.,* v. 45, no. 6, p. 886
235. *Bull.,* v. 46, no. 6, p. 936
788. *Bull. 8,* La. Geol. Svy., pp. 206-207, 263-275
96. *Bull. 11,* La. Geol. Svy., pp. 32, 38, 49, 61, 77, 87, 111, 182
942a. *Bull. 4,* SIPES, Figs. 1, 3
427. *GAGC,* pp. 228, 238, 270
717. *GAS,* pp. 685, 712
363. *Geophysics,* v. 1, no. 1, Fig. 3 (between pp. 142-143), Fig. 8 (between pp. 146-147)
647. *Lockwood's* (Louisiana 1940), pp. 120-121
645. *NOGS,* v. 2, pp. 58-59
327. *OGJ,* v. 28, no. 45, p. 160
515. *OGJ,* v. 28, no. 49, p. 118
393. *OGJ,* v. 32, no. 7, p. 36
484. *OGJ,* v. 32, no. 20, p. 10
334. *OW,* v. 69, no. 1, p. 65
524. *OW,* v. 90, no. 7, p. 220
161. *OW,* v. 123, no. 3, pp. 82, 84-85
409. *OW,* v. 123, no. 3, p. 149
434. *PROB.,* pp. 632-633
631. *Trans.,* GCAGS, v. 10, p. 218
525. *WO,* v. 130, no. 7, p. 59
410. *WO,* v. 130, no. 7, p. 108

Gibsland, Beinville Parish:

6a. *BMIC*
601. *Bull.,* v. 10, no. 1, p. 14; *SD,* p. 222
427. *GAGC,* p. 269

Gibsland, Beinville Parish: (cont.)

634. *Guidebook,* Shreveport Geol. Soc. (1960), p. 57
24. *Guidebook,* Shreveport Geol. Soc. (1960), p. 64
421. *Guidebook,* Shreveport Geol. Soc. (1960), p. 96, Plate A-49, p. 97
434. *PROB.,* pp. 632-633

Gilbert, Franklin Parish:

6a. *BMIC*
599. *Bull.,* v. 24, no. 3, p. 486
242. *Bull.,* v. 24, no. 6, p. 1028
427. *GAGC,* p. 269
434. *Guidebook,* Shreveport Geol. Soc. (1960), p. 59
24. *Guidebook,* Shreveport Geol. Soc. (1960), p. 68

Golden Meadow, Lafourche Parish:

6a. *BMIC*
210. *Bull.,* v. 23, no. 6, p. 884
212. *Bull.,* v. 24, no. 6, p. 1009
222. *Bull.,* v. 33, no. 6, pp. 987-988
225. *Bull.,* v. 36, no. 6, p. 1217
227. *Bull.,* v. 38, no. 6, p. 1228
647. *Lockwood's* (Louisiana 1940), pp. 126-129
645. *NOGS,* v. 2, pp. 52-53
491. *OGJ,* v. 38, no. 18, pp. 24-25, 34
490. *OGJ,* v. 38, no. 39, pp. 29-31
524. *OW,* v. 90, no. 7, p. 218
161. *OW,* v. 123, no. 3, pp. 82, 84-85
170. *OW,* v. 123, no. 3, p. 87
409. *OW,* v. 123, no. 3, p. 148
410. *WO,* v. 123, no. 7, p. 106

Good Hope, St. Charles Parish

Grande Cote, Iberia Parish: (see Weeks Island)

Grand Ecaille, Plaquemines Parish: (see Lake Washington)

Grand Isle Area Blocks: (see Offshore)

Grosse Tete, Iberville Parish: (see Bayou Choctaw)

Gueydan, Vermilion Parish:

6a. *BMIC*
847. *Bull.,* v. 20, no. 6, p. 731; *GC,* p. 115
555a. *Bull.,* v. 50, no. 3, p. 465
91. *Bull. 6,* La. Geol. Svy., pp. 160-166, 186, 205, 212

Gueydan, Vermilion Parish: (cont.)
96. *Bull. 11,* La. Geol. Svy., pp. 51, 53, 55, 111
1. *Bull. 36,* La. Geol. Svy., p. 49
427. *GAGC,* pp. 238, 270
717. *GAS,* pp. 685, 695
363. *Geophysics,* v. 1, no. 1, Fig. 3 (between pp. 142-143), Fig. 8 (between pp. 146-147)
647. *Lockwood's* (Louisiana 1940), pp. 136-137
645. *NOGS,* v. 2, pp. 82-83
722. *OFNA,* p. 135
515. *OGJ,* v. 28, no. 49, p. 118
484. *OGJ,* v. 32, no. 20, p. 10
473. *OGJ,* v. 31, no. 8, p. 16
524. *OW,* v. 90, no. 7, p. 228
161. *OW,* v. 123, no. 3, p. 85
409. *OW,* v. 123, no. 3, p. 159
8. *Trans.,* GCAGS, v. 7, p. 235
410. *WO,* v. 130, no. 7, p. 120

Hackberry, Cameron Parish: (see West Hackberry)

Hager-Martin, St. Martin Parish: (see Section 28)

Harang, Lafourche Parish: (see Valentine)

Hester, St. James Parish: (Hester-Vacherie, Convent)
6a. *BMIC*
647. *Lockwood's* (Louisiana 1940), pp. 150-151
645. *NOGS,* v. 2, pp. 64-65
300. *OGJ,* v. 37, no. 12, p. 34
582. *OGJ,* v. 37, no. 43, p. 28
524. *OW,* v. 90, no. 7, p. 222
409. *OW,* v. 123, no. 3, p. 152

Hester-Vacherie, St. James Parish: (see Hester)

Iberia, Iberia Parish: (New Iberia, Little Bayou)
6a. *BMIC*
883. *Bull.,* v. 9, no. 3, p. 569; *SD,* p. 751
723. *Bull.,* v. 9, no. 5, p. 866; *SD,* p. 36
843. *Bull.,* v. 9, no. 9, p. 1229; *SD,* p. 169
54. *Bull.,* v. 19, no. 5, p. 648; *GC,* p. 1037
229. *Bull.,* v. 40, no. 6, p. 1257
96. *Bull. 11,* La. Geol. Svy., pp. 52, 86, 110, 115
427. *GAGC,* p. 222
363. *Geophysics,* v. 1, no. 1, Fig. 2 (between pp. 142-143), Fig. 7 (between pp. 146-147)
647. *Lockwood's* (Louisiana 1940), pp. 206-207

Iberia, Iberia Parish: (New Iberia, Little Bayou) (cont.)
645. *NOGS,* v. 2, pp. 32-33
722. *OFNA,* p. 134
327. *OGJ,* v. 28, no. 45, p. 159
876. *OGJ,* v. 35, no. 27, p. 11
718. *OGJ,* v. 35, no. 33, p. 316
337. *OGJ,* v. 38, no. 50, p. 92
311. *OGJ,* v. 39, no. 49, pp 84-86
520. *OGJ,* v. 39, no. 49, p. 138
524. *OW,* v. 90, no. 7, p. 216
161. *OW,* v. 123, no. 3, pp. 82, 84-85
409. *OW,* v. 123, no. 3, p. 144
434. *PROB.,* pp. 632-633
410. *WO,* v. 130, no. 7, p. 102

Iowa, Jefferson Davis Parish: (Iowa Junction)
6a. *BMIC*
511. *Bull.,* v. 19, no. 1, pp. 19-21; *EGP,* pp. 679-681; *Trans.,* SEG, v. 5, pp. 19-21
847. *Bull.,* v. 20, no. 6, p. 731; *GC,* p. 115
431. *Bull.,* v. 21, no. 2, p. 207
221. *Bull.,* v. 32, no. 6, p. 1037
222. *Bull.,* v. 33, no. 6, p. 987
223. *Bull.,* v. 34, no. 6, p. 1196
224. *Bull.,* v. 35, no. 6, pp. 1342-1343
225. *Bull.,* v. 36, no. 6, p. 1217
652. *Bull.,* v. 37, no. 2, p. 404
407. *Bull.,* v. 37, no. 2, pp. 419, 430
227. *Bull.,* v. 38, no. 6, p. 1226
650. *Bull.,* v. 43, no. 11, pp. 2592, 2603, 2614-2617
555a. *Bull.,* v. 50, no. 3, p. 470
1. *Bull. 36,* La. Geol. Svy., pp. 49-50, 52, 55, 172-175
403. *EGP,* p. 343; *Trans.,* SEG, v. 3, p. 15
427. *GAGC,* p, 270
717. *GAS,* pp. 685, 695, 732
363. *Geophysics,* v. 1, no. 1, Fig. 3 (between pp. 142-143), Fig. 8 (between pp. 146-147), p. 147
475. *Geophysics,* v. 1, no. 3, p. 309
361. *Geophysics,* v. 3, no. 1, pp. 30, 33-34
547. *Geophysics,* v. 3, no. 2, pp. 100-101
469. *Geophysics,* v. 8, no. 4, pp. 348-355; *GCH,* v. 1, pp. 153-160
647. *Lockwood's* (Louisiana 1940), pp. 154-157
645. *NOGS,* v. 1, pp. 42-43; v. 1, first rev., pp. 30-31
722. *OFNA,* p. 135
515. *OGJ,* v. 28, no. 49, p. 118
790. *OGJ,* v. 30, no. 37, p. 71
473. *OGJ,* v. 31, no. 8, p. 16

Iowa, Jefferson Davis Parish: (Iowa Junction) (cont.)

393. *OGJ*, v. 32, no. 7, p. 8
395. *OGJ*, v. 32, no. 13, p. 12
484. *OGJ*, v. 32, no. 20, p. 10
603. *OGJ*, v. 32, no. 26, pp. 13-14
79. *OGJ*, v. 36, no. 34, p. 48
605. *OGJ*, v. 39, no. 27, pp. 82, 85
520. *OGJ*, v. 39, no. 49, p. 140
527. *OW*, v. 69, no. 1, p. 16
604. *OW*, v. 71, no. 13, pp. 12-13, 16
376. *OW*, v. 82, no. 10, p. 14
524. *OW*, v. 90, no. 7, p. 205
161. *OW*, v. 123, no. 3, pp. 82, 84-85
409. *OW*, v. 123, no. 3, p. 138
449. *Pet. Geol.*, p. 436
434. *PROB.*, pp. 632-633
851. *Proc.*, Fourth World Pet. Cong., sec. 1, p. 95
8. *Trans.*, GCAGS, v. 7, p. 234
410. *WO*, v. 130, no. 7, p. 96

Iowa Junction, Jefferson Davis Parish: (see Iowa)

Jeanerette, St. Mary Parish:
6a. *BMIC*
847. *Bull.*, v. 20, no. 6, p. 731; *GC*, p. 116
219. *Bull.*, v. 30, no. 6, pp. 1004, 1006
800. *Bull.*, v. 30, no. 8, p. 1307
236. *Bull.*, v. 47, no. 6, p. 1095
427. *GAGC*, p. 270
647. *Lockwood's* (Louisiana 1940), pp. 158-159
645. *NOGS*, v. 1, pp. 92-93; v. 1, first rev., pp. 80-81
79. *OGJ*, v. 36, no. 34, pp. 48-50
524. *OW*, v. 90, no. 7, p. 224
161. *OW*, v. 123, no. 3, pp. 82, 84-85
409. *OW*, v. 123, no. 3, p. 156
410. *WO*, v. 130, no. 7, p. 116

Jefferson Island, Iberia Parish: (Lake Peigneur)
6a. *BMIC*
883. *Bull.*, v. 9, no. 3, pp. 565, 567, 569; *SD*, pp. 747, 749, 751
380. *Bull.*, v. 9, no. 4, pp. 758-761; *SD*, pp. 358-361
723. *Bull.*, v. 9, no. 5, pp. 841, 853; *SD*, pp. 11, 23
385. *Bull.*, v. 17, no. 9, p. 1074; *GC*, p. 69
54. *Bull.*, v. 19, no. 5, p. 649; *GC*, p. 1038
614. *Bull.*, v. 19, no. 11, pp. 1602-1644; *GC*, pp. 983-1025
137. *Bull.*, v. 20, no. 2, p. 183; *GC*, p. 1030
847. *Bull.*, v. 20, no. 6, p. 732; *GC*, p. 116
849. *Bull.*, v. 31, no. 7, pp. 1295, 1298, 1299
615. *Bull.*, v. 37, no. 2, pp. 433-443; (abs.) *Trans.*, GCAGS, v. 2, p. 1

Jefferson Island, Iberia Parish: (Lake Peigneur) (cont.)

613. *Bull.*, v. 37, no. 11, pp. 2455-2474
753. *Bull.*, v. 41, no. 8, pp. 1828-1830
231. *Bull.*, v. 42, no. 6, p. 1312
234. *Bull.*, v. 45, no. 6, p. 886
931. *Bull.*, v. 46, no. 8, pp. 1460-1461
932. *Bull.*, v. 46, no. 8, pp. 1454-1455, 1459
554. *Bull.*, v. 47, no. 1, p. 180
555a. *Bull.*, v. 50, no. 3, pp. 448, 458, 470, 472-474
440. *Bull. 1*, La. Geol. Svy., pp. 15, 22-23, 25, 33, 38-39, 41-43, 49-52, 55-58, 60-62, 65-67, 70-71, 75-76, 86, 92-94, 107, 110, 112, 115-116, 118, 120, 162-70, 180-181, 183.
91. *Bull. 6*, La. Geol. Svy., p. 73
942a. *Bull. 4*, SIPES, Figs. 1, 3
427. *GAGC*. pp. 206, 209, 211-212, 217, 221-222, 228, 231, 233, 236, 240, 246, 267, 270
402. *GCH*, v. 1, pp. 266-271
363. *Geophysics*, v. 1, no. 1, Fig. 2 (between pp. 142-143), Fig. 7 (between 146-147), p. 143
647. *Lockwood's* (Louisiana 1940), pp. 160-161, 329
645. *NOGS*, v. 2, p. 34-35
722. *OFNA*, pp. 134, 136
327. *OGJ*, v. 28, no. 45, p. 159
300. *OGJ*, v. 37, no. 12, p. 33
520. *OGJ*, v. 39, no. 49, pp. 64, 130
337. *OGJ*, v. 38, no. 50, p. 95
524. *OW*, v. 90, no. 7, pp. 214, 216
161. *OW*, v. 123, no. 3, p. 85
409. *OW*, v. 123, no. 3, p. 144
449. *Pet. Geol.*, p. 436
434. *PROB.*, pp. 632-633
515a. *SOS*, pp. 105-107, 110-111, 113, 118, 121
314a. *SOS*, p. 390
136. *Trans.*, GCAGS, v. 5, pp. 173-174
701. *Trans.*, GCAGS, v. 10, p. 2
631. *Trans.*, GCAGS, v. 10, pp. 217-218, 236
373. *Trans.*, GCAGS, v. 11, p. 165
410. *WO*, v. 130, no. 7, p. 102

Jennings, Acadia Parish: (Evangeline)
6a. *BMIC*
923. *Bull.*, v. 9, no. 3, p. 611; *SD*, p. 495
601. *Bull.*, v. 10, no. 1, pp. 72-92; *SD*, pp. 398-418
963. *Bull.*, v. 16, no. 6, pp. 609-610
640. *Bull.*, v. 17, no. 6, pp. 634, 642, 646; *GC*, pp. 404, 412, 416
654. *Bull.*, v. 18, no. 4, p. 504; *GC*, p. 5

Lake Barre, Terrebonne Parish:

6a. *BMIC*
902.   *Bull.*, v. 16, no. 12, pp. 1228; *GCH*,
             v. 1, p. 142; *EGP*, p. 388; *Trans.*,
             SEG, v. 3, p. 58
329.   *Bull.*, v. 17, no. 12, pp. 1493-1496, 1509-
             1510; *GC*, pp. 142-145, 158-159,
             OW, v. 71, no. 12, pp. 18-22;
             OGJ, v. 32, no. 22, pp. 18, 22
847.   *Bull.*, v. 20, no. 6, p. 732; *GC*, p. 116
219.   *Bull.*, v. 30, no. 6, p. 1004
231.   *Bull.*, v. 42, no. 6, pp. 1314, 1317
232.   *Bull.*, v. 43, no. 6, pp. 1314, 1317, 1320
235.   *Bull.*, v. 46, no. 6, pp. 929, 934-936
236.   *Bull.*, v. 47, no. 6, pp. 1088, 1094, 1096
158.   *Bull.*, v. 47, no. 12, p. 2014
555a. *Bull.*, v. 50, no. 3, p. 447
360.   *EGP*, p. 262; *Jour.*, Soc. of Pet. Geo-
             physicists, v. 6, no. 1, p. 18
427.   *GAGC*, pp. 222, 270
363.   *Geophysics*, v. 1, no. 1, Fig. 3 (pp. 142-143),
             Fig. 8 (between pp. 146-147)
509.   *Geophysics*, v. 5, no. 3, p. 221; *GCH*,
             v. 1, p. 13
647.   *Lockwood's* (Louisiana 1940), pp. 180-181
645.   *NOGS*, v. 1, pp. 104-105; v. 1, first rev.,
             pp. 92-93
722.   *OFNA*, p. 134
478.   *OGJ*, v. 27, no. 25, p. 35
327.   *OGJ*, v. 28, no. 45, p. 160
515.   *OGJ*, v. 28, no. 49, p. 118
484.   *OGJ*, v. 32, no. 20, p. 10
79.   *OGJ*, v. 36, no. 34, pp. 46, 48, 50
311.   *OGJ*, v. 39, no. 49, p. 84
520.   *OGJ*, v. 39, no. 49, p. 140
637.   *OGJ*, v. 57, no. 48, pp. 126, 128
527.   *OW*, v. 69, no. 1, pp. 16-17
758.   *OW*, v. 69, no. 1, p. 59
334.   *OW*, v. 69, no. 1, pp. 65-66, 68
376.   *OW*, v. 82, no. 10, p. 14
524.   *OW*, v. 90, no. 7, p. 226
161.   *OW*, v. 123, no. 3, p. 85
409.   *OW*, v. 123, no. 3, p. 159
434.   *PROB.*, pp. 632-633
644.   *Trans.*, GCAGS, v. 9, pp. 78, 84
410.   *WO*, v. 130, no. 7, p. 118

Lake Chicot, St. Martin Parish:

6a. *BMIC*
427.   *GAGC*, p. 270
645.   *NOGS*, v. 1, pp. 82-83; v. 1, first rev.,
             pp. 70-71
422.   *OGJ*, v. 54, no. 59, p. 222
161.   *OW*, v. 123, no. 3, p. 85

Lake Chicot, St. Martin Parish: (cont.)

409.   *OW*, v. 123, no. 3, p. 155
8.   *Trans.*, GCAGS, v. 7, p. 235
410.   *WO*, v. 130, no. 7, p. 114

Lake Hermitage, Plaquemines Parish:

6a. *BMIC*
847.   *Bull.*, v. 20, no. 6, p. 732; *GC*, p 116
219.   *Bull.*, v. 30, no. 6, p. 1004
221.   *Bull.*, v. 32, no. 6, p. 1037
407.   *Bull.*, v. 37, no. 2, p. 419
555a. *Bull.*, v. 50, no. 3, p. 446
788.   *Bull. 8*, La. Geol. Svy., pp. 201, 206-207,
             242-256
96.   *Bull. 11*, La. Geol. Svy., pp. 33, 36, 38, 119
648.   *Bull.*, GSA, v. 70, p. 1284
427.   *GAGC*, p. 270
363.   *Geophysics*, v. 1, no. 1, Fig. 3 (between
             pp. 142-143), Fig. 8 (between pp.
             146-147)
647.   *Lockwood's* (Louisiana 1940), pp. 182-183
645.   *NOGS*, v. 1, pp. 60-61; v. 1, first rev.,
             pp. 48-49
327.   *OGJ*, v. 28, no. 45, p. 160
515.   *OGJ*, v. 28, no. 49, p. 118
524.   *OW*, v. 90, no. 7, p. 220
161.   *OW*, v. 123, no. 3, p. 85
409.   *OW*, v. 123, no. 3, p. 149
410.   *WO*, v. 130, no. 7, p. 108

Lake Mongoulis, St. Martin Parish:

6a. *BMIC*
847.   *Bull.*, v. 20, no. 6, p. 732; *GC*, p. 116
324.   *Bull.*, v. 28, no. 9, pp. 1298-1302
222.   *Bull.*, v. 33, no. 6, p. 987
224.   *Bull.*, v. 35, no. 6, p. 1343
227.   *Bull.*, v. 38, no. 6, p. 1229
555a. *Bull.*, v. 50, no. 3, pp. 452, 461-462
427.   *GAGC*, pp. 217, 225, 270
363.   *Geophysics*, v. 1, no. 1, Fig. 3 (between
             pp. 142-143), Fig. 8 (between pp.
             146-147)
647.   *Lockwood's* (Louisiana 1940), pp. 186-187
645.   *NOGS*, v. 2, pp. 68-69
300.   *OGJ*, v. 37, no. 12, p. 34
520.   *OGJ*, v. 39, no. 49, p. 138
879.   *OGJ*, v. 54, no. 53, p. 144
524.   *OW*, v. 90, no. 7, p. 223
161.   *OW*, v. 123, no. 3, p. 85
409.   *OW*, v. 123, no. 3, p. 155
8.   *Trans.*, GCAGS, v. 7, p. 235
373.   *Trans.*, GCAGS, v. 11, p. 143
410.   *WO*, v. 130, no. 7, p 114

Lake Peigneur, Iberia Parish: (see Jefferson Island)

Lake Pelto, Terrebonne Parish:
  6a. *BMIC*
847. *Bull.*, v. 20, no. 6, p. 732; *GC*, p 116
223. *Bull.*, v. 34, no. 6, p. 1196
224. *Bull.*, v. 35, no. 6, pp. 1343-1344
227. *Bull.*, v. 38, no. 6, p. 1230
234. *Bull.*, v. 45, no. 6, p. 886
942a. *Bull. 4*, SIPES, Figs. 1, 3
427. *GAGC*, pp. 227, 270
363. *Geophysics*, v. 1, no. 1, Fig. 3 (between
       pp. 142-143), Fig. 8 (between pp.
       146-147)
626. *JPT*, v. 12, no. 10, pp. 15-19
647. *Lockwood's* (Louisiana 1940), pp. 188-189
645. *NOGS*, v. 2, pp. 80-81
327. *OGJ*, v. 28, no. 45, p. 160
515. *OGJ*, v. 28, no. 49, p. 118
484. *OGJ*, v. 32, no. 20, p. 10
637. *OGJ*, v. 57, no. 48, pp. 126, 128
334. *OW*, v. 69, no. 1, p. 68
524. *OW*, v. 90, no. 7, p. 226
161. *OW*, v.123, no. 3, p. 85
409. *OW*, v. 123, no. 3, p. 159
146. *PROB.*, p. 115
434. *PROB.*, pp. 632-633
644. *Trans.*, GCAGS, v. 9, pp. 78, 84
410. *WO*, v. 130, no. 7, p. 118

Lake Salvador, St. Charles Parish:
  6a. *BMIC*
212. *Bull.*, v. 25, no. 6, p. 1013
227. *Bull.*, v. 38, no. 6, p. 1229
231. *Bull.*, v. 42, no. 6, p. 1312
 50. *Geophysics*, v. 18, no. 2, p. 372
647. *Lockwood's* (Louisiana 1940), pp. 190-191
645. *NOGS*, v. 2, pp. 62-63
478. *OGJ*, v. 27, no. 25, p. 35
327. *OGJ*, v. 28, no. 45, p. 160
515. *OGJ*, v. 28, no. 49, p. 118
524. *OW*, v. 90, no. 7, p. 222
161. *OW*, v. 123, no. 3, pp. 82, 84-85
409. *OW*, v. 123, no. 3, p. 152
616. *Trans.*, GCAGS, v. 8, pp. 105-107, 109-
       110, 115
410. *WO*, v. 130, no. 7, p. 112

Lake Washington, Plaquemines Parish:
 (Grand Ecaille, Myrtle Grove)
  6a. *BMIC*
847. *Bull.*, v. 20, no. 6, p. 732; *GC*, p. 116
223. *Bull.*, v. 34, no. 6, p. 1196
224. *Bull.*, v. 35, no. 6, pp. 1342-1343
225. *Bull.*, v. 36, no. 6, p. 1217
226. *Bull.*, v. 37, no. 6, p. 1447
227. *Bull.*, v. 38, no. 6, p. 1228

Lake Washington, Plaquemines Parish: (Grand Ecaille, Myrtle Grove) (cont.)
228. *Bull.*, v. 39, no. 6, p. 994
229. *Bull.*, v. 40, no. 6, p. 1258
230. *Bull.*, v. 41, no. 6, p. 1195
753. *Bull.*, v. 41, no. 8, p. 1833
231. *Bull.*, v. 42, no. 6, p. 1313
232. *Bull.*, v. 43, no. 6, p. 1316
650. *Bull.*, v. 43, no. 11, pp. 2592, 2600, 2603,
       2617-2621
233. *Bull.*, v. 44, no. 6, p. 830
235. *Bull.*, v. 46, no. 6, p. 934
236. *Bull.*, v. 47, no. 6, p. 1094
555a. *Bull.*, v. 50, no. 3, pp. 446, 472-474
645. *Bull.*, GSA, v. 70, pp. 1285, 1287-1289
788. *Bull. 8*, La. Geol. Svy., pp. 201, 206-242,
       261
 96. *Bull. 11*, La. Geol. Svy., pp. 15, 22, 33,
       38-40, 49-55, 57, 59-62, 65-67, 70-
       71, 75-76, 86, 107, 112, 115-116,
       118, 120, 128, 134, 159, 171-181
942a. *Bull. 4*, SIPES, Figs. 1, 3
115. *Chron. Hist.*, pp. 169-170
427. *GAGC*, pp. 206, 217, 220, 222, 228, 240,
       247, 260, 270
717. *GAS*, pp. 685, 694, 712
402. *GCH*, v. 1, pp. 263-266, 271
363. *Geophysics*, v. 1, no. 1, Fig. 3 (between
       pp. 142-143), Fig. 8 (between pp.
       146-147)
512. *Geophysics*, v. 22, no. 3, p. 633
647. *Lockwood's* (Louisiana 1940), pp. 192-
       193, 330
645. *NOGS*, v. 1, pp. 62-63; v. 1, first rev.,
       pp. 50-51
722. *OFNA*, pp. 135, 138
327. *OGJ*, v. 28, no. 45, p. 160
515. *OGJ*, v. 28, no. 49, p. 118
790. *OGJ*, v. 30, no. 37, p. 71
484. *OGJ*, v. 32, no. 20, p. 10
520. *OGJ*, v. 39, no. 49, p. 138
879. *OGJ*, v. 54, no. 53, p. 144
377. *OGJ*, v. 54, no. 59, p. 214
422. *OGJ*, v. 54, no. 59, p. 222
334. *OW*, v. 69, no. 1, p. 65
524. *OW*, v. 90, no. 7, p. 220
161. *OW*, v. 123, no. 3, p. 85
409. *OW* , v. 123, no. 3, p. 149
364. *Paper 5*, Fifth World Pet. Cong., sec. 1,
       p. 2; *Oil*, v. 19, no. 8, p. 36
146. *PROB.*, p. 115
434. *PROB.*, pp. 632-633
851. *Proc.*, Fourth World Pet. Cong., sec. 1,
       p. 95

Lake Washington, Plaquemines Parish: (Grand Ecaille, Myrtle Grove) (cont.)
497. *Tech. Pub.* 533, AIME, pp. 3-18
644. *Trans.,* GCAGS, v. 9, pp. 78, 84
631. *Trans.,* GCAGS, v. 10, p. 218
410. *WO,* v. 130, no. 7, p. 108
335. *WO,* v. 142, no. 7, p. 158

La Rose, Lafourche Parish: (see Valentine)

Leeville, Lafourche Parish:
6a. *BMIC*
847. *Bull.,* v. 20, no. 6, p. 732; *GC,* p. 116
219. *Bull.,* v. 30, no. 6, p. 1004
221. *Bull.,* v. 32, no. 6, p. 1037
222. *Bull.,* v. 33, no. 6, p. 984
223. *Bull.,* v. 34, no. 6, p. 1196
225. *Bull.,* v. 36, no. 6, pp. 1217-1218
227. *Bull.,* v. 38, no. 6, p. 1228
236. *Bull.,* v. 47, no. 6, p. 1093
427. *GAGC.* pp. 222, 270
717. *GAS,* pp. 685, 695
363. *Geophysics,* v. 1, no. 1, Fig. 3 (between pp. 142-143), Fig. 8 (between pp. 146-147)
901. *Geophysics,* v. 5, no. 3, p. 221; *GCH,* v. 1, p. 13
647. *Lockwood's* (Louisiana 1940), pp. 194-195
645. *NOGS,* v. 2, pp. 54-55
722. *OFNA,* p. 135
327. *OGJ,* v. 28, no. 45, p. 160
515. *OGJ,* v. 28, no. 49, p. 118
790. *OGJ,* v. 30, no. 37, pp. 70-71
484. *OGJ,* v. 32, no. 20, p. 10
627. *OGJ,* v. 32, no. 50, pp. 13, 36
311. *OGJ,* v. 39, no. 49, p. 84
520. *OGJ,* v. 39, no. 49, p. 140
637. *OGJ,* v. 57, no. 48, pp. 126, 128
334. *OW,* v. 69, no. 1, p. 68
376. *OW,* v. 82, no. 10, p. 14
524. *OW,* v. 90, no. 7, p. 218
161. *OW,* v. 123, no. 3, pp. 82, 84-85
409. *OW* v. 123, no. 3, p. 148
434. *PROB.,* pp. 632-633
644. *Trans.,* GCAGS, v. 9, pp. 78, 84

Little Bayou, Iberia Parish: (see Iberia)

Lockport, Calcasieu Parish:
6a. *BMIC*
640. *Bull.,* v. 1 no. 6, p. 642; *GC,* p. 412
847. *Bull.,* v. 20, no. 6, p. 732; *GC,* p. 116
219. *Bull.,* v. 30, no. 6, p. 1004
652. *Bull.,* v. 37, no. 2, p. 404
403. *EGP,* p. 343; *Trans.,* SEG, v. 3, p. 15
427. *GAGC,* p. 270

Lockport, Calcasieu Parish: (cont.)
717. *GAS,* pp. 685, 695, 732-733
363. *Geophysics,* v. 1, no. 1, Fig. 2 (between pp. 142-143), Fig. 7 (between pp. 146-147)
89. *Geophysics,* v. 10, no. 1, p. 3; *GCH,* v. 1, p. 163
647. *Lockwood's* (Louisiana 1940), pp. 198-199
645. *NOGS,* v. 1, pp. 22-23, v. 1, first rev., pp. 10-11
722. *OFNA,* pp. 134-135
532. *OGJ,* v. 25, no. 40, p. 152
478. *OGJ,* v. 27, no. 25, p. 88
515. *OGJ,* v. 28, no. 49, p. 43
790. *OGJ,* v. 30, no. 37, p. 76
79. *OGJ,* v. 36, no. 34, p. 48
520. *OGJ,* v. 39, no. 49, pp. 138, 140
334. *OW,* v. 69, no. 1, p. 16
376. *OW,* v. 82, no. 10, p. 14
524. *OW,* v. 90, no. 7, p. 205
161. *OW,* v. 123, no. 3, p. 85
409. *OW,* v. 123, no. 3, p. 138
146. *PROB.,* p. 115
434. *PROB.,* pp. 632-633
410. *WO,* v. 130, no. 7, p. 96

Lonnie, Winn Parish: (Chester)
6a. *BMIC*
427. *GAGC,* p. 269
634. *Guidebook,* Shreveport Geol. Soc. (1960), p. 58
24. *Guidebook,* Shreveport Geol. Soc. (1960), p. 66

Loureauville, Iberia and St. Martin Parishes: (see Fausse Point)

Milam, Winn Parish:
6a. *BMIC*
634. *Guidebook,* Shreveport Geol. Soc. (1960), p. 58
24. *Guidebook,* Shreveport Geol. Soc. (1960), p. 65

Minden, Webster Parish:
6a. *BMIC*
832. *Bull.,* v. 27, no. 1, p. 60
181. *Bull.,* v. 42, no. 6, p. 1320
182. *Bull.,* v. 43, no. 6, p. 1957
183. *Bull.,* v. 44, no. 6, p. 840
184. *Bull.,* v. 45, no. 6, p. 897
185. *Bull.,* v. 46, no. 6, p. 948
461. *Bull. 29,* La. Geol. Svy., pp. 84, 88, 94, 99, 102, 108, 111, 117-120, 225
427. *GAGC,* p. 269

Minden, Webster Parish: (cont.)

602. *Guidebook,* Shreveport Geol. Soc. (1960),
        p. 5, 13-16
689. *Guidebook,* Shreveport Geol. Soc. (1960),
        pp. 17-26
688. *Guidebook,* Shreveport Geol. Soc. (1960),
        pp. 27-28
634. *Guidebook,* Shreveport Geol. Soc. (1960),
        p. 57
 24. *Guidebook,* Shreveport Geol. Soc. (1960),
        p. 63
421. *Guidebook,* Shreveport Geol. Soc. (1960),
        pp. 93-94, Plate A-34 +, p. 95
818. *OGJ,* v. 55, no. 22, p. 167
 86. *OGJ,* v. 56, no. 30, p. 263
364. *Paper 5,* Fifth World Pet. Cong., sec.
        1, pp. 3, 9; *Oil,* v. 19, no. 8, pp.
        34, 39
631. *Trans.,* GCAGS, v. 10, pp. 217-218

**Myrtle Grove, Plaquemines Parish: (see Lake
Washington)**

Napoleonville, Assumption Parish:
  6a. *BMIC*
847. *Bull.,* v. 20, no. 6, p. 732; *GC,* p. 116
219. *Bull.,* v. 30, no. 6, p. 1004
222. *Bull.,* v. 33, no. 6, p. 988
225. *Bull.,* v. 36, no. 6, p. 1217
227. *Bull.,* v. 38, no. 6, p. 1226
229. *Bull.,* v. 40, no. 6, p. 1256
 96. *Bull. 11,* La. Geol. Svy., p. 119
427. *GAGC,* p. 270
363. *Geophysics,* v. 1, no. 1, Fig. 3 (between pp.
        142-143), Fig. 8 (between pp. 146-
        147)
647. *Lockwood's* (Louisiana 1940), pp. 202-203
645. *NOGS,* v. 1, pp. 18-19; v. 1, first rev.,
        pp. 6-7
532. *OGJ,* v. 25, no. 40, pp. 151-152
478. *OGJ,* v. 27, no. 25, pp. 35, 91
327. *OGJ,* v. 28, no. 45, p. 159
515. *OGJ,* v. 28, no. 49, p. 118
484. *OGJ,* v. 32, no. 20, p. 10
300. *OGJ,* v. 37, no. 12, p. 34
337. *OGJ,* v. 38, no. 50, pp. 95, 102
524. *OW,* v. 90, no. 7, p. 204
161. *OW,* v. 123, no. 3, p. 85
409. *OW,* v. 123, no. 3, p. 137
434. *PROB.,* pp. 632-633
851. *Proc.,* Fourth World Pet. Cong., sec. 1,
        p. 95
  8. *Trans.,* GCAGS, v. 7, p. 234
787. *Trans.,* GCAGS, v. 9, p. 91
410. *WO,* v. 130, no. 7, p. 94

Newellton, Tensas Parish:
  6a. *BMIC*
599. *Bull.,* v. 24, no. 3, pp. 484-485
242. *Bull.,* v. 24, no. 6, p. 1028
427. *GAGC,* p. 269
634. *Guidebook,* Shreveport Geol. Soc. (1960),
        p. 59
 24. *Guidebook,* Shreveport Geol. Soc. (1960),
        pp. 68-69

New Iberia, Iberia Parish: (see Iberia)

North Crowley, Acadia Parish: (Bayou Wikoff)
  6a. *BMIC*
645. *NOGS,* v. 1, first rev., p. VI, index map, p. 1

**North Lake Salvador, St. Charles Parish: (see
Bayou Couba)**

North Mallard Bay, Cameron Parish:
  6a. *BMIC*
645. *NOGS,* v. 1, first rev., p. VI, index map, p. 1

North Starks, Calcasieu Parish:
  6a. *BMIC*
227. *Bull.,* v. 38, no. 6, p. 1226
645. *NOGS,* v. 2, pp. 24-25
  8. *Trans.,* GCAGS, v. 7, p. 234
631. *Trans.,* GCAGS, v. 10, p. 235

North Tallulah, Madison Parish: (Tallulah)
  6a. *BMIC*
634. *Guidebook,* Shreveport Geol. Soc. (1960),
        p. 59
 24. *Guidebook,* Shreveport Geol. Soc. (1960),
        p. 68

Packton, Winn Parish:
  6a. *BMIC*
172. *Bull.,* v. 32, no. 6, p. 1045
427. *GAGC,* p. 269
 23. *Geophysics,* v. 16, no. 3, p. 405
634. *Guidebook,* Shreveport Geol. Soc. (1960),
        p. 58
 24. *Guidebook,* Shreveport Geol. Soc. (1960),
        p. 65

Paradis, St. Charles Parish:
  6a. *BMIC*
211. *Bull.,* v. 24, no. 6, p. 1088
214. *Bull.,* v. 27, no. 6, p. 737
225. *Bull.,* v. 36, no. 6, p. 1216
427. *GAGC,* pp. 218, 257, 270
647. *Lockwood's* (Louisiana 1940), pp. 216-217

Potash, Plaquemines Parish: (Cockrell)
  6a. *BMIC*
  211. *Bull.*, v. 24, no. 6, p. 1090
  219. *Bull.*, v. 30, no. 6, p. 1005
  222. *Bull.*, v. 33, no. 6, p. 984
  225. *Bull.*, v. 36, no. 6, p. 1217
  227. *Bull.*, v. 38, no. 6, p. 1228
  236. *Bull.*, v. 47, no. 6, p. 1094
  788. *Bull. 8,* La. Geol. Svy., pp. 201, 276-277
   96. *Bull. 11,* La. Geol. Svy., pp. 115, 119
  648. *Bull.*, GSA, v. 70, p. 1284
  427. *GAGC,* p. 270
  647. *Lockwood's* (Louisiana 1940), pp. 226-227
  645. *NOGS,* v. 2, pp. 60-61
  515. *OGJ,* v. 28, no. 49, p. 118
  300. *OGJ,* v. 37, no. 12, p. 34
  304. *OGJ,* v. 43, no. 31, pp. 66-68
  524. *OW,* v. 90, no. 7, p. 220
  161. *OW,* v. 123, no. 3, p. 85
  409. *OW,* v. 123, no. 3, p. 149
  434. *PROB.,* pp. 632-633
  410. *WO,* v. 130, no. 7, p. 110

Price's, Winn Parish:
  6a. *BMIC*
  601. *Bull.*, v. 10, no. 1, pp. 14, 55-56; *SD,* pp. 222, 263-264
  598. *Bull.*, v. 10, no. 3, pp. 222-224, 265-271; *SD,* pp. 274-276, 317-323
   89. *Bull. 15,* La. Geol. Svy., pp. 190-191, 224, 232, 238, 252-260, 288, 295
  427. *GAGC,* p. 269
  634. *Guidebook,* Shreveport Geol. Soc. (1960), p. 57
  434. *PROB.,* pp. 632-633

Prothro, Bienville Parish:
  6a. *BMIC*
  796. *Bull.*, v. 9, no. 5, pp. 904-906
  601. *Bull.*, v. 10, no. 1, p. 14; *SD,* p. 222
  598. *Bull.*, v. 10, no. 3, pp. 224, 245-252; *SD,* pp. 276, 297-304
  640. *Bull.*, v. 17, no. 6, p. 614; *GC,* p. 384
  142. *Bull. 32,* La. Geol. Svy.
  427. *GAGC,* p. 269
  634. *Guidebook,* Shreveport Geol. Soc. (1960), p. 57
  421. *Guidebook,* Shreveport Geol. Soc. (1960), Plate A-107 +, Plate A-110, p. 103
  434. *PROB.,* pp. 632-633

Rabbit Island, Iberia Parish:
  6a. *BMIC*
  223. *Bull.*, v. 34, no. 6, p. 1196

Rabbit Island, Iberia Parish: (cont.)
  427. *GAGC,* p. 270
  645. *NOGS,* v. 2, pp. 36-37
  161. *OW,* v. 123, no. 3, p. 85

Raceland, Lafourche Parish:
  6a. *BMIC*
  210. *Bull.*, v. 23, no. 6, p. 885
  222. *Bull.*, v. 33, no. 6, p. 987
  231. *Bull.*, v. 42, no. 6, p. 1312
  361. *Geophysics,* v. 3, no. 1, p. 27
  547. *Geophysics,* v. 3, no. 2, p. 114
  427. *GAGC,* p. 270
  647. *Lockwood's* (Louisiana 1940), pp. 230-231
  645. *NOGS,* v. 1, pp. 54-55; v. 1, first rev., pp. 42-43
  524. *OW,* v. 90, no. 7, pp. 218, 220
  161. *OW,* v. 123, no. 3, p. 85
  409. *OW,* v. 123, no. 3, pp. 148-149
  373. *Trans.,* GCAGS, v. 11, pp. 147, 157
  410. *WO,* v. 130, no. 7, p. 108

Rayburn's, Bienville Parish:
  6a. *BMIC*
  601. *Bull.*, v. 10, no. 1, pp. 4, 14; *SD,* pp. 212, 222
  640. *Bull.*, v. 10, no. 3, pp. 222-224, 229, 260-265; *SD,* pp. 274-276, 281, 312-317
  141. *Bull. 32,* La. Geol. Svy.
  427. *GAGC,* p. 269
  634. *Guidebook,* Shreveport Geol. Soc. (1960), p. 57
   24. *Guidebook,* Shreveport Geol. Soc. (1960), p. 64
  421. *Guidebook,* Shreveport Geol. Soc. (1960), Plate A-93 p. 101
  885. *OW* (Aug. 7, 1931), p. 17
  434. *PROB.,* pp. 632-633

Roanoke, Jefferson Davis Parish:
  6a. *BMIC*
  519. *Bull.*, v. 17, no. 12, p. 1449; *GC,* p. 195
  511. *Bull.*, v. 19, no. 1, pp. 19, 21; *EGP,* pp. 679, 681; *Trans.,* SEG, v. 5, pp. 19, 21
  847. *Bull.*, v. 20, no. 6, pp. 732-733; *GC,* p. 116
  324. *Bull.*, v. 28, no. 9, pp. 1289-1292
  652. *Bull.*, v. 37, no. 2, p. 405
  407. *Bull.*, v. 37, no. 2, p. 419
    1. *Bull. 36,* La. Geol. Svy., pp. 49-50, 52, 190-192
  360. *EGP,* p. 260; *Jour.,* Soc. of Pet. Geophysicists, v. 6, no. 1, p. 16
  403. *EGP,* p. 343; *Trans.,* SEG, v. 3, p. 15

Roanoke, Jefferson Davis Parish: (cont.)

427. *GAGC,* p. 270
717. *GAS,* pp. 685, 695
363. *Geophysics,* v. 1, no. 1, Fig. 3 (between
        pp. 142-143), Fig. 8 (between pp.
        146-147)
510. *GCH,* v. 1, p. 182
647. *Lockwood's* (Louisiana 1940), pp. 232-
        233
645. *NOGS,* v. 1, pp. 44-45; v. 1, first rev.,
        pp. 32-33
722. *OFNA,* p. 135
834. *Oil Forum,* Special Oil Finders' Issue
        (April, 1955), p. 130
327. *OGJ,* v. 28, no. 45, p. 159
515. *OGJ,* v. 28, no. 49, p. 118
474. *OGJ,* v. 28, no. 50, p. 143
473. *OGJ,* v. 31, no. 8, p. 16
484. *OGJ,* v. 32, no. 20, p. 10
524. *OW,* v. 90, no. 7, p. 217
161. *OW,* v. 123, no. 3, p. 85
409. *OW,* v. 123, no. 3, p. 148
146. *PROB.,* p. 115
373. *Trans.,* GCAGS, v. 11, p. 154
410. *WO,* v. 130, no. 7, p. 106

Rose, Plaquemines Parish: (see Venice)

Sikes, Winn Parish:
    6a. *BMIC*

St. Gabriel, Iberville Parish:
    6a. *BMIC*
213. *Bull.,* v. 26, no. 6, p. 989
324. *Bull.,* v. 28, no. 9, pp. 1277-1280, 1302
222. *Bull.,* v. 33, no. 6, p. 987
407. *Bull.,* v. 37, no. 2, p. 419
427. *GAGC,* p. 270
645. *NOGS,* v. 1, pp. 36-37; v. 1, first rev.,
        pp. 24-25
161. *OW,* v. 123, no. 3, p. 85

St. Martinville, St. Martin Parish:
    6a. *BMIC*
847. *Bull.,* v. 20, no. 6, p. 732; *GC,* p. 116
225. *Bull.,* v. 36, no. 6, p. 1217
236. *Bull.,* v. 47, no. 6, p. 1094
363. *Geophysics,* v. 1, no. 1, Fig. 3 (between
        pp. 142-143), Fig. 8 (between pp.
        146-147)
361. *Geophysics,* v. 3, no. 1, p. 32
547. *Geophysics,* v. 3, no. 2, pp. 100-101
647. *Lockwood's* (Louisiana 1940), pp. 234-235
645. *NOGS,* v. 2, no. 1, pp. 70-71

St. Martinville, St. Martin Parish: (cont.)

327. *OGJ,* v. 28, no. 45, p. 159
813. *OGJ,* v. 34, no. 27, p. 13
520. *OGJ,* v. 39, no. 49, p. 138
524. *OW,* v. 90, no. 7, p. 223
161. *OW,* v. 123, no. 3, p. 85
409. *OW,* v. 123, no. 3, p. 155
  8. *Trans.,* GCAGS, v. 7, p. 235
410. *WO,* v. 130, no. 7, p. 114
649. *WO,* v. 142, no. 7, p. 218

Scully, Lafourche Parish: (see Clovelly)

Section 28, St. Martin Parish: (Hager-Martin)
    6a. *BMIC*
549. *Bull.,* v. 9, no. 1, p. 37; *SD,* p. 776
899. *Bull.,* v. 9, no. 9, pp. 1290-1293; *SD,* pp.
        352-355
847. *Bull.,* v. 20, no. 6, p. 732; *GC,* p. 116
212. *Bull.,* v. 25, no. 6, p. 1013
218. *Bull.,* v. 29, no. 6, p. 798
221. *Bull.,* v. 32, no. 6, p. 1037
222. *Bull.,* v. 33, no. 6, p. 988
223. *Bull.,* v. 34, no. 6, p. 1196
234. *Bull.,* v. 45, no. 6, p. 887
555a. *Bull.,* v. 50, no. 3, pp. 449, 461-462
427. *GAGC,* pp. 217, 225, 270
363. *Geophysics,* v. 1, no. 1, Fig. 2 (between
        pp. 142-143); Fig. 7 (between pp.
        146-147)
431. *Geophysics,* v. 2, no. 1, p. 66
647. *Lockwood's* (Louisiana 1940), pp. 236-237
645. *NOGS,* v. 2, pp. 72-73
300. *OGJ,* v. 37, no. 12, p. 34
337. *OGJ,* v. 38, no. 50, pp. 95, 102
520. *OGJ,* v. 39, no. 49, p. 138
524. *OW,* v. 90, no. 7, p. 223
161. *OW,* v. 123, no. 3, p. 85
409. *OW,* v. 123, no. 3, p. 155
434. *PROB.,* pp. 632-633
  8. *Trans.,* GCAGS, v. 7, p. 235
410. *WO,* v. 130, no. 7, p. 114

Ship Shoal Area Blocks: (see Offshore)

Sikes, Winn Parish:
    6a. *BMIC*
177. *Bull.,* v. 37, no. 6, p. 1454
 96. *Bull. 11,* La. Geol. Svy., pp. 34, 38
 88. *Bull. 15,* La. Geol. Svy., pp. 58-59, 61,
        244, 252, 260-268, 277, 293, 297, 303
427. *GAGC,* p. 269
634. *Guidebook,* Shreveport Geol. Soc. (1960),
        p. 58

Sikes, Winn Parish: (cont.)
   24.   *Guidebook,* Shreveport Geol. Soc. (1960),
            p. 65
  434.   *PROB.,* pp. 632-633

Singer, Madison Parish:
   6a.   *BMIC*
  599.   *Bull.,* v. 24, no. 3, pp. 483-485
  427.   *GAGC,* p. 269
  634.   *Guidebook,* Shreveport Geol. Soc. (1960),
            p. 59
   24.   *Guidebook,* Shreveport Geol. Soc. (1960),
            p. 68

Snake Bayou, Tensas Parish: (Killens Ferry)
   6a.   *BMIC*

Somerset, Tensas Parish: (see Ashwood)

Sorrento, Ascension Parish:
   6a.   *BMIC*
  640.   *Bull.,* v. 17, no. 6, p. 642; *GC,* p. 412
  847.   *Bull.,* v. 20, no. 6, p. 732; *GC,* p. 116
  227.   *Bull.,* v. 38, no. 6, p. 1226
   96.   *Bull. 11,* La. Geol. Svy., pp. 49, 55, 111,
            115, 119
   27.   *Bull. 13,* La. Geol. Svy., pp. 1-2, 46-47,
            81-82, 88, 114-135, 209-211
  427.   *GAGC,* pp. 238, 270
  363.   *Geophysics,* v. 1, no. 1, Fig. 3 (between
            pp. 142-143), Fig. 8 (between pp.
            146-147)
  647.   *Lockwood's* (Louisiana 1940), pp. 238-239
  645.   *NOGS,* v. 1, pp. 16-17; v. 1, first rev.,
            pp. 4-5
  722.   *OFNA,* p. 138
  905.   *OGJ,* v. 26, no. 43, pp. 33, 86
  904.   *OGJ,* v. 26, no. 44, pp. 34, 92
  478.   *OGJ,* v. 27, no. 25, pp. 35, 88, 91
  515.   *OGJ,* v. 28, no. 49, p. 118
  790.   *OGJ,* v. 30, no. 37, p. 76
  484.   *OGJ,* v. 32, no. 20, p. 10
  520.   *OGJ,* v. 39, no. 49, p. 138
  524.   *OW,* v. 90, no. 7, pp. 202, 204
  370.   *OW,* v. 100, no. 10, p. 20
  161.   *OW,* v. 123, no. 3, p. 85
  409.   *OW,* v. 123, no. 3, p. 137
  434.   *PROB.,* pp. 632-633
  410.   *WO,* v. 130, no. 7, p. 94

South Coleman, Madison Parish: (see Coleman)

South Crowley, Acadia Parish: (see Crowley)

South Marsh Island Area Blocks: (see Offshore)

South Pass Area Block: (see Offshore)

South Pelto Area Block: (see Offshore)

South Section 28, St. Martin Parish:
   6a.   *BMIC*
  645.   *NOGS,* v. 2, pp. 74-75.
  524.   *OW,* v. 90, no. 7, p. 223

South Tallulah, Madison Parish:
   6a.   *BMIC*
  427.   *GAGC,* p. 269
  634.   *Guidebook,* Shreveport Geol. Soc. (1960),
            p. 59
   24.   *Guidebook,* Shreveport Geol. Soc. (1960),
            p. 68

South Tigre Lagoon, Iberia Parish:
   6a.   *BMIC*
  427.   *GAGC,* pp. 222, 270
  645.   *NOGS,* v. 1, pp. 28-29; v. 1, first rev.,
            pp. 16-17.

South Timbalier Area Blocks: (see Offshore)

Spanish Pass, Plaquemines Parish: (see Venice)

Starks, Calcasieu Parish:
   6a.   *BMIC*
  640.   *Bull.,* v. 17, no. 6, pp. 634, 642; *GC,* pp.
            404, 412
  655.   *Bull.,* v. 18, no. 2, p. 222; *GC,* p. 129
  847.   *Bull.,* v. 20, no. 6, p. 732; *GC,* p. 116
  570.   *Bull.,* v. 23, no. 12, pp. 1835-1836
  218.   *Bull.,* v. 29, no. 6, p. 798
  775.   *Bull.,* v. 33, no. 7, p. 1253
  753.   *Bull.,* v. 41, no. 8, p. 1844
   96.   *Bull. 11,* La. Geol. Svy, pp. 115, 119
  942a. *Bull. 4,* SIPES, Figs. 1, 3
  360.   *EGP,* pp. 259, 262; *Jour.,* Soc. of Pet.
            Geophysicists, v. 6, no. 1, pp. 15, 18
  427.   *GAGC,* p. 270
  717.   *GAS,* pp. 685, 694, 711
  363.   *Geophysics,* v. 1, no. 1, Fig. 3 (between
            pp. 142-143), Fig. 8 (between pp.
            146-147)
  361.   *Geophysics,* v. 3, no. 1, p. 32
  637.   *Lockwood's* (Louisiana 1940), pp. 250-251
  645.   *NOGS,* v. 2, pp. 6-7
  722.   *OFNA,* pp. 135-138
  927.   *OGJ,* v. 26, no. 19, pp. 184-185
  478.   *OGJ,* v. 27, no. 25, pp. 35, 91
  327.   *OGJ,* v. 28, no. 45, p. 42
  515.   *OGJ,* v. 28, no. 49, p. 118
  484.   *OGJ,* v. 32, no. 20, p. 10

Timbalier Bay, Lafourche Parish:
6a. *BMIC*
210. *Bull.,* v. 23, no. 6, p. 885
225. *Bull.,* v. 36, no. 6, pp. 1217-1218
227. *Bull.,* v. 38, no. 6, p. 1228
229. *Bull.,* v. 40, no. 6, p. 1257
230. *Bull.,* v. 41, no. 6, p. 1194
231. *Bull.,* v. 42, no. 6, p. 1312
232. *Bull.,* v. 43, no. 6, pp. 1316, 1320
650. *Bull.,* v. 43, no. 11, pp. 2601-2602
233. *Bull.,* v. 44, no. 6, p. 830
555a. *Bull.,* v. 50, no. 3, pp. 441, 444
96. *Bull. 11,* La. Geol. Svy., p. 110
115. *Chron. Hist.,* p. 197
427. *GAGC,* pp. 222-223, 236, 270
957. *JPT,* v. 15, no. 2, pp. 127-132
647. *Lockwood's* (Louisiana 1940), pp. 260-261
645. *NOGS,* v. 2, pp. 56-57
478. *OGJ,* v. 27, no. 25, p. 35
637. *OGJ,* v. 57, no. 48, pp. 126, 128
524. *OW,* v. 90, no. 7, p. 220
161. *OW,* v. 123, no. 3, p. 85
409. *OW,* v. 123, no. 3, p. 149
434. *PROB.,* pp. 632-633
644. *Trans.,* GCAGS, v. 9, pp. 78, 84
383. *Trans.,* GCAGS, v. 12, p. 302 (abs.)
410. *WO,* 130, no. 7, p. 108

Vacherie, Bienville and Webster Parishes:
6a. *BMIC*
601. *Bull.,* v. 10, no. 1, pp. 14, 56; *SD,* pp. 222, 264
598. *Bull.,* v. 10, no. 3, pp. 217-218, 222-224, 238-245; *SD,* pp. 269-270, 274-276, 290-297
640. *Bull.,* v. 17, no. 6, p. 614; *GC,* p. 384
177. *Bull.,* v. 37, no. 6, p. 1454
185. *Bull.,* v. 46, no. 6, p. 950
96. *Bull. 11,* La. Geol. Svy., p. 57
461. *Bull. 29,* La. Geol. Svy., pp. 56, 71, 73, 76, 78, 80, 108, 110-111, 121-127, 225
427. *GAGC,* p. 269
634. *Guidebook,* Shreveport Geol. Soc. (1960), p. 57
24. *Guidebook,* Shreveport Geol. Soc. (1960), pp. 63-64
434. *PROB.,* pp. 632-633

Valentine, Lafourche Parish: (LaRose, Harang)
6a. *BMIC*
959. *Bull.,* v. 18, no. 4, p. 543; *GC,* p. 1040
847. *Bull.,* v. 20, no. 6, p. 732; *GC,* p. 116

Valentine, Lafourche Parish: (LaRose, Harang) (cont.)
221. *Bull.,* v. 32, no. 6, p. 1037
222. *Bull.,* v. 33, no. 6, p. 984
775. *Bull.,* v. 33, no. 7, p. 1255 (Fig. 2)
224. *Bull.,* v. 35, no. 6, pp. 1342-1344
225. *Bull.,* v. 36, no. 6, p. 1217
650. *Bull.,* v. 43, no. 11, pp. 2592, 2595-2600
555a. *Bull.,* v. 50, no. 3, p. 470
360. *EGP,* p. 254; *Jour.,* Soc. of Pet. Geophysicists, v. 6, no. 1, p. 10
403. *EGP,* p. 262; *Jour.,* Soc. of Pet. Geophysicists, v. 6, no. 1, p. 18
427. *GAGC,* p. 270
363. *Geophysics,* v. 1, no. 1, Fig. 3 (between pp. 142-143), Fig. 8, (between pp. 146-147)
647. *Lockwood's* (Louisiana 1940), pp. 266-267
645. *NOGS,* v. 1, pp. 56-57; v. 1, first rev., pp. 44-45
524. *OW,* v. 90, no. 7, p. 220
370. *OW,* v. 100, no. 10, p. 20
161. *OW,* v. 123, no. 3, p. 85
409. *OW,* v. 123, no. 3, p. 149
373. *Trans.,* GCAGS, v. 11, pp. 147, 170
776. *Trans.,* GCAGS, v. 12, pp. 232, 234
410. *WO,* v. 130, no. 7, p. 108

Venice, Plaquemines Parish: (Rose, Spanish Pass)
6a. *BMIC*
847. *Bull.,* v. 20, no. 6, p. 732; *GC,* p. 116
211. *Bull.,* v. 24, no. 6, p. 1090
219. *Bull.,* v. 30, no. 6, p. 1005
222. *Bull.,* v. 33, no. 6, p. 988
436. *Bull.,* v. 34, no. 3, p. 382
223. *Bull.,* v. 34, no. 6, p. 1196
407. *Bull.,* v. 37, no. 2, p. 419
227. *Bull.,* v. 38, no. 6, p. 1228
235. *Bull.,* v. 46, no. 6, p. 934
555a. *Bull.,* v. 50, no. 3, p. 450
648. *Bull.,* GSA, v. 70 pp. 1286-1287
788. *Bull. 8,* La. Geol. Svy., pp. 201, 206-207, 257-262
96. *Bull. 11,* La. Geol. Svy., pp. 34, 38
427. *GAGC,* p. 270
717. *GAS,* 685, 712
363. *Geophysics,* v. 1, no. 1, Fig. 3 (Between pp. 142-143), Fig. 8 (between pp. 146-147)
647. *Lockwood's* (Louisiana 1940), pp. 268-269
645. *NOGS,* v. 1, pp. 66-67, v. 1, first rev., pp. 54-55
393. *OGJ,* v. 32, no. 7, p. 36
484. *OGJ,* v. 32, no. 20, p. 10

Venice, Plaquemines Parish: (Rose, Spanish Pass) (cont.)

520. *OGJ,* v. 39, no. 49, p. 138
437. *OGJ,* v. 47, no. 8, p. 250
961. *OGJ,* v. 51, no. 11, pp. 62-64
962. *OGJ,* v. 54, no. 10, pp. 122-123
637. *OGJ,* v. 57, no. 48, pp. 126, 128
524. *OW,* v. 90, no. 7, p. 222
161. *OW,* v. 123, no. 3, pp. 82, 84-85
409. *OW,* v. 123, no. 3, p. 149
434. *PROB.,* pp. 632-633
644. *Trans.,* GCAGS, v. 9, pp. 78, 84
373. *Trans.,* GCAGS, v. 11, p. 142
410. *WO,* v. 130, no. 7, p. 110

Vermilion Bay, Iberia Parish:

6a. *BMIC*
902. *Bull.,* v. 16, no. 12, pp. 1221-1229; *GCH,* v. 1, pp. 135-143; *EGP,* v. 1, pp. 381-389; *Trans.,* SEG, v. 3, pp. 51-59
847. *Bull.,* v. 20, no. 6, p. 732; *GC,* p. 116
210. *Bull.,* v. 23, no. 6, p. 884
211. *Bull.,* v. 24, no. 6, p. 1087
396. *Bull.,* v. 24, no. 8, p. 1408
221. *Bull.,* v. 32, no. 6, p. 1037
227. *Bull.,* v. 38, no. 6, p. 1227
96. *Bull. 11,* La. Geol. Svy., pp. 5, 11
427. *GAGC,* pp. 222, 238, 270
363. *Geophysics,* v. 1, no. 1, Fig. 3 (between pp. 142-143), Fig. 7, Fig. 8 (between pp. 146-147)
647. *Lockwood's* (Louisiana 1940), pp. 270-271
645. *NOGS,* v. 2, pp. 38-39
478. *OGJ,* v. 27, no. 25, pp. 35, 91
327. *OGJ,* v. 28, no. 45, p. 159
515. *OGJ,* v. 28, no. 49, p. 118
484. *OGJ,* v. 32, no. 20, p. 10
300. *OGJ,* v. 37, no. 12, p. 34
86. *OGJ,* v. 56, no. 30, p. 263
524. *OW,* v. 90, no. 7, p. 216
161. *OW,* v. 123, no. 3, p. 85
409. *OW,* v. 123, no. 3, p. 144
449. *Pet. Geol,* p. 436
434. *PROB.,* pp. 632-633
410. *WO,* v. 130, no. 7, p. 102

Vermilion Area Blocks: (see Offshore)

Vinton, Calcasieu Parish:

6a. *BMIC*
127. *Bull.,* v. 1, no. 1, pp. 47, 84
964. *Bull.,* v. 5, no. 2, pp. 333, 339
843. *Bull.,* v. 9, no. 9, pp. 1229, 1263; *SD,* pp. 169, 203

Vinton, Calcasieu Parish: (cont.)

883. *Bull.,* v. 9, no. 3, pp. 571, 580; *SD,* pp. 753, 762
965. *Bull.,* v. 12, no. 4, pp. 385-394
640. *Bull.,* v. 17, no. 6, pp. 634, 642; *GC,* pp. 404, 412
385. *Bull.,* v. 17, no. 9, pp. 1074, 1080; *GC,* pp. 69, 75
329. *Bull.,* v. 17, no. 12, pp. 1494-1497, 1500, 1502, 1507, 1508; *GC,* pp. 143-146, 149, 151, 156-157; *OW,* v. 71 no. 12, pp. 18-22; *OGJ,* v. 32, no. 22, pp. 18, 22
654. *Bull.,* v. 18, no. 4, p. 510; *GC,* p. 11
54. *Bull.,* v. 19, no. 5, p. 648; *GC,* p. 1037
847. *Bull.,* v. 20, no. 6, p. 732; *GC,* p. 116
215. *Bull.,* v. 28, no. 6, p. 856
221. *Bull.,* v. 32, no. 6, p. 1037
222. *Bull.,* v. 33, no. 6, p. 988
225. *Bull.,* v. 36, no. 6, pp. 1217-1218
96. *Bull. 11,* La. Geol. Svy., pp. 53, 119
427. *GAGC,* p. 270
717. *GAS,* pp. 685-686, 694, 711
363. *Geophysics,* v. 1, no. 1, Fig. 2 (between pp. 142-143), Fig. 7 (between pp. 146-147)
647. *Lockwood's* (Louisiana 1940), pp. 276-278
645. *NOGS,* v. 1, pp. 26-27; v. 1, first rev., pp. 14-15
722. *OFNA,* pp. 134-135
969. *OGJ,* v. 22, no. 27, p. 86
327. *OGJ,* v. 28, no. 45, p. 42
311. *OGJ,* v. 39, no. 49, pp. 82, 84
520. *OGJ,* v. 39, no. 49, pp. 133, 135, 138
376. *OW,* v. 82, no. 10, pp. 14-15
161. *OW,* v. 90, no. 7, p. 208
169. *OW,* v. 99, no. 3, p. 47
389. *OW,* v. 112, no. 1, pp. 12-13
161. *OW,* v. 123, no. 3, pp. 82, 84-86
409. *OW,* v. 123, no. 3, p. 142
449. *Pet. Geol.,* pp. 258, 435-436
434. *PROB.,* pp. 632-633
851. *Proc.,* Fourth World Pet Cong., sec. 1, p. 96
723. *SD,* p. 41
8. *Trans.,* GCAGS, v. 7, p. 234
410. *WO,* v. 130, no. 7, p. 98

Walnut Bayou, Madison Parish: (East Tallulah)

6a. *BMIC*
634. *Guidebook,* Shreveport Geol. Soc. (1960), p. 59
24. *Guidebook,* Shreveport Geol. Soc. (1960), p. 68

Weeks Island, Iberia Parish: (Grand Cote)

6a. *BMIC*

883. *Bull.,* v. 9, no. 3, pp. 565, 567; *SD,* pp. 747, 749
380. *Bull.,* v. 9, no. 4, pp. 774-780; *SD,* pp. 374-380
385. *Bull.,* v. 17, no. 9, p. 1051; *GC,* p. 46
54. *Bull.,* v. 19, no. 5, p. 649; *GC,* p. 1038
847. *Bull.,* v. 20, no. 6, p. 732; *GC,* p. 116
219. *Bull.,* v. 30, no. 6, pp. 1000-1001, 1003, 1005-1006
160. *Bull.,* v. 31, no. 7, pp. 1128, 1133
849. *Bull.,* v. 31, no. 7, pp. 1295, 1297
221. *Bull.,* v. 32, no. 6, p. 1037
222. *Bull.,* v. 33, no. 6, p. 984
223. *Bull.,* v. 34, no. 6, p. 1196
224. *Bull.,* v. 35, no. 6, pp. 1343-1344
225. *Bull.,* v. 36, no. 6, p. 1216
407. *Bull.,* v. 37, no. 2, pp. 419, 422
227. *Bull.,* v. 38, no. 6, pp. 1227, 1231
229. *Bull.,* v. 40, no. 6, p. 1257
753. *Bull.,* v. 41, no. 8, pp. 1828-1830
231. *Bull.,* v. 42, no. 6, p. 1313
650. *Bull.,* v. 43, no. 11, pp. 2592, 2603-2610
931. *Bull.,* v. 46, no. 8, pp. 1460-1467
554. *Bull.,* v. 47, no. 1, p. 180
158. *Bull.,* v. 47, no. 12, p. 2014
555a. *Bull.,* v. 50, no. 3, pp. 454, 457, 470
96. *Bull. 11,* La. Geol. Svy., pp. 34, 38-40, 159, 161
403. *EGP,* p. 343
427. *GAGC,* pp. 205, 222, 270, 272
363. *Geophysics,* v. 1, no. 1, Fig. 2 (between pp. 142-143), Fig. 7 (between pp. 146-147)
647. *Lockwood's* (Louisiana 1940), pp. 280-281, 329
645. *NOGS,* v. 2, pp. 40-41
722. *OFNA,* pp. 134, 136
327. *OGJ,* v. 28, no. 45, p. 159
300. *OGJ,* v. 37, no. 12, pp. 33-34
967. *OGJ,* v. 47, no. 18, pp. 58-60, 89
337. *OGJ,* v. 38, no. 50, pp. 95, 102
520. *OGJ,* v. 39, no. 49, p. 130
450. *OGJ,* v. 46, no. 4, pp. 137, 194
541. *OGJ,* v. 52, no. 7, p. 357
868. *OGJ,* v. 54, no. 14, p. 155
745. *OGJ,* v. 54, no. 23, p. 324
879. *OGJ,* v. 54, no. 53, p. 144
377. *OGJ,* v. 54, no. 59, p. 214
365. *OGJ,* v. 57, no. 24, p. 135
637. *OGJ,* v. 57, no. 48, pp. 126, 128-129
966. *OGJ,* v. 61, no. 37, pp. 106-115
524. *OW,* v. 90, no. 7, p. 216

Weeks Island, Iberia Parish: (Grand Cote) (cont.)

161. *OW,* v. 123, no. 3, pp. 81, 83, 85-86
170. *OW,* v. 123, no. 3, p. 87
409. *OW,* v. 123, no. 3, p. 144
364. *Paper 5,* Fifth World Pet. Cong., sec. 1, p. 2; *Oil,* v. 19, no. 8, p. 36
965a. *Pet. Eng.* (March, 1952), pp. B-7—B-10
434. *PROB.,* pp. 632-633
851. *Proc.,* Fourth World Pet. Cong., sec. 1, pp. 94-95
515a. *SOS,* pp. 104-107, 110-113, 115-118
314a. *SOS,* p. 390
136. *Trans.,* GCAGS, v. 5, pp. 173-174, 177, 179
644. *Trans.,* GCAGS, v. 9, pp. 78-79, 81, 83-84
701. *Trans.,* GCAGS, v. 10, p. 2
631. *Trans.,* GCAGS, v. 10, p. 218
525. *WO,* v. 130, no. 7, p. 59
410. *WO,* v. 130, no. 7, p. 102

Welsh, Jefferson Davis Parish:

6a. *BMIC*

127. *Bull.,* v. 1, no. 1, p. 46
970. *Bull.,* v. 9, no. 3, pp. 464-478; *SD,* pp. 437-451
847. *Bull.,* v. 20, no. 6, p. 732; *GC,* p. 116
223. *Bull.,* v. 34, no. 6, pp. 1196-1197
1. *Bull. 36,* La. Geol. Svy., pp. 49-50, 52-53, 209-211
427. *GAGC,* p. 270
717. *GAS,* pp. 685, 695, 734
363. *Geophysics,* v. 1, no. 1, Fig. 2 (between pp. 142-143), Fig. 7 (between pp. 146-147), p. 147
469. *Geophysics,* v. 8, no. 4, p. 354; *GCH,* v. 1, p. 159
647. *Lockwood's* (Louisiana 1940), pp. 282-283
645. *NOGS,* v. 1, pp. 46-47; v. 1, first rev., pp. 34-35
722. *OFNA,* pp. 134-135
327. *OGJ,* v. 28, no. 45, p. 159
473. *OGJ,* v. 31, no. 8, p. 16
520. *OGJ,* v. 39, no. 49, pp. 133, 135, 138
376. *OW,* v. 82, no. 10, p. 14
524. *OW,* v. 90, no. 7, p. 218
370. *OW,* v. 100, no. 10, p. 20
161. *OW,* v. 123, no. 3, p. 85
409. *OW,* v. 123, no. 3, p. 148
434. *PROB.,* pp. 632-633
8. *Trans.,* GCAGS, v. 7, p. 234
403. *Trans.,* SEG, v. 3, p. 15; *EGP,* p. 343
410. *WO,* v. 130, no. 7, p. 106

West Bay, Plaquemines Parish:
6a. *BMIC*
212. *Bull.,* v. 25, no. 6, p. 1013
215. *Bull.,* v. 28, no. 6, p. 856
436. *Bull.,* v. 34, no. 3, p. 382
223. *Bull.,* v. 34, no. 6, p. 1196
224. *Bull.,* v. 35, no. 6, pp. 1342-1343
225. *Bull.,* v. 36, no. 6, p. 1217
407. *Bull.,* v. 37, no. 2, p. 419
227. *Bull.,* v. 38, no. 6, p. 1228
230. *Bull.,* v. 41, no. 6, p. 1195
234. *Bull.,* v. 45, no. 6, p. 886
235. *Bull.,* v. 46, no. 6, p. 934
427. *GAGC,* p. 270
645. *NOGS,* v. 1, pp. 68-69; v. 1, first rev., pp. 56-57
437. *OGJ,* v. 47, no. 8, p. 250
637. *OGJ,* v. 57, no. 48, pp. 126,128
161. *OW,* v. 123, no. 3, p. 85
409. *OW,* v. 123, no. 3, p. 149
644. *Trans.,* GCAGS, v. 9, pp. 78, 84

West Cameron Block 2, Cameron Parish: (see Creole)

West Cote Blanche Bay, St. Mary Parish:
6a. *BMIC*
212. *Bull.,* v. 25, no. 6, p. 1011
214. *Bull.,* v. 27, no. 6, p. 737
227. *Bull.,* v. 38, no. 6, p. 1229
427. *GAGC,* pp. 222, 270
647. *Lockwood's* (Louisiana 1940), pp. 284-285
422. *OGJ,* v. 54, no. 59, p. 222
161. *OW,* v. 123, no. 3, p. 85
409. *OW,* v. 123, no. 3, p. 156

West Delta Area Blocks: (see Offshore)

West Hackberry, Cameron Parish: (Hackberry)
6a. *BMIC*
640. *Bull.,* v. 17, no. 6, p. 634; *GC,* p. 404
226. *Bull.,* v. 37, no. 6, p. 1447
227. *Bull.,* v. 38, no. 6, p. 1227
236. *Bull.,* v. 47, no. 6, p. 1093
555a. *Bull.,* v. 50, no. 3, pp. 441, 443, 473
91. *Bull. 6,* La. Geol. Svy., pp. 73, 77-78, 84-86, 88-90, 93-101, 182, 185-186, 205
96. *Bull. 11,* La. Geol. Svy., pp. 26, 30, 52, 115
574. *Bull. 1,* Tex. Gulf Coast, So. La. Oil Scouts Assn., pp. 121-123
427. *GAGC,* pp. 222, 260, 270, 274
717. *GAS,* pp. 685-686
363. *Geophysics,* v. 1, no. 1, Fig. 2 (between pp. 142-143), Fig. 7 (between pp. 146-147)

West Hackberry, Cameron Parish: (Hackberry) (cont.)
793. *JPT,* v. 4, no. 7, p. 16
647. *Lockwood's* (Louisiana 1940), pp. 143-147
645. *NOGS,* v. 2, pp. 22-23
327. *OGJ,* v. 28, no. 45, p. 42
515. *OGJ,* v. 28, no. 49, p. 42
876. *OGJ,* v. 35, no. 27, p. 12
337. *OGJ,* v. 38, no. 50, pp. 92, 95
311. *OGJ,* v. 39, no. 49, p. 86
520. *OGJ,* v. 39, no. 49, p. 138
422. *OGJ,* v. 54, no. 59, p. 222
376. *OW,* v. 82, no. 10, p. 14
524. *OW,* v. 90, no. 7, p. 210
370. *OW,* v. 100, no. 10, p. 20
161. *OW,* v. 123, no. 3, pp. 82, 84-86, 88
409. *OW,* v. 123, no. 3, p. 144
434. *PROB.,* pp. 632-633, 659, 661
8. *Trans.,* GCAGS, v. 7, p. 234
406. *Trans.,* GCAGS, v. 8, pp. 17-18
410. *WO,* v. 130, no. 7, p. 98
581. *WP* (May, 1936), pp. 271-272

White Castle, Iberville Parish:
6a. *BMIC*
640. *Bull.,* v. 17, no. 6, p. 642; *GC,* p. 412
847. *Bull.,* v. 20, no. 6, p. 732; *GC,* p. 116
96. *Bull. 11,* La. Geol. Svy., pp. 34, 38, 49, 52, 55, 93, 112
27. *Bull. 13,* La. Geol. Svy., pp. 1-2, 88, 135-154
427. *GAGC,* pp. 240, 270
717. *GAS,* pp. 685, 712
363. *Geophysics,* v. 1, no. 1, Fig. 3 (between pp. 142-143), Fig. 8 (between pp. 146-147)
647. *Lockwood's* (Louisiana 1940), pp. 290-291
645. *NOGS,* v. 1, pp. 38-39; v. 1, first rev., pp. 26-27
478. *OGJ,* v. 27, no. 25, pp. 34, 91
515. *OGJ,* v. 28, no. 49, p. 118
484. *OGJ,* v. 32, no. 20, p. 10
339. *OGJ,* v. 38, no. 50, p. 102
524. *OW,* v. 90, no. 7, p. 216
161. *OW,* v. 123, no. 3, p. 85
409. *OW,* v. 123, no. 3, p. 147
434. *PROB.,* pp. 632-633
8. *Trans.,* GCAGS, v. 7, p. 234
410. *WO,* v. 130, no. 7, p. 104

Winnfield, Winn Parish:
6a. *BMIC*
99. *Am. Mineralogist,* v. 18, pp. 335-340
723. *Bull.,* v. 9, no. 5, p. 842; *SD,* p. 12

Winnfield, Winn Parish: (cont.)

601.   *Bull.,* v. 10, no. 1, pp. 14, 17; *SD,* pp. 222, 225

598.   *Bull.,* v. 10, no. 3, pp. 276-282; *SD,* pp. 328-334

655.   *Bull.,* v. 18, no. 2, pp. 216, 224; *GC,* pp. 123, 131

849.   *Bull.,* v. 31, no. 7, pp. 1295, 1297

753.   *Bull.,* v. 41, no. 8, pp. 1828-1832

932.   *Bull.,* v. 46, no. 8, pp. 1444-1459

931.   *Bull.,* v. 46, no. 8, p. 1465

554.   *Bull.,* v. 47, no. 1, p. 180

933.   *Bull.,* v. 48, no. 3, pp. 360-361

555a. *Bull.,* v. 50, no. 3, pp. 455, 460

 96.   *Bull. 11,* La. Geol. Svy., pp. 5, 9, 25, 29, 34, 38, 41, 49-50, 55, 57, 61-62, 69-70, 75, 77, 89-90, 106, 112-114, 158

 88.   *Bull. 15,* La. Geol. Svy., pp. 42, 61, 70, 185-186, 188, 190, 193-224, 237-238, 284, 289-293, 297, 345-346

429.   *Bull. 1869,* Tex. U., p. 143

403.   *EGP,* p. 340; *Trans.,* SEG, v. 3, p. 12

427.   *GAGC,* pp. 209, 223, 228-230, 240, 269

499.   *GCH,* v. 1, p. 120; Geophysics, v. 10, no. 3, p. 391

977.   *Guidebook,* Shreveport Geol. Soc. (1960), pp. 29-47

634.   *Guidebook,* Shreveport Geol. Soc. (1960), p. 58

 24.   *Guidebook,* Shreveport Geol. Soc. (1960), p. 65

421.   *Guidebook,* Shreveport Geol. Soc. (1960), p. 129

885.   *OW* (Aug. 7, 1931), p. 17

434.   *PROB.,* pp. 632-633, 651

515a. *SOS,* pp. 104-109, 111, 113, 115, 117, 119

631.   *Trans.,* GCAGS, v. 10, p. 218

Woodlawn, Jefferson Davis Parish:

 6a.   *BMIC*

210.   *Bull.,* v. 23, no. 6, p. 879

225.   *Bull.,* v. 36, no. 6, pp. 1217-1218

  1.   *Bull. 36,* La. Geol. Svy., pp. 49-50, 52, 222-224

427.   *GAGC,* pp. 217, 242

647.   *Lockwood's* (Louisiana 1940), pp. 294-295

645.   *NOGS,* v. 1, pp. 48-49; v. 1, first rev., pp. 36-37

524.   *OW,* v. 90, no. 7, p. 218

161.   *OW,* v. 123, no. 3, p. 85

409.   *OW,* v. 123, no. 3, p. 148

934.   *Trans.,* GCAGS, v. 1, pp. 200-210

  8.   *Trans.,* GCAGS, v. 7, p. 234

410.   *WO,* v. 130, no. 7, p. 106

Offshore

East Cameron Area:

Block 115 (Block 104)

 6a.   *BMIC*

645.   *NOGS,* v. 2, pp. 84-85

Block 118

 6a.   *BMIC*

645.   *NOGS,* v. 1, first rev., (index map, p. 1)

Block 126

 6a.   *BMIC*

231.   *Bull.,* v. 42, no. 6, p. 1315

234.   *Bull.,* v. 45, no. 6, p. 885

555a. *Bull.,* v. 50, no. 3, p. 454

427.   *GAGC,* p. 270

645.   *NOGS,* v. 2, pp. 86-87

Block 139

Block 151

Block 152

Block 155

 6a.   *BMIC*

645.   *NOGS,* v. 1, first rev. (index map, p. 1)

Block 160

 6a.   *BMIC*

230.   *Bull.,* v. 41, no. 6, p. 1196

645.   *NOGS,* v. 1, pp. 106-107; v. 1, first rev., pp. 94-95

Block 187 (Block 194)

 6a.   *BMIC*

645.   *NOGS,* v. 1, first rev., (index map, p. 1)

Block 189

Eugene Island Area:

Block 32

 6a.   *BMIC*

223.   *Bull.,* v. 34, no. 6, p. 1195

224.   *Bull.,* v. 35, no. 6, pp. 1343-1344

652.   *Bull.,* v. 37, no. 2, p. 405

645.   *NOGS,* v. 1, pp. 108-109; v. 1, first rev., pp. 96-97

410.   *WO,* v. 130, no. 7, p. 116

Block 77

 6a.   *BMIC*

230.   *Bull.,* v. 41, no. 6, p. 1197

232.   *Bull.,* v. 43, no. 6, p. 1318

233.   *Bull.,* v. 44, no. 6, p. 831

427.   *GAGC,* p. 270

645.   *NOGS,* v. 1, pp. 110-111; v. 1, first rev., pp. 98-99

Block 110

 6a.   *BMIC*

223.   *Bull.,* v. 34, no. 6, p. 1194

Eugene Island: (cont.)

233. *Bull.,* v. 44, no. 6, p. 831
234. *Bull.,* v. 45, no. 6, p. 887
555a. *Bull.,* v. 50, no. 3, p. 447
427. *GAGC,* p. 270
645. *NOGS,* v. 2, pp. 88-89
410. *WO,* v. 130, no. 7, p. 102

Block 126

6a. *BMIC*
224. *Bull.,* v. 35, no. 6, pp. 1341, 1344
225. *Bull.,* v. 36, no. 6, p. 1217
226. *Bull.,* v. 37, no. 6, p. 1447
 60. *Bull.,* v. 40, no. 1, pp. 173-177
234. *Bull.,* v. 45, no. 6, p. 887
427. *GAGC,* p. 270
645. *NOGS,* v. 2, pp. 90-91
313. *OGJ,* v. 57, no. 31, pp. 250, 252
132. *Trans.,* GCAGS, v. 9, pp. 131, 137, 141-144
631. *Trans.,* GCAGS, v. 10, p. 236
410. *WO,* v. 130, no. 7, p. 116

Block 128

6a. *BMIC*
229. *Bull.,* v. 40, no. 6, pp. 1253-1255, 1259
230. *Bull.,* v. 41, no. 6, p. 1197
427. *GAGC,* p. 270
645. *NOGS,* v. 1, pp. 112-113; v. 1, first rev.,
        pp. 100-101

Block 175

6a. *BMIC*
230. *Bull.,* v. 41, no. 6, p. 1197
645. *NOGS,* v. 1, pp. 114-115; v. 1, first rev.,
        pp. 102-103

Block 184

6a. *BMIC*
230. *Bull.,* v. 41, no. 6, p. 1197
235. *Bull.,* v. 46, no. 6, p. 935
645. *NOGS,* v. 2, pp. 92-93

Block 188

6a. *BMIC*
230. *Bull.,* v. 41, no. 6, pp. 1192, 1197
231. *Bull.,* v. 42, no. 6, p. 1315
233. *Bull.,* v. 44, no. 6, p. 831
234. *Bull.,* v. 45, no. 6, p. 879
133. *Bull.,* GSA, v. 70, pp. 1379, 1385-1387, 1391
645. *NOGS,* v. 1, pp. 116-117; v. 1, first rev.,
        pp. 104-105

Block 205

6a. *BMIC*
235. *Bull.,* v. 46, no. 6, p. 933
645. *NOGS,* v. 2, pp. 94-95

Eugene Island: (cont.)

Block 208

6a. *BMIC*
232. *Bull.,* v. 43, no. 6, p. 1318
233. *Bull.,* v. 44, no. 6, p. 831
234. *Bull.,* v. 45, no. 6, p. 887
645. *NOGS,* v. 1, pp. 118-119; v. 1, first rev.,
        pp. 106-107

Block 231

6a. *BMIC*

Block 238

Block 292

6a. *BMIC*

Grand Isle Area:

Block 16

6a. *BMIC*
222. *Bull.,* v. 33, no. 6, pp. 981-982, 985
225. *Bull.,* v. 36, no. 6, p. 1217
229. *Bull.,* v. 40, no. 6, p. 1259
231. *Bull.,* v. 42, no. 6, p. 1315
232. *Bull.,* v. 43, no. 6, p. 1320
650. *Bull.,* v. 43, no. 11, p. 2602
234. *Bull.,* v. 45, no. 6, p. 885
235. *Bull.,* v. 46, no. 6, p. 935
427. *GAGC,* p. 270
645. *NOGS,* v. 1, pp. 120-121; v. 1, first rev.,
        pp. 108-109
410. *WO,* v. 130, no. 7, p. 104

Block 18

6a. *BMIC*
222. *Bull.,* v. 33, no. 6, pp. 981-982, 984-985
228. *Bull.,* v. 39, no. 6, p. 993
753. *Bull.,* v. 41, no. 8, pp. 1830, 1832
650. *Bull.,* v. 43, no. 11, p. 2602
942a. *Bull. 4,* SIPES, p. 2, Figs. 1, 3
427. *GAGC,* pp. 222, 270
468. *GCH,* v. 2, pp. 103-112
645. *NOGS,* v. 1, pp. 122-123; v. 1, first rev.,
        pp. 110-111
132. *Trans.,* GCAGS, v. 9, pp. 131, 137, 143-145
410. *WO,* v. 130, no. 7, p. 104

Block 72

6a. *BMIC*

Main Pass Area:

Block 46

Ship Shoal Area:

Block 32

6a. *BMIC*
225. *Bull.,* v. 36, no. 6, p. 1217

Ship Shoal Area: (cont.)
233. *Bull.,* v. 44, no. 6, p. 831
427. *GAGC,* p. 270
645. *NOGS,* v. 2, pp. 96-97
556. *OGJ,* v. 46, no. 46, pp. 96-99, 113-114
333. *OGJ,* v. 47, no. 22, pp. 64-65
525. *WO,* v. 130, no. 7, p. 59
410. *WO,* v. 130, no. 7, p. 120

Block 38: (see Coon Point)

Block 72
6a.   *BMIC*
222. *Bull.,* v. 33, no. 6, pp. 981-982, 986
652. *Bull.,* v. 37, no. 2, p. 405
229. *Bull.,* v. 40, no. 6, p. 1259
555a. *Bull.,* v. 50, no. 3, p. 454
427. *GAGC,* p. 270
645. *NOGS,* v. 1, pp. 124-125; v. 1, first rev.,
          pp., 112-113
333. *OGJ,* v. 47, no. 22, pp. 66-67
410. *WO,* v. 130, no. 7, p. 120

Block 113 (Block 114)
6a.   *BMIC*
229. *Bull.,* v. 40, no. 6, p. 1259
234. *Bull.,* v. 45, no. 6, pp. 887-888
555a. *Bull.,* v. 50, no. 3, p. 451
645. *NOGS,* v. 2, pp. 98-99

Block 154
6a.   *BMIC*
229. *Bull.,* v. 40, no. 6, p. 1259
230. *Bull.,* v. 41, no. 6, p. 1192
232. *Bull.,* v. 43, no. 6, p. 1318
233. *Bull.,* v. 44, no. 6, p. 831
427. *GAGC,* p. 270
645. *NOGS,* v. 1, pp. 126-127; v. 1, first rev.,
          pp. 114-115

Block 208
6a.   *BMIC*
236. *Bull.,* v. 47, no. 6, p. 1095
645. *NOGS,* v. 1, first rev., (index map, p. 1)

Block 230
6a.   *BMIC*
236. *Bull.,* v. 47, no. 6, pp. 1090, 1092
645. *NOGS,* v. 1, first rev., (index map, p. 1)

South Marsh Island Area:
Block 6
6a.   *BMIC*
645. *NOGS,* v. 1, first rev., (index map, p. 1)

Block 7
6a.   *BMIC*

South Marsh Island: (cont.)
Block 8
6a.   *BMIC*

Block 38
6a.   *BMIC*
645. *NOGS,* v. 2, pp. 100-101

Block 41
6a.   *BMIC*
645. *NOGS,* v. 1, first rev., (index map, p. 1)

Block 48
6a.   *BMIC*
235. *Bull.,* v. 46, no. 6, p. 933
645. *NOGS,* v. 2, pp. 102-103

Block 57

Block 66
6a.   *BMIC*
645. *NOGS,* v. 1, first rev., (index map, p. 1)

Block 73
6a.   *BMIC*
645. *NOGS,* v. 1, first rev., (index map, p. 1)

Block 79

South Pass Area:
Block 27
6a.   *BMIC*
230. *Bull.,* v. 41, no. 6, p. 1199
231. *Bull.,* v. 42, no. 6, p. 1317
232. *Bull.,* v. 43, no. 6, p. 1320
908. *Bull.,* v. 45, no. 1, pp. 51-71
234. *Bull.,* v. 45, no. 6, pp. 879, 884, 887
645. *NOGS,* v. 2, pp. 104-105
637. *OGJ,* v. 57, no. 48, pp. 126, 128
644. *Trans.,* GCAGS, v. 9, pp. 78, 84

South Pelto Area:
Block 20
6a.   *BMIC*
225. *Bull.,* v. 36, no. 6, p. 1214
234. *Bull.,* v. 45, no. 6, p. 887
427. *GAGC,* p. 270
645. *NOGS,* v. 1, pp. 128-129; v. 1, first rev.,
          pp. 116-117

South Timbalier Area:
Block 54
6a.   *BMIC*
229. *Bull.,* v. 40, no. 6, p. 1259
231. *Bull.,* v. 42, no. 6, p. 1316
133. *Bull.,* GSA, v. 70, pp. 1379, 1390, 1392
427. *GAGC,* p. 270

South Timbalier Area: (cont.)

645.   *NOGS*, v. 1, pp. 130-131; v. 1, first rev., pp. 118-119

Block 86

6a.   *BMIC*
230.   *Bull.*, v. 41, no. 6, p. 1198
231.   *Bull.*, v. 42, no. 6, p. 1316
555a.   *Bull.*, v. 50, no. 3, p. 451
645.   *NOGS*, v. 1, pp. 132-133; v. 1, first rev., pp. 120-121

Block 131

6a.   *BMIC*
232.   *Bull.*, v. 43, no. 6, p. 1319
645.   *NOGS*, v. 1, pp. 134-135; v. 1, first rev., pp. 122-123

Block 135

6a.   *BMIC*
230.   *Bull.*, v. 41, no. 6, p. 1198
231.   *Bull.*, v. 42, no. 6, p. 1316
234.   *Bull.*, v. 45, no. 6, p. 887
555a.   *Bull.*, v. 50, no. 3, p. 453
645.   *NOGS*, v. 1, pp. 136-137; v. 1, first rev., pp. 124-125

Block 176

6a.   *BMIC*

Vermilion Area:

Block 102

6a.   *BMIC*
230.   *Bull.*, v. 41, no. 6, p. 1198
645.   *NOGS*, v. 1, pp. 138-139; v. 1, first rev., pp. 126-127

Block 111

6a.   *BMIC*
645.   *NOGS*, v. 1, pp. 140-141; v. 1, first rev., pp. 128-129

Block 120

6a.   *BMIC*
231.   *Bull.*, v. 42, no. 6, p. 1316
645.   *NOGS*, v. 2, pp. 106-107

Vermilion Area: (cont.)

Block 162

6a.   *BMIC*
236.   *Bull.*, v. 47, no. 6, pp. 1090, 1092
645.   *NOGS*, v. 1, first rev., (index map, p. 1)

Block 164

6a.   *BMIC*
231.   *Bull.*, v. 42, no. 6, p. 1316
233.   *Bull.*, v. 44, no. 6, p. 831
645.   *NOGS*, v. 1, pp. 142-143; v. 1, first rev., pp. 130-131

Block 190 (Block 191)

6a.   *BMIC*

Block 203

6a.   *BMIC*
645.   *NOGS*, v. 1, first rev., (index map, p. 1)

Block 245

6a.   *BMIC*

West Cameron Area: Block 2 (see Creole)

Block 386

West Delta Area:

Block 30

6a.   *BMIC*
223.   *Bull.*, v. 34, no. 6, p. 1194
229.   *Bull.*, v. 40, no. 6 p. 1259
230.   *Bull.*, v. 41, no. 6, p. 1198
231.   *Bull.*, v. 42, no. 6, p. 1316
232.   *Bull.*, v. 43, no. 6, p. 1320
234.   *Bull.*, v. 45, no. 6, p. 885
235.   *Bull.*, v. 46, no. 6, p. 935
427.   *GAGC*, pp. 222, 270
645.   *NOGS*, v. 1, pp. 144, 145; v. 1, first rev., pp. 132-133
637.   *OGJ*, v. 57, no. 48, pp. 126, 128
644.   *Trans.*, GCAGS, v. 9, pp. 78, 84

Block 133

6a.   *BMIC*
645.   *NOGS*, v. 1, first rev., (index map, p. 1)

Salt Domes of Mississippi
Alphabetical Listing
(Alternate Name in Parenthesis)

Dome	County	Dome	County
Allen	Copiah	Kola	Covington
Arm	Lawrence	Lampton	Marion
Brownsville	Hinds	Laurel	Jones
Bruinsburg	Claiborne	Learned	Hinds
Burns	Smith	Leedo	Jefferson
Byrd	Greene	McBride	Jefferson
Carmichael	Hinds	McLaurin	Forrest
Carson	Jefferson Davis	Midway (Scanlon)	Lamar
Caseyville	Lincoln	Monticello	Lawrence
Centerville	Jones	Moselle	Jones
(Chapparal) Hiwanee	Wayne	New Home	Smith
County Line	Greene	Newman	Warren
D'lo	Simpson	Oak Ridge	Warren
Dont	Covington	Oakley	Hinds
Dry Creek	Covington	Oakvale	Jefferson Davis
Eagle Bend	Warren	Ovett	Jones
Edwards	Hinds	Petal	Forrest
Ellisville	Jones	Prentiss	Jefferson Davis
Eminence	Covington	Raleigh	Smith
Eucutta	Wayne	Richmond	Covington
Galloway	Claiborne and Warren	Richton	Perry
		Rufus	Rankin
Glass	Warren	Ruth	Lincoln
Glazier	Perry	Sardis Church	Copiah
Grange	Jefferson Davis	(Scanlon) Midway	Lamar
Gwinville	Jefferson Davis	Sunrise	Forrest
Halifax	Hinds	Tatum	Lamar
Hazelhurst	Copiah	Utica	Copiah
Heidelberg	Jasper	Valley Park	Issaquena-Sharkey
Hervey	Claiborne	Vicksburg	Warren
Hiwanee (Chapparal)	Wayne	Wesson	Copiah
Kings	Warren	Yellow Creek	Wayne

By County

Claiborne County
Bruinsburg
Galloway
Hervey

Copiah County
Allen
Hazelhurst

Copiah County (cont.)
Sardis Church
Utica
Wesson

Covington County
Dont
Dry Creek

Covington County (cont.)
Eminence
Kola
Richmond

Forrest County
McLaurin
Petal
Sunrise

Greene County
Byrd
County Line

Hinds County
Brownsville
Carmichael
Edwards
Halifax
Learned
Oakley

Issaquena-Sharkey County
Valley Park

Jasper County
Heidelberg

Jefferson County
Leedo
McBride

Jefferson Davis County
Carson
Grange
Gwinville
Oakvale
Prentiss

Jones County
Centerville
Ellisville
Laurel
Moselle
Ovett

Lamar County
Midway (Scanlon)
Tatum

Lawrence County
Arm
Monticello

Lincoln County
Caseyville
Ruth

Marion County
Lampton

Perry County
Glazier
Richton

Rankin County
Rufus

Simpson County
D'lo

Smith County
Burns
New Home
Raleigh

Warren County
Eagle Bend
Galloway
Glass
Kings
Newman
Oak Ridge
Vicksburg

Wayne County
Eucutta
Hiwannee (Chapparal)
Yellow Creek

Salt Dome Index

Brownsville, Hinds County:
6a. *BMIC*
262.   *Bull.,* v. 32, no. 6, p. 1074
700.   *Bull.,* v. 34, no. 7, pp. 1506-1508

Bruinsburg, Claiborne County:
6a. *BMIC*
673.   *Bull.,* v. 28, no. 7, p. 1049
260.   *Bull.,* v. 29, no. 6, pp. 826, 828
261.   *Bull.,* v. 30, no. 6, pp. 1022, 1035
700.   *Bull.,* v. 34, no. 7, p. 1506
427.   *GAGC,* p. 269
314.   *OGJ,* v. 50, no. 37, pp. 58-59
693.   *OGJ,* v. 60, no. 29, p. 131
722.   *OFNA,* pp. 141, 143
364.   *Paper 5,* Fifth World Pet. Cong., sec. 1, p. 10; *Oil,* v. 19, no. 8, p. 40
449.   *Pet. Geol.,* pp. 455, 458
515a. *SOS,* pp. 105-106

Burns, Smith County:
6a. *BMIC*

Byrd, Green County:
6a. *BMIC*
673.   *Bull.,* v. 28, no. 7, p. 1047
260.   *Bull.,* v. 29, no. 6, p. 829
261.   *Bull.,* v. 30, no. 6, pp. 1022, 1042
427.   *GAGC,* p. 269

Carmichael, Hinds County:
6a. *BMIC*
264.   *Bull.,* v. 34, no. 6, p. 1221
427.   *GAGC,* p. 269
697.   *Trans.,* GCAGS, v. 10, p. 154

Carson, Jefferson Davis County:
6a. *BMIC*
673.   *Bull.,* v. 28, no. 7, p. 1048
261.   *Bull.,* v. 30, no. 6, pp. 1022, 1043
427.   *GAGC,* p. 269

Caseyville, Lincoln County:
6a. *BMIC*
427.   *GAGC,* p. 269

Centerville, Jones County:
6a. *BMIC*
264.   *Bull.,* v. 34, no. 6, p. 1221
274.   *Bull.,* v. 46, no. 6, p. 957
427.   *GAGC,* p. 269
697.   *Trans.,* GCAGS, v. 10, p. 154

Chapparal, Wayne County: (see Hiwanee)

County Line, Green County:
6a. *BMIC*
263.   *Bull.,* v. 33, no. 6, p. 1008
427.   *GAGC,* p. 269
697.   *Trans.,* GCAGS, v. 10, p. 154

D'Lo, Simpson County:
6a. *BMIC*
260.   *Bull.,* v. 29, no. 6, p. 831
261.   *Bull.,* v. 30, no. 6, p. 1022
555a. *Bull.,* v. 50, no. 3, pp. 452, 461
427.   *GAGC,* pp. 205, 209, 212, 269
471.   *GCH,* v. 1, pp. 239, 244-247; *Geophysics,* v. 12, no. 1, pp. 30, 35, 38
697.   *Trans.,* GCAGS, v. 10, p. 154

Dont, Covington County:
6a. *BMIC*
274.   *Bull.,* v. 46, no. 6, pp. 956-957
427.   *GAGC,* p. 269

Dry Creek, Covington County:
6a. *BMIC*
427.   *GAGC,* p. 269

Eagle Bend, Warren County:
6a. *BMIC*
262.   *Bull.,* v. 32, no. 6, p. 1074
700.   *Bull.,* v. 34, no. 7, pp. 1506-1508
427.   *GAGC,* p. 269

Edwards, Hinds County:
6a. *BMIC*
261.   *Bull.,* v. 30, no. 6, p. 1022
427.   *GAGC,* p. 269
722.   *OFNA,* p. 141
698.   *OGJ,* v. 37, no. 5, pp. 20, 22

Ellisville, Jones County:
6a. *BMIC*

Eminence, Covington County:
6a. *BMIC*
274.   *Bull.,* v. 46, no. 6, p. 957
427.   *GAGC,* p. 269

Eucutta, Wayne County:
6a. *BMIC*
277.   *Bull.,* v. 28, no. 6, p. 802
673.   *Bull.,* v. 28, no. 7, p. 1047
260.   *Bull.,* v. 29, no. 6, pp. 827-828
142.   *Bull.,* v. 29, no. 7, pp. 1009-1011
261.   *Bull.,* v. 30, no. 6, pp. 1022, 1037, 1048
263.   *Bull.,* v. 33, no. 6, p. 1009
264.   *Bull.,* v. 34, no. 6, p. 1223

Eucutta, Wayne County: (Cont.)

700. *Bull.,* v. 34, no. 7, pp. 1510-1514
135. *Bull.,* v. 34, no. 10, pp. 2029, 2044, 2047
271. *Bull.,* v. 42, no. 6, pp. 1335-1336
427. *GAGC,* p. 269
722. *OFNA,* pp. 139, 144
693. *OGJ,* v. 60, no. 29, p. 131
732. *Ref. Rept.,* Shreveport Geol. Soc. (1945),
        v. 1, pp. 255-259
697. *Trans.,* GCAGS, v. 10, pp. 154, 158

Galloway, Claiborne, and Warren Counties:

6a. *BMIC*
261. *Bull.,* v. 30, no. 6, p. 1042
427. *GAGC,* p. 269

Glass, Warren County:

6a. *BMIC*
261. *Bull.,* v. 30, no. 6, p. 1022
427. *GAGC,* p. 269
722. *OFNA,* p. 141

Glazier, Perry County:

6a. *BMIC*
427. *GAGC,* p. 269
314. *OGJ,* v. 50, no. 37, p. 58
693. *OGJ,* v. 60, no. 29, p. 131
600. *Guidebook,* Shreveport Geol. Soc. (1960), p. 5

Grange, Jefferson Davis County:

6a. *BMIC*

Gwinville, Jefferson Davis County:

6a. *BMIC*

Halifax, Hinds County:

6a. *BMIC*
276. *Bull.,* v. 26, no. 6, p. 995
261. *Bull.,* v. 30, no. 6, p. 1022
427. *GAGC,* p. 269
722. *OFNA,* p. 141

Hazelhurst, Copiah County:

6a. *BMIC*
427. *GAGC,* p. 269

Heidelberg, Jasper County:

6a. *BMIC*
673. *Bull.,* v. 28, no. 7, p. 1097
260. *Bull.,* v. 29, no. 6, p. 821
142. *Bull.,* v. 29, no. 7, pp. 1010, 1012
261. *Bull.,* v. 30, no. 6, pp. 1022, 1039, 1048
263. *Bull.,* v. 33, no. 6, p. 1009
264. *Bull.,* v. 34, no. 6, p. 1223

Heidelberg, Jasper County: (Cont.)

700. *Bull.,* v. 34, no. 7, pp. 1508, 1510-1512,
        1514-1515
835. *Bull.,* v. 40, no. 1, pp. 1-8, 14-15
272. *Bull.,* v. 44, no. 6, p. 848
273. *Bull.,* v. 45, no. 6, pp. 903, 906
555a. *Bull.,* v. 50, no. 3, p. 467
427. *GAGC,* pp. 217, 240, 269
398. *Geophysics,* v. 10, no. 4, pp. 487, 489-493
516. *Habitat of Oil,* p. 518
722. *OFNA,* pp. 139, 144
693. *OGJ,* v. 60, no. 29, p. 131
438. *Oil,* v. 4, no. 8, pp. 8-9
732. *Ref. Rept.,* Shreveport Geol. Soc. (1945),
        v. 1, pp. 275-279
697. *Trans.,* GCAGS, v. 10, pp. 157-159, 161
631. *Trans.,* GCAGS, v. 10, p. 221

Hervey, Claiborne County:

6a. *BMIC*
261. *Bull.,* v. 30, no. 6, p. 1042
427. *GAGC,* p. 269

Hiwanee, Wayne County: (Chapparal)

6a. *BMIC*
427. *GAGC,* p. 269

King's, Warren County:

6a. *BMIC*
640. *Bull.,* v. 17, no. 6, p. 614; *GC,* p. 384
261. *Bull.,* v. 30, no. 6, pp. 1022, 1043
262. *Bull.,* v. 32, no. 6, p. 1071
700. *Bull.,* v. 34, no. 7, p. 1506
427. *GAGC,* p. 269
722. *OFNA,* pp. 141, 144
314. *OGJ,* v. 50, no. 37, pp. 58-59
693. *OGJ,* v. 60, no. 29, p. 131
449. *Pet. Geol.,* pp. 455, 458

Kola, Covington County:

6a. *BMIC*
263. *Bull.,* v. 33, no. 6. p. 1008
274. *Bull.,* v. 45, no. 6, p. 957
427. *GAGC,* p. 269

Lampton, Marion County:

6a. *BMIC*
673. *Bull.,* v. 28, no. 7, p. 1049
260. *Bull.,* v. 29, no. 6, pp. 830-831
261. *Bull.,* v. 30, no. 6, pp. 1022, 1043
427. *GAGC,* p. 269

Laurel, Jones County:

6a. *BMIC*

Laurel, Jones County: (Cont.)
275. *Bull.,* v. 47, no. 6, p. 1112
693. *OGJ,* v. 60, no. 29, p. 131
697. *Trans.,* GCAGS, v. 10, p. 158

Learned, Hinds County:
6a. *BMIC*
264. *Bull.,* v. 34, no. 6, p. 1221
427. *GAGC,* p. 269

Leedo, Jefferson County:
6a. *BMIC*
673. *Bull.,* v. 28, no. 7, pp. 1047-1048
260. *Bull.,* v. 29, no. 6, p. 830
261. *Bull.,* v. 30, no. 6, pp. 1022, 1043
700. *Bull.,* v. 34, no. 7, p. 1506
 71. *Bull.,* v. 38, no. 8, p. 1726
427. *GAGC,* p. 269
833. *OGJ,* v. 53, no. 26, p. 93

McBride, Jefferson County:
6a. *BMIC*
262. *Bull.,* v. 32, no. 6, p. 1071
700. *Bull.,* v. 34, no. 7, p. 1506
427. *GAGC,* p .269
314. *OGJ,* v. 50, no. 37, pp. 58-59
693. *OGJ,* v. 60, no. 29, p. 131

McLaurin, Forest County:
6a. *BMIC*
427. *GAGC,* p. 269

Midway, Lamar County: (Scanlon)
6a. *BMIC*
684. *Bull.,* v. 22, no. 7, pp. 816-822; *OGJ,* v. 36, no. 44, pp. 58-62; *World Pet.,* v. 9, no. 10, p. 70
261. *Bull.,* v. 30, no. 6, p. 1022
700. *Bull.,* v. 34, no. 7, p. 1507
427. *GAGC,* p. 269
722. *OFNA,* p. 139
698. *OGJ,* v. 37, no. 5, pp. 20, 22
476. *OGJ,* v. 51, no. 7, p. 94
695. *OW,* v. 118, no. 7, p. 52

Monticello, Lawrence County:
6a. *BMIC*
673. *Bull.,* v. 28, no. 7, p. 1048
261. *Bull.,* v. 30, no. 6, p. 1022
427. *GAGC,* p. 269

Moselle, Jones County:
6a. *BMIC*
673. *Bull.,* v. 28, no. 7, p. 1048

Moselle, Jones County: (Cont.)
261. *Bull.,* v. 30, no. 6, p. 1022
427. *GAGC,* p. 269

New Home, Smith County:
6a. *BMIC*
673. *Bull.,* v. 28, no. 7, p. 1049
261. *Bull.,* v. 30, no. 6, pp. 1022, 1043
700. *Bull.,* v. 34, no. 7, pp. 1506, 1509
427. *GAGC,* p. 269
471. *GCH,* v. 1, pp. 239-244; *Geophysics,* v. 12, no. 1, pp. 30-35
697. *Trans.,* GCAGS, v. 10, p. 154

Newman, Warren County:
6a. *BMIC*
720. *Bull.,* v. 25, no. 3, p. 424
261. *Bull.,* v. 30, no. 6, p. 1022
427. *GAGC,* p. 269
722. *OFNA,* p. 141

Oak Ridge, Warren County:
6a. *BMIC*
270. *Bull.,* v. 40, no. 6, 1273, 1277

Oakley, Hinds County:
6a. *BMIC*
264. *Bull.,* v. 34, no. 6, p. 1221
269. *Bull.,* v. 39, no. 6, pp. 1010-1011
427. *GAGC,* p .269
697. *Trans.,* GCAGS, v. 10, p. 154

Oakvale, Jefferson Davis County:
6a. *BMIC*
673. *Bull.,* v. 28, no. 7, p. 1048
261. *Bull.,* v. 30, no. 6, p. 1022
427. *GAGC,* p. 269

Ovett, Jones County:
6a. *BMIC*
262. *Bull.,* v. 32, no. 6, p. 1075
263. *Bull.,* v. 33, no. 6, pp. 1004-1005, 1009
700. *Bull.,* v. 34, no. 7, pp. 1508, 1510-1511, 1514
265. *Bull.,* v. 35, no. 6, pp. 1359, 1363-1364
427. *GAGC,* p. 269
516. *Habitat of Oil,* pp. 518, 521
693. *OGJ,* v. 60, no. 29, p. 131
449. *Pet. Geol.,* p. 455
697. *Trans.,* GCAGS, v. 10, p. 154

Petal, Forrest County:
6a. *BMIC*
427. *GAGC,* p. 269

Prentiss, Jefferson Davis County:
6a.   *BMIC*
673.   *Bull.,* v. 28, no. 7, p. 1048
261.   *Bull.,* v. 30, no. 6, p. 1022
427.   *GAGC,* p. 269

Raleigh, Smith County:
6a.   *BMIC*

Richmond, Covington County:
6a.   *BMIC*
260.   *Bull.,* v. 29, no. 6, p. 829
261.   *Bull.,* v. 30, no. 6, p. 1022

Richton, Perry County:
6a.   *BMIC*
260.   *Bull.,* v. 29, no. 6, p. 829
261.   *Bull.,* v. 30, no. 6, pp. 1022, 1043
700.   *Bull.,* v. 34, no. 7, p. 1506
427.   *GAGC,* p. 269

Rufus, Rankin County:
6a.   *BMIC*

Ruth, Lincoln County:
6a.   *BMIC*
673.   *Bull.,* v. 28, no. 7, p. 1049
260.   *Bull.,* v. 29, no .6, p. 830
261.   *Bull.,* v. 30, no. 6, p. 1020
427.   *GAGC,* p. 269
476.   *OGJ,* v. 51, no. 7, p. 94

Sardis Church, Copiah County:
6a.   *BMIC*
673.   *Bull.,* v. 28, no. 7, p. 1047

Scanlon, Lamar County: (see Midway)

Sunrise, Forrest County:
6a.   *BMIC*
427.   *GAGC,* p. 269

Tatum, Lamar County:
6a.   *BMIC*
946.   *Bull.,* v. 25, no. 3, p. 424
260.   *Bull.,* v. 29, no. 6, p. 830
261.   *Bull.,* v. 30, no. 6, p. 1022
427.   *GAGC,* p. 269
722.   *OFNA,* p. 139
476.   *OGJ,* v. 51, no. 7, p. 94
515a. *SOS,* pp. 105-106

Utica, Copiah County:
6a.   *BMIC*
427.   *GAGC,* p. 269

Valley Park, Issaquena-Sharkey County:
6a.   *BMIC*

Vicksburg, Warren County:
6a.   *BMIC*
263.   *Bull.,* v. 33, no. 6, p. 1008
427.   *GAGC,* p. 269

Wesson, Copiah County:
6a.   *BMIC*

Yellow Creek, Wayne County:
6a.   *BMIC*
262.   *Bull.,* v. 32, no. 6, p. 1072
263.   *Bull.,* v. 33, no. 6, p. 1009
700.   *Bull.,* v. 34, no. 7, pp. 1510-1515
266.   *Bull.,* v. 36, no. 6, p. 1234
275.   *Bull.,* v. 47, no. 6, pp. 1112, 1114
427.   *GAGC,* p. 269
697.   *Trans.,* GCAGS, v. 10, pp. 154, 158

Salt Domes of Alabama

McIntosh, Washington County:
6a.   *BMIC*
263.   *Bull.,* v. 33, no. 6, p. 1003
6.   *OGJ,* v. 51, no. 6, p. 340

631.   *Trans.,* GCAGS, v. 10, pp. 217, 234, 237

South Carlton, Clarke County:
6a.   *BMIC*

Salt Domes of Mexico

Alphabetical Listing

(Alternate Name in Parenthesis)

Dome	State	Dome	State
Abanicos	Veracruz	Mazate	Veracruz
Acalapa	Veracruz	Medellin	Chiapas
Achotal	Veracruz	Medias Aguas	Veracruz
Almagres	Veracruz	(Mesquital) Amezquite	Veracruz
Amezquite (Mesquital, Salinas)	Veracruz	Metate	Veracruz
Buena Vista	Veracruz	Minatitlan (Tierra Nueva)	Veracruz
Cabritos	Veracruz	Moloacan	Veracruz
Cascajal	Veracruz	Moralar	Veracruz
(Chichon) Chichon Tecuanapa	Veracruz	Nopalapa	Veracruz
Chichon Tecuanapa (Chichon, Tecuanapa S.E.)	Veracruz	Nuevo Teapa	Veracruz
Chichonal	Veracruz	Ogarrio	Tabasco
Chinameca (Tonalapa)	Veracruz	Pailebot	Tabasco
(Cinco Presidentes) Yucateco	Tabasco	Pajaritos	Veracruz
Coatzacoalcos	Veracruz	Pedregal	Veracruz
Colorado	Veracruz	Pochitoque	Veracruz
Cosoleacaque	Veracruz	(Potrerillos) Jaltipan	Veracruz
(El Burro) Tonala	Veracruz	Punta Gordo	Veracruz
El Dorado	Tabasco	Rabon Grande	Veracruz (Offshore)
El Encanto	Veracruz		
El Juile	Veracruz	Remolino del Carmen (Tecuanapa West)	Veracruz
El Plan	Veracruz	(Rincon del Diablo)	
El Roble	Tabasco	Los Muertos	Veracruz
El Rosario	Tabasco	Romero Rubio	Veracruz
El Venado	Veracruz	(Salinas) Amezquite	Veracruz
Encantada	Veracruz	San Cristobal	Veracruz
Filisola	Veracruz	San Jose del Carmen	Veracruz
Hidalgotitlan	Veracruz	San Pedro	Veracruz
Ixhuatlan	Veracruz	Santa Ana	Tabasco (Offshore)
Jaltipan (Potrerillos)	Veracruz		
Jalupa	Tabasco	Santa Rosa (Teapa)	Veracruz
La Central	Tabasco	Soledad	Veracruz
Laguna Nueva	Veracruz	Tabasqueno	Veracruz
La Venta	Tabasco	Tancamichapan	Veracruz
Las Limas	Veracruz	(Teapa) Santa Rosa	Veracruz
Los Muertos (Rincon del Diablo, Tecuanapa N.E.)	Veracruz	(Tecuanapa N.E.) Los Muertos	Veracruz
Los Soldados	Veracruz	(Tecuanapa S.E.) Chichon Tecuanapa	Veracruz
Magallanes	Tabasco	(Tecuanapa West)	
Manati	Veracruz	Remolino del Carmen	Veracruz

Salt Dome Index

Los Soldados, Veracruz: (Cont.)

148.   *Bol.,* v. 3, nos. 7-8, p. 251
607.   *OGJ,* v. 58, no. 7, p. 162
680.   *OGJ,* v. 58, no. 8, p. 155
694.   *Paper,* V Conv. An. de la AIPM, en Abril de Coatzacoalcos, pp. 7, 15, 20, 23
608.   *SOS,* p. 275
424.   *Symposium Sobre Petroleo,* pp. 522-523

Magallanes, Tabasco:

607.   *OGJ,* v. 58, no. 7, pp. 162-163
680.   *OGJ,* v. 58, no. 8, p. 158
678.   *Pet. Inter.,* v. 22, no. 2, p. 48
608.   *SOS,* p. 275

Manati, Veracruz:

33a.   *Bol. 51,* Consejo de Recursos Naturales No Renovables, p. 44
33e.   *Bol. 64,* Consejo de Recursos Naturales No Renovables, pp. 71, 76; Lam. 17

Mazate, Veracruz:

15.   *Bol.,* v. 2, no. 7, p. 456
608.   *SOS,* p. 275

Medellin, Chiapas:

331.   *Bol.,* v. 5, nos. 1-2, p. 58
33e.   *Bol. 64,* Consejo de Recursos Naturales No Renovables, p. 7
680.   *OGJ,* v. 58, no. 8, pp. 150, 152, 155
674.   *Paper,* V Conv. An. de la AIPM, en Abril de 1963 en Coatzacoalcos, p. 15

Medias Aguas, Veracruz:

33a.   *Bol. 51,* Consejo de Recursos Naturales no Renovables, pp. 11, 27, 30-31, 33, 44-45, 47, 56, 61, 65, 83, 91; Lams. 2-4
33e.   *Bol. 64,* Consejo de Recursos Naturales No Renovables, pp. 52, 56-57, 64

Mesquital, Veracruz: (see Amezquite)

Metate, Veracruz:

33e.   *Bol. 64,* Consejo de Recursos Naturales No Renovables, pp. 71, 76

Minatitlan, Veracruz: (Tierra Nueva)

Moloacan, Veracruz:

15.   *Bol.,* v. 2, no. 7, p. 455
147.   *Bol.,* v. 2, no. 7, pp. 469-470
148.   *Bol.,* v. 3, nos. 7-8, pp. 247; Tablas 9-10, 19, 23, 26
427.   *GAGC,* p. 224

Moloacan, Veracruz: (Cont.)

680.   *OGJ,* v. 58, no. 8, p. 155
674.   *Paper,* V Conv. An. de la AIPM, en Abril de 1963 en Coatzacoalcos, pp. 14, 23
608.   *SOS,* p. 275
424.   *Symposium Sobre Petroleo,* pp. 522-523

Moralar, Veracruz

Nopalapa, Veracruz:

33a.   *Bol. 51,* Consejo de Recursos Naturales No Renovables, pp. 10, 12, 37-38, 84, 87-89
33e.   *Bol. 64,* Consejo de Recursos Naturales No Renovables, pp. 10, 18, 52, 56-58, 64, 68, 75

Nuevo Teapa, Veracruz:

149.   *Bol.,* v. 2, no. 7, p. 450
147.   *Bol.,* v. 2, no. 7, pp. 468-469
710.   *Bol.,* v. 2, no. 7, pp. 478-479, 482-484
427.   *GAGC,* p. 224
680.   *OGJ,* v. 58, no. 8, p. 155
674.   *Paper,* V Conv. An. de la AIPM, en Abril de 1963 en Coatzacoalcos, p. 23
608.   *SOS,* p. 275
349.   *WO,* v. 135, no. 2, p. 122

Ogarrio, Tabasco:

607.   *OGJ,* v. 58, no. 7, p. 162
680.   *OGJ,* v. 58, no. 8, pp. 150, 155, 158
674.   *Paper,* V Conv. An. de la AIPM, en Abril de 1963 en Coatzacoalcos, pp. 15, 20, 22-23
678.   *Pet. Inter.,* v. 22, no. 2, p. 48
608.   *SOS,* p. 275

Pailebot, Tabasco:

608.   *SOS,* p. 275

Pajaritos, Veracruz:

15.   *Bol.,* v. 2, no. 7, p. 455
147.   *Bol.,* v. 2, no. 7, pp. 468-469
148.   *Bol.,* v. 3, nos. 7-8, p. 247; Tablas 10, 19, 23, 26, 29
33e.   *Bol. 64,* Consejo de Recursos Naturales No Renovables, p. 33
427.   *GAGC,* p. 224
674.   *Paper,* V Conv. An. de la AIPM, en Abril de 1963 en Coatzacoalcos, p. 13
608.   *SOS,* p. 275

Pedregal, Veracruz:

555a.   *Bull.,* v. 50, no. 3, p. 469
427.   *GAGC,* p. 220

Tonala, Veracruz: (El Burro) (Cont.)

147. *Bol.,* v. 2, no. 7, p. 470
148. *Bol.,* v. 3, nos. 7-8, pp. 245-250, 253; Tablas 4, 15, 20, 24, 29, 31
331. *Bol.,* v. 5, nos. 1-2, pp. 57-58, 70, 73
427. *GAGC,* pp. 219, 224
677. *OGJ,* v. 38, no. 2, p. 29
607. *OGJ,* v. 58, no. 7, pp. 159, 162
674. *Paper,* V Conv. An. de la AIPM, en Abril de 1963 en Coatzacoalcos, pp. 7, 10, 23
608. *SOS,* p. 275
424. *Symposium Sobre Petroleo,* pp. 522-523
349. *WO,* v. 135, no. 2, p. 122

Tonalapa, Veracruz: (see Chinameca)

Tortuguero, Veracruz:

149. *Bol.,* v. 2, no. 7, p. 450
148. *Bol.,* v. 3, nos. 7-8, pp. 248, 250, 252; Tablas 15-16, 20, 24, 27, 29, 31-32
33e. *Bol. 64,* Consejo de Recursos Naturales No Renovables, p. 57
427. *GAGC,* p. 224
674. *Paper,* V Conv. An. de la AIPM, en Abril de 1963 en Coatzacoalcos, pp. 7, 23
608. *SOS,* p. 275
424. *Symposium Sobre Petroleo,* pp. 522-523

Tuzandepetl, Veracruz:

147. *Bol.,* v. 2, no. 7, pp. 468-469

Tuzandepetl, Veracruz: (Cont.)

148. *Bol.,* v. 3, nos. 7-8, pp. 245, 248; Tablas 16, 21, 24
33e. *Bol. 64,* Consejo de Recursos Naturales No Renovables, pp. 33-34, 39
427. *GAGC,* p. 224
674. *Paper,* V Conv. An. de la AIPM, en Abril de 1963 en Coatzacoalcos, pp. 13-14
608. *SOS,* p. 275
474. *Symposium Sobre Petroleo,* p. 504

Yucatecal, Veracruz

Yucateco, Tabasco: (Cinco Presidentes)

674. *Paper,* V Conv. An. de la AIPM, en Abril de 1963 en Coatzacoalcos, pp. 22-23
678. *Pet. Inter.,* v. 22, no. 2, p. 48
608. *SOS,* p. 275

Zanapa, Tabasco:

15. *Bol.,* v. 2, no. 7, pp. 454-455, 457
147. *Bol.,* v. 2, no. 7, pp. 465-466
148. *Bol.,* v. 3, nos. 7-8; Tablas 16-17, 24, 27, 29, 31
331. *Bol.,* v. 5, nos. 1-2, pp. 57, 59
607. *OGJ,* v. 58, no. 7, p. 160
680. *OGJ,* v. 58, no. 8, pp. 153, 155
674. *Paper,* V Conv. An. de la AIPM, en Abril de 1963 en Coatzacoalcos, pp. 15, 20
608. *SOS,* pp. 265-266, 278

Addendum to Bibliographies
Bibliography Arranged According to Author

Amstutz, D. E., Nowlin, W. D., Jr. and Harding, J. L.: "A Reconnaissance Study of the Sigsbee Knolls of the Gulf of Mexico," *Jour. Geophys. Res.* (1965), v. 70, no. 6, pp. 1339-1349.

Anderson, Robert A.: "Big Lake Field, Cameron Parish, Louisiana," *Typical Oil and Gas Fields of Southwestern Louisiana,* Lafayette Geol. Soc. (1964), pp. 2-2d.

Antoine, J., Bryant, W. and Jones. B: "Structural Features of Continental Shelf, Slope, and Scarp, Northeastern Gulf of Mexico," *Bull.,* AAPG (1967), v. 51, no. 2, pp. 257-262.

Antoine, J. and Ewing, M.: "New Seismic Data Concerning Sediments and Diapiric Structures in Sigsbee Deep and Upper Continental Slope," *Bull.,* AAPG (1966), v. 50, no. 3, pp. 479-504.

Archambeau, C. B., Flinn, E. A. and Lambert, D. G.: "Detection Analysis, and Interpretation of Seismic Signals. 1. Compressional Phases from the Salmon Event," *Jour. Geophys. Res.* (1966), v. 71, no. 14, pp. 3483-3501.

Boardman, C., Wheeler, V., Rawson, D. and Randolph, P.: "Post-explosion Environment Resulting from the Salmon Event," *Jour. Geophys. Res.* (1966), v. 71, no. 14, pp. 3507-3521.

Braunstein, Jules (ed.): *Oil and Gas Fields of Southeast Louisiana, Vol. 1,* New Orleans Geol. Soc. (1965), 195 pp.

Bryant, W., Jones, B. and Antoine, J.: "Structural Features of Continental Shelf, Slope, and Scarp, Northeastern Gulf of Mexico," *Bull.,* AAPG (1967), v. 51, no. 2, pp. 257-262.

Bryant, W. and Pyle, T.: "Tertiary Sediments from Sigsbee Knolls, Gulf of Mexico," *Bull.,* AAPG (1965), v. 49, no. 9, pp. 1517-1518.

Burckle, Lloyd H., Peter, George and Heirtzler, J. R.: "Magnetic Anomalies in the Gulf of Mexico," *Jour. Geophys. Res.* (1966), v. 71, no. 2, pp. 519-526.

Clark, D. M., Jordan, J. N., Mickey, W. W. and Helterbran, W.: "Travel Times and Amplitudes from the Salmon Explosion," *Jour. Geophys. Res.* (1966), v. 71, no. 14, pp. 3469-3482.

Copeland, R. R., Jr., Gimbrede, L. delA., Paine, W. R. and Mitchell, M. W.: "Frio and Anahuac Sediment Inclusions, Belle Isle Salt Dome, St. Mary Parish, Louisiana," *Bull.,* AAPG (1965), v. 49, no. 5, pp. 616-620.

Curray, Joseph R. and Lankford, Robert R.: "Mid-Tertiary Rock Outcrop on Continental Shelf, Northwest Gulf of Mexico," *Bull.,* AAPG (1957), v. 41, no. 9, pp. 2113-2117.

Curray, Joseph R. and Parker, Robert H.: "Fauna and Bathymetry of Banks on Continental Shelf, Northwest Gulf of Mexico," *Bull.,* AAPG (1956), v. 40, no. 10, pp. 2428-2439.

Diaz G., Teodoro, Wall, James R. and Murray, G. E.: "Geologic Occurrence of Intrusive Gypsum and Its Effect on Structural Forms in Coahuila Marginal Folded Province of Northeastern Mexico," *Bull.,* AAPG (1961), v. 45, no. 9, pp. 1504-1522.

Dumble, E. T.: "The Occurrence of Petroleum in Eastern Mexico as Contrasted with Those in Texas and Louisiana," *Trans.,* AIME (1916), v. 52, p. 263.

Eby, Thomas J., Jr.: "Franklin Field, St. Mary Parish, Louisiana," *Typical Oil and Gas Fields of Southwestern Louisiana,* Lafayette Geol. Soc. (1964), pp. 10-10d.

Ewing, J. and Ewing, M.: "Rate of Salt-dome Growth," *Bull.,* AAPG (1962), v. 46, no. 5, pp. 708-709.

Ewing, J., Wortzel, J. L. and Ewing, M.: "Sediments and Oceanic Structural History of the Gulf of Mexico," *Jour. Geophys. Res.* (1962), v. 67, no. 6, pp. 2509-2527.

Ewing, M. and Antoine, J.: "New Seismic Data Concerning Sediments and Diapiric Structures in

Sigsbee Deep and Upper Continental Slope," *Bull.,* AAPG (1966), v. 50, no. 3, pp. 479-504.

Ewing, M. and Ewing, J.: "Rate of Salt-dome Growth," *Bull.,* AAPG (1962), v. 46, no. 5, pp. 708-709.

Ewing, M., Ewing, J. and Wortzel, J. L.: "Sediments and Oceanic Structural History of the Gulf of Mexico," *Jour. Geophys. Res.* (1962), v. 67, no. 6, pp. 2509-2527.

Ewing, M. and Talwani, Manik: "A Continuous Gravity Profile Over the Sigsbee Knolls," *Jour. Geophys. Res.* (1966), v. 71, no. 18, pp. 4434-4438.

Fails, Thomas G.: "Lake Pelto Field, Terrebonne Parish, Louisiana," *Oil and Gas Fields of Southeast Louisiana, Vol. 1,* New Orleans Geol. Soc. (1965), pp. 115-120.

Flinn, E. A., Lambert, D. G. and Archambeau, C. B.: "Detection Analysis, and Interpretation of Seismic Signals. 1. Compressional Phases from the Salmon Event," *Jour. Geophys. Res.* (1966), v. 71, no. 14, pp. 3483-3501.

Forman, M. J. and Schlanger, S. O.: "Tertiary Reef and Associated Limestone Facies from Louisiana and Guam," *Jour. Geol.* (1957), v. 65, no. 6, pp. 611-627.

Freeman, Paul S.: "Caillou Island (East) Field, Terrebonne Parish, Louisiana," *Oil and Gas Fields of Southeast Louisiana, Vol. 1,* New Orleans Geol. Soc. (1965), pp. 61-65.

George, Peter, Heirtzler, J. R. and Burckle, Lloyd H.: "Magnetic Anomalies in the Gulf of Mexico," *Jour. Geophys. Res.* (1966), v. 71, no. 2, pp. 519-526.

Gimbrede, L. deA., Paine, W. R., Mitchell, M. W. and Copeland, R. R., Jr.: "Frio and Anahuac Sediment Inclusions, Belle Island Salt Dome, St. Mary Parish, Louisiana," *Bull.,* AAPG (1965), v. 49, no. 5, pp. 616-620.

Goedicke, T. R.: "Origin of the Pinnacles on the Continental Shelf and Slope in the Gulf of Mexico," *Tex. Jour. Sci.* (1955), v. 7, no. 2, pp. 149-159.

Harding, J. L., Amstutz, D. E. and Nowlin, W. D., Jr.: "A Reconnaissance Study of the Sigsbee Knolls of the Gulf of Mexico," *Jour. Geophys. Res.* (1965), v. 70, no. 6, pp. 1339-1349.

Hatten, C. W. and Meyerhoff, A. A.: (abs.) "Pre-Portlandian Rocks of Western Cuba," *Spec. Paper 82,* GSA (1965), p. 301.

Hatten, C. W. and Meyerhoff, A. A.: "Diapiric Structures in Central Cuba, *in* Diapirism and Diapirs," *Memoir,* AAPG (in press).

Healy, J. H., Jackson, W. H. and Warren, D. H.: "Crustal Seismic Measurements in Southern Missis-

sippi," *Jour. Geophys. Res.* (1966), v. 71, no. 14, pp. 3437-3458.

Heirtzler, J. R., Burckle, Lloyd H. and Peter, George: "Magnetic Anomalies in the Gulf of Mexico," *Jour. Geophys. Res.* (1966), v. 71, no. 2, pp. 519-526.

Halterbran, W., Clark, D. M., Jordan, J. N. and Mickey, W. W.: "Travel Times and Amplitudes from the Salmon Explosion," *Jour. Geophys. Res.* (1966), v. 71, no. 14, pp. 3469-3482.

Herrin, E. and Taggart, J.: "Epicenter Determination for the Salmon Event," *Jour. Geophys. Res.* (1966), v. 71, no. 14, pp. 3503-3506.

Holyoak, Dale Maxwell: "St. Gabriel Field, Ascension and Iberville Parishes, Louisiana," *Oil and Gas Fields of Southeast Louisiana, Vol 1,* New Orleans Geol. Soc. (1946), pp. 177-180.

Imlay, R. W.: "Correlation of the Jurassic Formations of North America, Exclusive of Canada," *Bull.,* GSA (1952), v. 63, no. 9, pp. 953-992.

Jackson, W. H., Warren, D. H. and Healy, J. H.: "Crustal Seismic Measurements in Southern Mississippi," *Jour. Geophys. Res.* (1966), v. 71, no. 14, pp. 3437-3458.

Jones, B., Antoine, J. and Bryant, W.: "Structural Features of Continental Shelf, Slope, and Scarp, Northeastern Gulf of *Mexico,*" *Bull.,* AAPG (1967), v. 51, no. 2, pp. 257-262.

Jordan, J. N., Mickey, W. V., Helterbran, W. and Clark, D. M.: "Travel Times and Amplitudes from the Salmon Explosion," *Jour. Geophys. Res.* (1966), v. 71, no. 14, pp. 3469-3482.

Kepner, Thomas: "Cameron Meadows Field, Cameron Parish, Louisiana," *Typical Oil and Gas Fields of Southwestern Louisiana,* Lafayette Geol. Soc. (1964), pp. 3-3d.

Khudoley, K. M.: "Principal Features of Cuban Geology," *Bull.,* AAPG (1967), v. 51, no. 5, pp. 668-677.

Lambert, D. G., Archambeau, C. B. and Flinn, E. A.: "Detection Analysis, and Interpretation of Seismic Signals. 1. Compressional Phases from the Salmon Event," *Jour. Geophys. Res.* (1966), v. 71, no. 14, pp. 3483-3501.

Lankford, Robert R. and Curray, Joseph R.: "Mid-Tertiary Rock Outcrop on Continental Shelf, Northwest Gulf of Mexico," *Bull.,* AAPG (1957), v. 41, no. 9, pp. 2113-2117.

Lysinger, Scott J.: "Sweet Lake Field, Cameron Parish, Louisiana," *Typical Oil and Gas Fields of Southwestern Louisiana,* Lafayette Geol. Soc. (1964), pp. 31-31c.

Marsh, Owen T.: (abs.) "Deep-lying Salt Deposits in Florida Panhandle Suggested by Faulting and Gravity Anomalies," *Spec. Paper 82,* GSA (1965), pp. 304-305.

Marsh, Owen T.: "Evidence for Deep Salt Deposits in Western Florida Panhandle," *Bull.,* AAPG (1967), v. 51, no. 2, pp. 212-222.

Matteson, W. G.: "Principles and Problems of Oil Prospecting in the Gulf Coast Country," *AIME* (1918), v. 59, pp. 435-491.

McCampbell, John C. and Sheller, James W. (eds.): *Typical Oil and Gas Fields of Southwestern Louisiana,* Lafayette Geol. Soc. (1964), pp. 1-32e.

Melton, John R.: "Lake Chicot Field, St. Martin Parish, Louisiana," *Typical Oil and Gas Fields of Southwestern Louisiana,* Lafayette Geol. Soc. (1964), pp. 21-21d.

Meyerhoff, A. A.: (abs.) "Cuban Evaporite Diapirs," *Bull.,* AAPG (1965), v. 49, no. 3, pp. 350-351.

Meyerhoff, A. A. and Hatten, C. W.: (abs.) "Diapiric Portlandian Rocks of Western Cuba," *Spec. Paper 82,* GSA (1965), p. 301.

Meyerhoff, A. A. and Hatten, C. W.: "Diapiric Structures in Central Cuba, *in* Diapirism and Diapirs," *Memoir,* AAPG (in press).

Mickey, W. V., Helterbran, W., Clark, D. M. and Jordan, J. N.: "Travel Times and Amplitudes from the Salmon Explosion," *Jour. Geophys. Res.* (1966), v. 71, no. 14, pp. 3469-3482.

Mississippi State Geological Survey: *Bull. 43, Warren County Mineral Resources* (1941), 140 pp.

Mitchell, M. W., Copeland, R. R., Jr., Gimbrede, L. deA., and Paine, W. R.: "Frio and Anahuac Sediment Inclusions, Belle Isle Salt Dome, St. Mary Parish, Louisiana," *Bull.,* AAPG (1965), v. 49, no. 5, pp. 616-620.

Moore, David G. and Curray, Joseph R.: "Structural Framework of the Continental Terrace, Northwest Gulf of Mexico," *Jour. Geophys. Res.* (1963), v. 68, no. 6, pp. 1725-1747.

Murray, G. E.: "Geologic Occurrence of Hydrocarbons in Gulf Coastal Province of the United States," *Trans.,* GCAGS, v. 7 (1957), pp. 253-299; *Symposium on the Occurrence of Oil and Gas,* XX International Geological Congress, Mexico City (1956).

Murray, G. E., Diaz, G., Teodoro and Wall, James R.: "Geologic Occurrence of Intrusive Gypsum and Its Effect on Structural Forms in Coahuila Marginal Folded Province of Northeastern Mexico," *Bull.,* AAPG (1961), v. 45, no. 9, 1504-1522.

Murray, G. E. and Weidie, Alfred E., Jr.: "Tectonics of Parras Basin, States of Coahuila and Nuevo Leon, Mexico," *Trans.,* GCAGS (1961), v. 11, pp. 47-56.

New Orleans Geol. Soc.: "Stella Field, Plaquemines Parish, Louisiana," *Oil and Gas Fields of Southeast Louisiana, Vol 1,* New Orleans Geol. Soc. (1965), pp. 181-184.

Nowlin, W. D., Jr., Harding, J. L. and Amstutz, D. E.: "A Reconnaissance Study of the Sigsbee Knolls of the Gulf of Mexico," *Jour. Geophys. Res.* (1965), v. 70, no. 6, pp. 1339-1349.

Paine, W. R., Mitchell, M. W., Copeland, R. R., Jr. and Gimbrede, L. deA.: "Frio and Anahuac Sediment Inclusions, Belle Isle Salt Dome, St. Mary Parish, Louisiana," *Bull.,* AAPG (1965), v. 49, no. 5, pp. 616-620.

Parker, Robert H. and Curray, Joseph R.: "Fauna and Bathymetry of Banks on Continental Shelf, Northwest Gulf of Mexico," *Bull.,* AAPG (1956), v. 40, no. 10, pp. 2428-2439.

Patterson, D. W.: "Nuclear Decoupling, Full and Partial," *Jour. Geophys. Res.* (1966), v. 71, no. 14, pp. 3427-3436.

Posepny, F.: "Studien aus dem Salinargebiete Siebenburgens, zweite Abteilung," *K. K. Geol. Reichsanstalt Jahrb.* (1871), Bd. 21, Heft 1, pp. 123-188.

Pyle, T. and Bryant, W.: "Tertiary Sediments from Sigsbee Knolls, Gulf of Mexico," *Bull.,* AAPG (1965), v. 49, no. 9, pp. 1517-1518.

Randolph, P., Boardman, C., Wheeler, V. and Rawson, D.: "Post-explosion Environment Resulting from the Salmon Event," *Jour. Geophys. Res.* (1966), v. 71, no. 14, pp. 3507-3521.

Randolph, P. and Werth, G.: "The Salmon Seismic Experiment," *Jour. Geophys. Res.* (1966), v. 71, no. 14, pp. 3405-3413.

Rawson, D., Randolph, P., Boardman, C. and Wheeler, V.: "Post-explosion Environment Resulting from the Salmon Event," *Jour. Geophys. Res.* (1966), v. 71, no. 14, pp. 3507-3521.

Robinson, E. C.: "Gueydan Field, Acadia and Vermilion Parishes, Louisiana," *Typical Oil and Gas Fields of Southwestern Louisiana,* Lafayette Geol. Soc. (1964), pp. 12-12d.

Rogers, G. S.: 'Intrusive Orgin of the Gulf Coast Salt Domes," *Econ. Geol.* (1918), v. 13, p. 468.

Rogers, L. A.: "Free-field Motion Near a Nuclear Explosion in Salt: Project Salmon," *Jour. Geophys. Res.* (1966), v. 71, no. 14, pp. 3415-3426.

Schlanger, S. O. and Forman, M. J.: "Tertiary Reef and Associated Limestone Facies from Louisiana and Guam," *Jour. Geol.* (1957), v. 65, no. 6, pp. 611-627.

Sheller, James W. and McCampbell, John C. (eds.): *Typical Oil and Gas Fields of Southwestern Louisiana,* Lafayette Geol. Soc. (1964), pp. 1-32e.

Springer, D. L.: "Calculation of First-zone *P* Wave Amplitudes for Salmon Event and for Decoupled Sources," *Jour. Geophys. Res.* (1966), v. 71, no. 14, pp. 3459-3467.

Taggart, J. and Herrin, E.: "Epicenter Determination for the Salmon Event," *Jour. Geophys. Res.* (1966), v. 71, no. 14, pp. 3503-3506.

Talwani, Manik and Ewing, M.: "A Continuous Gravity Profile Over the Sigsbee Knolls," *Jour. Geophys. Res.* (1966), v. 71, no. 18, pp. 4434-4438.

Thorsen, Carl E.: "Age of Growth Faulting in Southeast Louisiana," *Trans., GCAGS* (1963), v. 13, pp. 103-110.

Van der Gracht, W. A. I. M. von Waterschoot: "The Saline Domes of Northwestern Europe," *Southwestern Assoc. Pet. Geol.* (1917), v. 1, pp. 85-92.

Wall, James R., Murray, G. E. and Diaz G.,

Teodoro: "Geologic Occurrence of Intrusive Gypsum and Its Effect on Structural Forms in Coahuila Marginal Folded Province of Northeastern Mexico," *Bull.,* AAPG (1961), v. 45, no. 9, pp. 1504-1522.

Warren, D. H., Healy, J. H. and Jackson, W. H.: "Crustal Seismic Measurements in Southern Mississippi," *Jour. Geophys. Res.* (1966), v. 71, no. 14, pp. 3437-3458.

Weidie, Alfred E., Jr. and Murray, G. E.: "Tectonics of Parras Basin, States of Coahuila and Nuevo Leon, Mexico," *Trans., GCAGS* (1961), v. 11, pp. 47-56.

Werth, G. and Randolph, P.: "The Salmon Seismic Experiment," *Jour. Geophys. Res.* (1966), v. 71, no. 14, pp. 3405-3413.

Wheeler, V., Rawson, D., Randolph, P. and Boardman, C.: "Post-explosion Environment Resulting from the Salmon Event," *Jour. Geophys. Res.* (1966), v. 71, no. 14, pp. 3507-3521.

Williamson, J. D. M.: "Gulf Coast Cenozoic History," *Trans., GCAGS* (1959), v. 9, pp. 14-29.

Wortzel, J. L., Ewing, M. and Ewing, J. I.: "Sediments and Oceanic Structural History of the Gulf of Mexico," *Jour. Geophys. Res.* (1962), v. 67, no. 6, pp. 2509-2527.

*For references on page 227, Rojas, Antonio Garcia should be Garcia Rojas, Antonio; Roldan, Pascual Gutierrez should be Gutierrez Roldan, Pascual.

Addendum to Bibliographies
Bibliography Arranged According to Subject Matter

978. "Anahuac and Frio Sediment Inclusions, Belle Isle Salt Dome, St. Mary, Parish, Louisiana": Paine, W. R., Mitchell, M. W., Copeland, R. R., Jr. and Gimbrede, L. deA., *Bull.,* AAPG (1965), v. 49, no. 5, pp. 616-620.

979. "Bathymetry of Banks on Continental Shelf, Northwest Gulf of Mexico, Fauna and": Parker, Robert H. and Curray, Joseph R., *Bull.,* AAPG (1956), v. 40, no. 10, pp. 2428-2439.

978. "Belle Isle Salt Dome, St. Mary Parish, Louisiana, Frio and Anahuac Sediment Inclusions": Paine, W. R., Mitchell, M. W., Copeland, R. R., Jr. and Gimbrede, L. deA., *Bull.,* AAPG (1965), v. 49, no. 5, pp. 616-620.

980. "Big Lake Field, Cameron Parish, Louisiana": Anderson, Robert A., *Typical Oil and Gas Fields of Southwestern Louisiana,* Lafayette Geol. Soc. (1964), pp. 2-2d.

981. "Caillou Island (East) Field, Terrebonne Parish, Louisiana": Freeman, Paul S., *Oil and Gas Fields of Southeast Louisiana, Vol. 1,* New Orleans Geol. Soc. (1965), pp. 61-65.

982. "Cameron Meadows Field, Cameron Parish, Louisiana": Kepner, Thomas, *Typical Oil and Gas Fields of Southwestern Louisiana,* Lafayette Geol. Soc. (1964), pp. 3-3d.

983. "Cenozoic History, Gulf Coast": Williamson, J. D. M., *Trans.,* GCAGS (1959), v. 9, pp. 14-29.

979. "Continental Shelf, Northwest Gulf of Mexico, Fauna and Bathymetry of Banks on": Parker, Robert H. and Curray, Joseph R., *Bull.,* AAPG (1956), v. 40, no. 10, pp. 2428-2439.

984. "Continental Shelf, Northwest Gulf of Mexico, Mid-tertiary Rock Outcrop on": Lankford, Robert R. and Curray, Joseph R., *Bull.,* AAPG (1957), v. 41, no. 9, pp. 2113-2117.

985. "Continental Shelf and Slope in the Gulf of Mexico, Origin of the Pinnacles on the": Goedicke, T. R., *Tex. Jour. Sci.* (1955), v. 7, no. 2, pp. 149-159.

986. "Continental Shelf, Slope, and Scarp, Northeastern Gulf of Mexico, Structural Features Deep and Upper": Ewing, M. and Antonie, J., *Bull.,* AAPG (1967), v. 51, no. 2, pp. 257-262.

987. "Continental Slope, New Seismic Data Concerning Sediments and Diapiric Structures in Sigsbee Deep and": Ewing, M. and Antonie, J., *Bull.,* AAPG (1966), v. 50, no. 3, pp. 479-504.

988. "Continental Terrace, Northwest Gulf of Mexico, Structural Framework of the": Moore, David G. and Curray, Joseph R., *Jour. Geophys. Res.* (1963), v. 68, no. 6, pp. 1725-1747.

989. "Correlation of the Jurassic Formations of North America, Exclusive of Canada": Imlay, R. W., *Bull.,* GSA (1952), v. 63, no. 9, pp. 953-992.

990. "Cuba, *in* Diapirism and Diapirs, Diapiric Structures in Central": Hatten C. W. and Meyerhoff, A. A., *Memoir,* AAPG (in press).

991. "Cuba, Pre-Portlandian Rocks of Western" (abs.): Hatten, C. W. and Meyerhoff, A. A., *Spec. Paper 82,* GSA (1965), p. 301.

992. "Cuban Evaporite Diapirs" (abs.): Meyerhoff, A. A., *Bull.,* AAPG (1965), v. 49, no. 3, pp. 350-351.

993. "Cuban Geology, Principal Features of": Khudoley, K. M., *Bull.,* AAPG (1967), v. 51, no. 5, pp. 668-677.

994. "Detection Analysis and Interpretation of Seismic Signals. 1. Compressional Phases from the Salmon Event": Archambeau, C. B., Flinn, E. A. and Lambert, D. G., *Jour. Geophys. Res.* (1966), v. 71, no. 14, pp. 3483-3501.

990. "Diapiric Structures in Central Cuba, *in* Diapirism and Diapirs": Meyerhoff, A. A. and Hatten, C. W., *Memoir,* AAPG (in press).

987. "Diapiric Structures in Sigebee Deep and Upper Continental Slope, New Seismic Concerning Sediments and": Ewing, M. and Antoine, J., *Bull.,* AAPG (1966), v. 50, no. 3, pp. 479-504.

995. "Epicenter Determination for the Salmon Event": Herrin, E. and Taggart, J., *Jour. Geophys. Res.* (1966), v. 71, no. 14, pp. 3503-3506.

996. "Europe, The Saline Domes of Northwestern": Van der Gracht, W.A.I.M. von Waterschoot, *Southwestern Assoc. Pet. Geol.* (1917), v. 1, pp. 85-92.

992. "Evaporite Diapirs, Cuban" (abs.): Meyerhoff, A. A., *Bull.,* AAPG (1965), v. 49, no. 3, pp. 350-351.

997. "Faulting and Gravity Anomalies, Deep-lying Salt Deposits in Florida Panhandle Suggested by" (abs.): Marsh, Owen T., *Spec. Paper 82,* GSA (1965), pp. 304-305.

979. "Fauna and Baythymetry of Banks on Continental Shelf, Northwest Gulf of Mexico": Parker, Robert H. and Curray, Joseph R., *Bull.,* AAPG (1956), v. 40, no. 10, pp. 2428-2439.

998. "Florida Panhandle, Evidence for Deep Salt Deposits in Western": Marsh, Owen T., *Bull.,* AAPG (1967), v. 51, no. 2, pp. 212-222.

997. "Florida Panhandle Suggested by Faulting and Gravity Anomalies, Deep-lying Salt Deposits in" (abs.): Marsh, Owen T., *Spec. Paper 82,* GSA (1965), pp. 304-305.

999. "Franklin Field, St. Mary Parish, Louisiana": Eby, Thomas J., Jr., *Typical Oil and Gas Fields of Southwestern Louisiana,* Lafayette Geol. Soc. (1964), pp. 10-10d.

978. "Frio and Anahuac Sediment Inclusions, Belle Isle Salt Dome, St. Mary Parish, Louisiana": Paine, W. R., Mitchell, M. W., Copeland, R. R., Jr. and Gimbrede, L. deA., *Bull.,* AAPG (1965), v. 49, no. 5, pp. 616-620.

1000. "Geologic Occurrence of Hydrocarbons in Gulf Coastal Province of the United States": Murray, G. E., *Trans.,* GCAGS, v. 7 (1957), pp. 253-299; *Symposium on the Occurrence of Oil and Gas,* XX International Geological Congress, Mexico City (1956).

1001. "Geologic Occurrence of Intrusive Gypsum and Its Effect on Structural Forms in Coahuila Marginal Folded Province of Northeastern Mexico": Wall, James R. Murray, G. E. and Diaz G., Teodoro, *Bull.,* AAPG (1961), v. 45, no. 9, pp. 1504-1522.

997. "Gravity and Faulting Anomalies, Deep-lying Salt Deposits in Florida Panhandle Suggested by" (abs.): Marsh, Owen T., *Spec. Paper 82,* GSA (1964), pp. 304-305.

1002. "Gravity Profile Over the Sigsbee Knolls, A Continuous": Ewing, M. and Talwani, Manik, *Jour. Geophys. Res.* (1966), v. 71, no. 18, pp. 4434-4438.

1003. "Growth Faulting in Southeast Louisiana, Age of": Thorsen, Carl E., *Trans.,* GCAGS (1963), v. 13, pp. 103-110.

1004. "Guam and Louisiana, Tertiary Reef and Associated Limestone Facies from": Forman, M. J. and Schlanger, S. O., *Jour. Geol.* (1957), v. 65, no. 6, pp. 611-627.

1005. "Gueydan Field, Acadia and Vermilion Parishes, Louisiana": Robinson, E. C., *Typical Oil and Gas Fields of Southwestern Louisiana,* Lafayette Geol. Soc. (1964), pp. 12-12d.

983. "Gulf Coast Cenozoic History": Williamson, J. D. M., Trans., GCAGS (1959), v. 9, pp. 14-29.

1006. "Gulf Coast Country, Principles and Problems of Oil Prospecting in the": Matteson, W., *AIME* (1918), v. 59, pp. 435-491.

1007. "Gulf Coast Salt Domes, Intrusive Origin of the": Rogers, G. S., *Econ. Geol.* (1918), v. 13, p. 468.

1000. "Gulf Coastal Province of the United States, Geologic Occurrence of Hydrocarbons in": Murray, G. E., *Trans.,* GCAGS, v. 7 (1957), pp. 253-299; *Symposium on the Occurrence of Oil and Gas,* XX International Geological Congress, Mexico City (1956).

1008. "Gulf of Mexico, A Reconnaissance Study of the Sigsbee Knolls of the": Nowlin, W. D., Jr., Hardin, J. L. and Amstutz, D. E., *Jour. Geophys. Res.* (1965), v. 70, no. 6, pp. 1339-1349.

1009. "Gulf of Mexico, Magnetic Anomalies in the": Heirtzler, J. R., Burckle, Lloyd H., Peter, George, *Jour. Geophys. Res.* (1966), v. 71, no. 2, pp. 519-526.

986. "Gulf of Mexico, structural Features of Continental Shelf, Slope, and Scarp, Northeastern": Jones, B., Antoine, J. and Bryant, W., *Bull.,* AAPG (1967), v. 51, no. 2, pp. 257-262.

979. "Gulf of Mexico, Fauna and Bathymetry of Banks on Continental Shelf, Northwest": Parker, Robert H. and Curray, Joseph R., *Bull.,* AAPG (1956), v. 40, no. 10, pp. 2428-2439.

984. "Gulf of Mexico, Mid-Tertiary Rock Outcrop on Continental Shelf, Northwest": Lankford,

Robert R. and Curray, Joseph R., *Bull.*, AAPG (1957), v. 41, no. 9, pp. 2113-2117.

988. "Gulf of Mexico, Structural Framework of the Continental Terrace, Northwest": Moore, David G. and Curray, Joseph R., *Jour. Geophys. Res.* (1963), v. 68, no. 6, pp. 1725-1747.

985. "Gulf of Mexico, Origin of the Pinnacles on the Continental Shelf and Slope in the": Goedicke, T. R., *Tex. Jour. Sci.* (1955), v. 7, no. 2, pp. 149-159.

1010. "Gulf of Mexico, Sediments and Oceanic Structural History of the": Ewing, J., Ewing, M. and Wortzel, J. L., *Jour Geophys. Res.* (1962), v. 67, no. 6, pp. 2509-2527.

1011. "Gulf of Mexico, Tertiary Sediments from Sigsbee Knolls": Bryant, W. and Pyle, T., *Bull.*, AAPG (1965), v. 49, no. 9, pp. 1517-1518.

1000. "Hydrocarbons in Gulf Coastal Province of the United States, Geologic Occurrence of": Murray, G. E., *Trans.*, GCAGS, v. 7 (1957), pp. 253-299; *Symposium on the Occurrence of Oil and Gas*, XX International Geological Congress, Mexico City (1956).

1001. "Intrusive Gypsum and Its Effect on Structural Forms in Coahuila Marginal Folded Province of Northeastern Mexico, Geologic Occurrence of": Wall, James R., Murray, G. E. and Diaz G., Teodoro, *Bull.*, AAPG (1961), v. 45, no. 9, pp. 1504-1522.

1007. "Intrusive Origin of the Gulf Coast Salt Domes": Rogers, G. S., *Econ. Geol.* (1918), v. 13, p. 468.

989. "Jurassic Formations of North America, Exclusive of Canada, Correlation of the," Imlay, R. W., *Bull.*, GSA (1952), v. 63, no. 9, pp. 953-992.

1012. "Lake Chicot Field, St. Martin Parish, Louisiana": Melton, John R., *Typical Oil and Gas Fields of Southwestern Louisiana*, Lafayette Geol. Soc. (1964), pp. 21-21d.

1013. "Lake Pelto Field, Terrebonne Parish, Louisiana": Fails, Thomas G., *Oil and Gas Fields of Southeast Louisiana, Vol 1*, New Orleans Geol. Soc. (1965), pp. 115-120.

1003. "Louisiana, Age of Growth Faulting in Southeast": Thorsen, Carl E., *Trans.*, GCAGS (1963), v. 13, pp. 103-110.

1004. "Louisiana and Guam, Tertiary Reef and Associated Limestone Facies from": Forman, M. J. and Schlanger, S. O., *Jour. Geol.* (1957), v. 65, no. 6, pp. 611-627.

1014. "Louisiana and Texas, The Occurrence of Petroleum in Eastern Mexico as Contrasted with Those in": Dumble, E. T., *Trans.*, AIME (1916), v. 52, p. 263.

1015. *Louisiana, Oil and Gas Fields of Southeast, Vol. 1:* Braunstein, Jules (ed.), New Orleans Geol. Soc. (1965), 195 pp.

1016. *Louisiana, Typical Oil and Gas Fields of Southwestern:* McCampbell, John C. and Sheller, James W. (eds.), Lafayette Geol. Soc. (1964), pp. 1-32e.

1009. "Magnetic Anomalies in the Gulf of Mexico": Heirtzler, J. R., Burckle, Lloyd H. and Peter, George, *Jour. Geophys. Res.* (1966), v. 71, no. 2, pp. 519-526.

1014. "Mexico, as Contrasted with Those in Texas and Louisiana, The Occurrence of Petroleum in Eastern": Dumble, E. T., *Trans.*, AIME (1916), v. 52, p. 623.

1001. "Mexico, Geologic Occurrence of Intrusive Gypsum and Its Effect on Structural Forms in Coahuila Marginal Folded Province of Northeastern," Diaz, G., Teodoro, Wall, James R. and Murray, G. E., *Bull.*, AAPG (1961), v. 45, no. 9, pp. 1504-1522.

1015. "Mexico, Tectonics of Parras Basin, States of Coahuila and Nuevo Leon": Weidie, Alfred E., Jr. and Murray, G. E., *Trans.*, GCAGS (1961), v. 11, pp. 47-56.

984. "Mid-Tertiary Rock Outcrop on Continental Shelf, Northwest Gulf of Mexico": Lankford, Robert R. and Curry, Joseph R., *Bull.*, AAPG (1957), v. 41, no. 9, pp. 2113-2117.

1006. "Mississippi, Crustal Seismic Measurements in Southern": Warren, D. H., Healy, J. H. and Jackson, W. H., *Jour. Geophys. Res.* (1966), v. 71, no. 14, pp. 3437-3458.

1017. "Nuclear Decoupling, Full and Partial": Patterson, D. W., *Jour. Geophys. Res.* (1966), v. 71, no. 14, pp. 3427-3436.

1018. "Nuclear Explosion in Salt, Free-field Motion Near a: Project Salmon": Rogers, L. A., *Jour. Geophys. Res.* (1966), v. 71, no. 14, pp. 3415-3426.

1015. *Oil and Gas Fields of Southeast Louisiana, Vol. 1:* Braunstein, Jules (ed.), New Orleans Geol. Soc. (1965), 195 pp.

1016. *Oil and Gas Fields of Southwestern Louisiana, Typical:* McCampbell, John C. and Sheller, James W. (eds.), Lafayette Geol. Soc. (1964), pp. 1-32e.

1006. "Oil Prospecting in the Gulf Coast Country, Principles and Problems of": Matteson, W., *AIME* (1918), v. 59, pp. 435-491.

985. "Origin of the Pinnacles on the Continental Shelf and Slope in the Gulf of Mexico": Goedicke, T. R., *Tex. Jour. Sci.* (1955), v. 7, no. 2, pp. 149-159.

1015. "Parras Basin, States of Coahuila and Nuevo Leon, Mexico, Tectonics of": Weidie, Alfred E., Jr. and Murray G. E., *Trans.*, GCAGS (1961), v. 11, pp. 47-56.

1014. "Petroleum in Eastern Mexico as Contrasted with Those in Texas and Louisiana, The Occurrence of": Dumble, E. T., *Trans.*, AIME (1916), v. 52, p. 263.

985. "Pinnacles on the Continental Shelf and Slope in the Gulf of Mexico, Origin of the": Goedicke, T. R., *Tex. Jour. Sci.* (1955), v. 7, no. 2, pp. 149-159.

991. "Pre-Portlandian Rocks of Western Cuba" (abs.): Hatten, C. W. and Meyerhoff, A. A., *Spec. Paper 82*, GSA (1965), p. 301.

1019. "St. Gabriel Field, Ascension and Iberville Parishes, Louisiana": Holyoak, Dale Maxwell, *Oil and Gas Fields of Southeast Louisiana, Vol. 1*, New Orleans Geol. Soc. (1965), pp. 177-180.

1020. "Salinargebiete Siebenburgens, zweite Abteilung, Studien aus dem": Posepny, F., *K. K. Geol. Reichsanstalt Jahrb.* (1871), Bd. 21, Heft 1, pp.123-188.

996. "Saline Domes of Northwestern Europe, The": Van der Gracht, W.A.I.M. von Waterschoot, *Southwestern Assoc. Pet Geol.* (1917), v. 1, pp. 85-92.

1021. "Salmon Event and for Decoupled Sources, Calculation of First-zone *P* Wave Amplitudes for": Springer, D. L., *Jour. Geophys. Res.* (1966), v. 71, no. 14, pp. 3459-3467.

994. "Salmon Event, Detection Analysis, and Interpretation of Seismic Signals. 1. Compressional Phases from the": Archambeau, C. B., Flinn, E. A. and Lambert, D. G., *Jour. Geophys. Res.* (1966), v. 71, no. 14, pp. 3483-3501.

995. "Salmon Event, Epicenter Determination for the": Herrin, E. and Taggart, J., *Jour Geophys. Res.* (1966), v. 71, no. 14, pp. 3503-3506.

1022. "Salmon Event, Post-explosion Environment Resulting from the": Rawson, D., Randolph, P., Boardman, C. and Wheeler, V., *Jour. Geophys. Res.* (1966), v. 71, no. 14, pp. 3507-3521.

1023. "Salmon Explosion, Travel Times and Amplitudes from the": Jordan, J. N., Mickey,

W. V., Helterbran, W. and Clark, D. M., *Jour. Geophys. Res.* (1966), v. 71, no. 14, pp. 3469-3482.

1018. "Salmon, Project, Nuclear Explosion in Salt, Free-field Motion Near a": Rogers, L. A., *Jour. Geophys. Res.* (1966), v. 71, no. 14, pp. 3415-3426.

1024. "Salmon Seismic Experiment, The": Werth, G. and Randolph, P., *Jour. Geophys. Res.* (1966), v. 71, no. 14, pp. 3405-3413.

997. "Salt Deposits in Florida Panhandle Suggested by Faulting and Gravity Anomalies, Deep-lying (abs.)": Marsh, Owen T., *Spec. Paper 82*, GSA (1965), pp. 304-305.

998. "Salt Deposits in Western Florida Panhandle, Evidence for Deep": Marsh, Owen T., *Bull.*, AAPG (1967), v. 51, no. 2, pp. 212-222.

1025. "Salt-dome Growth, Rate of": Ewing, M. and Ewing, J., *Bull*, AAPG (1962), v. 46, no. 5, pp. 708-709.

1007. "Salt Domes, Intrusive Origin of the Gulf Coast": Rogers, G. S., *Econ. Geol.* (1918), v. 13, p. 468.

987. "Sediments and Diapiric Structures in Sigsbee Deep and Upper Continental Slope, New Seismic Data Concerning": Antoine, J. and Ewing, M., *Bull.*, AAPG (1966) v. 50, no. 3, pp. 479-504.

1010. "Sediments and Oceanic Structural History of the Gulf of Mexico": Ewing, J., Wortzel, J. L. and Ewing, M., *Jour Geophys. Res.* (1962), v. 67, no. 6. pp. 2509-2527.

1016. Seismic, Measurements in Southern Mississippi Crustal": Warren, D. H., Healy, J. H. and Jackson, W. H., *Jour. Geophys. Res.* (1966), v. 71, no. 14, pp. 3437-3458.

987. "Seismic Data Concerning Sediments and Diapiric Structures in Sigsbee Deep and Upper Continental Slope, New": Ewing, M. and Antoine, J., *Bull.*, AAPG (1966), v. 50, no. 3, pp. 479-504.

987. "Sigsbee Deep and Upper Continental Slope, New Seismic Data Concerning Sediments and Diapiric Structures in": Ewing, M. and Antoine, J., *Bull.*, AAPG (1966), v. 50, no. 3, pp. 479-504.

1002. "Sigsbee Knolls, A Continuous Gravity Profile Over the": Ewing, M. and Talwani, Manik, *Jour. Geophys. Res.* (1966), v. 71, no. 18, pp. 4434-4438.

1011. "Sigsbee Knolls, Gulf of Mexico, Tertiary Sediments from ": Bryant, W. and Pyle, T., *Bull.*, AAPG (1965), v. 49, no. 9, pp. 1517-1518.

1008. "Sigsbee Knolls of the Gulf of Mexico, A Reconnaissance Study of the": Nowlin, W. D., Jr.,

Harding, J. L. and Amstutz, D. E., *Jour. Geophys. Res.* (1965), v. 70, no. 6, pp. 1339-1349.

1026. "Stella Field, Plaquemines Parish, Louisiana": New Orleans Geol. Soc., *Oil and Gas Fields of Southeast Louisiana, Vol. 1,* New Orleans Geol. Soc. (1965) pp. 181-184.

986. "Structural Features of Continental Shelf, Slope, and Scarp, Northeastern Gulf of Mexico": Antoine, J., Bryant, W. and Jones, B., *Bull.,* AAPG (1967), v. 51, no. 2, pp. 257-262.

988. "Structural Framework of the Continental Terrace, Northwest Gulf of Mexico": Moore, David G. and Curray, Joseph R., *Jour Geophys Res.* (1963), v. 68, no. 6, pp. 1725-1747.

1010. "Structural History of the Gulf of Mexico, Sediments and Oceanic": Ewing, M., Ewing, J. and Wortzel, J. L., *Jour. Geophys, Res.* (1962), v. 67, no. 6, pp. 2509-2527.

1027. "Sweet Lake Field, Cameron Parish, Louisiana": Lysinger, Scott J., *Typical Oil and Gas Fields of Southwestern Louisiana,* Lafayette Geol. Soc. (1964), pp. 31-31c.

1015. "Tectonics of Parras Basin, States of Coahuila and Nuevo Leon, Mexico": Weidie, Alfred E., Jr. and Murray, G. E., *Trans.,* GCAGS (1961), v. 11, pp. 47-56.

1004. "Tertiary Reef and Associated Limestone Facies from Louisiana and Guam": Forman, M. J. and Schlanger, S. O., *Jour Geol.* (1957), v. 65, no. 6, pp. 611-627.

1011. "Tertiary Sediments from Sigsbee Knolls, Gulf of Mexico": Bryant, W. and Pyle, T., *Bull.,* AAPG (1965), v. 49, no. 9, pp. 1517-1518.

1014. "Texas and Louisiana, The Occurrence of Petroleum in Eastern Mexico as Contrasted with Those in": Dumble, E. T., *Trans.,* AIME (1916), v. 52, p. 263.

1028. *Warren County Mineral Resources, Bull. 43:* Mississippi State Geological Survey (1941), 140 pp.

Addendum to Salt Dome Indices

Louisiana

Belle Isle, St. Mary Parish:
978. *Bull.*, v. 49, no. 5, pp. 616-620.

Big Lake, Cameron Parish:
980. *Typical Oil and Gas Fields of Southwestern Louisiana*, Lafayette Geol. Soc. (1964)), pp. 2-2d.

Caillou Island, Terrebonne Parish:
981. *Oil and Gas Fields of Southeast Louisiana, Vol. 1,* New Orleans Geol. Soc. (1965), pp. 61-65.

Cameron Meadows, Cameron Parish:
982. *Typical Oil and Gas Fields of Southwestern Louisiana*, Lafayette Geol. Soc. (1964), pp. 3-3d.

Franklin, St. Mary Parish:
999. *Typical Oil and Gas Fields of Southwestern Louisiana*, Lafayette Geol. Soc. (1964), pp. 10-10d.

Gueydan, Vermilion Parish:
1005. *Typical Oil and Gas Fields of Southwestern Louisiana*, Lafayette Geol. Soc. (1964), pp. 12-12d.

Lake Chicot, St. Martin Parish:
1012. *Typical Oil and Gas Fields of Southwestern Louisiana*, Lafayette Geol. Soc. (1964), pp. 21-21d.

Lake Pelto, Terrebonne Parish:
1013. *Oil and Gas Fields of Southeast Louisiana, Vol. 1,* New Orleans Geol. Soc. (1965), pp. 115-120.

St. Gabriel, Iberville Parish:
1019. *Oil and Gas Fields of Southeast Louisiana, Vol. 1,* New Orleans Geol. Soc. (1965), pp. 177-180.

Stella, Plaquemines Parish:
1026. *Oil and Gas Fields of Southeast Louisiana, Vol. 1,* New Orleans Geol. Soc. (1965), pp. 181-184.

Sweet Lake, Cameron Parish:
1027. *Typical Oil and Gas Fields of Southwestern Louisiana*, Lafayette Geol. Soc. (1964), pp. 31-31c.

Mississippi

Glass Dome, Warren County:
1028. *Bull. 43,* Miss. State Geol. Svy., pp. 61-63.

Newman Dome, Warren County:
1028. *Bull. 43,* Miss. State Geol. Svy., p. 66.

Tatum Dome, Lamar County:
994. *Jour. Geophys. Res.,* v. 71, no. 14, pp. 3483-3501.
995. *Jour. Geophys. Res.,* v. 71, no. 14, pp. 3503-3506.
1006. *Jour. Geophys. Res.,* v. 71, no. 14, pp. 3437-3458.

1017. *Jour. Geophys. Res.,* v. 71, no. 14, pp. 3427-3436.
1018. *Jour. Geophys. Res.,* v. 71, no. 14, pp. 3415-3426.
1021. *Jour. Geophys. Res.,* v. 71, no. 14, pp. 3459-3467.
1022. *Jour. Geophys. Res.,* v. 71, no. 14, pp. 3507-3521.
1023. *Jour. Geophys. Res.,* v. 71, no. 14, pp. 3469-3482.
1024. *Jour. Geophys. Res.,* v. 71, no. 14, pp. 3405-3413.

Subject Index